Pearson New International Edition

Nonlinear Systems

Hassan K. Khalil
Third Edition

PEARSON®

Pearson Education Limited
Edinburgh Gate
Harlow
Essex CM20 2JE
England and Associated Companies throughout the world

Visit us on the World Wide Web at: www.pearsoned.co.uk

ISBN 10: 1-292-03921-3
ISBN 13: 978-1-292-03921-3

British Library Cataloguing-in-Publication Data
A catalogue record for this book is available from the British Library

ARP Impression 98
Printed in Great Britain by Clays Ltd, St Ives plc

Table of Contents

Chapter 1

Introduction

When engineers analyze and design nonlinear dynamical systems in electrical circuits, mechanical systems, control systems, and other engineering disciplines, they need to absorb and digest a wide range of nonlinear analysis tools. In this book, we introduce some of the these tools. In particular, we present tools for the stability analysis of nonlinear systems, with emphasis on Lyapunov's method. We give special attention to the stability of feedback systems from input–output and passivity perspectives. We present tools for the detection and analysis of "free" oscillations, including the describing function method. We introduce the asymptotic tools of perturbation theory, including averaging and singular perturbations. Finally, we introduce nonlinear feedback control tools, including linearization, gain scheduling, integral control, feedback linearization, sliding mode control, Lyapunov redesign, backstepping, passivity-based control, and high-gain observers.

1.1   Nonlinear Models and Nonlinear Phenomena

We will deal with dynamical systems that are modeled by a finite number of coupled first-order ordinary differential equations

$$
\begin{aligned}
\dot{x}_1 &= f_1(t, x_1, \ldots, x_n, u_1, \ldots, u_p) \\
\dot{x}_2 &= f_2(t, x_1, \ldots, x_n, u_1, \ldots, u_p) \\
&\vdots \qquad \vdots \\
\dot{x}_n &= f_n(t, x_1, \ldots, x_n, u_1, \ldots, u_p)
\end{aligned}
$$

where $\dot{x}_i$ denotes the derivative of x_i with respect to the time variable t and u_1, u_2, ..., u_p are specified input variables. We call the variables x_1, x_2, ..., x_n the state variables. They represent the memory that the dynamical system has of its past.

We usually use vector notation to write these equations in a compact form. Define

$$
x = \begin{bmatrix} x_1 \\ x_2 \\ \vdots \\ \vdots \\ x_n \end{bmatrix}, \quad u = \begin{bmatrix} u_1 \\ u_2 \\ \vdots \\ u_p \end{bmatrix}, \quad f(t, x, u) = \begin{bmatrix} f_1(t, x, u) \\ f_2(t, x, u) \\ \vdots \\ \vdots \\ f_n(t, x, u) \end{bmatrix}
$$

and rewrite the n first-order differential equations as one n-dimensional first-order vector differential equation

$$\dot{x} = f(t, x, u) \tag{1.1}$$

We call (1.1) the state equation and refer to x as the *state* and u as the *input*. Sometimes, another equation

$$y = h(t, x, u) \tag{1.2}$$

is associated with (1.1), thereby defining a q-dimensional *output* vector y that comprises variables of particular interest in the analysis of the dynamical system, (e.g., variables that can be physically measured or variables that are required to behave in a specified manner). We call (1.2) the output equation and refer to equations (1.1) and (1.2) together as the state-space model, or simply the state model. Mathematical models of finite-dimensional physical systems do not always come in the form of a state model. However, more often than not, we can model physical systems in this form by carefully choosing the state variables. Examples and exercises that will appear later in the chapter will demonstrate the versatility of the state model.

A good part of our analysis in this book will deal with the state equation, many times without explicit presence of an input u, that is, the so-called unforced state equation

$$\dot{x} = f(t, x) \tag{1.3}$$

Working with an unforced state equation does not necessarily mean that the input to the system is zero. It could be that the input has been specified as a given function of time, $u = \gamma(t)$, a given feedback function of the state, $u = \gamma(x)$, or both, $u = \gamma(t, x)$. Substituting $u = \gamma$ in (1.1) eliminates u and yields an unforced state equation.

A special case of (1.3) arises when the function f does not depend explicitly on t; that is,

$$\dot{x} = f(x) \tag{1.4}$$

in which case the system is said to be *autonomous* or *time invariant*. The behavior of an autonomous system is invariant to shifts in the time origin, since changing the time variable from t to $\tau = t - a$ does not change the right-hand side of the state equation. If the system is not autonomous, then it is called *nonautonomous* or *time varying*.

An important concept in dealing with the state equation is the concept of an equilibrium point. A point $x = x^*$ in the state space is said to be an equilibrium point of (1.3) if it has the property that whenever the state of the system starts at x^*, it will remain at x^* for all future time. For the autonomous system (1.4), the equilibrium points are the real roots of the equation

$$f(x) = 0$$

An equilibrium point could be isolated; that is, there are no other equilibrium points in its vicinity, or there could be a continuum of equilibrium points.

For linear systems, the state model (1.1)–(1.2) takes the special form

$$\begin{aligned} \dot{x} &= A(t)x + B(t)u \\ y &= C(t)x + D(t)u \end{aligned}$$

We assume that the reader is familiar with the powerful analysis tools for linear systems, founded on the basis of the *superposition principle*. As we move from linear to nonlinear systems, we are faced with a more difficult situation. The superposition principle does not hold any longer, and analysis tools involve more advanced mathematics. Because of the powerful tools we know for linear systems, the first step in analyzing a nonlinear system is usually to linearize it, if possible, about some nominal operating point and analyze the resulting linear model. This is a common practice in engineering, and it is a useful one. There is no question that, whenever possible, we should make use of linearization to learn as much as we can about the behavior of a nonlinear system. However, linearization alone will not be sufficient; we must develop tools for the analysis of nonlinear systems. There are two basic limitations of linearization. First, since linearization is an approximation in the neighborhood of an operating point, it can only predict the "local" behavior of the nonlinear system in the vicinity of that point. It cannot predict the "nonlocal" behavior far from the operating point and certainly not the "global" behavior throughout the state space. Second, the dynamics of a nonlinear system are much richer than the dynamics of a linear system. There are "essentially nonlinear phenomena" that can take place only in the presence of nonlinearity; hence, they cannot be described or predicted by linear models. The following are examples of essentially nonlinear phenomena:

- *Finite escape time.* The state of an unstable linear system goes to infinity as time approaches infinity; a nonlinear system's state, however, can go to infinity in finite time.

- *Multiple isolated equilibria.* A linear system can have only one isolated equilibrium point; thus, it can have only one steady-state operating point that attracts the state of the system irrespective of the initial state. A nonlinear system can have more than one isolated equilibrium point. The state may converge to one of several steady-state operating points, depending on the initial state of the system.

- *Limit cycles.* For a linear time-invariant system to oscillate, it must have a pair of eigenvalues on the imaginary axis, which is a nonrobust condition that is almost impossible to maintain in the presence of perturbations. Even if we do, the amplitude of oscillation will be dependent on the initial state. In real life, stable oscillation must be produced by nonlinear systems. There are nonlinear systems that can go into an oscillation of fixed amplitude and frequency, irrespective of the initial state. This type of oscillation is known as a limit cycle.

- *Subharmonic, harmonic, or almost-periodic oscillations.* A stable linear system under a periodic input produces an output of the same frequency. A nonlinear system under periodic excitation can oscillate with frequencies that are submultiples or multiples of the input frequency. It may even generate an almost-periodic oscillation, an example is the sum of periodic oscillations with frequencies that are not multiples of each other.

- *Chaos.* A nonlinear system can have a more complicated steady-state behavior that is not equilibrium, periodic oscillation, or almost-periodic oscillation. Such behavior is usually referred to as chaos. Some of these chaotic motions exhibit randomness, despite the deterministic nature of the system.

- *Multiple modes of behavior.* It is not unusual for two or more modes of behavior to be exhibited by the same nonlinear system. An unforced system may have more than one limit cycle. A forced system with periodic excitation may exhibit harmonic, subharmonic, or more complicated steady-state behavior, depending upon the amplitude and frequency of the input. It may even exhibit a discontinuous jump in the mode of behavior as the amplitude or frequency of the excitation is smoothly changed.

In this book, we will encounter only the first three of these phenomena.[1] Multiple equilibria and limit cycles will be introduced in the next chapter, as we examine second-order autonomous systems, while the phenomenon of finite escape time will be introduced in Chapter 3.

---

[1]To read about forced oscillation, chaos, bifurcation, and other important topics, the reader may consult [70], [74], [187], and [207].

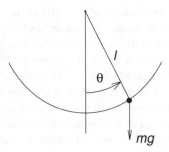

Figure 1.1: Pendulum.

1.2 Examples

1.2.1 Pendulum Equation

Consider the simple pendulum shown in Figure 1.1, where l denotes the length of the rod and m denotes the mass of the bob. Assume the rod is rigid and has zero mass. Let θ denote the angle subtended by the rod and the vertical axis through the pivot point. The pendulum is free to swing in the vertical plane. The bob of the pendulum moves in a circle of radius l. To write the equation of motion of the pendulum, let us identify the forces acting on the bob. There is a downward gravitational force equal to mg, where g is the acceleration due to gravity. There is also a frictional force resisting the motion, which we assume to be proportional to the speed of the bob with a coefficient of friction k. Using Newton's second law of motion, we can write the equation of motion in the tangential direction as

$$ml\ddot{\theta} = -mg\sin\theta - kl\dot{\theta}$$

Writing the equation of motion in the tangential direction has the advantage that the rod tension, which is in the normal direction, does not appear in the equation. We could have arrived at the same equation by writing the moment equation about the pivot point. To obtain a state model for the pendulum, let us take the state variables as $x_1 = \theta$ and $x_2 = \dot{\theta}$. Then, the state equations are

$$\dot{x}_1 \;=\; x_2 \tag{1.5}$$

$$\dot{x}_2 \;=\; -\frac{g}{l}\sin x_1 - \frac{k}{m}x_2 \tag{1.6}$$

To find the equilibrium points, we set $\dot{x}_1 = \dot{x}_2 = 0$ and solve for x_1 and x_2:

$$0 \;=\; x_2$$

$$0 \;=\; -\frac{g}{l}\sin x_1 - \frac{k}{m}x_2$$

The equilibrium points are located at $(n\pi, 0)$, for $n = 0, \pm 1, \pm 2, \ldots$. From the physical description of the pendulum, it is clear that the pendulum has only two equilibrium positions corresponding to the equilibrium points $(0, 0)$ and $(\pi, 0)$. Other equilibrium points are repetitions of these two positions, which correspond to the number of full swings the pendulum would make before it rests at one of the two equilibrium positions. For example, if the pendulum makes m complete 360° revolutions before it rests at the downward vertical position, then, mathematically, we say that the pendulum approaches the equilibrium point $(2m\pi, 0)$. In our investigation of the pendulum, we will limit our attention to the two "nontrivial" equilibrium points at $(0, 0)$ and $(\pi, 0)$. Physically, we can see that these two equilibrium positions are quite distinct from each other. While the pendulum can indeed rest at the $(0, 0)$ equilibrium point, it can hardly maintain rest at the $(\pi, 0)$ equilibrium point because infinitesimally small disturbance from that equilibrium will take the pendulum away. The difference between the two equilibrium points is in their stability properties, a topic we will study in some depth.

Sometimes it is instructive to consider a version of the pendulum equation where the frictional resistance is neglected by setting $k = 0$. The resulting system

$$\dot{x}_1 = x_2 \tag{1.7}$$

$$\dot{x}_2 = -\frac{g}{l}\sin x_1 \tag{1.8}$$

is conservative in the sense that if the pendulum is given an initial push, it will keep oscillating forever with a nondissipative energy exchange between kinetic and potential energies. This, of course, is not realistic, but gives insight into the behavior of the pendulum. It may also help in finding approximate solutions of the pendulum equation when the friction coefficient k is small. Another version of the pendulum equation arises if we can apply a torque T to the pendulum. This torque may be viewed as a control input in the equation

$$\dot{x}_1 = x_2 \tag{1.9}$$

$$\dot{x}_2 = -\frac{g}{l}\sin x_1 - \frac{k}{m}x_2 + \frac{1}{ml^2}T \tag{1.10}$$

Interestingly enough, several unrelated physical systems are modeled by equations similar to the pendulum equation. Such examples are the model of a synchronous generator connected to an infinite bus (Exercise 1.8), the model of a Josephson junction circuit (Exercise 1.9), and the model of a phase-locked loop (Exercise 1.11). Consequently, the pendulum equation is of great practical importance.

1.2.2 Tunnel-Diode Circuit

Consider the tunnel-diode circuit shown in Figure 1.2,[2] where the tunnel diode is characterized by $i_R = h(v_R)$. The energy-storing elements in this circuit are the

---

[2]This figure, as well as Figures 1.3 and 1.7, are taken from [39].

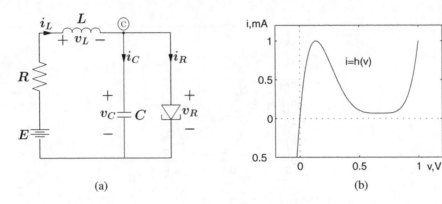

Figure 1.2: (a) Tunnel-diode circuit; (b) Tunnel-diode v_R–i_R characteristic.

capacitor C and the inductor L. Assuming they are linear and time invariant, we can model them by the equations

$$i_C = C\frac{dv_C}{dt} \quad \text{and} \quad v_L = L\frac{di_L}{dt}$$

where i and v are the current through and the voltage across an element, with the subscript specifying the element. To write a state model for the system, let us take $x_1 = v_C$ and $x_2 = i_L$ as the state variables and $u = E$ as a constant input. To write the state equation for x_1, we need to express i_C as a function of the state variables x_1, x_2 and the input u. Using Kirchhoff's current law, we can write an equation that the algebraic sum of all currents leaving node ⓒ is equal to zero:

$$i_C + i_R - i_L = 0$$

Therefore,

$$i_C = -h(x_1) + x_2$$

Similarly, we need to express v_L as a function of the state variables x_1, x_2 and the input u. Using Kirchhoff's voltage law, we can write an equation that the algebraic sum of all voltages across elements in the left loop is equal to zero:

$$v_C - E + Ri_L + v_L = 0$$

Hence,

$$v_L = -x_1 - Rx_2 + u$$

We can now write the state model for the circuit as

$$\dot{x}_1 = \frac{1}{C}[-h(x_1) + x_2] \tag{1.11}$$

$$\dot{x}_2 = \frac{1}{L}[-x_1 - Rx_2 + u] \tag{1.12}$$

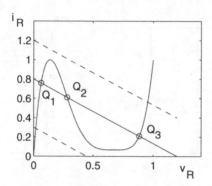

Figure 1.3: Equilibrium points of the tunnel-diode circuit.

The equilibrium points of the system are determined by setting $\dot{x}_1 = \dot{x}_2 = 0$ and solving for x_1 and x_2:

$$
\begin{aligned}
0 &= -h(x_1) + x_2 \\
0 &= -x_1 - Rx_2 + u
\end{aligned}
$$

Therefore, the equilibrium points correspond to the roots of the equation

$$
h(x_1) = \frac{E}{R} - \frac{1}{R}x_1
$$

Figure 1.3 shows graphically that, for certain values of E and R, this equation has three isolated roots which correspond to three isolated equilibrium points of the system. The number of equilibrium points might change as the values of E and R change. For example, if we increase E for the same value of R, we will reach a point beyond which only the point Q_3 will exist. On the other hand, if we decrease E for the same value of R, we will end up with the point Q_1 as the only equilibrium. Suppose that we are in the multiple equilibria situation, which of these equilibrium points can we observe in an experimental setup of this circuit? The answer depends on the stability properties of the equilibrium points. We will come back to this example in Chapter 2 and answer the question.

1.2.3   Mass–Spring System

In the mass–spring mechanical system, shown in Figure 1.4, we consider a mass m sliding on a horizontal surface and attached to a vertical surface through a spring. The mass is subjected to an external force F. We define y as the displacement from a reference position and write Newton's law of motion

$$
m\ddot{y} + F_f + F_{sp} = F
$$

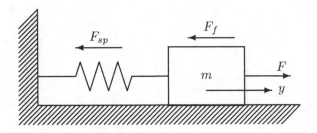

Figure 1.4: Mass-spring mechanical system.

where F_f is a resistive force due to friction and F_{sp} is the restoring force of the spring. We assume that F_{sp} is a function only of the displacement y and write it as $F_{sp} = g(y)$. We assume also that the reference position has been chosen such that $g(0) = 0$. The external force F is at our disposal. Depending upon F, F_f, and g, several interesting autonomous and nonautonomous second-order models arise.

For a relatively small displacement, the restoring force of the spring can be modeled as a linear function $g(y) = ky$, where k is the spring constant. For a large displacement, however, the restoring force may depend nonlinearly on y. For example, the function

$$g(y) = k(1 - a^2 y^2)y, \quad |ay| < 1$$

models the so-called *softening spring*, where, beyond a certain displacement, a large displacement increment produces a small force increment. On the other hand, the function

$$g(y) = k(1 + a^2 y^2)y$$

models the so-called *hardening spring*, where, beyond a certain displacement, a small displacement increment produces a large force increment.

The resistive force F_f may have components due to static, Coulomb, and viscous friction. When the mass is at rest, there is a static friction force F_s that acts parallel to the surface and is limited to $\pm\mu_s mg$, where $0 < \mu_s < 1$ is the static friction coefficient. This force takes whatever value, between its limits, to keep the mass at rest. For motion to begin, there must be a force acting on the mass to overcome the resistance to motion caused by static friction. In the absence of an external force, $F = 0$, the static friction force will balance the restoring force of the spring and maintain equilibrium for $|g(y)| \leq \mu_s mg$. Once motion has started, the resistive force F_f, which acts in the direction opposite to motion, is modeled as a function of the sliding velocity $v = \dot{y}$. The resistive force due to *Coulomb friction* F_c has a constant magnitude $\mu_k mg$, where μ_k is the kinetic friction coefficient, that is,

$$F_c = \begin{cases} -\mu_k mg, & \text{for} \quad v < 0 \\ \mu_k mg, & \text{for} \quad v > 0 \end{cases}$$

As the mass moves in a viscous medium, such as air or lubricant, there will be a frictional force due to viscosity. This force is usually modeled as a nonlinear

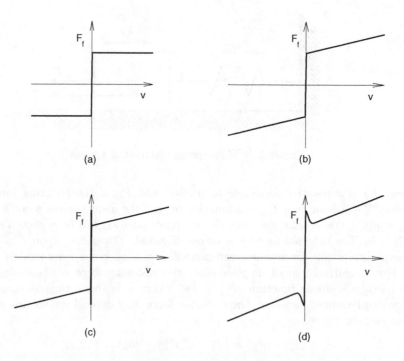

Figure 1.5: Examples of friction models. (a) Coulomb friction; (b) Coulomb plus linear viscous friction; (c) static, Coulomb, and linear viscous friction; (d) static, Coulomb, and linear viscous friction—Stribeck effect.

function of the velocity; that is, $F_v = h(v)$, where $h(0) = 0$. For small velocity, we can assume that $F_v = cv$. Figures 1.5(a) and (b) show examples of friction models for Coulomb friction and Coulombs plus linear viscous friction, respectively. Figure 1.5(c) shows an example where the static friction is higher than the level of Coulomb friction, while Figure 1.5(d) shows a similar situation, but with the force decreasing continuously with increasing velocity, the so-called *Stribeck effect*.

The combination of a hardening spring, linear viscous friction, and a periodic external force $F = A\cos\omega t$ results in the Duffing's equation

$$m\ddot{y} + c\dot{y} + ky + ka^2y^3 = A\cos\omega t \tag{1.13}$$

which is a classical example in the study of periodic excitation of nonlinear systems.

The combination of a linear spring, static friction, Coulomb friction, linear viscous friction, and zero external force results in

$$m\ddot{y} + ky + c\dot{y} + \eta(y, \dot{y}) = 0$$

where

$$\eta(y, \dot{y}) = \begin{cases} \mu_k mg \ \text{sign}(\dot{y}), & \text{for} \quad |\dot{y}| > 0 \\ -ky, & \text{for} \quad \dot{y} = 0 \ \text{ and } \ |y| \le \mu_s mg/k \\ -\mu_s mg \ \text{sign}(y), & \text{for} \quad \dot{y} = 0 \ \text{ and } \ |y| > \mu_s mg/k \end{cases}$$

The value of $\eta(y, \dot{y})$ for $\dot{y} = 0$ and $|y| \le \mu_s mg/k$ is obtained from the equilibrium condition $\ddot{y} = \dot{y} = 0$. With $x_1 = y$ and $x_2 = \dot{y}$, the state model is

$$\dot{x}_1 = x_2 \tag{1.14}$$

$$\dot{x}_2 = -\frac{k}{m}x_1 - \frac{c}{m}x_2 - \frac{1}{m}\eta(x_1, x_2) \tag{1.15}$$

Let us note two features of this state model. First, it has an equilibrium set, rather than isolated equilibrium points. Second, the right-hand side function is a discontinuous function of the state. The discontinuity is a consequence of the idealization we adopted in modeling friction. One would expect the physical friction to change from its static friction mode into its sliding friction mode in a smooth way, not abruptly as our idealization suggests.[3] The discontinuous idealization, however, simplifies the analysis. For example, when $x_2 > 0$, we can model the system by the linear model

$$\dot{x}_1 = x_2$$

$$\dot{x}_2 = -\frac{k}{m}x_1 - \frac{c}{m}x_2 - \mu_k g$$

Similarly, when $x_2 < 0$, we can model it by the linear model

$$\dot{x}_1 = x_2$$

$$\dot{x}_2 = -\frac{k}{m}x_1 - \frac{c}{m}x_2 + \mu_k g$$

Thus, in each region, we can predict the behavior of the system via linear analysis. This is an example of the so-called *piecewise linear analysis*, where a system is represented by linear models in various regions of the state space, certain coefficients changing from region to region.

1.2.4   Negative-Resistance Oscillator

Figure 1.6 shows the basic circuit structure of an important class of electronic oscillators. The inductor and capacitor are assumed to be linear, time invariant and passive, that is, $L > 0$ and $C > 0$. The resistive element is an active circuit characterized by the v–i characteristic $i = h(v)$, shown in the figure. The function

---

[3]The smooth transition from static to sliding friction can be captured by dynamic friction models; see, for example, [12] and [144].

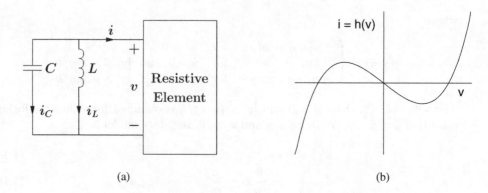

(a)   (b)

Figure 1.6: (a) Basic oscillator circuit; (b) Typical driving-point characteristic.

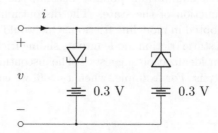

Figure 1.7: A negative-resistance twin-tunnel-diode circuit.

$h(\cdot)$ satisfies the conditions

$$h(0) = 0, \quad h'(0) < 0$$

$$h(v) \to \infty \text{ as } v \to \infty, \quad \text{and} \quad h(v) \to -\infty \text{ as } v \to -\infty$$

where $h'(v)$ is the first derivative of $h(v)$ with respect to v. Such v–i characteristic can be realized, for example, by the twin-tunnel-diode circuit of Figure 1.7, with the tunnel-diode characteristic shown in Figure 1.2. Using Kirchhoff's current law, we can write the equation

$$i_C + i_L + i = 0$$

Hence,

$$C\frac{dv}{dt} + \frac{1}{L} \int_{-\infty}^{t} v(s) \, ds + h(v) = 0$$

Differentiating once with respect to t and multiplying through by L, we obtain

$$CL\frac{d^2v}{dt^2} + v + Lh'(v)\frac{dv}{dt} = 0$$

The foregoing equation can be written in a form that coincides with some well-known equations in nonlinear systems theory. To do that, let us change the time variable from t to $\tau = t/\sqrt{CL}$. The derivatives of v with respect to t and τ are related by

$$\frac{dv}{d\tau} = \sqrt{CL}\frac{dv}{dt} \quad \text{and} \quad \frac{d^2v}{d\tau^2} = CL\frac{d^2v}{dt^2}$$

Denoting the derivative of v with respect to τ by $\dot{v}$, we can rewrite the circuit equation as

$$\ddot{v} + \varepsilon h'(v)\dot{v} + v = 0$$

where $\varepsilon = \sqrt{L/C}$. This equation is a special case of *Liénard's equation*

$$\ddot{v} + f(v)\dot{v} + g(v) = 0 \tag{1.16}$$

When

$$h(v) = -v + \tfrac{1}{3}v^3$$

the circuit equation takes the form

$$\ddot{v} - \varepsilon(1 - v^2)\dot{v} + v = 0 \tag{1.17}$$

which is known as the *Van der Pol equation*. This equation, which was used by Van der Pol to study oscillations in vacuum tube circuits, is a fundamental example in nonlinear oscillation theory. It possesses a periodic solution that attracts every other solution except the zero solution at the unique equilibrium point $v = \dot{v} = 0$. To write a state model for the circuit, let us take $x_1 = v$ and $x_2 = \dot{v}$ to obtain

$$\dot{x}_1 = x_2 \tag{1.18}$$
$$\dot{x}_2 = -x_1 - \varepsilon h'(x_1)x_2 \tag{1.19}$$

Note that an alternate state model could have been obtained by choosing the state variables as the voltage across the capacitor and the current through the inductor. Denoting the state variables by $z_1 = i_L$ and $z_2 = v_C$, the state model is given by

$$\frac{dz_1}{dt} = \frac{1}{L}z_2$$
$$\frac{dz_2}{dt} = -\frac{1}{C}[z_1 + h(z_2)]$$

Since the first state model has been written with respect to the time variable $\tau = t/\sqrt{CL}$, let us write this model with respect to τ.

$$\dot{z}_1 = \frac{1}{\varepsilon}z_2 \tag{1.20}$$
$$\dot{z}_2 = -\varepsilon[z_1 + h(z_2)] \tag{1.21}$$

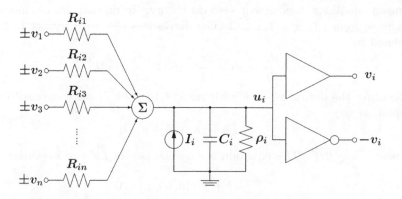

Figure 1.8: Hopfield neural network model.

The state models in x and z look different, but they are equivalent representations of the system. This equivalence can be seen by noting that these models can be obtained from each other by a change of coordinates

$$z = T(x)$$

Since we have chosen both x and z in terms of the physical variables of the circuit, it is not hard to find the map $T(\cdot)$. We have

$$x_1 = v = z_2$$
$$x_2 = \frac{dv}{d\tau} = \sqrt{CL}\frac{dv}{dt} = \sqrt{\frac{L}{C}}[-i_L - h(v_C)] = \varepsilon[-z_1 - h(z_2)]$$

Thus,

$$z = T(x) = \begin{bmatrix} -h(x_1) - (1/\varepsilon)x_2 \\ x_1 \end{bmatrix}$$

and the inverse mapping is

$$x = T^{-1}(z) = \begin{bmatrix} z_2 \\ -\varepsilon z_1 - \varepsilon h(z_2) \end{bmatrix}$$

1.2.5 Artificial Neural Network

Artificial neural networks, in analogy to biological structures, take advantage of distributed information processing and their inherent potential for parallel computation. Figure 1.8 shows an electric circuit that implements one model of neural networks, known as the *Hopfield model*. The circuit is based on an RC network con-

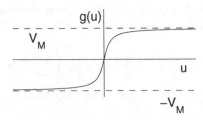

Figure 1.9: A typical input–output characteristic for the amplifiers in Hopfield network.

necting amplifiers. The input–output characteristics of the amplifiers are given by $v_i = g_i(u_i)$, where u_i and v_i are the input and output voltages of the ith amplifier. The function $g_i(\cdot) : R \to (-V_M, V_M)$ is a sigmoid function with asymptotes $-V_M$ and V_M, as shown in Figure 1.9. It is continuously differentiable, odd, monotonically increasing, and $g_i(u_i) = 0$ if and only if $u_i = 0$. Examples of possible $g_i(\cdot)$ are

$$g_i(u_i) = \frac{2V_M}{\pi} \tan^{-1}\left(\frac{\lambda \pi u_i}{2V_M}\right), \quad \lambda > 0$$

and

$$g_i(u_i) = V_M \frac{e^{\lambda u_i} - e^{-\lambda u_i}}{e^{\lambda u_i} + e^{-\lambda u_i}} = V_M \tanh(\lambda u_i), \quad \lambda > 0$$

where λ determines the slope of $g_i(u_i)$ at $u_i = 0$. Such sigmoid input–output characteristics can be realized by using operational amplifiers. For each amplifier, the circuit contains an inverting amplifier whose output is $-v_i$, which permits a choice of the sign of the amplifier output that is connected to a given input line. The outputs v_i and $-v_i$ are usually provided by two output terminals of the same operational amplifier circuit. The pair of nonlinear amplifiers is referred to as a "neuron." The circuit also contains an RC section at the input of each amplifier. The capacitance $C_i > 0$ and the resistance $\rho_i > 0$ represent the total shunt capacitance and shunt resistance at the ith amplifier input. Writing Kirchhoff's current law at the input node of the ith amplifier, we obtain

$$C_i \frac{du_i}{dt} = \sum_j \frac{1}{R_{ij}}(\pm v_j - u_i) - \frac{1}{\rho_i} u_i + I_i = \sum_j T_{ij} v_j - \frac{1}{R_i} u_i + I_i$$

where

$$\frac{1}{R_i} = \frac{1}{\rho_i} + \sum_j \frac{1}{R_{ij}}$$

T_{ij} is a signed conductance whose magnitude is $1/R_{ij}$, and whose sign is determined by the choice of the positive or negative output of the jth amplifier, and I_i is a constant input current. For a circuit containing n amplifiers, the motion is described by n first-order differential equations. To write a state model for the circuit, let us choose the state variables as $x_i = v_i$ for $i = 1, 2, \ldots, n$. Then

$$\dot{x}_i = \frac{dg_i}{du_i}(u_i) \times \dot{u}_i = \frac{dg_i}{du_i}(u_i) \times \frac{1}{C_i}\left(\sum_j T_{ij}x_j - \frac{1}{R_i}u_i + I_i\right)$$

By defining

$$h_i(x_i) = \left.\frac{dg_i}{du_i}(u_i)\right|_{u_i = g_i^{-1}(x_i)}$$

we can write the state equation as

$$\dot{x}_i = \frac{1}{C_i}h_i(x_i)\left[\sum_j T_{ij}x_j - \frac{1}{R_i}g_i^{-1}(x_i) + I_i\right] \tag{1.22}$$

for $i = 1, 2, \ldots, n$. Note that, due to the sigmoid characteristic of $g_i(\cdot)$, the function $h_i(\cdot)$ satisfies

$$h_i(x_i) > 0, \quad \forall\, x_i \in (-V_M, V_M)$$

The equilibrium points of the system are the roots of the n simultaneous equations

$$0 = \sum_j T_{ij}x_j - \frac{1}{R_i}g_i^{-1}(x_i) + I_i, \quad 1 \le i \le n$$

They are determined by the sigmoid characteristics, the linear resistive connection, and the input currents. We can obtain an equivalent state model by choosing the state variables as u_i for $i = 1, 2, \ldots, n$.

Stability analysis of this neural network depends critically on whether the symmetry condition $T_{ij} = T_{ji}$ is satisfied. An example of the analysis when $T_{ij} = T_{ji}$ is given in Section 4.2, while an example when $T_{ij} \ne T_{ji}$ is given in Section 9.5.

1.2.6 Adaptive Control

Consider a first-order linear system described by the model

$$\dot{y}_p = a_p y_p + k_p u$$

where u is the control input and y_p is the measured output. We refer to this system as the plant. Suppose that it is desirable to obtain a closed-loop system whose input–output behavior is described by the reference model

$$\dot{y}_m = a_m y_m + k_m r$$

where r is the reference input and the model has been chosen such that $y_m(t)$ represents the desired output of the closed-loop system. This goal can be achieved by the linear feedback control

$$u(t) = \theta_1^* r(t) + \theta_2^* y_p(t)$$

provided that the plant parameters a_p and k_p are known, $k_p \neq 0$, and the controller parameters θ_1^* and θ_2^* are chosen as

$$\theta_1^* = \frac{k_m}{k_p} \quad \text{and} \quad \theta_2^* = \frac{a_m - a_p}{k_p}$$

When a_p and k_p are unknown, we may consider the controller

$$u(t) = \theta_1(t)r(t) + \theta_2(t)y_p(t)$$

where the time-varying gains $\theta_1(t)$ and $\theta_2(t)$ are adjusted on-line by using the available data, namely, $r(\tau)$, $y_m(\tau)$, $y_p(\tau)$, and $u(\tau)$ for $\tau < t$. The adaptation should be such that $\theta_1(t)$ and $\theta_2(t)$ evolve to their nominal values θ_1^* and θ_2^*. The adaptation rule is chosen based on stability considerations. One such rule, known as the gradient algorithm,[4] is to use

$$\begin{aligned} \dot{\theta}_1 &= -\gamma(y_p - y_m)r \\ \dot{\theta}_2 &= -\gamma(y_p - y_m)y_p \end{aligned}$$

where γ is a positive constant that determines the speed of adaptation. This adaptive control law assumes that the sign of k_p is known and, without loss of generality, takes it to be positive. To write a state model that describes the closed-loop system under the adaptive control law, it is more convenient to define the output error e_o and the parameter errors ϕ_1 and ϕ_2 as

$$e_o = y_p - y_m, \quad \phi_1 = \theta_1 - \theta_1^*, \quad \text{and} \quad \phi_2 = \theta_2 - \theta_2^*$$

By using the definition of θ_1^* and θ_2^*, the reference model can be rewritten as

$$\dot{y}_m = a_p y_m + k_p(\theta_1^* r + \theta_2^* y_m)$$

On the other hand, the plant output y_p satisfies the equation

$$\dot{y}_p = a_p y_p + k_p(\theta_1 r + \theta_2 y_p)$$

Subtracting the above two equations, we obtain the error equation

$$\begin{aligned} \dot{e}_o &= a_p e_o + k_p(\theta_1 - \theta_1^*)r + k_p(\theta_2 y_p - \theta_2^* y_m) \\ &= a_p e_o + k_p(\theta_1 - \theta_1^*)r + k_p(\theta_2 y_p - \theta_2^* y_m + \theta_2^* y_p - \theta_2^* y_p) \\ &= (a_p + k_p \theta_2^*)e_o + k_p(\theta_1 - \theta_1^*)r + k_p(\theta_2 - \theta_2^*)y_p \end{aligned}$$

Thus, the closed-loop system is described by the nonlinear, nonautonomous, third-order state model

$$\dot{e}_o = a_m e_o + k_p \phi_1 r(t) + k_p \phi_2 [e_o + y_m(t)] \tag{1.23}$$

$$\dot{\phi}_1 = -\gamma e_o r(t) \tag{1.24}$$

$$\dot{\phi}_2 = -\gamma e_o [e_o + y_m(t)] \tag{1.25}$$

---

[4]This adaptation rule will be justified in Section 8.3.

where we used $\dot{\phi}_i(t) = \dot{\theta}_i(t)$ and wrote $r(t)$ and $y_m(t)$ as explicit functions of time to emphasize the nonautonomous nature of the system. The signals $r(t)$ and $y_m(t)$ are the external driving inputs of the closed-loop system.

A simpler version of this model arises if we know k_p. In this case, we can take $\theta_1 = \theta_1^*$ and only θ_2 needs to be adjusted on-line. The closed-loop model reduces to

$$\dot{e}_o = a_m e_o + k_p \phi [e_o + y_m(t)] \tag{1.26}$$

$$\dot{\phi} = -\gamma e_o [e_o + y_m(t)] \tag{1.27}$$

where we dropped the subscript from ϕ_2. If the goal of the control design is to regulate the plant output y_p to zero, we take $r(t) \equiv 0$ (hence, $y_m(t) \equiv 0$) and the closed-loop model simplifies to the autonomous second-order model

$$\dot{e}_o = (a_m + k_p \phi) e_o$$

$$\dot{\phi} = -\gamma e_o^2$$

The equilibrium points of this system are determined by setting $\dot{e}_o = \dot{\phi} = 0$ to obtain the algebraic equations

$$0 = (a_m + k_p \phi) e_o$$

$$0 = -\gamma e_o^2$$

The system has equilibrium at $e_o = 0$ for all values of ϕ; that is, it has an equilibrium set $e_o = 0$. There are no isolated equilibrium points.

The particular adaptive control scheme described here is called *direct model reference adaptive control*. The term "model reference" stems from the fact that the controller's task is to match a given closed-loop reference model, while the term "direct" is used to indicate that the controller parameters are adapted directly as opposed, for example, to an adaptive control scheme that would estimate the plant parameters a_p and k_p on-line and use their estimates to calculate the controller parameters.[5] The adaptive control problem generates some interesting nonlinear models that will be used to illustrate some of the stability and perturbation techniques of this book.

1.2.7   Common Nonlinearities

In the foregoing examples, we saw some typical nonlinearities that arise in modeling physical systems, such as nonlinear resistance, nonlinear friction, and sigmoid nonlinearities. In this section, we cover some other typical nonlinearities. Figure 1.10 shows four typical memoryless nonlinearities. They are called memoryless, zero memory, or static because the output of the nonlinearity at any instant of time is

---

[5]For a comprehensive treatment of adaptive control, the reader may consult [5], [15], [87], [139], or [168].

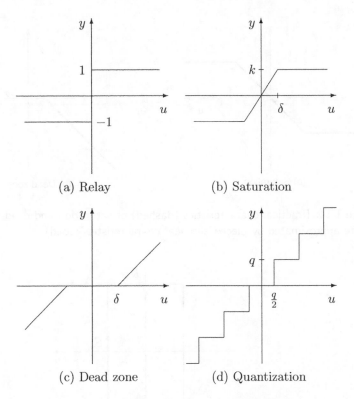

(a) Relay

(b) Saturation

(c) Dead zone

(d) Quantization

Figure 1.10: Typical memoryless nonlinearities.

determined uniquely by its input at that instant; it does not depend on the history of the input.

Figure 1.10(a) shows an ideal relay described by the signum function

$$\text{sgn}(u) = \begin{cases} 1, & \text{if } u > 0 \\ 0, & \text{if } u = 0 \\ -1, & \text{if } u < 0 \end{cases} \tag{1.28}$$

Such nonlinear characteristic can model electromechanical relays, thyristor circuits, and other switching devices.

Figure 1.10(b) shows an ideal saturation nonlinearity. Saturation characteristics are common in all practical amplifiers (electronic, magnetic, pneumatic, or hydraulic), motors, and other devices. They are also used, intentionally, as limiters to restrict the range of a variable. We define the saturation function

$$\text{sat}(u) = \begin{cases} u, & \text{if } |u| \leq 1 \\ \text{sgn}(u), & \text{if } |u| > 1 \end{cases} \tag{1.29}$$

to represent a normalized saturation nonlinearity and generate the graph of Fig-

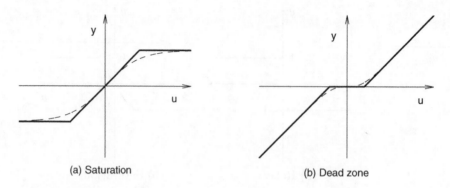

(a) Saturation   (b) Dead zone

Figure 1.11: Practical characteristics (dashed) of saturation and dead-zone nonlinearities are approximated by piecewise linear characteristics (solid).

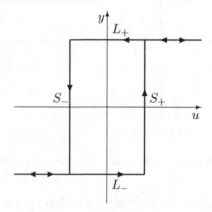

Figure 1.12: Relay with hysteresis.

ure 1.10(b) as $k \, \text{sat}(u/\delta)$.

Figure 1.10(c) shows an ideal dead-zone nonlinearity. Such characteristic is typical of valves and some amplifiers at low input signals. The piecewise linear functions used in Figure 1.10(b) and (c) to represent saturation and dead-zone characteristics are approximations of more realistic smooth functions, as shown in Figure 1.11

Figure 1.10(d) shows a quantization nonlinearity, which is typical in analog-to-digital conversion of signals.

Quite frequently, we encounter nonlinear elements whose input–output characteristics have memory; that is, the output at any instant of time may depend on the whole history of the input. Figures 1.12, 1.15(b), and 1.16 show three such characteristics of the hysteresis type. The first of the three elements, Figure 1.12, is a relay with hysteresis. For highly negative values of the input, the output will

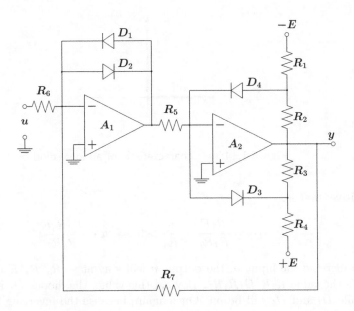

Figure 1.13: An operational amplifier circuit that realizes the relay with hysteresis characteristic of Figure 1.12.

be at the lower level L_-. As the input is increased, the output stays at L_- until the input reaches S_+. Increasing the input beyond S_+, the output switches to the higher level L_+ and stays there for higher values of the input. Now, if we decrease the input, the output stays at the higher level L_+ until the input crosses the value S_- at which point the output switches to the lower level L_- and stays there for lower values of the input. Such input–output characteristic can be generated, for example, by the operational amplifier circuit of Figure 1.13.[6] The circuit features ideal operational amplifiers and ideal diodes. An ideal operational amplifier has the voltage at its inverting (-) input equal to the voltage at its noninverting (+) input and has zero input currents at both inputs. An ideal diode has the v–i characteristic shown in Figure 1.14. When the input voltage u is highly negative, the diodes D_1 and D_3 will be *on* while D_2 and D_4 will be *off*.[7] Because the inverting inputs of both amplifiers are at virtual ground, the currents in R_5 and D_3 will be zero and the output of D_3 will be at virtual ground. Therefore, the output voltage y will be given by $y = -(R_3/R_4)E$. This situation will remain as long as the current in D_1

---

[6]This circuit is taken from [204].

[7]To see why D_3 is *on* when D_1 is *on*, notice that when D_1 is *on*, the voltage at the output of A_1 will be V_d, the offset voltage of the diode. This will cause a current V_d/R_5 to flow in R_5 heading towards A_2. Since the input current to A_2 is zero, the current in R_5 must flow through D_3. In modeling the diodes, we neglect the offset voltage V_d; therefore, the currents in R_5 and D_3 are neglected.

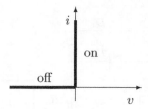

Figure 1.14: v–i characteristic of an ideal diode.

is positive; that is,

$$i_{D1} = \frac{R_3 E}{R_4 R_7} - \frac{u}{R_6} > 0 \Leftrightarrow u < \frac{R_3 R_6 E}{R_4 R_7}$$

As we increase the input u, the output y will stay at $-(R_3/R_4)E$ until the input reaches the value $R_3 R_6 E / R_4 R_7$. Beyond this value, the diodes D_1 and D_3 will be *off* while D_2 and D_4 will be *on*. Once again, because the inverting inputs of both amplifiers are at virtual ground, the currents in R_5 and D_4 will be zero, and the input of D_4 will be at virtual ground. Therefore, the output y will be given by $y = (R_2/R_1)E$. This situation will remain as long as the current in D_2 is positive; that is,

$$i_{D2} = \frac{u}{R_6} + \frac{R_2 E}{R_1 R_7} > 0 \Leftrightarrow u > -\frac{R_2 R_6 E}{R_1 R_7}$$

Thus, we obtain the input–output characteristic of Figure 1.12 with

$$L_- = -\frac{R_3 E}{R_4}, \quad L_+ = \frac{R_2 E}{R_1}, \quad S_- = -\frac{R_2 R_6 E}{R_1 R_7}, \quad S_+ = \frac{R_3 R_6 E}{R_4 R_7}$$

We will see in Example 2.1 that the tunnel-diode circuit of Section 1.2.2 produces a similar characteristic when its input voltage is much slower than the dynamics of the circuit.

Another type of hysteresis nonlinearity is the backlash characteristic shown in Figure 1.15(b), which is common in gears. To illustrate backlash, the sketch of Figure 1.15(a) shows a small gap between a pair of mating gears. Suppose that the driven gear has a high friction to inertia ratio so that when the driving gear starts to decelerate, the surfaces will remain in contact at L. The input–output characteristic shown in Figure 1.15(b) depicts the angle of the driven gear y versus the angle of the driving gear u. Starting from the position shown in Figure 1.15(a), when the driving gear rotates an angle smaller than a, the driven gear does not move. For rotation larger than a, a contact is established at L and the driven gear follows the driving one, corresponding to the $A_o A$ piece of the input–output characteristic. When the driving gear reverses direction, it rotates an angle $2a$ before a contact is established at U. During this motion, the angle y remains constant, producing the AB piece of

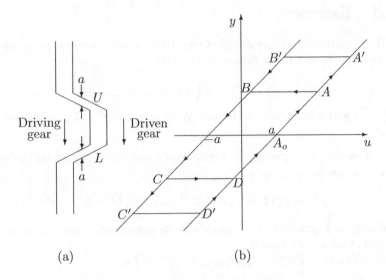

Figure 1.15: Backlash nonlinearity.

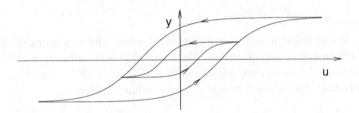

Figure 1.16: Hysteresis nonlinearity.

the characteristic. After a contact is established at U, the driven gear follows the driving one, producing the BC piece, until another reversal of direction produces the CDA piece. Thus, a periodic input of amplitude higher than a produces the $ABCD$ hysteresis loop of Figure 1.15(b). Notice that for a larger amplitude, the hysteresis loop will be $A'B'C'D'$—an important difference between this type of hysteresis characteristic and the relay with hysteresis characteristic of Figure 1.12, where the hysteresis loop is independent of the amplitude of the input.

Similar to backlash, the hysteresis characteristic of Figure 1.16, which is typical in magnetic material, has a hysteresis loop that is dependent on the amplitude of the input.[8]

---

[8]Modeling the hysteresis characteristics of Figures 1.15(b) and 1.16 is quite complex. Various modeling approaches are given in [106], [126] and [203].

1.3   Exercises

1.1 A mathematical model that describes a wide variety of physical nonlinear systems is the nth-order differential equation

$$y^{(n)} = g\left(t, y, \dot{y}, \ldots, y^{(n-1)}, u\right)$$

where u and y are scalar variables. With u as input and y as output, find a state model.

1.2 Consider a single-input–single-output system described by the nth-order differential equation

$$y^{(n)} = g_1\left(t, y, \dot{y}, \ldots, y^{(n-1)}, u\right) + g_2\left(t, y, \dot{y}, \ldots, y^{(n-2)}\right)\dot{u}$$

where g_2 is a differentiable function of its arguments. With u as input and y as output, find a state model.
Hint: Take $x_n = y^{(n-1)} - g_2\left(t, y, \dot{y}, \ldots, y^{(n-2)}\right)u$.

1.3 Consider a single-input–single-output system described by the nth-order differential equation

$$y^{(n)} = g\left(y, \ldots, y^{(n-1)}, z, \ldots, z^{(m)}\right), \quad m < n$$

where z is the input and y is the output. Extend the dynamics of the system by adding a series of m integrators at the input side and define $u = z^{(m)}$ as the input to the extended system; see Figure 1.17. Using $y, \ldots, y^{(n-1)}$ and $z, \ldots, z^{(m-1)}$ as state variables, find a state model of the extended system.

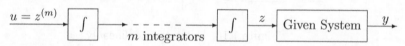

Figure 1.17: Exercise 1.3.

1.4 The nonlinear dynamic equations for an m-link robot [171, 185] take the form

$$M(q)\ddot{q} + C(q, \dot{q})\dot{q} + + D\dot{q} + g(q) = u$$

where q is an m-dimensional vector of generalized coordinates representing joint positions, u is an m-dimensional control (torque) input, and $M(q)$ is a symmetric inertia matrix, which is positive definite for all $q \in R^m$. The term $C(q, \dot{q})\dot{q}$ accounts for centrifugal and Coriolis forces. The matrix C has the property that $\dot{M} - 2C$ is a skew-symmetric matrix for all $q, \dot{q} \in R^m$, where $\dot{M}$ is the total derivative of $M(q)$ with respect to t. The term $D\dot{q}$ account for viscous damping, where D is a positive semidefinite symmetric matrix. The term $g(q)$, which accounts for gravity forces, is given by $g(q) = [\partial P(q)/\partial q]^T$, where $P(q)$ is the total potential energy of the links due to gravity. Choose appropriate state variables and find the state equation.

1.5 The nonlinear dynamic equations for a single-link manipulator with flexible joints [185], damping ignored, is given by

$$I\ddot{q}_1 + MgL\sin q_1 + k(q_1 - q_2) = 0$$
$$J\ddot{q}_2 - k(q_1 - q_2) = u$$

where q_1 and q_2 are angular positions, I and J are moments of inertia, k is a spring constant, M is the total mass, L is a distance, and u is a torque input. Choose state variables for this system and write down the state equation.

1.6 The nonlinear dynamic equations for an m-link robot with flexible joints [185] take the form

$$M(q_1)\ddot{q}_1 + h(q_1, \dot{q}_1) + K(q_1 - q_2) = 0$$
$$J\ddot{q}_2 - K(q_1 - q_2) = u$$

where q_1 and q_2 are m-dimensional vectors of generalized coordinates, $M(q_1)$ and J are symmetric nonsingular inertia matrices, and u is an m-dimensional control input. The term $h(q, \dot{q})$ accounts for centrifugal, Coriolis, and gravity forces, and K is a diagonal matrix of joint spring constants. Choose state variables for this system and write down the state equation.

1.7 Figure 1.18 shows a feedback connection of a linear time-invariant system represented by the transfer function $G(s)$ and a nonlinear time-varying element defined by $z = \psi(t, y)$. The variables r, u, y, and z are vectors of the same dimension, and $\psi(t, y)$ is a vector-valued function. With r as input and y as output, find a state model.

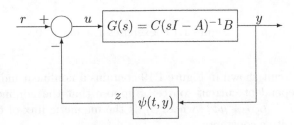

Figure 1.18: Exercise 1.7.

1.8 A synchronous generator connected to an infinite bus can be represented [148] by

$$M\ddot{\delta} = P - D\dot{\delta} - \eta_1 E_q \sin\delta$$
$$\tau\dot{E}_q = -\eta_2 E_q + \eta_3 \cos\delta + E_{FD}$$

where δ is an angle in radians, E_q is voltage, P is mechanical input power, E_{FD} is field voltage (input), D is damping coefficient, M is inertial coefficient, τ is time constant, and η_1, η_2, and η_3 are constant parameters.

(a) Using δ, $\dot{\delta}$, and E_q as state variables, find the state equation.

(b) Let $P = 0.815$, $E_{FD} = 1.22$, $\eta_1 = 2.0$, $\eta_2 = 2.7$, $\eta_3 = 1.7$, $\tau = 6.6$, $M = 0.0147$, and $D/M = 4$. Find all equilibrium points.

(c) Suppose that τ is relatively large so that $\dot{E}_q \approx 0$. Show that assuming E_q to be constant reduces the model to a pendulum equation.

1.9 The circuit shown in Figure 1.19 contains a nonlinear inductor and is driven by a time-dependent current source. Suppose that the nonlinear inductor is a Josephson junction [39], described by $i_L = I_0 \sin k\phi_L$, where ϕ_L is the magnetic flux of the inductor and I_0 and k are constants.

(a) Using ϕ_L and v_C as state variables, find the state equation.

(b) Is it easier to choose i_L and v_C as state variables?

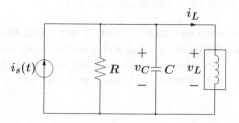

Figure 1.19: Exercises 1.9 and 1.10.

1.10 The circuit shown in Figure 1.19 contains a nonlinear inductor and is driven by a time-dependent current source. Suppose that the nonlinear inductor is described by $i_L = L\phi_L + \mu\phi_L^3$, where ϕ_L is the magnetic flux of the inductor and L and μ are positive constants.

(a) Using ϕ_L and v_C as state variables, find the state equation.

(b) Find all equilibrium points when $i_s = 0$.

1.11 A phase-locked loop [64] can be represented by the block diagram of Figure 1.20. Let $\{A, B, C\}$ be a minimal realization of the scalar, strictly proper transfer function $G(s)$. Assume that all eigenvalues of A have negative real parts, $G(0) \neq 0$, and $\theta_i = $ constant. Let z be the state of the realization $\{A, B, C\}$.

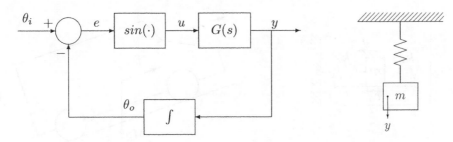

Figure 1.20: Exercise 1.11.   Figure 1.21: Exercise 1.12.

(a) Show that the closed-loop system can be represented by the state equations

$$\dot{z} = Az + B\sin e, \qquad \dot{e} = -Cz$$

(b) Find all equilibrium points of the system.

(c) Show that when $G(s) = 1/(\tau s + 1)$, the closed-loop model coincides with the model of a pendulum equation.

1.12 Consider the mass–spring system shown in Figure 1.21. Assuming a linear spring and nonlinear viscous damping described by $c_1\dot{y} + c_2\dot{y}|\dot{y}|$, find a state equation that describes the motion of the system.

1.13 An example of a mechanical system in which friction can be negative in a certain region is the structure shown in Figure 1.22 [7]. On a belt moving uniformly with velocity v_0, there lies a mass m fixed by linear springs, with spring constants k_1 and k_2. The friction force $h(v)$ exerted by the belt on the mass is a function of the relative velocity $v = v_0 - \dot{y}$. We assume that $h(v)$ is a smooth function for $|v| > 0$. In addition to this friction, assume that there is a linear viscous friction proportional to $\dot{y}$.

(a) Write down the equation of motion of the mass m.

(b) By restricting our analysis to the region $|\dot{y}| \ll v_0$, we can use a Taylor series to approximate $h(v)$ by $h(v_0) - \dot{y}h'(v_0)$. Using this approximation, simplify the model of the system.

(c) In view of the friction models discussed in Section 1.3, describe what kind of friction characteristic $h(v)$ would result in a system with negative friction.

1.14 Figure 1.23 shows a vehicle moving on a road with grade angle θ, where v the vehicle's velocity, M is its mass, and F is the tractive force generated by the engine. Assume that the friction is due to Coulomb friction, linear viscous friction, and a drag force proportional to v^2. Viewing F as the control input and θ as a disturbance input, find a state model of the system.

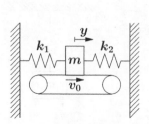

Figure 1.22: Exercise 1.13.

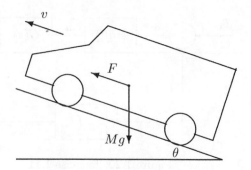

Figure 1.23: Exercise 1.14.

1.15 Consider the inverted pendulum of Figure 1.24 [110]. The pivot of the pendulum is mounted on a cart that can move in a horizontal direction. The cart is driven by a motor that exerts a horizontal force F on the cart. The figure shows also the forces acting on the pendulum, which are the force mg at the center of gravity, a horizontal reaction force H, and a vertical reaction force V at the pivot. Writing horizontal and vertical Newton's laws at the center of gravity of the pendulum yields

$$m \frac{d^2}{dt^2}(y + L\sin\theta) = H \quad \text{and} \quad m \frac{d^2}{dt^2}(L\cos\theta) = V - mg$$

Taking moments about the center of gravity yields the torque equation

$$I\ddot{\theta} = VL\sin\theta - HL\cos\theta$$

while a horizontal Newton's law for the cart yields

$$M\ddot{y} = F - H - k\dot{y}$$

Here m is the mass of the pendulum, M is the mass of the cart, L is the distance from the center of gravity to the pivot, I is the moment of inertia of the pendulum with respect to the center of gravity, k is a friction coefficient, y is the displacement of the pivot, θ is the angular rotation of the pendulum (measured clockwise), and g is the acceleration due to gravity.

(a) Carrying out the indicated differentiation and eliminating V and H, show that the equations of motion reduce to

$$I\ddot{\theta} = mgL\sin\theta - mL^2\ddot{\theta} - mL\ddot{y}\cos\theta$$

$$M\ddot{y} = F - m\left(\ddot{y} + L\ddot{\theta}\cos\theta - L\dot{\theta}^2\sin\theta\right) - k\dot{y}$$

(b) Solving the foregoing equations for $\ddot{\theta}$ and $\ddot{y}$, show that

$$\begin{bmatrix} \ddot{\theta} \\ \ddot{y} \end{bmatrix} = \frac{1}{\Delta(\theta)} \begin{bmatrix} m+M & -mL\cos\theta \\ -mL\cos\theta & I+mL^2 \end{bmatrix} \begin{bmatrix} mgL\sin\theta \\ F + mL\dot{\theta}^2\sin\theta - k\dot{y} \end{bmatrix}$$

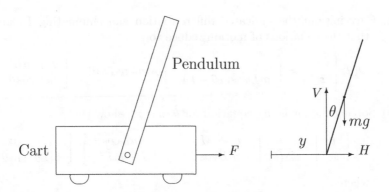

Figure 1.24: Inverted pendulum of Exercise 1.15.

where

$$\Delta(\theta) = (I + mL^2)(m + M) - m^2L^2\cos^2\theta \geq (I + mL^2)M + mI > 0$$

(c) Using $x_1 = \theta$, $x_2 = \dot{\theta}$, $x_3 = y$, and $x_4 = \dot{y}$ as the state variables and $u = F$ as the control input, write down the state equation.

1.16 Figure 1.25 shows a schematic diagram of a Translational Oscillator with Rotating Actuator (TORA) system [205]. The system consists of a platform of mass M connected to a fixed frame of reference by a linear spring, with spring constant k. The platform can only move in the horizontal plane, parallel to the spring axis. On the platform, a rotating proof mass is actuated by a DC motor. It has mass m and moment of inertial I around its center of mass, located at a distance L from its rotational axis. The control torque applied to the proof mass is denoted by u. The rotating proof mass creates a force which can be controlled to dampen the translational motion of the platform. We will derive a model for the system, neglecting friction. Figure 1.25 shows that the proof mass is subject to forces F_x and F_y and a torque u. Writing Newton's law at the center of mass and taking moments about the center of mass yield the equations

$$m\,\frac{d^2}{dt^2}(x_c + L\sin\theta) = F_x, \quad m\,\frac{d^2}{dt^2}(L\cos\theta) = F_y, \quad \text{and} \quad I\ddot{\theta} = u + F_yL\sin\theta - F_xL\cos\theta$$

where θ is the angular position of the proof mass (measured counter clockwise). The platform is subject to the forces F_x and F_y, in the opposite directions, as well as the restoring force of the spring. Newton's law for the platform yields

$$M\ddot{x}_c = -F_x - kx_c$$

where x_c is the translational position of the platform.

(a) Carrying out the indicated differentiation and eliminating F_x and F_y, show that the equations of motion reduce to

$$D(\theta) \begin{bmatrix} \ddot{\theta} \\ \ddot{x}_c \end{bmatrix} = \begin{bmatrix} u \\ mL\dot{\theta}^2 \sin\theta - kx_c \end{bmatrix}, \text{ where } D(\theta) = \begin{bmatrix} I + mL^2 & mL\cos\theta \\ mL\cos\theta & M + m \end{bmatrix}$$

(b) Solving the foregoing equation for $\ddot{\theta}$ and $\ddot{x}_c$, show that

$$\begin{bmatrix} \ddot{\theta} \\ \ddot{x}_c \end{bmatrix} = \frac{1}{\Delta(\theta)} \begin{bmatrix} m+M & -mL\cos\theta \\ -mL\cos\theta & I + mL^2 \end{bmatrix} \begin{bmatrix} u \\ mL\dot{\theta}^2 \sin\theta - kx_c \end{bmatrix}$$

where

$$\Delta(\theta) = (I + mL^2)(m+M) - m^2L^2\cos^2\theta \geq (I + mL^2)M + mI > 0$$

(c) Using $x_1 = \theta$, $x_2 = \dot{\theta}$, $x_3 = x_c$, and $x_4 = \dot{x}_c$ as the state variables and u as the control input, write down the state equation.

(d) Find all equilibrium points of the system.

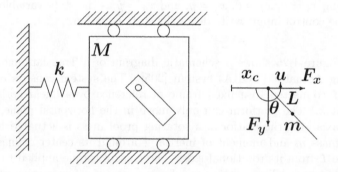

Figure 1.25: Translational Oscillator with Rotating Actuator (TORA) system.

1.17 The dynamics of a DC motor [178] can be described by

$$v_f = R_f i_f + L_f \frac{di_f}{dt}$$

$$v_a = c_1 i_f \omega + L_a \frac{di_a}{dt} + R_a i_a$$

$$J\frac{d\omega}{dt} = c_2 i_f i_a - c_3 \omega$$

The first equation is for the field circuit with v_f, i_f, R_f, and L_f being its voltage, current, resistance, and inductance. The variables v_a, i_a, R_a, and L_a are the corresponding variables for the armature circuit described by the second equation. The third equation is a torque equation for the shaft, with J as the rotor inertia and c_3 as a damping coefficient. The term $c_1 i_f \omega$ is the back e.m.f. induced in the armature circuit, and $c_2 i_f i_a$ is the torque produced by the interaction of the armature current with the field circuit flux.

(a) For a separately excited DC motor, the voltages v_a and v_f are independent control inputs. Choose appropriate state variables and find the state equation.

(b) Specialize the state equation of part(a) to the field controlled DC motor, where v_f is the control input, while v_a is held constant.

(c) Specialize the state equation of part(a) to the armature controlled DC motor, where v_a is the control input, while v_f is held constant. Can you reduce the order of the model in this case?

(d) In a shunt wound DC motor, the field and armature windings are connected in parallel and an external resistance R_x is connected in series with the field winding to limit the field flux; that is, $v = v_a = v_f + R_x i_f$. With v as the control input, write down the state equation.

1.18 Figure 1.26 shows a schematic diagram of a magnetic suspension system, where a ball of magnetic material is suspended by means of an electromagnet whose current is controlled by feedback from the, optically measured, ball position [211, pp. 192–200]. This system has the basic ingredients of systems constructed to levitate mass, used in gyroscopes, accelerometers, and fast trains. The equation of motion of the ball is

$$m\ddot{y} = -k\dot{y} + mg + F(y, i)$$

where m is the mass of the ball, $y \geq 0$ is the vertical (downward) position of the ball measured from a reference point ($y = 0$ when the ball is next to the coil), k is a viscous friction coefficient, g is the acceleration due to gravity, $F(y, i)$ is the force generated by the electromagnet, and i is its electric current. The inductance of the electromagnet depends on the position of the ball and can be modeled as

$$L(y) = L_1 + \frac{L_0}{1 + y/a}$$

where L_1, L_0, and a are positive constants. This model represents the case that the inductance has its highest value when the ball is next to the coil and decreases to a constant value as the ball is removed to $y = \infty$. With $E(y, i) = \frac{1}{2} L(y) i^2$ as the energy stored in the electromagnet, the force $F(y, i)$ is given by

$$F(y, i) = \frac{\partial E}{\partial y} = -\frac{L_0 i^2}{2a(1 + y/a)^2}$$

When the electric circuit of the coil is driven by a voltage source with voltage v, Kirchhoff's voltage law gives the relationship $v = \dot{\phi} + Ri$, where R is the series resistance of the circuit and $\phi = L(y)i$ is the magnetic flux linkage.

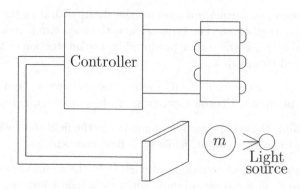

Figure 1.26: Magnetic suspension system of Exercise 1.18.

(a) Using $x_1 = y$, $x_2 = \dot{y}$, and $x_3 = i$ as state variables and $u = v$ as control input, find the state equation.

(b) Suppose it is desired to balance the ball at a certain position $r > 0$. Find the steady-state values I_{ss} and V_{ss} of i and v, respectively, which are necessary to maintain such balance.

The next three exercises give examples of hydraulic systems [41].

1.19 Figure 1.27 shows a hydraulic system where liquid is stored in an open tank. The cross-sectional area of the tank, $A(h)$, is a function of h, the height of the liquid level above the bottom of the tank. The liquid volume v is given by $v = \int_0^h A(\lambda)\, d\lambda$. For a liquid of density ρ, the absolute pressure p is given by $p = \rho g h + p_a$, where p_a is the atmospheric pressure (assumed constant) and g is the acceleration due to gravity. The tank receives liquid at a flow rate w_i and loses liquid through a valve that obeys the flow-pressure relationship $w_o = k\sqrt{\Delta p}$. In the current case, $\Delta p = p - p_a$. Take $u = w_i$ to be the control input and $y = h$ to be the output.

(a) Using h as the state variable, determine the state model.

(b) Using $p - p_a$ as the state variable, determine the state model.

(c) Find u_{ss} that is needed to maintain the output at a constant value r.

1.20 The hydraulic system shown in Figure 1.28 consists of a constant speed centrifugal pump feeding a tank from which liquid flows through a pipe and a valve that obeys the relationship $w_o = k\sqrt{p - p_a}$. The pump characteristic for the specified pump speed is shown in Figure 1.29. Let us denote this relationship by $\Delta p = \phi(w_i)$ and denote its inverse, whenever defined, by $w_i = \phi^{-1}(\Delta p)$. For the current pump, $\Delta p = p - p_a$. The cross-sectional area of the tank is uniform; therefore, $v = Ah$ and $p = p_a + \rho g v / A$, where the variables are defined in the previous exercise.

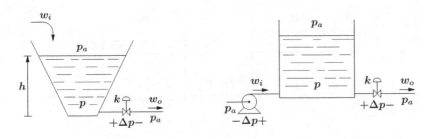

Figure 1.27: Exercise 1.19. Figure 1.28: Exercise 1.20.

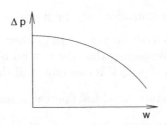

Figure 1.29: Typical centrifugal pump characteristic.

(a) Using $(p - p_a)$ as the state variable, find the state model.

(b) Find all equilibrium points of the system.

1.21 The valves in the hydraulic system of Figure 1.30 obey the flow relationships $w_1 = k_1\sqrt{p_1 - p_2}$ and $w_2 = k_2\sqrt{p_2 - p_a}$. The pump has the characteristic shown in Figure 1.29 for $(p_1 - p_a)$ versus w_p. The various components and variables are defined in the previous two exercises.

(a) Using $(p_1 - p_a)$ and $(p_2 - p_a)$ as the state variables, find the state equation.

(b) Find all equilibrium points of the system.

1.22 Consider a biochemical reactor with two components—biomass and substrate—where the biomass cells consume the substrate [23]; a schematic is shown in Figure 1.31. Assume that the reactor is perfectly mixed and the volume V is constant. Let x_1 and x_2 be the concentrations (mass/volume) of the biomass cells and substrate, respectively, and x_{1f} and x_{2f} be the corresponding concentrations in the feed stream. Let r_1 be the rate of biomass cell generation (mass/volume/time), r_2 be the rate of the substrate consumption, and F be the flow rate (volume/time). The dynamic model is developed by writing material balances on the biomass and substrate; that is,

rate of biomass accumulation = in by flow − out by flow + generation

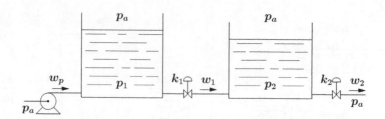

Figure 1.30: The hydraulic system of Exercise 1.21.

rate of substrate accumulation = in by flow − out by flow − consumption

The generation rate r_1 is modeled as $r_1 = \mu x_1$, where the specific growth coefficient μ is a function of x_2. We assume that there is no biomass in the feed stream, so $x_{1f} = 0$, the dilution rate $d = F/V$ is constant, and the yield $Y = r_1/r_2$ is constant.

(a) Using x_1 and x_2 as state variables, find the state model.

(b) Find all equilibrium points when $\mu = \mu_m x_2/(k_m + x_2)$ for some positive constants μ_m and k_m. Assume that $d < \mu_m$.

(c) Find all equilibrium points when $\mu = \mu_m x_2/(k_m + x_2 + k_1 x_2^2)$ for some positive constants μ_m, k_m, and k_1. Assume that $d < \max_{x_2 \geq 0}\{\mu(x_2)\}$.

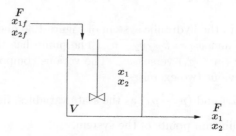

Figure 1.31: Biochemical reactor of Exercise 1.22.

Chapter 2

Second-Order Systems

Second-order autonomous systems occupy an important place in the study of nonlinear systems because solution trajectories can be represented by curves in the plane. This allows for easy visualization of the qualitative behavior of the system. The purpose of this chapter is to use second-order systems to introduce, in an elementary context, some of the basic ideas of nonlinear systems. In particular, we will look at the behavior of a nonlinear system near equilibrium points, the phenomenon of nonlinear oscillation, and bifurcation.

A second-order autonomous system is represented by two scalar differential equations

$$\dot{x}_1 = f_1(x_1, x_2) \tag{2.1}$$

$$\dot{x}_2 = f_2(x_1, x_2) \tag{2.2}$$

Let $x(t) = (x_1(t), x_2(t))$ be the solution[1] of (2.1)–(2.2) that starts at a certain initial state $x_0 = (x_{10}, x_{20})$; that is, $x(0) = x_0$. The locus in the x_1–x_2 plane of the solution $x(t)$ for all $t \geq 0$ is a curve that passes through the point x_0. This curve is called a *trajectory* or *orbit* of (2.1)–(2.2) from x_0. The x_1–x_2 plane is usually called the *state plane* or *phase plane*. The right-hand side of (2.1)–(2.2) expresses the tangent vector $\dot{x}(t) = (\dot{x}_1(t), \dot{x}_2(t))$ to the curve. Using the vector notation

$$\dot{x} = f(x)$$

where $f(x)$ is the vector $(f_1(x), f_2(x))$, we consider $f(x)$ as a *vector field* on the state plane, which means that to each point x in the plane, we assign a vector $f(x)$. For easy visualization, we represent $f(x)$ as a vector based at x; that is, we assign to x the directed line segment from x to $x + f(x)$. For example, if $f(x) = (2x_1^2, x_2)$, then at $x = (1, 1)$, we draw an arrow pointing from $(1, 1)$ to $(1, 1) + (2, 1) = (3, 2)$. (See Figure 2.1.) Repeating this at every point in a grid covering the plane, we

---

[1]It is assumed that there is a unique solution.

From Chapter 2 of *Nonlinear Systems*, Third Edition. Hassan K. Khalil.

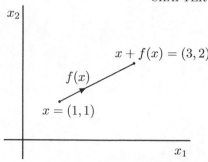

Figure 2.1: Vector field representation.

obtain a *vector field diagram*, such as the one shown in Figure 2.2 for the pendulum equation without friction:

$$\dot{x}_1 = x_2$$
$$\dot{x}_2 = -10\sin x_1$$

In the figure, the length of the arrow at a given point x is proportional to the length of $f(x)$, that is, $\sqrt{f_1^2(x) + f_2^2(x)}$. Sometimes, for convenience, we draw arrows of equal length at all points. Since the vector field at a point is tangent to the trajectory through that point, we can, in essence, construct trajectories from the vector field diagram. Starting at a given initial point x_0, we can construct the trajectory from x_0 by moving along the vector field at x_0. This motion takes us to a new point x_a, where we continue the trajectory along the vector field at x_a. If the process is repeated carefully and the consecutive points are chosen close enough to each other, we can obtain a reasonable approximation of the trajectory through x_0. In the case of Figure 2.2, a careful implementation of the foregoing process would show that the trajectory through $(2,0)$ is a closed curve.

The family of all trajectories or solution curves is called the *phase portrait* of (2.1)–(2.2). An (approximate) picture of the phase portrait can be constructed by plotting trajectories from a large number of initial states spread all over the x_1–x_2 plane. Since numerical subroutines for solving general nonlinear differential equations are widely available, we can easily construct the phase portrait by using computer simulations. (Some hints are given in Section 2.5.) Note that since the time t is suppressed in a trajectory, it is not possible to recover the solution $(x_1(t), x_2(t))$ associated with a given trajectory. Hence, a trajectory gives only the *qualitative*, but not *quantitative*, behavior of the associated solution. For example, a closed trajectory shows that there is a periodic solution; that is, the system has a sustained oscillation, whereas a shrinking spiral shows a decaying oscillation. In the rest of this chapter, we will qualitatively analyze the behavior of second-order systems by using their phase portraits.

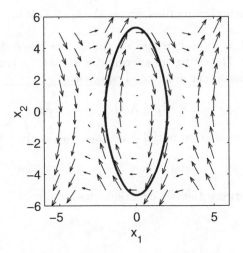

Figure 2.2: Vector field diagram of the pendulum equation without friction.

2.1 Qualitative Behavior of Linear Systems

Consider the linear time-invariant system

$$\dot{x} = Ax \tag{2.3}$$

where A is a 2×2 real matrix. The solution of (2.3) for a given initial state x_0 is given by

$$x(t) = M \exp(J_r t) M^{-1} x_0$$

where J_r is the real Jordan form of A and M is a real nonsingular matrix such that $M^{-1}AM = J_r$. Depending on the eigenvalues of A, the real Jordan form may take one of three forms

$$\begin{bmatrix} \lambda_1 & 0 \\ 0 & \lambda_2 \end{bmatrix}, \quad \begin{bmatrix} \lambda & k \\ 0 & \lambda \end{bmatrix}, \quad \text{and} \quad \begin{bmatrix} \alpha & -\beta \\ \beta & \alpha \end{bmatrix}$$

where k is either 0 or 1. The first form corresponds to the case when the eigenvalues λ_1 and λ_2 are real and distinct, the second form corresponds to the case when the eigenvalues are real and equal, and the third form corresponds to the case of complex eigenvalues $\lambda_{1,2} = \alpha \pm j\beta$. In our analysis, we have to distinguish between these three cases. Moreover, with real eigenvalues, we have to isolate the case when at least one of the eigenvalues is zero. In that situation, the origin is not an isolated equilibrium point and the qualitative behavior is quite different from the behavior in the other cases.

Case 1. Both eigenvalues are real: $\lambda_1 \neq \lambda_2 \neq 0$.

In this case, $M = [v_1, v_2]$, where v_1 and v_2 are the real eigenvectors associated with λ_1 and λ_2. The change of coordinates $z = M^{-1}x$ transforms the system into two decoupled first-order differential equations,

$$\dot{z}_1 = \lambda_1 z_1, \qquad \dot{z}_2 = \lambda_2 z_2$$

whose solution, for a given initial state (z_{10}, z_{20}), is given by

$$z_1(t) = z_{10}e^{\lambda_1 t}, \qquad z_2(t) = z_{20}e^{\lambda_2 t}$$

Eliminating t between the two equations, we obtain

$$z_2 = cz_1^{\lambda_2/\lambda_1} \tag{2.4}$$

where $c = z_{20}/(z_{10})^{\lambda_2/\lambda_1}$. The phase portrait of the system is given by the family of curves generated from (2.4) by allowing the constant c to take arbitrary values in R. The shape of the phase portrait depends on the signs of λ_1 and λ_2.

Consider first the case when both eigenvalues are negative. Without loss of generality, let $\lambda_2 < \lambda_1 < 0$. Here, both exponential terms $e^{\lambda_1 t}$ and $e^{\lambda_2 t}$ tend to zero as $t \to \infty$. Moreover, since $\lambda_2 < \lambda_1 < 0$, the term $e^{\lambda_2 t}$ tends to zero faster than the term $e^{\lambda_1 t}$. Hence, we call λ_2 the fast eigenvalue and λ_1 the slow eigenvalue. For later reference, we call v_2 the fast eigenvector and v_1 the slow eigenvector. The trajectory tends to the origin of the z_1–z_2 plane along the curve of (2.4), which now has a ratio λ_2/λ_1 that is greater than one. The slope of the curve is given by

$$\frac{dz_2}{dz_1} = c\frac{\lambda_2}{\lambda_1}z_1^{[(\lambda_2/\lambda_1)-1]}$$

Since $[(\lambda_2/\lambda_1) - 1]$ is positive, the slope of the curve approaches zero as $|z_1| \to 0$ and approaches ∞ as $|z_1| \to \infty$. Therefore, as the trajectory approaches the origin, it becomes tangent to the z_1-axis; as it approaches ∞, it becomes parallel to the z_2-axis. These observations allow us to sketch the typical family of trajectories shown in Figure 2.3. When transformed back into the x-coordinates, the family of trajectories will have the typical portrait shown in Figure 2.4(a). Note that in the x_1–x_2 plane, the trajectories become tangent to the slow eigenvector v_1 as they approach the origin and parallel to the fast eigenvector v_2 far from the origin. In this situation, the equilibrium point $x = 0$ is called a *stable node*.

When λ_1 and λ_2 are positive, the phase portrait will retain the character of Figure 2.4(a), but with the trajectory directions reversed, since the exponential terms $e^{\lambda_1 t}$ and $e^{\lambda_2 t}$ grow exponentially as t increases. Figure 2.4(b) shows the phase portrait for the case $\lambda_2 > \lambda_1 > 0$. The equilibrium point $x = 0$ is referred to in this instance as an *unstable node*.

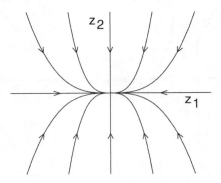

Figure 2.3: Phase portrait of a stable node in modal coordinates.

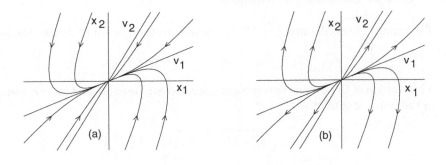

Figure 2.4: Phase portraits for (a) a stable node; (b) an unstable node.

Suppose now that the eigenvalues have opposite signs. In particular, let $\lambda_2 < 0 < \lambda_1$. In this case, $e^{\lambda_1 t} \to \infty$, while $e^{\lambda_2 t} \to 0$ as $t \to \infty$. Hence, we call λ_2 the stable eigenvalue and λ_1 the unstable eigenvalue. Correspondingly, v_2 and v_1 are called the stable and unstable eigenvectors, respectively. Equation (2.4) will have a negative exponent (λ_2/λ_1). Thus, the family of trajectories in the z_1–z_2 plane will take the typical form shown in Figure 2.5(a). Trajectories have hyperbolic shapes. They become tangent to the z_1-axis as $|z_1| \to \infty$ and tangent to the z_2-axis as $|z_1| \to 0$. The only exception to these hyperbolic shapes are the four trajectories along the axes. The two trajectories along the z_2-axis are called the stable trajectories since they approach the origin as $t \to \infty$, while the two trajectories along the z_1-axis are called the unstable trajectories since they approach infinity as $t \to \infty$. The phase portrait in the x_1–x_2 plane is shown in Figure 2.5(b). Here the stable trajectories are along the stable eigenvector v_2 and the unstable trajectories are along the unstable eigenvector v_1. In this case, the equilibrium point is called a *saddle*.

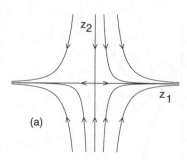
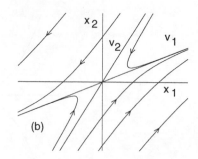

Figure 2.5: Phase portrait of a saddle point (a) in modal coordinates; (b) in original coordinates.

Case 2. Complex eigenvalues: $\lambda_{1,2} = \alpha \pm j\beta$.

The change of coordinates $z = M^{-1}x$ transforms the system (2.3) into the form

$$\dot{z}_1 = \alpha z_1 - \beta z_2, \qquad \dot{z}_2 = \beta z_1 + \alpha z_2$$

The solution of these equations is oscillatory and can be expressed more conveniently in the polar coordinates

$$r = \sqrt{z_1^2 + z_2^2}, \qquad \theta = \tan^{-1}\left(\frac{z_2}{z_1}\right)$$

where we have two uncoupled first-order differential equations:

$$\dot{r} = \alpha r \quad \text{and} \quad \dot{\theta} = \beta$$

The solution for a given initial state (r_0, θ_0) is given by

$$r(t) = r_0 e^{\alpha t} \quad \text{and} \quad \theta(t) = \theta_0 + \beta t$$

which define a logarithmic spiral in the z_1–z_2 plane. Depending on the value of α, the trajectory will take one of the three forms shown in Figure 2.6. When $\alpha < 0$, the spiral converges to the origin; when $\alpha > 0$, it diverges away from the origin. When $\alpha = 0$, the trajectory is a circle of radius r_0. Figure 2.7 shows the trajectories in the x_1–x_2 plane. The equilibrium point $x = 0$ is referred to as a *stable focus* if $\alpha < 0$, *unstable focus* if $\alpha > 0$, and *center* if $\alpha = 0$.

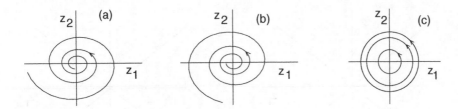

Figure 2.6: Typical trajectories in the case of complex eigenvalues.
(a) $\alpha < 0$; (b) $\alpha > 0$; (c) $\alpha = 0$.

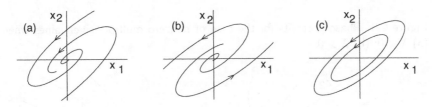

Figure 2.7: Phase portraits for (a) a stable focus; (b) an unstable focus; (c) a center.

Case 3. Nonzero multiple eigenvalues: $\lambda_1 = \lambda_2 = \lambda \neq 0$.

The change of coordinates $z = M^{-1}x$ transforms the system (2.3) into the form

$$\dot{z}_1 = \lambda z_1 + k z_2, \qquad \dot{z}_2 = \lambda z_2$$

whose solution, for a given initial state (z_{10}, z_{20}), is given by

$$z_1(t) = e^{\lambda t}(z_{10} + k z_{20} t), \qquad z_2(t) = e^{\lambda t} z_{20}$$

Eliminating t, we obtain the trajectory equation

$$z_1 = z_2 \left[\frac{z_{10}}{z_{20}} + \frac{k}{\lambda} \ln \left(\frac{z_2}{z_{20}} \right) \right]$$

Figure 2.8 shows the form of the trajectories when $k = 0$, while Figure 2.9 shows their form when $k = 1$. The phase portrait has some similarity with the portrait of a node. Therefore, the equilibrium point $x = 0$ is usually referred to as a stable node if $\lambda < 0$ and unstable node if $\lambda > 0$. Note, however, that the phase portraits of Figures 2.8 and 2.9 do not have the asymptotic slow–fast behavior that we saw in Figures 2.3 and 2.4.

Before we discuss the degenerate case when one or both of the eigenvalues are zero, let us summarize our findings about the qualitative behavior of the system when the equilibrium point $x = 0$ is isolated. We have seen that the system can display six qualitatively different phase portraits, which are associated with different

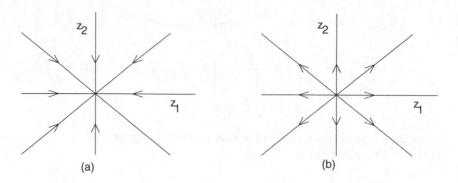

Figure 2.8: Phase portraits for the case of nonzero multiple eigenvalues when $k = 0$: (a) $\lambda < 0$; (b) $\lambda > 0$.

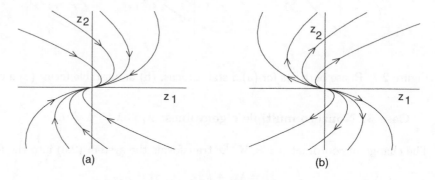

Figure 2.9: Phase portraits for the case of nonzero multiple eigenvalues when $k = 1$: (a) $\lambda < 0$; (b) $\lambda > 0$.

types of equilibria: stable node, unstable node, saddle point, stable focus, unstable focus, and center. The type of equilibrium point is completely specified by the location of the eigenvalues of A. Note that the global (throughout the phase plane) qualitative behavior of the system is determined by the type of equilibrium point. This is a characteristic of linear systems. When we study the qualitative behavior of nonlinear systems in the next section, we shall see that the type of equilibrium point can only determine the qualitative behavior of the trajectories in the vicinity of that point.

Case 4. One or both eigenvalues are zero.

When one or both eigenvalues of A are zero, the phase portrait is in some sense degenerate. Here, the matrix A has a nontrivial null space. Any vector in the null space of A is an equilibrium point for the system; that is, the system has an

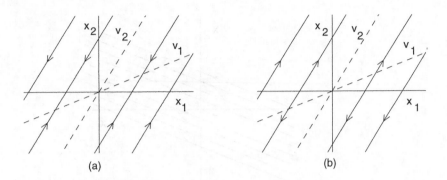

Figure 2.10: Phase portraits for (a) $\lambda_1 = 0$, $\lambda_2 < 0$; (b) $\lambda_1 = 0$, $\lambda_2 > 0$.

equilibrium subspace, rather than an equilibrium point. The dimension of the null space could be one or two; if it is two, the matrix A will be the zero matrix. This is a trivial case where every point in the plane is an equilibrium point. When the dimension of the null space is one, the shape of the Jordan form of A will depend on the multiplicity of the zero eigenvalue. When $\lambda_1 = 0$ and $\lambda_2 \neq 0$, the matrix M is given by $M = [v_1, v_2]$ where v_1 and v_2 are the associated eigenvectors. Note that v_1 spans the null space of A. The change of variables $z = M^{-1}x$ results in

$$\dot{z}_1 = 0, \qquad \dot{z}_2 = \lambda_2 z_2$$

whose solution is

$$z_1(t) = z_{10}, \qquad z_2(t) = z_{20}e^{\lambda_2 t}$$

The exponential term will grow or decay, depending on the sign of λ_2. Figure 2.10 shows the phase portrait in the x_1–x_2 plane. All trajectories converge to the equilibrium subspace when $\lambda_2 < 0$, and diverge away from it when $\lambda_2 > 0$.

When both eigenvalues are at the origin, the change of variables $z = M^{-1}x$ results in

$$\dot{z}_1 = z_2, \qquad \dot{z}_2 = 0$$

whose solution is

$$z_1(t) = z_{10} + z_{20}t, \qquad z_2(t) = z_{20}$$

The term $z_{20}t$ will increase or decrease, depending on the sign of z_{20}. The z_1-axis is the equilibrium subspace. Figure 2.11 shows the phase portrait in the x_1–x_2 plane; the dashed line is the equilibrium subspace. The phase portrait in Figure 2.11 is quite different from that in Figure 2.10. Trajectories starting off the equilibrium subspace move parallel to it.

The study of the behavior of linear systems about the equilibrium point $x = 0$ is important because, in many cases, the local behavior of a nonlinear system near an equilibrium point can be deduced by linearizing the system about that point and

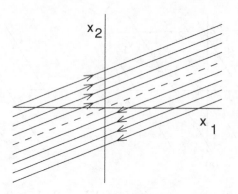

Figure 2.11: Phase portrait when $\lambda_1 = \lambda_2 = 0$.

studying the behavior of the resultant linear system. How conclusive the linearization approach is depends to a great extent on how the various qualitative phase
portraits of a linear system persist under perturbations. We can gain insight into
the behavior of a linear system under perturbations by examining the special case
of linear perturbations. Suppose A has distinct eigenvalues and consider $A + \Delta A$,
where ΔA is a 2×2 real matrix whose elements have arbitrarily small magnitudes.
From the perturbation theory of matrices,[2] we know that the eigenvalues of a matrix depend continuously on its parameters. This means that, given any positive
number ε, there is a corresponding positive number δ such that if the magnitude
of the perturbation in each element of A is less than δ, the eigenvalues of the perturbed matrix $A + \Delta A$ will lie in open discs of radius ε centered at the eigenvalues
of A. Consequently, any eigenvalue of A that lies in the open right-half plane (positive real part) or in the open left-half plane (negative real part) will remain in
its respective half of the plane after arbitrarily small perturbations. On the other
hand, eigenvalues on the imaginary axis, when perturbed, might go into either the
right-half or the left-half of the plane, since a disc centered on the imaginary axis
will extend in both halves no matter how small ε is. Consequently, we can conclude
that if the equilibrium point $x = 0$ of $\dot{x} = Ax$ is a node, focus, or saddle point,
then the equilibrium point $x = 0$ of $\dot{x} = (A + \Delta A)x$ will be of the same type for
sufficiently small perturbations. The situation is quite different if the equilibrium
point is a center. Consider the perturbation of the real Jordan form in the case of
a center

$$\begin{bmatrix} \mu & 1 \\ -1 & \mu \end{bmatrix}$$

where μ is a perturbation parameter. When μ is positive, the equilibrium point of
the perturbed system is an unstable focus; when μ is negative, it is a stable focus.

---

[2]See [67, Chapter 7].

This is true no matter how small μ is, as long as it is different from zero. Because the phase portraits of a stable focus and unstable focus are qualitatively different from the phase portrait of a center, we see that a center equilibrium point will not persist under perturbations. The node, focus, and saddle equilibrium points are said to be *structurally stable* because they maintain their qualitative behavior under infinitesimally small perturbations,[3] while the center equilibrium point is not structurally stable. The distinction between the two cases is due to the location of the eigenvalues of A, with the eigenvalues on the imaginary axis being vulnerable to perturbations. This brings in the definition of a *hyperbolic equilibrium point*. The origin $x = 0$ is said to be a hyperbolic equilibrium point of $\dot{x} = Ax$ if A has no eigenvalues with zero real part.[4]

When A has multiple nonzero real eigenvalues, infinitesimally small perturbations could result in a pair of complex eigenvalues. Hence, a stable (respectively, unstable) node would either remain a stable (respectively, unstable) node or become a stable (respectively, unstable) focus.

When A has eigenvalues at zero, one would expect perturbations to move these eigenvalues away from zero, resulting in a major change in the phase portrait. It turns out, however, that there is an important difference between the case when there is only one eigenvalue at zero and the case when both eigenvalues are at zero $(A \neq 0)$. In the first case, perturbation of the zero eigenvalue results in a real eigenvalue $\lambda_1 = \mu$, where μ could be positive or negative. Since the other eigenvalue λ_2 is different from zero, its perturbation will keep it away from zero. Moreover, since we are talking about arbitrarily small perturbations, $|\lambda_1| = |\mu|$ will be much smaller than $|\lambda_2|$. Thus, we end up with two real distinct eigenvalues, which means that the equilibrium point of the perturbed system will be a node or a saddle point, depending on the signs of λ_2 and μ. This is already an important change in the phase portrait. However, a careful examination of the phase portrait gives more insight into the qualitative behavior of the system. Since $|\lambda_1| \ll |\lambda_2|$, the exponential term $e^{\lambda_2 t}$ will change with t much faster than the exponential term $e^{\lambda_1 t}$, resulting in the typical phase portraits of a node and a saddle shown in Figure 2.12, for the case $\lambda_2 < 0$. Comparing these phase portraits with Figure 2.10(a) shows some similarity. In particular, similar to Figure 2.10, trajectories starting off the eigenvector v_1 converge to that vector along lines (almost) parallel to the eigenvector v_2. As they approach the vector v_1, they become tangent to it and move along it. When $\mu < 0$, the motion along v_1 converges to the origin (stable node), while when $\mu > 0$ the motion along v_1 tends to infinity (saddle point). This qualitative behavior is characteristic of singularly perturbed systems, which will be studied in Chapter 11.

When both eigenvalues of A are zeros, the effect of perturbations is more dra-

---

[3]See [81, Chapter 16] for a rigorous and more general definition of structural stability.

[4]This definition of a hyperbolic equilibrium point extends to higher-dimensional systems. It also carries over to equilibria of nonlinear systems by applying it to the eigenvalues of the linearized system.

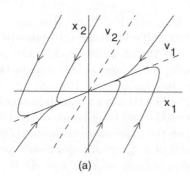 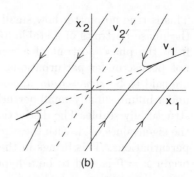

(a)　　　　　　　　　　　　　　　　　　　　(b)

Figure 2.12: Phase portraits of a perturbed system when $\lambda_1 = 0$ and $\lambda_2 < 0$: (a) $\mu < 0$; (b) $\mu > 0$.

matic. Consider the four possible perturbations of the Jordan form

$$\begin{bmatrix} 0 & 1 \\ -\mu^2 & 0 \end{bmatrix}, \quad \begin{bmatrix} \mu & 1 \\ -\mu^2 & \mu \end{bmatrix}, \quad \begin{bmatrix} \mu & 1 \\ 0 & \mu \end{bmatrix}, \quad \text{and} \quad \begin{bmatrix} \mu & 1 \\ 0 & -\mu \end{bmatrix}$$

where μ is a perturbation parameter that could be positive or negative. It can easily be seen that the equilibrium points in these four cases are a center, a focus, a node, and a saddle point, respectively. In other words, all the possible phase portraits of an isolated equilibrium point could result from perturbations.

2.2　Multiple Equilibria

The linear system $\dot{x} = Ax$ has an isolated equilibrium point at $x = 0$ if A has no zero eigenvalues, that is, if $\det A \neq 0$. When $\det A = 0$, the system has a continuum of equilibrium points. These are the only possible equilibria patterns that a linear system may have. A nonlinear system can have multiple isolated equilibrium points. In the following two examples, we explore the qualitative behavior of the tunnel-diode circuit of Section 1.2.2 and the pendulum equation of Section 1.2.1. Both systems exhibit multiple isolated equilibria.

Example 2.1 The state model of a tunnel-diode circuit is given by

$$\dot{x}_1 = \frac{1}{C}[-h(x_1) + x_2]$$

$$\dot{x}_2 = \frac{1}{L}[-x_1 - Rx_2 + u]$$

Assume that the circuit parameters are[5] $u = 1.2\ V$, $R = 1.5\ k\Omega = 1.5 \times 10^3\ \Omega$, $C = 2\ pF = 2 \times 10^{-12}\ F$, and $L = 5\ \mu H = 5 \times 10^{-6}\ H$. Measuring time in

---

[5]The numerical data are taken from [39].

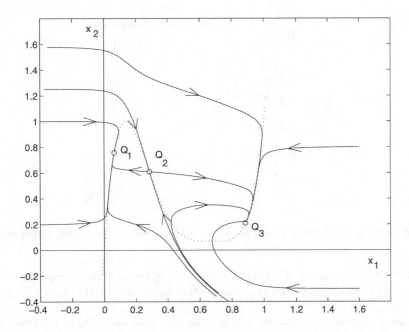

Figure 2.13: Phase portrait of the tunnel-diode circuit of Example 2.1.

nanoseconds and the currents x_2 and $h(x_1)$ in mA, the state model is given by

$$\dot{x}_1 = 0.5[-h(x_1) + x_2]$$
$$\dot{x}_2 = 0.2(-x_1 - 1.5x_2 + 1.2)$$

Suppose that $h(\cdot)$ is given by

$$h(x_1) = 17.76x_1 - 103.79x_1^2 + 229.62x_1^3 - 226.31x_1^4 + 83.72x_1^5$$

By setting $\dot{x}_1 = \dot{x}_2 = 0$ and solving for the equilibrium points, we can verify that there are three equilibrium points at $(0.063, 0.758)$, $(0.285, 0.61)$, and $(0.884, 0.21)$. The phase portrait of the system, generated by a computer program, is shown in Figure 2.13. The three equilibrium points are denoted in the portrait by Q_1, Q_2, and Q_3, respectively. Examination of the phase portrait shows that, except for two special trajectories, which approach Q_2, all trajectories eventually approach either Q_1 or Q_3. Near the equilibrium points, the trajectories take the form of a saddle for Q_2 and stable nodes for Q_1 and Q_3. The two special trajectories, which approach Q_2, are the stable trajectories of the saddle. They form a curve that divides the plane into two halves. All trajectories originating from the left side of the curve will approach Q_1, while all trajectories originating from the right side will approach Q_3. This special curve is called a *separatrix*, because it partitions the

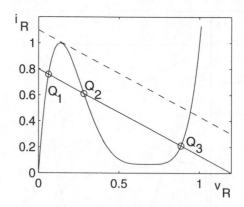

Figure 2.14: Adjustment of the load line of the tunnel-diode circuit during triggering.

plane into two regions of different qualitative behavior.[6] In an experimental setup, we shall observe one of the two steady-state operating points Q_1 or Q_3, depending on the initial capacitor voltage and inductor current. The equilibrium point at Q_2 is never observed in practice because the ever-present physical noise would cause the trajectory to diverge from Q_2 even if it were possible to set up the exact initial conditions corresponding to Q_2.

The phase portrait in Figure 2.13 tells us the global qualitative behavior of the tunnel-diode circuit. The range of x_1 and x_2 was chosen so that all essential qualitative features are displayed. The portrait outside this range does not contain any new qualitative features.

The tunnel-diode circuit with multiple equilibria is referred to as a *bistable* circuit, because it has two steady-state operating points. It has been used as a computer memory, where the equilibrium point Q_1 is associated with the binary state "0" and the equilibrium point Q_3 is associated with the binary state "1." Triggering from Q_1 to Q_3 or vice versa is achieved by a triggering signal of sufficient amplitude and duration that allows the trajectory to move to the other side of the separatrix. For example, if the circuit is initially at Q_1, then a positive pulse added to the supply voltage u will carry the trajectory to the right side of the separatrix. The pulse must be adequate in amplitude to raise the load line beyond the dashed line in Figure 2.14 and long enough to allow the trajectory to reach the right side of the separatrix.

Another feature of this circuit can be revealed if we view it as a system with input $u = E$ and output $y = v_R$. Suppose we start with a small value of u such that the only equilibrium point is Q_1. After a transient period, the system settles at Q_1. Let us now increase u gradually, allowing the circuit to settle at an equilibrium point

---

[6]In general, the state plane decomposes into a number of regions, within each of which the trajectories may show a different type of behavior. The curves separating these regions are called separatrices.

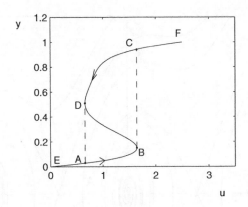

Figure 2.15: Hysteresis characteristics of the tunnel-diode circuit.

after each increment of u. For a range of values of u, Q_1 will be the only equilibrium point. On the input–output characteristic of the system, shown in Figure 2.15, this range corresponds to the segment EA. As the input is increased beyond the point A, the circuit will have two steady-state operating points at Q_1, on the segment AB, and Q_3, on the segment CD. Since we are increasing u gradually, the initial conditions will be near Q_1 and the circuit will settle there. Hence, the output will be on the segment AB. With further increase of u, we will reach a point where the circuit will have only one equilibrium point at Q_3. Therefore, after a transient period the circuit will settle at Q_3. On the input–output characteristic, it will appear as a jump from B to C. For higher values of u, the output will remain on the segment CF. Suppose now that we start decreasing u gradually. First, there will be only one equilibrium point Q_3; that is, the output will move along the segment FC. Beyond a certain value of u, corresponding to the point C, the circuit will have two steady-state operating points at Q_1 and Q_3, but will settle at Q_3 because its initial conditions will be closer to it. Hence, the output will be on the segment CD. Eventually, as we decrease u beyond the value corresponding to D, the circuit will have only one equilibrium point at Q_1 and the characteristic will exhibit another jump from D to A. Thus, the input–output characteristic of the system features a hysteresis behavior. Notice that by drawing the input–output characteristic of Figure 2.15, we ignore the dynamics of the system. Such viewpoint will be reasonable when the input is slowly varying relative to the dynamics of the system so that the transient time between different steady-state operating points can be neglected.[7] $\triangle$

Example 2.2 Consider the following pendulum equation with friction:

$$\dot{x}_1 = x_2$$

---

[7]This statement can be justified by the singular perturbation theory presented in Chapter 11.

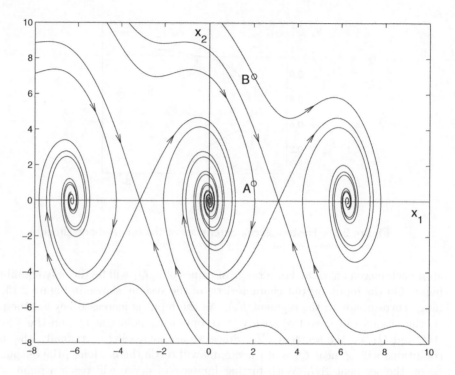

Figure 2.16: Phase portrait of the pendulum equation of Example 2.2.

$$\dot{x}_2 \;=\; -10\sin x_1 - x_2$$

A computer-generated phase portrait is shown in Figure 2.16. The phase portrait
is periodic in x_1 with period 2π. Consequently, all distinct features of the system's
qualitative behavior can be captured by drawing the portrait in the vertical strip
$-\pi \le x_1 \le \pi$. As we noted earlier, the equilibrium points $(0,0)$, $(2\pi,0)$, $(-2\pi,0)$,
etc., correspond to the downward equilibrium position $(0,0)$. Trajectories near
these equilibrium points have the pattern of a stable focus. On the other hand,
the equilibrium points at $(\pi,0)$, $(-\pi,0)$, etc., correspond to the upward equilibrium
position $(\pi,0)$. Trajectories near these equilibrium points have the pattern of a
saddle. The stable trajectories of the saddles at $(\pi,0)$ and $(-\pi,0)$ form separatrices
which contain a region with the property that all trajectories in its interior approach
the equilibrium point $(0,0)$. This picture is repeated periodically. The fact that
trajectories could approach different equilibrium points correspond to the number
of full swings a trajectory would take before it settles at the downward equilibrium
position. For example, the trajectories starting at points A and B have the same
initial position, but different speeds. The trajectory starting at A oscillates with
decaying amplitude until it settles down at equilibrium. The trajectory starting at
B, on the other hand, has more initial kinetic energy. It makes a full swing before it

starts to oscillate with decaying amplitude. Once again, notice that the "unstable" equilibrium position $(\pi, 0)$ cannot be maintained in practice, because noise would cause trajectories to diverge away from that position. $\triangle$

2.3 Qualitative Behavior Near Equilibrium Points

Examination of the phase portraits in Examples 2.1 and 2.2 shows that the qualitative behavior in the vicinity of each equilibrium point looks just like those we saw in Section 2.1 for linear systems. In particular, in Figure 2.13 the trajectories near Q_1, Q_2, and Q_3 are similar to those associated with a stable node, saddle point, and stable node, respectively. Similarly, in Figure 2.16 the trajectories near $(0,0)$ and $(\pi, 0)$ are similar to those associated with a stable focus and saddle point, respectively. In this section, we will see that we could have seen this behavior near the equilibrium points without drawing the phase portrait. It will follow from the general property that, except for some special cases, the qualitative behavior of a nonlinear system near an equilibrium point can be determined via *linearization* with respect to that point.

Let $p = (p_1, p_2)$ be an equilibrium point of the nonlinear system (2.1)–(2.2) and suppose that the functions f_1 and f_2 are continuously differentiable. Expanding the right-hand side of (2.1)–(2.2) into its Taylor series about the point (p_1, p_2), we obtain

$$
\begin{aligned}
\dot{x}_1 &= f_1(p_1, p_2) + a_{11}(x_1 - p_1) + a_{12}(x_2 - p_2) + \text{H.O.T.} \\
\dot{x}_2 &= f_2(p_1, p_2) + a_{21}(x_1 - p_1) + a_{22}(x_2 - p_2) + \text{H.O.T.}
\end{aligned}
$$

where

$$
a_{11} = \left. \frac{\partial f_1(x_1, x_2)}{\partial x_1} \right|_{x_1 = p_1, x_2 = p_2}, \qquad
a_{12} = \left. \frac{\partial f_1(x_1, x_2)}{\partial x_2} \right|_{x_1 = p_1, x_2 = p_2}
$$

$$
a_{21} = \left. \frac{\partial f_2(x_1, x_2)}{\partial x_1} \right|_{x_1 = p_1, x_2 = p_2}, \qquad
a_{22} = \left. \frac{\partial f_2(x_1, x_2)}{\partial x_2} \right|_{x_1 = p_1, x_2 = p_2}
$$

and H.O.T. denotes higher order terms of the expansion, that is, terms of the form $(x_1 - p_1)^2$, $(x_2 - p_2)^2$, $(x_1 - p_1) \times (x_2 - p_2)$, and so on. Since (p_1, p_2) is an equilibrium point, we have

$$
f_1(p_1, p_2) = f_2(p_1, p_2) = 0
$$

Moreover, since we are interested in the trajectories near (p_1, p_2), we define

$$
y_1 = x_1 - p_1 \quad \text{and} \quad y_2 = x_2 - p_2
$$

and rewrite the state equations as

$$
\begin{aligned}
\dot{y}_1 &= \dot{x}_1 = a_{11} y_1 + a_{12} y_2 + \text{H.O.T.} \\
\dot{y}_2 &= \dot{x}_2 = a_{21} y_1 + a_{22} y_2 + \text{H.O.T.}
\end{aligned}
$$

If we restrict attention to a sufficiently small neighborhood of the equilibrium point such that the higher-order terms are negligible, then we may drop these terms and approximate the nonlinear state equations by the linear state equations

$$\dot{y}_1 = a_{11}y_1 + a_{12}y_2$$
$$\dot{y}_2 = a_{21}y_1 + a_{22}y_2$$

Rewriting the equations in a vector form, we obtain

$$\dot{y} = Ay$$

where

$$A = \begin{bmatrix} a_{11} & a_{12} \\ a_{21} & a_{22} \end{bmatrix} = \begin{bmatrix} \frac{\partial f_1}{\partial x_1} & \frac{\partial f_1}{\partial x_2} \\ \frac{\partial f_2}{\partial x_1} & \frac{\partial f_2}{\partial x_2} \end{bmatrix}\Bigg|_{x=p} = \frac{\partial f}{\partial x}\Bigg|_{x=p}$$

The matrix $[\partial f/\partial x]$ is called the Jacobian matrix of $f(x)$, and A is the Jacobian matrix evaluated at the equilibrium point p.

It is reasonable to expect the trajectories of the nonlinear system in a small neighborhood of an equilibrium point to be "close" to the trajectories of its linearization about that point. Indeed, it is true that[8] *if the origin of the linearized state equation is a stable (respectively, unstable) node with distinct eigenvalues, a stable (respectively, unstable) focus, or a saddle point, then, in a small neighborhood of the equilibrium point, the trajectories of the nonlinear state equation will behave like a stable (respectively, unstable) node, a stable (respectively, unstable) focus, or a saddle point.* Consequently, we call an equilibrium point of the nonlinear state equation (2.1)–(2.2) a stable (respectively, unstable) node, a stable (respectively, unstable) focus, or a saddle point if the linearized state equation about the equilibrium point has the same behavior. The type of equilibrium points in Examples 2.1 and 2.2 could have been determined by linearization without the need to construct the global phase portrait of the system.

Example 2.3 The Jacobian matrix of the function $f(x)$ of the tunnel-diode circuit in Example 2.1 is given by

$$\frac{\partial f}{\partial x} = \begin{bmatrix} -0.5h'(x_1) & 0.5 \\ -0.2 & -0.3 \end{bmatrix}$$

where

$$h'(x_1) = \frac{dh}{dx_1} = 17.76 - 207.58x_1 + 688.86x_1^2 - 905.24x_1^3 + 418.6x_1^4$$

---

[8]The proof of this linearization property can be found in [76]. It is valid under the assumption that $f_1(x_1, x_2)$ and $f_2(x_1, x_2)$ have continuous first partial derivatives in a neighborhood of the equilibrium point (p_1, p_2). A related, but different, linearization result will be proved in Chapter 3 for higher-dimensional systems. (See Theorem 4.7.)

Evaluating the Jacobian matrix at the equilibrium points $Q_1 = (0.063, 0.758)$, $Q_2 = (0.285, 0.61)$, and $Q_3 = (0.884, 0.21)$, respectively, yields the three matrices

$$A_1 = \begin{bmatrix} -3.598 & 0.5 \\ -0.2 & -0.3 \end{bmatrix}, \quad \text{Eigenvalues}: -3.57, \ -0.33$$

$$A_2 = \begin{bmatrix} 1.82 & 0.5 \\ -0.2 & -0.3 \end{bmatrix}, \quad \text{Eigenvalues}: 1.77, \ -0.25$$

$$A_3 = \begin{bmatrix} -1.427 & 0.5 \\ -0.2 & -0.3 \end{bmatrix}, \quad \text{Eigenvalues}: -1.33, \ -0.4$$

Thus, Q_1 is a stable node, Q_2 is a saddle point, and Q_3 is a stable node. $\triangle$

Example 2.4 The Jacobian matrix of the function $f(x)$ of the pendulum equation in Example 2.2 is given by

$$\frac{\partial f}{\partial x} = \begin{bmatrix} 0 & 1 \\ -10 \cos x_1 & -1 \end{bmatrix}$$

Evaluating the Jacobian matrix at the equilibrium points $(0,0)$ and $(\pi, 0)$ yields, respectively, the two matrices

$$A_1 = \begin{bmatrix} 0 & 1 \\ -10 & -1 \end{bmatrix}, \quad \text{Eigenvalues}: -0.5 \pm j3.12$$

$$A_2 = \begin{bmatrix} 0 & 1 \\ 10 & -1 \end{bmatrix}, \quad \text{Eigenvalues}: -3.7, \ 2.7$$

Thus, the equilibrium point $(0,0)$ is a stable focus and the equilibrium point $(\pi, 0)$ is a saddle point. $\triangle$

Note that the foregoing linearization property dealt only with cases when the linearized state equation has no eigenvalues on the imaginary axis, that is, when the origin is a hyperbolic equilibrium point of the linear system. We extend this definition to nonlinear systems and say that an equilibrium point is hyperbolic if the Jacobian matrix, evaluated at that point, has no eigenvalues on the imaginary axis. If the Jacobian matrix has eigenvalues on the imaginary axis, then the qualitative behavior of the nonlinear state equation near the equilibrium point could be quite distinct from that of the linearized state equation. This should come as no surprise in view of our earlier discussion on the effect of linear perturbations on the qualitative behavior of a linear system when the origin is not a hyperbolic equilibrium point. The example that follows considers a case when the origin of the linearized state equation is a center.

Example 2.5 The system

$$\begin{aligned} \dot{x}_1 &= -x_2 - \mu x_1 (x_1^2 + x_2^2) \\ \dot{x}_2 &= x_1 - \mu x_2 (x_1^2 + x_2^2) \end{aligned}$$

has an equilibrium point at the origin. The linearized state equation at the origin has eigenvalues $\pm j$. Thus, the origin is a center equilibrium point for the linearized system. We can determine the qualitative behavior of the nonlinear system by representing it in the polar coordinates:

$$x_1 = r \cos \theta \quad \text{and} \quad x_2 = r \sin \theta$$

which yield

$$\dot{r} = -\mu r^3 \quad \text{and} \quad \dot{\theta} = 1$$

From these equations, it can be easily seen that the trajectories of the nonlinear system will resemble a stable focus when $\mu > 0$ and an unstable focus when $\mu < 0$.

$\triangle$

The preceding example shows that the qualitative behavior describing a center in the linearized state equation is not preserved in the nonlinear state equation.

The foregoing discussion excludes the case when the linearized state equation has a node with multiple eigenvalues. Exercise 2.5 shows a case where the linearization has a stable node, while the trajectories of the nonlinear state equation behave like a stable focus. It should be mentioned, however, that a smoother function $f(x)$ will not allow this to happen. In particular, if $f_1(x_1, x_2)$ and $f_2(x_1, x_2)$ are analytic functions[9] in a neighborhood of the equilibrium point, then it is true that[10] *if the origin of the linearized state equation is a stable (respectively, unstable) node, then, in a small neighborhood of the equilibrium point, the trajectories of the nonlinear state equation will behave like a stable (respectively, unstable) node whether or not the eigenvalues of the linearization are distinct.*

Determining the type of equilibrium points via linearization provides useful information that should be used when we construct a global phase portrait of a second-order system, whether we do that graphically or numerically. In fact, the first step in constructing a phase portrait should be the calculation of all equilibrium points and determining the type of isolated ones via linearization, which will give us a clear idea about the expected portrait in the neighborhood of the equilibrium points.

2.4   Limit Cycles

Oscillation is one of the most important phenomena that occur in dynamical systems. A system oscillates when it has a *nontrivial periodic solution*

$$x(t + T) = x(t), \quad \forall \, t \geq 0$$

for some $T > 0$. The word "nontrivial" is used to exclude constant solutions corresponding to equilibrium points. A constant solution satisfies the preceding equation,

---

[9]That is, f_1 and f_2 have convergent Taylor series representations.

[10]See [115, Theorem 3.4, page 188].

Figure 2.17: A linear LC circuit for the harmonic oscillator.

but it is not what we have in mind when we talk of oscillation or periodic solutions. Unless otherwise specified, from this point on whenever we refer to a periodic solution, we will mean a nontrivial one. The image of a periodic solution in the phase portrait is a closed trajectory, which is usually called a *periodic orbit* or a *closed orbit*.

We have already seen an example of oscillation in Section 2.1: the second-order linear system with eigenvalues $\pm j\beta$. The origin of that system is a center and the trajectories are closed orbits. When the system is transformed into its real Jordan form, the solution is given by

$$z_1(t) = r_0 \cos(\beta t + \theta_0), \qquad z_2(t) = r_0 \sin(\beta t + \theta_0)$$

where

$$r_0 = \sqrt{z_1^2(0) + z_2^2(0)}, \qquad \theta_0 = \tan^{-1}\left[\frac{z_2(0)}{z_1(0)}\right]$$

Therefore, the system has a sustained oscillation of amplitude r_0. It is usually referred to as the *harmonic oscillator*. If we think of the harmonic oscillator as a model for the linear LC circuit of Figure 2.17, then we can see that the physical mechanism leading to these oscillations is a periodic exchange (without dissipation) of the energy stored in the capacitor's electric field with the energy stored in the inductor's magnetic field. There are, however, two fundamental problems with this linear oscillator. The first problem is one of robustness. We have seen that infinitesimally small right-hand side (linear or nonlinear) perturbations will destroy the oscillation. That is, *the linear oscillator is not structurally stable.* In fact, it is impossible to build an LC circuit that realizes the harmonic oscillator, for the resistance in the electric wires alone will eventually consume whatever energy was initially stored in the capacitor and inductor. Even if we succeeded in building the linear oscillator, we would face the second problem: *the amplitude of oscillation is dependent on the initial conditions.*

The two fundamental problems of the linear oscillator can be eliminated in nonlinear oscillators. It is possible to build physical nonlinear oscillators such that

- The nonlinear oscillator is structurally stable.

- The amplitude of oscillation (at steady state) is independent of initial conditions.

The negative-resistance oscillator of Section 1.2.4 is an example of such nonlinear oscillators. The state equations of the system are given by

$$\begin{aligned} \dot{x}_1 &= x_2 \\ \dot{x}_2 &= -x_1 - \varepsilon h'(x_1)x_2 \end{aligned}$$

where the function h satisfies certain properties, stated in Section 1.2.4. The system has only one equilibrium point at $x_1 = x_2 = 0$. The Jacobian matrix at this point is given by

$$A = \left.\frac{\partial f}{\partial x}\right|_{x=0} = \begin{bmatrix} 0 & 1 \\ -1 & -\varepsilon h'(0) \end{bmatrix}$$

Since $h'(0) < 0$, the origin is either an unstable node or unstable focus, depending on the value of $\varepsilon h'(0)$. In either case, all trajectories starting near the origin would diverge away from it and head toward infinity. The repelling feature of the origin is due to the negative resistance of the resistive element near the origin, which means that the resistive element is "active" and supplies energy. This point can be seen analytically by writing an expression for the rate of change of energy. The total energy stored in the capacitor and inductor at any time t is given by

$$E = \tfrac{1}{2}Cv_C^2 + \tfrac{1}{2}Li_L^2$$

We have seen in Section 1.2.4 that

$$v_C = x_1 \quad \text{and} \quad i_L = -h(x_1) - \frac{1}{\varepsilon}x_2$$

Thus, recalling that $\varepsilon = \sqrt{L/C}$, we can rewrite the energy expression as

$$E = \tfrac{1}{2}C\{x_1^2 + [\varepsilon h(x_1) + x_2]^2\}$$

The rate of change of energy is given by

$$\begin{aligned} \dot{E} &= C\{x_1\dot{x}_1 + [\varepsilon h(x_1) + x_2][\varepsilon h'(x_1)\dot{x}_1 + \dot{x}_2]\} \\ &= C\{x_1x_2 + [\varepsilon h(x_1) + x_2][\varepsilon h'(x_1)x_2 - x_1 - \varepsilon h'(x_1)x_2]\} \\ &= C[x_1x_2 - \varepsilon x_1 h(x_1) - x_1x_2] \\ &= -\varepsilon C x_1 h(x_1) \end{aligned}$$

The preceding expression confirms that, near the origin, the trajectory gains energy since for small $|x_1|$ the term $x_1h(x_1)$ is negative. It also shows that there is a strip $-a \leq x_1 \leq b$ such that the trajectory gains energy within the strip and loses energy outside the strip. The strip boundaries $-a$ and b are roots of $h(x_1) = 0$, as shown in Figure 2.18. As a trajectory moves in and out of the strip, there is an exchange of energy with the trajectory gaining energy inside the strip and losing it outside. A stationary oscillation will occur if, along a trajectory, the net exchange of energy

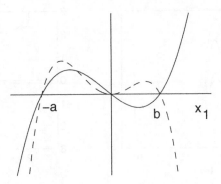

Figure 2.18: A sketch of $h(x_1)$ (solid) and $-x_1 h(x_1)$ (dashed), which shows that $\dot{E}$ is positive for $-a \leq x_1 \leq b$.

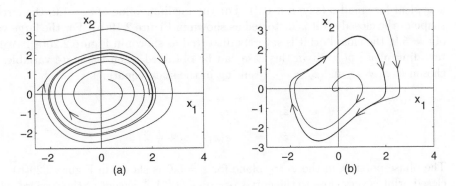

Figure 2.19: Phase portraits of the Van der Pol oscillator: (a) $\varepsilon = 0.2$; (b) $\varepsilon = 1.0$.

over one cycle is zero. Such a trajectory will be a closed orbit. It turns out that the negative-resistance oscillator has an isolated closed orbit, which is illustrated in the next example for the Van der Pol oscillator.

Example 2.6 Figures 2.19(a), 2.19(b), and 2.20(a) show the phase portraits of the Van der Pol equation

$$\dot{x}_1 = x_2 \tag{2.5}$$
$$\dot{x}_2 = -x_1 + \varepsilon(1 - x_1^2)x_2 \tag{2.6}$$

for three different values of the parameter ε: a small value of 0.2, a medium value of 1.0, and a large value of 5.0. In all three cases, the phase portraits show that there is a unique closed orbit that attracts all trajectories starting off the orbit. For $\varepsilon = 0.2$, the closed orbit is a smooth orbit that is close to a circle of radius 2. This

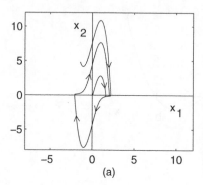 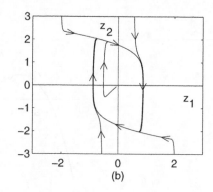

Figure 2.20: Phase portrait of the Van der Pol oscillator with $\varepsilon = 5.0$: (a) in x_1–x_2 plane; (b) in z_1–z_2 plane.

is typical for small ε (say, $\varepsilon < 0.3$). For the medium value of $\varepsilon = 1.0$, the circular shape of the closed orbit is distorted as shown in Figure 2.19(b). For the large value of $\varepsilon = 5.0$, the closed orbit is severely distorted as shown in Figure 2.20(a). A more revealing phase portrait in this case can be obtained when the state variables are chosen as $z_1 = i_L$ and $z_2 = v_C$, resulting in the state equations

$$\dot{z}_1 = \frac{1}{\varepsilon} z_2$$
$$\dot{z}_2 = -\varepsilon(z_1 - z_2 + \tfrac{1}{3} z_2^3)$$

The phase portrait in the z_1–z_2 plane for $\varepsilon = 5.0$ is shown in Figure 2.20(b). The closed orbit is very close to the curve $z_1 = z_2 - (1/3)z_2^3$, except at the corners, where it becomes nearly vertical. The vertical portion of the closed orbit can be viewed as if the closed orbit jumps from one branch of the curve to the other as it reaches the corner. Oscillations where the *jump phenomenon* takes place are usually referred to as *relaxation oscillations*. This phase portrait is typical for large values of ε (say, $\varepsilon > 3.0$). $\triangle$

The closed orbit we have seen in Example 2.6 is different from what we have seen in the harmonic oscillator. In the case of the harmonic oscillator, there is a continuum of closed orbits, while in the Van der Pol example, there is only one isolated periodic orbit. An isolated periodic orbit is called a *limit cycle*. The limit cycle of the Van der Pol oscillator has the property that all trajectories in the vicinity of the limit cycle ultimately tend toward the limit cycle as $t \to \infty$. A limit cycle with this property is classically known as a stable limit cycle. We shall also encounter *unstable limit cycles*, which have the property that all trajectories starting from points arbitrarily close to the limit cycle will tend away from it as $t \to \infty$. (See Figure 2.21.) To see an example of an unstable limit cycle, consider

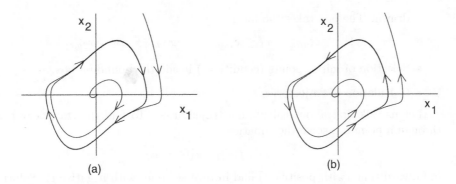

Figure 2.21: (a) A stable limit cycle; (b) an unstable limit cycle.

the Van der Pol equation in reverse time; that is,

$$\begin{aligned}
\dot{x}_1 &= -x_2 \\
\dot{x}_2 &= x_1 - \varepsilon(1 - x_1^2)x_2
\end{aligned}$$

The phase portrait of this system is identical to that of the Van der Pol oscillator, except that the arrowheads are reversed. Consequently, the limit cycle is unstable.

The limit cycle of the Van der Pol oscillator of Example 2.6 takes special forms in the limiting cases when ε is very small and very large. These special forms can be predicted analytically by using asymptotic methods. In Chapter 10, we will use the *averaging method* to derive the special form of the limit cycle as $\varepsilon \to 0$; while in Chapter 11, we will use the *singular perturbation method* to derive the special form of the limit cycle as $\varepsilon \to \infty$.

2.5 Numerical Construction of Phase Portraits

Computer programs for numerical solution of ordinary differential equations are widely available. They can be effectively used to construct phase portraits for second-order systems. In this section, we give some hints[11] that might be useful for beginners.

The first step in constructing the phase portrait is to find all equilibrium points and determine the type of isolated ones via linearization.

Drawing trajectories involves three tasks:[12]

- Selection of a bounding box in the state plane where trajectories are to be

---

[11]These hints are taken from [149, Chapter 10], which contains more instructions on how to generate informative phase portraits.

[12]A fourth task that we left out is placing arrowheads on the trajectory. For the purpose of this textbook, it can be conveniently done manually.

drawn. The box takes the form

$$x_{1min} \leq x_1 \leq x_{1max}, \qquad x_{2min} \leq x_2 \leq x_{2max}$$

- Selection of initial points (conditions) inside the bounding box.

- Calculation of trajectories.

Let us talk first about calculating trajectories. To find the trajectory passing through a point x_0, solve the equation

$$\dot{x} = f(x), \quad x(0) = x_0$$

in forward time (with positive t) and in reverse time (with negative t). Solution in reverse time is equivalent to solution in forward time of the equation

$$\dot{x} = -f(x), \quad x(0) = x_0$$

since the change of time variable $\tau = -t$ reverses the sign of the right-hand side. The arrowhead on the forward trajectory is placed heading away from x_0, while the one on the reverse trajectory is placed heading into x_0. Note that solution in reverse time is the only way we can get a good portrait in the neighborhood of unstable focus, unstable node, or unstable limit cycle. Trajectories are continued until they get out of the bounding box. If processing time is a concern, you may want to add a stopping criterion when trajectories converge to an equilibrium point.

The bounding box should be selected so that all essential qualitative features are displayed. Since some of these features will not be known *a priori*, we may have to adjust the bounding box interactively. However, our initial choice should make use of all prior information. For example, the box should include all equilibrium points. Care should be exercised when a trajectory travels out of bounds, for such a trajectory is either unbounded or is attracted to a stable limit cycle.

The simplest approach to select initial points is to place them uniformly on a grid throughout the bounding box. However, an evenly spaced set of initial conditions rarely yields an evenly spaced set of trajectories. A better approach is to select the initial points interactively after plotting the already calculated trajectories. Since most computer programs have sophisticated plotting tools, this approach should be quite feasible.

For a saddle point, we can use linearization to generate the stable and unstable trajectories. This is useful because, as we saw in Examples 2.1 and 2.2, the stable trajectories of a saddle define a separatrix. Let the eigenvalues of the linearization be $\lambda_1 > 0 > \lambda_2$ and the corresponding eigenvectors be v_1 and v_2. The stable and unstable trajectories of the nonlinear saddle will be tangent to the stable eigenvector v_2 and the unstable eigenvector v_1, respectively, as they approach the equilibrium point p. Therefore, the two unstable trajectories can be generated from the initial points $x_0 = p \pm \alpha v_1$, where α is a small positive number. Similarly, the two stable trajectories can be generated from the initial points $x_0 = p \pm \alpha v_2$. The major parts of the unstable trajectories will be generated by solution in forward time, while the major parts of the stable ones will be generated by solution in reverse time.

2.6 Existence of Periodic Orbits

Periodic orbits in the plane are special in that they divide the plane into a region inside the orbit and a region outside it. This makes it possible to obtain criteria for detecting the presence or absence of periodic orbits for second-order systems, which have no generalizations to higher order systems. The most celebrated of these criteria are the Poincaré–Bendixson theorem, the Bendixson criterion, and the index method.

We consider the second-order autonomous system

$$\dot{x} = f(x) \tag{2.7}$$

where $f(x)$ is continuously differentiable. Poincaré–Bendixson theorem gives a condition for the existence of periodic orbits of (2.7). We will not give the formal statement of the theorem,[13] but will give a corollary of the theorem which summarizes how the theorem is actually applied. We refer to this corollary as the Poincaré–Bendixson criterion.

Lemma 2.1 (Poincaré–Bendixson Criterion) *Consider the system* (2.7) *and let M be a closed bounded subset of the plane such that*

- *M contains no equilibrium points, or contains only one equilibrium point such that the Jacobian matrix* $[\partial f / \partial x]$ *at this point has eigenvalues with positive real parts. (Hence, the equilibrium point is unstable focus or unstable node.)*

- *Every trajectory starting in M stays in M for all future time.*

Then, M contains a periodic orbit of (2.7).

The intuition behind the criterion is that bounded trajectories in the plane will have to approach periodic orbits or equilibrium points as time tends to infinity. If M contains no equilibrium points, then it must contain a periodic orbit. If M contains only one equilibrium point that satisfies the stated conditions, then in the vicinity of that point all trajectories will be moving away from it. Therefore, we can choose a simple closed curve[14] around the equilibrium point such that the vector field on the curve points outward.[15] By redefining the set M to exclude the region enclosed by this curve (see Figure 2.22), we end up with a set that is free of equilibrium points, and all trajectories are trapped in it.

As a tool for investigating whether trajectories are trapped inside a set M, consider a simple closed curve defined by the equation $V(x) = c$, where $V(x)$ is continuously differentiable. The vector field $f(x)$ at a point x on the curve points

---

[13]For the statement and proof of the Poincaré–Bendixson theorem, see, for example, [135] or the second edition of this book.

[14]A simple closed curve divides the plane into a bounded region inside the curve and an unbounded region outside it (examples are circles, ellipses, and polygons).

[15]See Exercise 4.33.

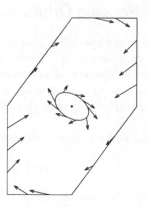

Figure 2.22: Redefinition of the set M to exclude the vicinity of an unstable focus or node.

inward if the inner product of $f(x)$ and the gradient vector $\nabla V(x)$ is negative; that is,

$$f(x) \cdot \nabla V(x) = \frac{\partial V}{\partial x_1}(x)f_1(x) + \frac{\partial V}{\partial x_2}(x)f_2(x) < 0$$

The vector field $f(x)$ points outward if $f(x) \cdot \nabla V(x) > 0$, and it is tangent to the curve if $f(x) \cdot \nabla V(x) = 0$. Trajectories can leave a set only if the vector field points outward at some point on its boundary. Therefore, for a set of the form $M = \{V(x) \leq c\}$, for some $c > 0$, trajectories are trapped inside M if $f(x) \cdot \nabla V(x) \leq 0$ on the boundary $V(x) = c$. For an annular region of the form $M = \{W(x) \geq c_1 \text{ and } V(x) \leq c_2\}$, for some $c_1 > 0$ and $c_2 > 0$, trajectories are trapped inside M if $f(x) \cdot \nabla V(x) \leq 0$ on $V(x) = c_2$ and $f(x) \cdot \nabla W(x) \geq 0$ on $W(x) = c_1$.

We illustrate the application of the Poincaré–Bendixson criterion in the next two examples, while the third example is a nontrivial application to the negative-resistance oscillator of Section 1.2.4.

Example 2.7 Consider the harmonic oscillator

$$\begin{aligned}
\dot{x}_1 &= x_2 \\
\dot{x}_2 &= -x_1
\end{aligned}$$

and the annular region $M = \{ c_1 \leq V(x) \leq c_2 \}$, where $V(x) = x_1^2 + x_2^2$ and $c_2 > c_1 > 0$. The set M is closed, bounded, and free of equilibrium points, since the only equilibrium point is at the origin $(0,0)$. Trajectories are trapped inside M since $f(x) \cdot \nabla V(x) = 0$ everywhere. Hence, by the Poincaré–Bendixson criterion, we conclude that there is a periodic orbit in M. $\triangle$

The preceding example emphasizes the fact that the Poincaré–Bendixson criterion assures the existence of a periodic orbit, but not its uniqueness. From our earlier study of the harmonic oscillator, we know that it has a continuum of periodic orbits in M.

Example 2.8 The system

$$\begin{aligned}
\dot{x}_1 &= x_1 + x_2 - x_1(x_1^2 + x_2^2) \\
\dot{x}_2 &= -2x_1 + x_2 - x_2(x_1^2 + x_2^2)
\end{aligned}$$

has a unique equilibrium point at the origin, and the Jacobian matrix

$$\left. \frac{\partial f}{\partial x} \right|_{x=0} = \left[\begin{array}{cc} 1 - 3x_1^2 - x_2^2 & 1 - 2x_1 x_2 \\ -2 - 2x_1 x_2 & 1 - x_1^2 - 3x_2^2 \end{array} \right]_{x=0} = \left[\begin{array}{cc} 1 & 1 \\ -2 & 1 \end{array} \right]$$

has eigenvalues $1 \pm j\sqrt{2}$. Let $M = \{V(x) \leq c\}$, where $V(x) = x_1^2 + x_2^2$ and $c > 0$. It is clear that M is closed, bounded, and contains only one equilibrium point at which the Jacobian matrix has eigenvalues with positive real parts. On the surface $V(x) = c$, we have

$$\begin{aligned}
\frac{\partial V}{\partial x_1} f_1 + \frac{\partial V}{\partial x_2} f_2 &= 2x_1[x_1 + x_2 - x_1(x_1^2 + x_2^2)] + 2x_2[-2x_1 + x_2 - x_2(x_1^2 + x_2^2)] \\
&= 2(x_1^2 + x_2^2) - 2(x_1^2 + x_2^2)^2 - 2x_1 x_2 \\
&\leq 2(x_1^2 + x_2^2) - 2(x_1^2 + x_2^2)^2 + (x_1^2 + x_2^2) \\
&= 3c - 2c^2
\end{aligned}$$

where we used the fact that $|2x_1 x_2| \leq x_1^2 + x_2^2$. By choosing $c \geq 1.5$, we can ensure that all trajectories are trapped inside M. Hence, by the Poincaré–Bendixson criterion, we conclude that there is a periodic orbit in M. $\triangle$

Example 2.9 The negative-resistance oscillator of Section 1.2.4 is modeled by the second-order differential equation

$$\ddot{v} + \varepsilon h'(v)\dot{v} + v = 0$$

where ε is a positive constant and h satisfies the conditions

$$h(0) = 0, \quad h'(0) < 0, \quad \lim_{v \to \infty} h(v) = \infty, \quad \text{and} \quad \lim_{v \to -\infty} h(v) = -\infty$$

To simplify the analysis, we impose the additional requirements

$$h(v) = -h(-v), \quad h(v) < 0 \text{ for } 0 < v < a, \quad \text{and} \quad h(v) > 0 \text{ for } v > a$$

These additional requirements are satisfied by the typical function of Figure 1.6(b), as well as by the function $h(v) = -v + (1/3)v^3$ of the Van der Pol oscillator. Choose the state variables as

$$x_1 = v \quad \text{and} \quad x_2 = \dot{v} + \varepsilon h(v)$$

to obtain the state model

$$\begin{aligned}
\dot{x}_1 &= x_2 - \varepsilon h(x_1) \\
\dot{x}_2 &= -x_1
\end{aligned} \tag{2.8}$$

which has a unique equilibrium point at the origin. We start our analysis by showing that every nonequilibrium solution rotates around the equilibrium point in the clockwise direction. To this end, we divide the state plane into four regions, which are determined by the intersection of the two curves

$$x_2 - \varepsilon h(x_1) = 0 \quad \text{and} \quad x_1 = 0$$

as shown in Figure 2.23. The figure also shows the general direction of the vector field $f(x)$ of (2.8) in the four regions as well as on the boundaries between them. It is not difficult to see that a solution starting at point $A = (0, p)$ on the upper half of the x_2-axis describes an orbit with an arc of the general nature shown in Figure 2.24. The point E where the arc intersects the lower half of the x_2-axis depends on the starting point A. Let us denote E by $(0, -\alpha(p))$. We will show that if p is chosen large enough, then $\alpha(p) < p$. Consider the function

$$V(x) = \tfrac{1}{2}(x_1^2 + x_2^2)$$

To show that $\alpha(p) < p$, it is enough to show that $V(E) - V(A) < 0$, since

$$V(E) - V(A) = \tfrac{1}{2}[\alpha^2(p) - p^2] \stackrel{\text{def}}{=} \delta(p)$$

The derivative of $V(x)$ is given by

$$\dot{V}(x) = x_1 \dot{x}_1 + x_2 \dot{x}_2 = x_1 x_2 - \varepsilon x_1 h(x_1) - x_1 x_2 = -\varepsilon x_1 h(x_1)$$

Thus, $\dot{V}$ is positive for $x_1 < a$ and negative for $x_1 > a$. Now,

$$\delta(p) = V(E) - V(A) = \int_{AE} \dot{V}(x(t))\, dt$$

where the right-hand side integral is taken along the arc from A to E. If p is small, the whole arc will lie inside the strip $0 < x_1 < a$. Then, $\delta(p)$ will be positive. As p increases, a piece of the arc will lie outside the strip, that is, the piece BCD in Figure 2.24. In this case, we evaluate the integral in different ways depending on whether the arc is inside or outside the strip $0 < x_1 < a$. We divide the integral into three parts

$$\delta(p) = \delta_1(p) + \delta_2(p) + \delta_3(p)$$

where

$$\delta_1(p) = \int_{AB} \dot{V}(x(t))\, dt, \quad \delta_2(p) = \int_{BCD} \dot{V}(x(t))\, dt, \quad \delta_3(p) = \int_{DE} \dot{V}(x(t))\, dt$$

Consider first the term

$$\delta_1(p) = -\int_{AB} \varepsilon x_1 h(x_1)\, dt = -\int_{AB} \varepsilon x_1 h(x_1)\, \frac{dt}{dx_1}\, dx_1$$

Substituting for dx_1/dt from (2.8), we obtain

$$\delta_1(p) = -\int_{AB} \varepsilon x_1 h(x_1) \frac{1}{x_2 - \varepsilon h(x_1)}\, dx_1$$

where, along the arc AB, x_2 is a given function of x_1. Clearly, $\delta_1(p)$ is positive. Note that as p increases, $x_2 - \varepsilon h(x_1)$ increases for the arc AB. Hence, $\delta_1(p)$ decreases as $p \to \infty$. Similarly, it can be shown that the third term $\delta_3(p)$ is positive and decreases as $p \to \infty$. Consider now the second term

$$\delta_2(p) = -\int_{BCD} \varepsilon x_1 h(x_1)\, dt = -\int_{BCD} \varepsilon x_1 h(x_1)\, \frac{dt}{dx_2}\, dx_2$$

Substituting for dx_2/dt from (2.8), we obtain

$$\delta_2(p) = \int_{BCD} \varepsilon h(x_1)\, dx_2$$

where along the arc BCD, x_1 is a given function of x_2. The integral on the right-hand side is negative since $h(x_1) > 0$ and $dx_2 < 0$. As p increases, the arc $ABCDE$ moves to the right and the domain of integration for $\delta_2(p)$ increases. It follows that $\delta_2(p)$ decreases as p increases and evidently $\lim_{p\to\infty} \delta_2(p) = -\infty$. In summary, we have shown that

- $\delta(p) > 0$, if $p < r$, for some $r > 0$.

- $\delta(p)$ decreases monotonically to $-\infty$ as $p \to \infty$, $p \geq r$.

A sketch of the function $\delta(p)$ is shown in Figure 2.25. It is now clear that by choosing p large enough, we can ensure that $\delta(p)$ is negative; hence, $\alpha(p) < p$.

Observe that, due to symmetry induced by the fact that $h(\cdot)$ is an odd function, if $(x_1(t), x_2(t))$ is a solution of (2.8), then so is $(-x_1(t), -x_2(t))$. Therefore, if we know that a path $ABCDE$ exists as in Figure 2.24, then the reflection of that path through the origin is another path. Consider $A = (0, p)$ and $E = (0, -\alpha(p))$, where $\alpha(p) < p$. Form a closed curve of the arc $ABCDE$, its reflection through the origin and segments on the x_2-axis connecting these arcs, to form a closed curve. (See Figure 2.26). Let M be the region enclosed by this closed curve. Every trajectory starting in M at $t = 0$ will remain inside for all $t \geq 0$. This is a consequence of the directions of the vector fields on the x_2-axis segments and the fact that trajectories do not intersect each other due to uniqueness of solutions. Now M is closed, bounded, and has a unique equilibrium point at the origin. The Jacobian

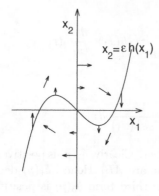   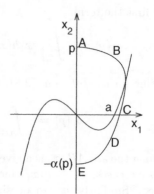

Figure 2.23: Vector field diagram for   Figure 2.24: The orbit $ABCDE$ of
Example 2.9.   Example 2.9.

matrix at the origin

$$A = \left.\frac{\partial f}{\partial x}\right|_{x=0} = \begin{bmatrix} 0 & 1 \\ -1 & -\varepsilon h'(0) \end{bmatrix}$$

has eigenvalues with positive real parts since $h'(0) < 0$. Thus, by the Poincaré–Bendixson criterion, we conclude that there is a closed orbit in M.

Using the same analysis, we can go beyond the Poincaré–Bendixson criterion and show that this closed orbit is unique. Notice that, due to the symmetry property alluded to earlier, the system can have a closed orbit if and only if $\alpha(p) = p$. From Figure 2.25, it is clear that there is only one value of p for which the condition is satisfied. Hence, there is only one closed orbit. Furthermore, we can show that every nonequilibrium solution spirals toward the unique closed orbit. To argue this point, let $p_0 > 0$ be the unique value of p for which $\alpha(p) = p$. Consider a point $(0, p)$ on the x_2-axis with $p > p_0$. As we argued earlier, the trajectory through $(0, p)$ intersects the lower half of the x_2-axis at a point $(0, -\alpha(p))$, where $\alpha(p) < p$. Due to symmetry, the trajectory through $(0, -\alpha(p))$ will meet the upper half of the x_2-axis at a point $(0, \sigma(p))$, where $p_0 \leq \sigma(p) < p$. The upper bound follows from the symmetry property, while the lower bound holds since for $\sigma(p)$ to be less than p_0, the trajectory must intersect the closed orbit. The map $p \to \sigma(p)$ is continuous due to continuous dependence of the solution on the initial states.[16] Starting again at the point $(0, \sigma(p))$, the trajectory comes back to the upper half of the x_2-axis at $(0, \sigma^2(p))$, where $p_0 \leq \sigma^2(p) < \sigma(p)$. By induction, we generate a sequence $\sigma^n(p)$, which satisfies

$$p_0 \leq \sigma^{n+1}(p) < \sigma^n(p), \quad n = 1, 2, \ldots$$

---

[16]This fact is shown in Theorem 3.4.

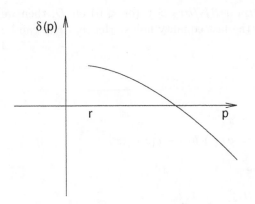

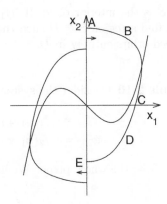

Figure 2.25: A sketch of the function $\delta(p)$ of Example 2.9.

Figure 2.26: The closed curve formed in Example 2.9.

The sequence $\sigma^n(p)$ has a limit $p_1 \geq p_0$. Note that, by continuity of $\sigma(\cdot)$, the limit p_1 satisfies

$$\sigma(p_1) - p_1 = \lim_{n \to \infty} \sigma(\sigma^n(p)) - p_1 = p_1 - p_1 = 0$$

By uniqueness of the closed orbit, it must be that $p_1 = p_0$. This shows that the trajectory of p spirals toward the unique closed orbit as $t \to \infty$. The same thing is true for $p < p_0$. $\triangle$

The next result, known as the *Bendixson criterion*, can be used to rule out the existence of periodic orbits in some cases.

Lemma 2.2 (Bendixson Criterion) *If, on a simply connected region[17] D of the plane, the expression $\partial f_1/\partial x_1 + \partial f_2/\partial x_2$ is not identically zero and does not change sign, then system (2.7) has no periodic orbits lying entirely in D.* $\diamond$

Proof: On any orbit of (2.7), we have $dx_2/dx_1 = f_2/f_1$. Therefore, on any closed orbit γ, we have

$$\int_\gamma f_2(x_1, x_2) \, dx_1 - f_1(x_1, x_2) \, dx_2 = 0$$

This implies, by Green's theorem, that

$$\int\int_S \left(\frac{\partial f_1}{\partial x_1} + \frac{\partial f_2}{\partial x_2} \right) \, dx_1 \, dx_2 = 0$$

---

[17]A region D is simply connected if, for every simple closed curve C in D, the inner region of C is a also a subset of D. The interior of any circle is simply connected, but the annular region $0 < c_1 \leq x_1^2 + x_2^2 \leq c_2$ is not simply connected. Intuitively speaking, simple connectedness is equivalent to the absence of "holes."

where S is the interior of γ. If $\partial f_1/\partial x_1 + \partial f_2/\partial x_2 > 0$ (or < 0) on D, then we cannot find a region $S \subset D$ such that the last equality holds. Hence, there can be no closed orbits entirely in D.   □

Example 2.10 Consider the system

$$
\begin{aligned}
\dot{x}_1 &= f_1(x_1, x_2) = x_2 \\
\dot{x}_2 &= f_2(x_1, x_2) = ax_1 + bx_2 - x_1^2 x_2 - x_1^3
\end{aligned}
$$

and let D be the whole plane. We have

$$
\frac{\partial f_1}{\partial x_1} + \frac{\partial f_2}{\partial x_2} = b - x_1^2
$$

Hence, there can be no periodic orbits if $b < 0$.   △

We conclude this section with a useful result that relates the existence of periodic orbits and equilibrium points. The result uses the (Poincaré) index of an equilibrium point. Given the second-order system (2.7), let C be a simple closed curve not passing through any equilibrium point of (2.7). Consider the orientation of the vector field $f(x)$ at a point $p \in C$. Letting p traverse C in the counterclockwise direction, the vector $f(x)$ rotates continuously and, upon returning to the original position, must have rotated an angle $2\pi k$ for some integer k, where the angle is measured counterclockwise. The integer k is called the index of the closed curve C. If C is chosen to encircle a single isolated equilibrium point $\bar{x}$, then k is called the index of $\bar{x}$. It is left to the reader (Exercise 2.25) to verify the next lemma by examining the vector fields.

Lemma 2.3

(a) *The index of a node, a focus, or a center is $+1$.*

(b) *The index of a (hyperbolic) saddle is -1.*

(c) *The index of a closed orbit is $+1$.*

(d) *The index of a closed curve not encircling any equilibrium points is 0.*

(e) *The index of a closed curve is equal to the sum of the indices of the equilibrium points within it.*   ◇

As a corollary to this lemma, we have the following:

Corollary 2.1 *Inside any periodic orbit γ, there must be at least one equilibrium point. Suppose the equilibrium points inside γ are hyperbolic, then if N is the number of nodes and foci and S is the number of saddles, it must be that $N - S = 1$.*   ◇

Recall that an equilibrium point is hyperbolic if the Jacobian at that point has no eigenvalues on the imaginary axis. If the equilibrium point is not hyperbolic, then its index may differ from ± 1. (See Exercise 2.26.)

The index method is usually useful in ruling out the existence of periodic orbits in certain regions of the plane.

Example 2.11 The system

$$
\begin{aligned}
\dot{x}_1 &= -x_1 + x_1 x_2 \\
\dot{x}_2 &= x_1 + x_2 - 2x_1 x_2
\end{aligned}
$$

has two equilibrium points at $(0,0)$ and $(1,1)$. The Jacobian matrices at these points are

$$
\left[\frac{\partial f}{\partial x} \right]_{(0,0)} = \left[\begin{array}{cc} -1 & 0 \\ 1 & 1 \end{array} \right]; \qquad \left[\frac{\partial f}{\partial x} \right]_{(1,1)} = \left[\begin{array}{cc} 0 & 1 \\ -1 & -1 \end{array} \right]
$$

Hence, $(0,0)$ is a saddle, while $(1,1)$ is a stable focus. The only combination of equilibrium points that can be encircled by a periodic orbit is a single focus. Other possibilities of periodic orbits, like a periodic orbit encircling both equilibria, are ruled out. $\triangle$

2.7 Bifurcation

The qualitative behavior of a second-order system is determined by the pattern of its equilibrium points and periodic orbits, as well as by their stability properties. One issue of practical importance is whether the system maintains its qualitative behavior under infinitesimally small perturbations. When it does so, the system is said to be structurally stable. In this section, we are interested in the complement of structural stability. In particular, we are interested in perturbations that will change the equilibrium points or periodic orbits of the system or change their stability properties. Consider, for example, the system

$$
\begin{aligned}
\dot{x}_1 &= \mu - x_1^2 \\
\dot{x}_2 &= -x_2
\end{aligned}
$$

which depends on a parameter μ. For $\mu > 0$, the system has two equilibrium points at $(\sqrt{\mu}, 0)$ and $(-\sqrt{\mu}, 0)$. Linearization at $(\sqrt{\mu}, 0)$ results in the Jacobian matrix

$$
\left[\begin{array}{cc} -2\sqrt{\mu} & 0 \\ 0 & -1 \end{array} \right]
$$

which shows that $(\sqrt{\mu}, 0)$ is a stable node, while linearization at $(-\sqrt{\mu}, 0)$ yields the Jacobian matrix

$$
\left[\begin{array}{cc} 2\sqrt{\mu} & 0 \\ 0 & -1 \end{array} \right]
$$

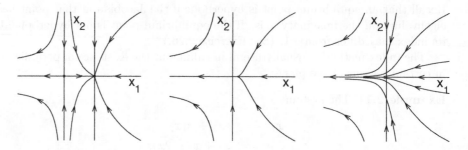

Figure 2.27: Phase portrait of the saddle–node bifurcation example for $\mu > 0$ (left), $\mu = 0$ (center), and $\mu < 0$ (right).

which shows that $(-\sqrt{\mu}, 0)$ is a saddle. As μ decreases, the saddle and node approach each other, collide at $\mu = 0$, and disappear for $\mu < 0$. As μ crosses zero, we witness a dramatic change in the phase portrait of the system. Figure 2.27 shows the phase portrait for positive, zero, and negative values of μ. While for positive μ, no matter how small it is, all trajectories in $\{x_1 > -\sqrt{\mu}\}$ reach steady state at the stable node, for negative μ all trajectories eventually escape to infinity. Such a change in the qualitative behavior of the system is called bifurcation. More generally, *bifurcation is a change in the equilibrium points or periodic orbits, or in their stability properties, as a parameter is varied.* The parameter is called *a bifurcation parameter*, and the values at which changes occur are called *bifurcation points*. In the foregoing example, the bifurcation parameter is μ, and the bifurcation point is $\mu = 0$.

The bifurcation we saw in the previous example can be represented by the *bifurcation diagram* shown in Figure 2.28(a). The diagram sketches a measure of the amplitude (or norm) of the equilibrium points versus the bifurcation parameter. The stable node is represented by a solid line, and the saddle by a dashed line. More generally, the ordinate of a bifurcation diagram is a measure of the amplitude of equilibrium points or periodic orbits, with solid lines representing stable nodes, stable foci, and stable limit cycles and dashed lines representing unstable nodes, unstable foci, saddles, and unstable limit cycles. The bifurcation represented in Figure 2.28(a) is called *saddle–node bifurcation* because it results from the collision of a saddle and a node. Note that the Jacobian matrix has a zero eigenvalue at the bifurcation point. This feature is common to the bifurcations shown in Figures 2.28(a) through (d), which are all examples of the so called *zero-eigenvalue bifurcation*. Figure 2.28(b) shows a *transcritical bifurcation*, where equilibrium points persist through the bifurcation, but their stability properties change. For example, the system

$$\begin{aligned} \dot{x}_1 &= \mu x_1 - x_1^2 \\ \dot{x}_2 &= -x_2 \end{aligned}$$

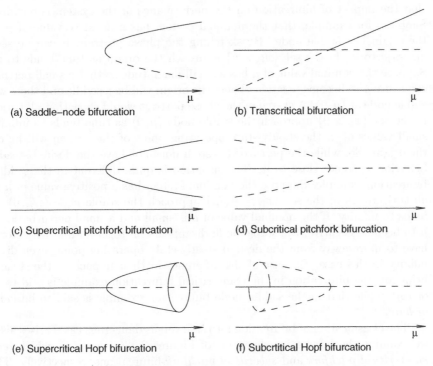

(a) Saddle–node bifurcation

(b) Transcritical bifurcation

(c) Supercritical pitchfork bifurcation

(d) Subcritical pitchfork bifurcation

(e) Supercritical Hopf bifurcation

(f) Subcrtitical Hopf bifurcation

Figure 2.28: Bifurcation diagrams.

has two equilibrium points at $(0,0)$ and $(\mu,0)$. The Jacobian at $(0,0)$ is

$$\begin{bmatrix} \mu & 0 \\ 0 & -1 \end{bmatrix}$$

which shows that $(0,0)$ is a stable node for $\mu < 0$ and a saddle for $\mu > 0$. On the other hand, the Jacobian at $(\mu,0)$ is

$$\begin{bmatrix} -\mu & 0 \\ 0 & -1 \end{bmatrix}$$

which shows that $(\mu,0)$ is a saddle for $\mu < 0$ and a stable node for $\mu > 0$. So, while the equilibrium points persist through the bifurcation point $\mu = 0$, $(0,0)$ changes from a stable node to a saddle and $(\mu,0)$ changes from a saddle to a stable node.

Before we proceed to describe the other bifurcations in Figure 2.28, let us note an important difference between the foregoing two examples. In the latter example, crossing the bifurcation point causes the equilibrium point at the origin to change from a stable node to a saddle, but at the same time it creates a stable node at $(\mu,0)$, which for small values of μ will be close to the origin. This could mean that the impact of bifurcation on the performance of the system is not dramatic. Suppose, for example, that the nominal system has a negative value of μ so that the origin is a stable node. By sketching the phase portrait, it can be seen that all trajectories in the set $\{x_1 > \mu\}$ approach the origin as time tends to infinity. Suppose the nominal value of μ has a small magnitude so that a small perturbation can cause μ to become positive. Then, the origin will be a saddle and there will be a stable node at $(\mu, 0)$. A sketch of the phase portrait would show that all trajectories in the set $\{x_1 > 0\}$ approach the stable node $(\mu, 0)$ as time tends to infinity. For small values of μ, the steady-state operating point of the system will be close to the origin. So, while the perturbed system does not have the desired steady-state behavior, it comes close to it. The situation is quite different in the saddle–node bifurcation example. Suppose the nominal system has a positive value of μ so that all trajectories in the set $\{x_1 > -\sqrt{\mu}\}$ approach the stable node $(\sqrt{\mu}, 0)$ as time tends to infinity. If the nominal value of μ is small and a small perturbation causes μ to become negative, the stable node disappears all together and trajectories will have to move away from the desired steady-state operating point, even diverge to infinity in this case. Because of the difference in their impact on the steady-state behavior, the bifurcation in the transcritical bifurcation example is said to be *safe* or *soft*, while that in the saddle–node bifurcation example is said to be *dangerous* or *hard*.

The classification of bifurcation into safe versus dangerous cases arises also when we examine the bifurcation diagrams of Figures 2.28(c) and (d), which represent *supercritical pitchfork* and *subcritical pitchfork* bifurcations, respectively. The first of the two cases is exemplified by the system

$$\begin{aligned} \dot{x}_1 &= \mu x_1 - x_1^3 \\ \dot{x}_2 &= -x_2 \end{aligned}$$

For $\mu < 0$, there is a unique equilibrium point at the origin. By calculating the Jacobian, we can see that the origin is a stable node. For $\mu > 0$, there are three equilibrium points at $(0, 0)$, $(\sqrt{\mu}, 0)$, and $(-\sqrt{\mu}, 0)$. Jacobian calculations show that $(0, 0)$ is a saddle and the other two equilibria are stable nodes. Thus, as μ crosses the bifurcation point $\mu = 0$, the stable node at the origin bifurcates into a saddle and gives birth to two stable nodes at $(\pm\sqrt{\mu}, 0)$. The amplitude of the newly created stable nodes grows with μ; hence, it is small for small μ. Subcritical pitchfork bifurcation is exemplified by the system

$$\begin{aligned} \dot{x}_1 &= \mu x_1 + x_1^3 \\ \dot{x}_2 &= -x_2 \end{aligned}$$

For $\mu < 0$, there are three equilibrium points: a stable node at $(0, 0)$ and two saddles at $(\pm\sqrt{-\mu}, 0)$. For $\mu > 0$, there is a unique equilibrium point at $(0, 0)$, which is a saddle. Thus, as μ crosses the bifurcation point $\mu = 0$, the stable node at the origin collides with the saddles at $(\pm\sqrt{-\mu}, 0)$ and bifurcates into a saddle. Comparing the supercritical and subcritical pitchfork bifurcations, we can easily see that the supercritical bifurcation is safe, while the subcritical one is dangerous. In particular, if the system has a nominal operating point at the stable node $(0,0)$ for $\mu < 0$, then supercritical pitchfork bifurcation ensures close steady-state operation when μ is perturbed to a small positive value, while in subcritical pitchfork bifurcation trajectories move away from the nominal operating point.

In the simplified examples we used to discuss zero-eigenvalue bifurcations, we noticed that in dangerous cases trajectories diverge to infinity. In more complicated examples, the system may have other equilibrium points or periodic orbits that are not affected by the bifurcation under consideration. Trajectories moving away from the bifurcating equilibrium point could be attracted by another equilibrium point or period orbit rather than diverge to infinity. This situation is illustrated by the next example.

Example 2.12 Consider the tunnel-diode circuit of Section 1.2.2:

$$
\begin{aligned}
\dot{x}_1 &= \frac{1}{C}\left[-h(x_1) + x_2\right] \\
\dot{x}_2 &= \frac{1}{L}\left[-x_1 - Rx_2 + \mu\right]
\end{aligned}
$$

The diode's v–i characteristic $h(\cdot)$ is sketched in Figure 1.2 and μ is a constant input. Let us study bifurcation as μ is varied. The equilibrium points of the system are the intersections of the curve $x_2 = h(x_1)$ with the load line $x_2 = (\mu - x_1)/R$. From Figure 2.29(a) and Examples 2.1 and 2.3, we know that for $\mu < A$, there is a stable node on the left branch; for $A < \mu < B$, there are three equilibrium points, a saddle on the middle branch and two stable nodes on the other two branches; and for $\mu > B$, there is a stable node on the right branch. The bifurcation diagram is shown in Figure 2.29(b). There are two saddle–node bifurcations at $\mu = A$ and $\mu = B$. Notice that when a stable node disappears upon collision with a saddle, trajectories that move away are attracted by the other stable node which is not affected by the bifurcation.   △

When a stable node loses stability at a bifurcation point, an eigenvalue of the Jacobian passes through zero. What about a stable focus losing stability? In this case, a pair of conjugate complex eigenvalues could pass through the imaginary axis. Figures 2.28(e) and (f) are examples of this situation, where Figures 2.28(e) is called *supercritical Hopf bifurcation* and Figures 2.28(f) is called *subcritical Hopf bifurcation*.[18] The supercritical Hopf bifurcation is exemplified by the system

$$
\begin{aligned}
\dot{x}_1 &= x_1(\mu - x_1^2 - x_2^2) - x_2 \\
\dot{x}_2 &= x_2(\mu - x_1^2 - x_2^2) + x_1
\end{aligned}
$$

---

[18]The names Andronov–Hopf bifurcation and Poincaré–Andronov–Hopf bifurcation are also used to acknowledge the earlier contributions of Poincaré and Andronov.

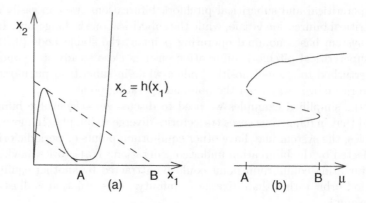

Figure 2.29: Example 2.12: (a) determining equilibrium points; (b) bifurcation diagram.

which is represented in the polar coordinates

$$x_1 = r \cos \theta \quad \text{and} \quad x_2 = r \sin \theta$$

by

$$\dot{r} = \mu r - r^3 \quad \text{and} \quad \dot{\theta} = 1$$

The system has a unique equilibrium point at the origin and the phase portraits for opposite signs of μ are shown in Figure 2.30. For $\mu < 0$, the origin is a stable focus and all trajectories are attracted to it, while for $\mu > 0$, the origin is an unstable focus, but there is a stable limit cycle that attracts all trajectories, except the zero solution. The limit cycle is $r = \sqrt{\mu}$, which shows that the amplitude of oscillation grows with μ and is small for small values of μ. This is a safe bifurcation because when the stable focus disappears due to small perturbation, the system will have a steady-state oscillation with a small amplitude. To see how the eigenvalues behave during bifurcation, notice that the Jacobian at the origin

$$\begin{bmatrix} \mu & -1 \\ 1 & \mu \end{bmatrix}$$

has eigenvalues $\mu \pm j$, which cross the imaginary axis from left to right as μ increases from negative to positive values.

The subcritical Hopf bifurcation is exemplified by the system

$$\begin{aligned} \dot{x}_1 &= x_1 \left[\mu + (x_1^2 + x_2^2) - (x_1^2 + x_2^2)^2 \right] - x_2 \\ \dot{x}_2 &= x_2 \left[\mu + (x_1^2 + x_2^2) - (x_1^2 + x_2^2)^2 \right] + x_1 \end{aligned}$$

which is represented in polar coordinates by

$$\dot{r} = \mu r + r^3 - r^5 \quad \text{and} \quad \dot{\theta} = 1$$

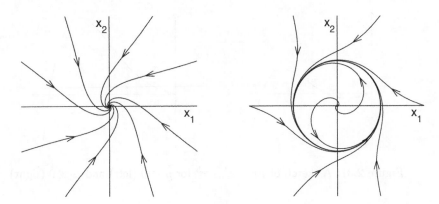

Figure 2.30: Phase portrait of the supercritical Hopf bifurcation example for $\mu < 0$ (left) and $\mu > 0$ (right).

There is a unique equilibrium point at the origin, which is a stable focus for $\mu < 0$ and unstable focus for $\mu > 0$. From the equation

$$0 = \mu + r^2 - r^4$$

we can determine the limit cycles of the system. For $\mu < 0$, there are two limit cycles at $r^2 = (1 \pm \sqrt{1 + 4\mu})/2$. By sketching $\dot{r} = r(\mu + r^2 - r^4)$ as a function of r (see Figure 2.31), it can be seen that the limit cycle at $r^2 = (1 + \sqrt{1 + 4\mu})/2$ is stable, while the limit cycle at $r^2 = (1 - \sqrt{1 + 4\mu})/2$ is unstable. For small $|\mu|$, the unstable limit cycle can be approximated by $r^2 = -\mu$. For $\mu > 0$, there is only one stable limit cycle at $r^2 = (1 + \sqrt{1 + 4\mu})/2$. Thus, as μ increases from negative to positive values, the stable focus at the origin merges with the unstable limit cycle and bifurcates into an unstable focus, as represented by the bifurcation diagram of Figures 2.28(f). Notice that the stable limit cycle is not shown in the bifurcation diagram because varying μ only varies its amplitude. The subcritical Hopf bifurcation is dangerous because small perturbation of a nominal stable focus at the origin could force trajectories to move away from the origin. Those trajectories are attracted by the stable limit cycle.

All the bifurcations represented in Figure 2.28 occur in the vicinity of an equilibrium point. Therefore, they are called *local bifurcations*. There are also *global bifurcations*, which involve large regions of the state plane and cannot be described in the vicinity of any equilibrium point. We give only one example of global bifurcations.[19] Consider the system

$$
\begin{aligned}
\dot{x}_1 &= x_2 \\
\dot{x}_2 &= \mu x_2 + x_1 - x_1^2 + x_1 x_2
\end{aligned}
$$

---

[19]See [187] for other examples.

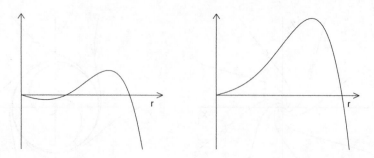

Figure 2.31: A sketch of $\mu r + r^3 - r^5$ for $\mu < 0$ (left) and $\mu > 0$ (right).

There are two equilibrium points at $(0,0)$ and $(1,0)$. By linearization, we can see that $(0,0)$ is always a saddle, while $(1,0)$ is an unstable focus for $-1 < \mu < 1$. Let us limit our analysis to the range $-1 < \mu < 1$. Figure 2.32 shows the phase portrait for four different values of μ. The phase portraits for $\mu = -0.95$ and -0.88 are typical for $\mu < \mu_c \approx -0.8645$, while that for $\mu = -0.8$ is typical for $\mu > \mu_c$. For $\mu < \mu_c$, there is a stable limit cycle that encircles the unstable focus. As μ increases towards μ_c, the limit cycle swells and finally touches the saddle at $\mu = \mu_c$, creating a trajectory that starts and ends at the saddle; such trajectory is called *homoclinic orbit*. For $\mu > \mu_c$, the limit cycle disappears. Note that this bifurcation occurs without any changes to the equilibrium points at $(0,0)$ and $(1,0)$. This type of global bifurcation is called *saddle–connection* or *homoclinic bifurcation*.

2.8   Exercises

2.1 For each of the following systems, find all equilibrium points and determine the type of each isolated equilibrium:

(1) $\quad \dot{x}_1 \;=\; -x_1 + 2x_1^3 + x_2,$ $\qquad\qquad \dot{x}_2 \;=\; -x_1 - x_2$

(2) $\quad \dot{x}_1 \;=\; x_1 + x_1 x_2,$ $\qquad\qquad\qquad \dot{x}_2 \;=\; -x_2 + x_2^2 + x_1 x_2 - x_1^3$

(3) $\quad \dot{x}_1 \;=\; [1 - x_1 - 2h(x)]\, x_1,$ $\qquad \dot{x}_2 \;=\; [2 - h(x)]\, x_2$

(4) $\quad \dot{x}_1 \;=\; x_2,$ $\qquad\qquad\qquad\qquad\quad \dot{x}_2 \;=\; -x_1 + x_2(1 - x_1^2 + 0.1x_1^4)$

(5) $\quad \dot{x}_1 \;=\; (x_1 - x_2)(1 - x_1^2 - x_2^2),$ $\quad \dot{x}_2 \;=\; (x_1 + x_2)(1 - x_1^2 - x_2^2)$

(6) $\quad \dot{x}_1 \;=\; -x_1^3 + x_2,$ $\qquad\qquad\qquad \dot{x}_2 \;=\; x_1 - x_2^3$

In the third system, $h(x) = x_2/(1 + x_1)$.

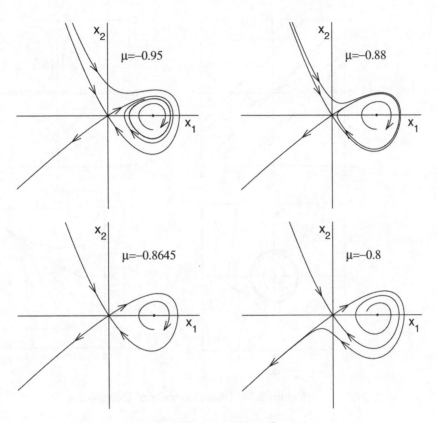

Figure 2.32: Saddle–connection bifurcation.

2.2 For each of the following systems, find all equilibrium points and determine the type of each isolated equilibrium:

$$(1) \qquad \dot{x}_1 \;=\; x_2, \qquad\qquad \dot{x}_2 \;=\; -x_1 + \tfrac{1}{16}x_1^5 - x_2$$

$$(2) \qquad \dot{x}_1 \;=\; 2x_1 - x_1 x_2, \qquad \dot{x}_2 \;=\; 2x_1^2 - x_2$$

$$(3) \qquad \dot{x}_1 \;=\; x_2, \qquad\qquad \dot{x}_2 \;=\; -x_2 - \psi(x_1 - x_2)$$

In the third system, $\psi(y) = y^3 + 0.5y$ if $|y| \le 1$ and $\psi(y) = 2y - 0.5\,\mathrm{sgn}(y)$ if $|y| > 1$.

2.3 For each of the systems in Exercise 2.1, construct the phase portrait and discuss the qualitative behavior of the system.

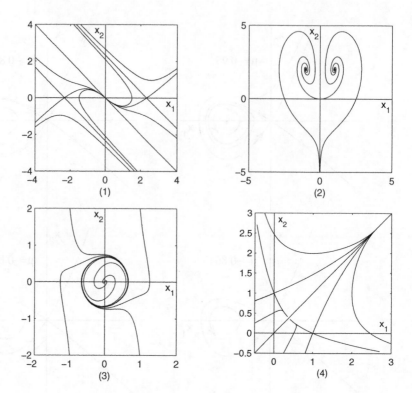

Figure 2.33: Phase portraits of Exercise 2.4.

2.4 The phase portraits of the following four systems are shown in Figure 2.33.

$$(1) \qquad \dot{x}_1 = x_2, \qquad\qquad\qquad \dot{x}_2 = x_1 - 2\tan^{-1}(x_1 + x_2)$$

$$(2) \qquad \dot{x}_1 = 2x_1 - x_1x_2, \qquad\qquad \dot{x}_2 = 2x_1^2 - x_2$$

$$(3) \qquad \dot{x}_1 = x_2, \qquad\qquad\qquad \dot{x}_2 = -x_1 + x_2(1 - 3x_1^2 - 2x_2^2)$$

$$(4) \qquad \dot{x}_1 = -(x_1 - x_1^2) + h(x), \qquad \dot{x}_2 = -(x_2 - x_2^2) + h(x)$$

In the fourth system, $h(x) = 1 - x_1 - x_2$. Mark the arrowheads and discuss the qualitative behavior of each system.

2.5 The system

$$\dot{x}_1 = -x_1 - \frac{x_2}{\ln\sqrt{x_1^2 + x_2^2}}, \qquad \dot{x}_2 = -x_2 + \frac{x_1}{\ln\sqrt{x_1^2 + x_2^2}}$$

has an equilibrium point at the origin.

(a) Linearize the system about the origin and show that the origin is a stable node of the linear system.

(b) Find the phase portrait of the nonlinear system near the origin and show that the portrait resembles a stable focus.
Hint: Transform the equations into polar coordinates.

(c) Explain the discrepancy between the results of parts (a) and (b).

2.6 Consider the system

$$\dot{x}_1 = -x_1 + ax_2 - bx_1x_2 + x_2^2$$
$$\dot{x}_2 = -(a + b)x_1 + bx_1^2 - x_1x_2$$

where $a > 0$ and $b \neq 0$.

(a) Find all equilibrium points of the system.

(b) Determine the type of each isolated equilibrium point, for all values of $a > 0$ and $b \neq 0$.

(c) For each of the following cases, construct the phase portrait and discuss the qualitative behavior of the system:

i. $a = b = 1$.
ii. $a = 1$, $b = -\frac{1}{2}$.
iii. $a = 1$, $b = -2$.

2.7 Consider the negative resistance oscillator of Section 1.2.4 with

$$h(v) = -v + v^3 - \tfrac{1}{5}v^5 + \tfrac{1}{105}v^7$$

and $\varepsilon = 1$. Construct the phase portrait in the x-coordinates and discuss the qualitative behavior of system.

2.8 Consider the system

$$\dot{x}_1 = x_2, \qquad \dot{x}_2 = -x_1 + \tfrac{1}{16}x_1^5 - x_2$$

(a) Find the equilibrium points and determine the type of each isolated one.

(b) Without using a computer program, sketch the phase portrait of the system.

2.9 For cruise control, the longitudinal motion of a vehicle on a flat road can be modeled, with the use of Newton's second law, by the first-order differential equation

$$m\dot{v} = u - K_c \, \text{sgn}(v) - K_f v - K_a v^2$$

where m is the vehicle's mass, v is its speed, u is the tractive force generated by the engine, $K_c \operatorname{sgn}(v)$ is the coulomb friction force, $K_f v$ is the viscous friction force, and $K_a v^2$ is the aerodynamic drag. The coefficients K_c, K_f and K_a are nonnegative. When a PI controller is used, $u = K_I \sigma + K_P(v_d - v)$, where v_d is the desired speed, σ is the state of the integrator $\dot{\sigma} = v_d - v$, and K_I and K_P are positive constants. We are only interested in the region $v \geq 0$.

(a) Using $x_1 = \sigma$ and $x_2 = v$ as the state variables, find the state model of the system.

(b) Let v_d be a positive constant. Find all equilibrium points and determine the type of each point.

(c) Construct the phase portrait and discuss the qualitative behavior of the system, for the following numerical data: $m = 1500$ kg, $K_c = 110$ N, $K_f = 2.5$ N/m/sec, $K_a = 1$ N/m^2/sec^2, $K_I = 15$, $K_P = 500$, and $v_d = 30$ m/sec.

(d) Repeat part (c) when K_I is increased to 150. Compare with the behavior in part (c).

(e) Repeat part (c) when saturation is used to limit u to the range $0 \leq u \leq 1800$ N. Compare with the behavior in part (c).

2.10 Consider the tunnel-diode circuit of Section 1.2.2 with the numerical data used in Example 2.1, except for R and E, which are taken as $E = 0.2V$ and $R = 0.2k\Omega$.

(a) Find all equilibrium points and determine the type of each point.

(b) Construct the phase portrait and discuss the qualitative behavior of the circuit.

2.11 Repeat the previous problem with $E = 0.4V$ and $R = 0.2k\Omega$.

2.12 Consider the Hopfield neural network model of Section 1.2.4 with $n = 2$, $V_M = 1$, and $T_{21} = T_{12} = 1$. For $i = 1, 2$, take $I_i = 0$, $C_i = 1$, $\rho_i = 1$, $T_{ii} = 0$, and $g_i(u) = (2/\pi) \tan^{-1}(\lambda \pi u/2)$.

(a) Find all equilibrium points and determine the type of each point.

(b) For $\lambda = 5$, construct the phase portrait and discuss the qualitative behavior of the system.

2.13 An equivalent circuit of the Wien–Bridge oscillator is shown in Figure 2.34 [40], where $g(v_2)$ is a nonlinear voltage-controlled voltage source.

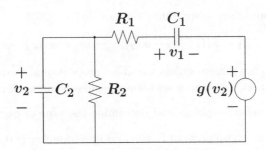

Figure 2.34: Exercise 2.13.

(a) With $x_1 = v_1$ and $x_2 = v_2$ as state variables, show that the state model is given by

$$\dot{x}_1 = \frac{1}{C_1 R_1}[-x_1 + x_2 - g(x_2)]$$

$$\dot{x}_2 = -\frac{1}{C_2 R_1}[-x_1 + x_2 - g(x_2)] - \frac{1}{C_2 R_2}x_2$$

(b) Let $C_1 = C_2 = R_1 = R_2 = 1$ and $g(v) = 3.234v - 2.195v^3 + 0.666v^5$. Construct the phase portrait and discuss the qualitative behavior of the system.

2.14 Consider the mass-spring system with Coulomb friction

$$\ddot{y} + ky + c\dot{y} + \eta(y, \dot{y}) = 0$$

where η is defined in Section 1.2.3. Use piecewise linear analysis to sketch the phase portrait (without numerical data) and discuss the qualitative behavior of the system.

2.15 Consider the system

$$\dot{x}_1 = x_2, \qquad \dot{x}_2 = u$$

where the control input u can take the values ± 1.

(a) Sketch the phase portrait when $u = 1$.

(b) Sketch the phase portrait when $u = -1$.

(c) By superimposing the two phase portraits, develop a strategy for switching the control between ± 1 so that any point in the state plane can be moved to the origin in finite time.

2.16 A prey–predatory system may be modeled by [202]

$$\dot{x}_1 = x_1(1 - x_1 - ax_2), \qquad \dot{x}_2 = bx_2(x_1 - x_2)$$

where x_1 and x_2 are dimensionless variables proportional to the prey and predator populations, respectively, and a and b are positive constants.

(a) Find all equilibrium points and determine the type of each point.

(b) Construct the phase portrait in the first quadrant $(x_1 \geq 0, x_2 \geq 0)$ when $a = 1$, $b = 0.5$ and discuss the qualitative behavior of the system.

2.17 For each of the following systems, use the Poincaré–Bendixson's criterion to show that the system has a periodic orbit:

(1) $\qquad \ddot{y} + y \;\; = \;\; \varepsilon \dot{y}(1 - y^2 - \dot{y}^2)$

(2) $\qquad \dot{x}_1 \;\; = \;\; x_2, \qquad\qquad\qquad\quad \dot{x}_2 \;\; = \;\; -x_1 + x_2(2 - 3x_1^2 - 2x_2^2)$

(3) $\qquad \dot{x}_1 \;\; = \;\; x_2, \qquad\qquad\qquad\quad \dot{x}_2 \;\; = \;\; -x_1 + x_2 - 2(x_1 + 2x_2)x_2^2$

(4) $\qquad \dot{x}_1 \;\; = \;\; x_1 + x_2 - x_1 h(x), \qquad \dot{x}_2 \;\; = \;\; -2x_1 + x_2 - x_2 h(x)$

In the fourth system, $h(x) = \max\{|x_1|, |x_2|\}$.

2.18 (Conservative Systems) Consider the second-order system

$$\dot{x}_1 = x_2, \qquad \dot{x}_2 = -g(x_1)$$

where g is continuously differentiable and $zg(z) > 0$ for $z \in (-a, a)$. Consider the energy function

$$V(x) = \tfrac{1}{2}x_2^2 + \int_0^{x_1} g(z) \, dz$$

(a) Show that $V(x)$ remains constant during the motion of the system.

(b) Show that, for sufficiently small $\|x(0)\|$, every solution is periodic.

(c) Suppose that $zg(z) > 0$ for $z \in (-\infty, \infty)$ and

$$\int_0^y g(z) \, dz \to \infty \text{ as } |y| \to \infty$$

Show that every solution is a periodic solution.

(d) Suppose that $g(z) = -g(-z)$ and let $G(y) = \int_0^y g(z) \, dz$. Show that the trajectory through $(A, 0)$ is given by

$$x_2 = \pm\sqrt{2[G(A) - G(x_1)]}$$

(e) Using part (d), show that the period of oscillation of a closed trajectory through $(A, 0)$ is

$$T(A) = 2\sqrt{2} \int_0^A \frac{dy}{[G(A) - G(y)]^{1/2}}$$

(f) Discuss how the trajectory equation in part (d) can be used to construct the phase portrait of the system.

2.19 Use the previous exercise to construct the phase portrait and study periodic solutions for each of the following systems:

$$\textbf{(1)} \ \ g(x_1) = \sin x_1, \qquad \textbf{(2)} \ \ g(x_1) = x_1 + x_1^3, \qquad \textbf{(3)} \ \ g(x_1) = x_1^3$$

In each case, give the period of oscillation of the periodic orbit through the point $(1, 0)$.

2.20 For each of the following systems, show that the system has no limit cycles:

$$\textbf{(1)} \qquad \dot{x}_1 = -x_1 + x_2, \qquad\qquad \dot{x}_2 = g(x_1) + ax_2, \ \ a \neq 1$$

$$\textbf{(2)} \qquad \dot{x}_1 = -x_1 + x_1^3 + x_1 x_2^2, \qquad \dot{x}_2 = -x_2 + x_2^3 + x_1^2 x_2$$

$$\textbf{(3)} \qquad \dot{x}_1 = 1 - x_1 x_2^2, \qquad\qquad \dot{x}_2 = x_1$$

$$\textbf{(4)} \qquad \dot{x}_1 = x_1 x_2, \qquad\qquad\qquad \dot{x}_2 = x_2$$

$$\textbf{(5)} \qquad \dot{x}_1 = x_2 \cos(x_1), \qquad\qquad \dot{x}_2 = \sin x_1$$

2.21 Consider the system

$$\dot{x}_1 = -x_1 + x_2(x_1 + a) - b, \qquad \dot{x}_2 = -cx_1(x_1 + a)$$

where a, b, and c are positive constants with $b > a$. Let

$$D = \left\{ x \in R^2 \ | \ x_1 < -a \text{ and } x_2 < \frac{x_1 + b}{x_1 + a} \right\}$$

(a) Show that every trajectory starting in D stays in D for all future time.

(b) Show that there can be no periodic orbits through any point $x \in D$.

2.22 Consider the system

$$\dot{x}_1 = ax_1 - x_1 x_2, \qquad \dot{x}_2 = bx_1^2 - cx_2$$

where a, b, and c are positive constants with $c > a$. Let $D = \{x \in R^2 \ | \ x_2 \geq 0\}$.

(a) Show that every trajectory starting in D stays in D for all future time.

(b) Show that there can be no periodic orbits through any point $x \in D$.

2.23 ([85]) Consider the system

$$\dot{x}_1 = x_2, \qquad \dot{x}_2 = -[2b - g(x_1)]ax_2 - a^2 x_1$$

where a and b are positive constants, and

$$g(x_1) = \begin{cases} 0, & |x_1| > 1 \\ k, & |x_1| \leq 1 \end{cases}$$

(a) Show, using Bendixson's criterion, that there are no periodic orbits if $k < 2b$.

(b) Show, using the Poincaré–Bendixson criterion, that there is a periodic orbit if $k > 2b$.

2.24 Consider a second-order system and suppose that the set $M = \{x_1^2 + x_2^2 \leq a^2\}$ has the property that every trajectory starting in M stays in M for all future time. Show that M contains an equilibrium point.

2.25 Verify Lemma 2.3 by examining the vector fields.

2.26 ([70]) For each of the following systems, show that the origin is not hyperbolic, find the index of the origin, and verify that it is different from ± 1:

$$\begin{array}{llll} (1) & \dot{x}_1 = x_1^2, & \dot{x}_2 = -x_2 \end{array}$$

$$\begin{array}{llll} (2) & \dot{x}_1 = x_1^2 - x_2^2, & \dot{x}_2 = 2x_1 x_2 \end{array}$$

2.27 For each of the following systems, find and classify bifurcations that occur as μ varies:

$$\begin{array}{llll} (1) & \dot{x}_1 = x_2, & \dot{x}_2 = \mu(x_1 + x_2) - x_2 - x_1^3 - 3x_1^2 x_2 \end{array}$$

$$\begin{array}{llll} (2) & \dot{x}_1 = -x_1^3 + x_2, & \dot{x}_2 = -(1 + \mu^2)x_1 + 2\mu x_2 - \mu x_1^3 + 2(x_2 - \mu x_1)^3 \end{array}$$

$$\begin{array}{llll} (3) & \dot{x}_1 = x_2, & \dot{x}_2 = \mu - x_2 - x_1^2 - 2x_1 x_2 \end{array}$$

$$\begin{array}{llll} (4) & \dot{x}_1 = x_2, & \dot{x}_2 = -(1 + \mu^2)x_1 + 2\mu x_2 + \mu x_1^3 - x_1^2 x_2 \end{array}$$

$$\begin{array}{llll} (5) & \dot{x}_1 = x_2, & \dot{x}_2 = \mu(x_1 + x_2) - x_2 - x_1^3 + 3x_1^2 x_2 \end{array}$$

$$\begin{array}{llll} (6) & \dot{x}_1 = x_2, & \dot{x}_2 = \mu(x_1 + x_2) - x_2 - x_1^2 - 2x_1 x_2 \end{array}$$

2.28 The model that follows is used to analyze the interaction between inhibitory and excitatory neurons in a biological system [195]. In its simplest form, the model describes the interaction of two neurons with x_1 as the output of the excitatory neuron and x_2 as the output of the inhibitory neuron. The evolution of x_1 and x_2 is described by

$$\dot{x}_1 = -\frac{1}{\tau}x_1 + \tanh(\lambda x_1) - \tanh(\lambda x_2)$$

$$\dot{x}_2 = -\frac{1}{\tau}x_2 + \tanh(\lambda x_1) + \tanh(\lambda x_2)$$

where $\tau > 0$ is a characteristic time constant and $\lambda > 0$ is an amplification gain.

(a) Using the Poincaré–Bendixson criterion, show that the system has a periodic orbit when $\lambda\tau > 1$.

(b) Construct the phase portrait for $\tau = 1$ and $\lambda = 2$ and discuss the qualitative behavior of the system.

(c) Repeat part (b) for $\tau = 1$ and $\lambda = 1/2$.

(d) Find and classify bifurcations that occur as $\mu = \lambda\tau$ varies.

2.29 A model that is used to analyze a class of experimental systems known as chemical oscillators [187] is given by

$$\dot{x}_1 = a - x_1 - \frac{4x_1 x_2}{1 + x_1^2}, \qquad \dot{x}_2 = bx_1\left(1 - \frac{x_2}{1 + x_1^2}\right)$$

where x_1 and x_2 are dimensionaless concentrations of certain chemicals and a, b are positive constants.

(a) Using the Poincaré–Bendixson criterion, show that the system has a periodic orbit when $b < 3a/5 - 25/a$.

(b) Construct the phase portrait in the first quadrant for $a = 10$, $b = 2$ and discuss the qualitative behavior of the system.

(c) Repeat part (b) for $a = 10$, $b = 4$.

(d) Find and classify bifurcations that occur as b varies, while a is fixed.

2.30 A biochemical reactor can be represented by the model

$$\dot{x}_1 = \left(\frac{\mu_m x_2}{k_m + x_2} - d\right)x_1, \qquad \dot{x}_2 = d(x_{2f} - x_2) - \frac{\mu_m x_1 x_2}{Y(k_m + x_2)}$$

where the state variables and the nonnegative constants d, μ_m, k_m, Y, and x_{2f} are defined in Exercise 1.22. Let $\mu_m = 0.5$, $k_m = 0.1$, $Y = 0.4$, and $x_{2f} = 4$.

(a) Find all equilibrium points for $d > 0$ and determine the type of each point.

(b) Study bifurcation as d varies.

(c) Construct the phase portrait and discuss the qualitative behavior of the system when $d = 0.4$.

2.31 A biochemical reactor can be represented by the model

$$\dot{x}_1 = \left(\frac{\mu_m x_2}{k_m + x_2 + k_1 x_2^2} - d \right) x_1, \qquad \dot{x}_2 = d(x_{2f} - x_2) - \frac{\mu_m x_1 x_2}{Y(k_m + x_2 + k_1 x_2^2)}$$

where the state variables and the nonnegative constants d, μ_m, k_m, k_1, Y, and x_{2f} are defined in Exercise 1.22. Let $\mu_m = 0.5$, $k_m = 0.1$, $k_1 = 0.5$, $Y = 0.4$, and $x_{2f} = 4$.

(a) Find all equilibrium points for $d > 0$ and determine the type of each point.

(b) Study bifurcation as d varies.

(c) Construct the phase portrait and discuss the qualitative behavior of the system when $d = 0.1$.

(d) Repeat part (c) when $d = 0.25$.

(e) Repeat part (c) when $d = 0.5$

Chapter 3

Fundamental Properties

This chapter states some fundamental properties of the solutions of ordinary differential equations, like existence, uniqueness, continuous dependence on initial conditions, and continuous dependence on parameters. These properties are essential for the state equation $\dot{x} = f(t,x)$ to be a useful mathematical model of a physical system. In experimenting with a physical system such as the pendulum, we expect that starting the experiment from a given initial state at time t_0, the system will move and its state will be defined in the (at least immediate) future time $t > t_0$. Moreover, with a deterministic system, we expect that if we could repeat the experiment exactly, we would get exactly the same motion and the same state at $t > t_0$. For the mathematical model to predict the future state of the system from its current state at t_0, the initial-value problem

$$\dot{x} = f(t,x), \quad x(t_0) = x_0 \tag{3.1}$$

must have a unique solution. This is the question of existence and uniqueness that is addressed in Section 3.1. It is shown that existence and uniqueness can be ensured by imposing some constraints on the right-hand side function $f(t,x)$. The key constraint used in Section 3.1 is the Lipschitz condition, whereby $f(t,x)$ satisfies the inequality[1]

$$\|f(t,x) - f(t,y)\| \le L\|x - y\| \tag{3.2}$$

for all (t,x) and (t,y) in some neighborhood of (t_0, x_0).

An essential factor in the validity of any mathematical model is the continuous dependence of its solutions on the data of the problem. The least we should expect from a mathematical model is that arbitrarily small errors in the data will not result in large errors in the solutions obtained by the model. The data of the initial-value problem (3.1) are the initial state x_0, the initial time t_0, and the right-hand side

---

[1] $\|\cdot\|$ denotes any p-norm, as defined in Appendix A.

function $f(t, x)$. Continuous dependence on the initial conditions (t_0, x_0) and on the parameters of f are studied in Section 3.2. If f is differentiable with respect to its parameters, then the solution will be differentiable with respect to these parameters. This is shown in Section 3.3 and is used to derive sensitivity equations that describe the effect of small parameter variations on the performance of the system. The continuity and differentiability results of Sections 3.2 and 3.3 are valid only on finite time intervals. Continuity results on the infinite time interval will be given later, after stability concepts have been introduced.[2]

The chapter ends with a brief statement of a comparison principle that bounds the solution of a scalar differential inequality $\dot{v} \leq f(t, v)$ by the solution of the differential equation $\dot{u} = f(t, u)$.

3.1   Existence and Uniqueness

In this section, we derive sufficient conditions for the existence and uniqueness of the solution of the initial-value problem (3.1). By a solution of (3.1) over an interval $[t_0, t_1]$, we mean a continuous function $x : [t_0, t_1] \rightarrow R^n$ such that $\dot{x}(t)$ is defined and $\dot{x}(t) = f(t, x(t))$ for all $t \in [t_0, t_1]$. If $f(t, x)$ is continuous in t and x, then the solution $x(t)$ will be continuously differentiable. We will assume that $f(t, x)$ is continuous in x, but only piecewise continuous in t, in which case, a solution $x(t)$ could only be piecewise continuously differentiable. The assumption that $f(t, x)$ be piecewise continuous in t allows us to include the case when $f(t, x)$ depends on a time-varying input that may experience step changes with time.

A differential equation with a given initial condition might have several solutions. For example, the scalar equation

$$\dot{x} = x^{1/3}, \quad \text{with} \quad x(0) = 0 \tag{3.3}$$

has a solution $x(t) = (2t/3)^{3/2}$. This solution is not unique, since $x(t) \equiv 0$ is another solution. In noting that the right-hand side of (3.3) is continuous in x, it is clear that continuity of $f(t, x)$ in its arguments is not sufficient to ensure uniqueness of the solution. Extra conditions must be imposed on the function f. The question of existence of a solution is less stringent. In fact, continuity of $f(t, x)$ in its arguments ensures that there is at least one solution. We will not prove this fact here.[3] Instead, we prove an easier theorem that employs the Lipschitz condition to show existence and uniqueness.

Theorem 3.1 (Local Existence and Uniqueness) *Let $f(t, x)$ be piecewise continuous in t and satisfy the Lipschitz condition*

$$\|f(t, x) - f(t, y)\| \leq L\|x - y\|$$

---

[2]See, in particular, Section 9.4.

[3]See [135, Theorem 2.3] for a proof.

$\forall\ x, y \in B = \{x \in R^n\ |\ \|x - x_0\| \le r\}$, $\forall\ t \in [t_0, t_1]$. *Then, there exists some* $\delta > 0$ *such that the state equation* $\dot{x} = f(t, x)$ *with* $x(t_0) = x_0$ *has a unique solution over* $[t_0, t_0 + \delta]$. $\diamondsuit$

Proof: See Appendix C.1.

The key assumption in Theorem 3.1 is the Lipschitz condition (3.2). A function satisfying (3.2) is said to be *Lipschitz in* x, and the positive constant L is called a *Lipschitz constant*. We also use the words *locally Lipschitz* and *globally Lipschitz* to indicate the domain over which the Lipschitz condition holds. Let us introduce the terminology first for the case when f depends only on x. A function $f(x)$ is said to be *locally Lipschitz* on a domain (open and connected set) $D \subset R^n$ if each point of D has a neighborhood D_0 such that f satisfies the Lipschitz condition (3.2) for all points in D_0 with some Lipschitz constant L_0. We say that f is Lipschitz on a set W if it satisfies (3.2) for all points in W, with the same Lipschitz constant L. A locally Lipschitz function on a domain D is not necessarily Lipschitz on D, since the Lipschitz condition may not hold uniformly (with the same constant L) for all points in D. However, a locally Lipschitz function on a domain D is Lipschitz on every compact (closed and bounded) subset of D (Exercise 3.19). A function $f(x)$ is said to be *globally Lipschitz* if it is Lipschitz on R^n. The same terminology is extended to a function $f(t, x)$, provided the Lipschitz condition holds uniformly in t for all t in a given interval of time. For example, $f(t, x)$ is locally Lipschitz in x on $[a, b] \times D \subset R \times R^n$ if each point $x \in D$ has a neighborhood D_0 such that f satisfies (3.2) on $[a, b] \times D_0$ with some Lipschitz constant L_0. We say that $f(t, x)$ is locally Lipschitz in x on $[t_0, \infty) \times D$ if it is locally Lipschitz in x on $[a, b] \times D$ for every compact interval $[a, b] \subset [t_0, \infty)$. A function $f(t, x)$ is Lipschitz in x on $[a, b] \times W$ if it satisfies (3.2) for all $t \in [a, b]$ and all points in W, with the same Lipschitz constant L.

When $f : R \to R$, the Lipschitz condition can be written as

$$\frac{|f(y) - f(x)|}{|y - x|} \le L$$

which implies that on a plot of $f(x)$ versus x, a straight line joining any two points of $f(x)$ cannot have a slope whose absolute value is greater than L. Therefore, any function $f(x)$ that has infinite slope at some point is not locally Lipschitz at that point. For example, any discontinuous function is not locally Lipschitz at the point of discontinuity. As another example, the function $f(x) = x^{1/3}$, which was used in (3.3), is not locally Lipschitz at $x = 0$ since $f'(x) = (1/3)x^{-2/3} \to \infty$ as $x \to 0$. On the other hand, if $|f'(x)|$ is bounded by a constant k over the interval of interest, then $f(x)$ is Lipschitz on the same interval with Lipschitz constant $L = k$. This observation extends to vector-valued functions, as demonstrated by Lemma 3.1.

Lemma 3.1 *Let* $f : [a, b] \times D \to R^m$ *be continuous for some domain* $D \subset R^n$. *Suppose that* $[\partial f / \partial x]$ *exists and is continuous on* $[a, b] \times D$. *If, for a convex subset*

$W \subset D$, there is a constant $L \geq 0$ such that

$$\left\| \frac{\partial f}{\partial x}(t, x) \right\| \leq L$$

on $[a, b] \times W$, then

$$\|f(t, x) - f(t, y)\| \leq L\|x - y\|$$

for all $t \in [a, b]$, $x \in W$, and $y \in W$.　　　　　　　　　　　　　$\diamond$

Proof: Let $\|\cdot\|_p$ be the underlying norm for any $p \in [1, \infty]$, and determine $q \in [1, \infty]$ from the relationship $1/p + 1/q = 1$. Fix $t \in [a, b]$, $x \in W$, and $y \in W$. Define $\gamma(s) = (1 - s)x + sy$ for all $s \in R$ such that $\gamma(s) \in D$. Since $W \subset D$ is convex, $\gamma(s) \in W$ for $0 \leq s \leq 1$. Take $z \in R^m$ such that[4]

$$\|z\|_q = 1 \quad \text{and} \quad z^T[f(t, y) - f(t, x)] = \|f(t, y) - f(t, x)\|_p$$

Set $g(s) = z^T f(t, \gamma(s))$. Since $g(s)$ is a real-valued function, which is continuously differentiable in an open interval that includes $[0, 1]$, we conclude by the mean value theorem that there is $s_1 \in (0, 1)$ such that

$$g(1) - g(0) = g'(s_1)$$

Evaluating g at $s = 0$, $s = 1$, and calculating $g'(s)$ by using the chain rule, we obtain

$$
\begin{aligned}
z^T[f(t, y) - f(t, x)] &= z^T \frac{\partial f}{\partial x}(t, \gamma(s_1))(y - x) \\
\|f(t, y) - f(t, x)\|_p &\leq \|z\|_q \left\| \frac{\partial f}{\partial x}(t, \gamma(s_1)) \right\|_p \|y - x\|_p \leq L\|y - x\|_p
\end{aligned}
$$

where we used the Hölder inequality $|z^T w| \leq \|z\|_q \|w\|_p$.　　　　　　$\square$

The lemma shows how a Lipschitz constant can be calculated using knowledge of $[\partial f/\partial x]$.

The Lipschitz property of a function is stronger than continuity. It can be easily seen that if $f(x)$ is Lipschitz on W, then it is uniformly continuous on W (Exercise 3.20). The converse is not true, as seen from the function $f(x) = x^{1/3}$, which is continuous, but not locally Lipschitz at $x = 0$. The Lipschitz property is weaker than continuous differentiability, as stated in the next lemma.

Lemma 3.2 If $f(t, x)$ and $[\partial f/\partial x](t, x)$ are continuous on $[a, b] \times D$, for some domain $D \subset R^n$, then f is locally Lipschitz in x on $[a, b] \times D$.　　　$\diamond$

---

[4]Such z always exists. (See Exercise 3.21.)

Proof: For $x_0 \in D$, let r be so small that the ball $D_0 = \{x \in R^n \mid \|x - x_0\| \leq r\}$ is contained in D. The set D_0 is convex and compact. By continuity, $[\partial f / \partial x]$ is bounded on $[a, b] \times D_0$. Let L_0 be a bound for $\|\partial f / \partial x\|$ on $[a, b] \times D_0$. By Lemma 3.1, f is Lipschitz on $[a, b] \times D_0$ with Lipschitz constant L_0. $\square$

It is left to the reader (Exercise 3.22) to extend the proof of Lemma 3.1 to prove the next lemma.

Lemma 3.3 *If $f(t, x)$ and $[\partial f / \partial x](t, x)$ are continuous on $[a, b] \times R^n$, then f is globally Lipschitz in x on $[a, b] \times R^n$ if and only if $[\partial f / \partial x]$ is uniformly bounded on $[a, b] \times R^n$.* $\diamond$

Example 3.1 The function

$$f(x) = \left[\begin{array}{c} -x_1 + x_1 x_2 \\ x_2 - x_1 x_2 \end{array} \right]$$

is continuously differentiable on R^2. Hence, it is locally Lipschitz on R^2. It is not globally Lipschitz since $[\partial f / \partial x]$ is not uniformly bounded on R^2. On any compact subset of R^2, f is Lipschitz. Suppose that we are interested in calculating a Lipschitz constant over the convex set $W = \{x \in R^2 \mid |x_1| \leq a_1, |x_2| \leq a_2\}$. The Jacobian matrix is given by

$$\left[\frac{\partial f}{\partial x} \right] = \left[\begin{array}{cc} -1 + x_2 & x_1 \\ -x_2 & 1 - x_1 \end{array} \right]$$

Using $\|.\|_\infty$ for vectors in R^2 and the induced matrix norm for matrices, we have

$$\left\| \frac{\partial f}{\partial x} \right\|_\infty = \max\{| - 1 + x_2| + |x_1|, \; |x_2| + |1 - x_1|\}$$

All points in W satisfy

$$| - 1 + x_2| + |x_1| \leq 1 + a_2 + a_1 \quad \text{and} \quad |x_2| + |1 - x_1| \leq a_2 + 1 + a_1$$

Hence,

$$\left\| \frac{\partial f}{\partial x} \right\|_\infty \leq 1 + a_1 + a_2$$

and a Lipschitz constant can be taken as $L = 1 + a_1 + a_2$. $\triangle$

Example 3.2 The function

$$f(x) = \left[\begin{array}{c} x_2 \\ -\text{sat}(x_1 + x_2) \end{array} \right]$$

is not continuously differentiable on R^2. Let us check its Lipschitz property by examining $f(x) - f(y)$. Using $\|.\|_2$ for vectors in R^2 and the fact that the saturation function $\text{sat}(\cdot)$ satisfies

$$|\text{sat}(\eta) - \text{sat}(\xi)| \leq |\eta - \xi|$$

we obtain

$$\|f(x) - f(y)\|_2^2 \leq (x_2 - y_2)^2 + (x_1 + x_2 - y_1 - y_2)^2$$
$$= (x_1 - y_1)^2 + 2(x_1 - y_1)(x_2 - y_2) + 2(x_2 - y_2)^2$$

Using the inequality

$$a^2 + 2ab + 2b^2 = \begin{bmatrix} a \\ b \end{bmatrix}^T \begin{bmatrix} 1 & 1 \\ 1 & 2 \end{bmatrix} \begin{bmatrix} a \\ b \end{bmatrix} \leq \lambda_{\max} \left\{ \begin{bmatrix} 1 & 1 \\ 1 & 2 \end{bmatrix} \right\} \times \left\| \begin{bmatrix} a \\ b \end{bmatrix} \right\|_2^2$$

we conclude that

$$\|f(x) - f(y)\|_2 \leq \sqrt{2.618} \, \|x - y\|_2, \quad \forall \, x, y \in R^2$$

Here we have used a property of positive semidefinite symmetric matrices; that is, $x^T P x \leq \lambda_{\max}(P) \, x^T x$, for all $x \in R^n$, where $\lambda_{\max}(\cdot)$ is the maximum eigenvalue of the matrix. A more conservative (larger) Lipschitz constant will be obtained if we use the more conservative inequality

$$a^2 + 2ab + 2b^2 \leq 2a^2 + 3b^2 \leq 3(a^2 + b^2)$$

resulting in a Lipschitz constant $L = \sqrt{3}$. $\triangle$

In these two examples, we have used $\|\cdot\|_\infty$ in one case and $\|\cdot\|_2$ in the other. Due to equivalence of norms, the choice of a norm on R^n does not affect the Lipschitz property of a function. It only affects the value of the Lipschitz constant (Exercise 3.5). Example 3.2 illustrates the fact that the Lipschitz condition (3.2) does not uniquely define the Lipschitz constant L. If (3.2) is satisfied with some positive constant L, it is satisfied with any constant larger than L. This nonuniqueness can be removed by defining L to be the smallest constant for which (3.2) is satisfied, but we seldom need to do that.

Theorem 3.1 is a local theorem since it guarantees existence and uniqueness only over an interval $[t_0, t_0 + \delta]$, where δ may be very small. In other words, we have no control on δ; hence, we cannot ensure existence and uniqueness over a given time interval $[t_0, t_1]$. However, one may try to extend the interval of existence by repeated applications of the local theorem. Starting at a time t_0, with an initial state $x(t_0) = x_0$, Theorem 3.1 shows that there is a positive constant δ (dependent on x_0) such that the state equation (3.1) has a unique solution over the time interval $[t_0, t_0 + \delta]$. Now, taking $t_0 + \delta$ as a new initial time and $x(t_0 + \delta)$ as a new initial state, one may try to apply Theorem 3.1 to establish existence of the solution beyond $t_0 + \delta$. If the conditions of the theorem are satisfied at $(t_0 + \delta, x(t_0 + \delta))$, then there exists $\delta_2 > 0$ such that the equation has a unique solution over $[t_0 + \delta, t_0 + \delta + \delta_2]$ that passes through the point $(t_0 + \delta, x(t_0 + \delta))$. We piece together the solutions over $[t_0, t_0 + \delta]$ and $[t_0 + \delta, t_0 + \delta + \delta_2]$ to establish the existence of a unique solution over $[t_0, t_0 + \delta + \delta_2]$. This idea can be repeated to keep extending the solution. However, in general, the interval of existence of the solution cannot be extended indefinitely because the conditions of Theorem 3.1 may cease to hold. There is a maximum interval $[t_0, T)$ where the unique solution starting at (t_0, x_0) exists.[5] In general, T may be less than t_1, in which case as $t \to T$, the solution leaves any compact set over which f is locally Lipschitz in x (Exercise 3.26).

Example 3.3 Consider the scalar system

$$\dot{x} = -x^2, \quad \text{with} \quad x(0) = -1$$

The function $f(x) = -x^2$ is locally Lipschitz for all $x \in R$. Hence, it is Lipschitz on any compact subset of R. The unique solution

$$x(t) = \frac{1}{t - 1}$$

exists over $[0, 1)$. As $t \to 1$, $x(t)$ leaves any compact set. $\triangle$

The phrase "finite escape time" is used to describe the phenomenon that a trajectory escapes to infinity at a finite time. In Example 3.3, we say that the trajectory has a finite escape time at $t = 1$.

In view of the discussion preceding Example 3.3, one may pose the following question: When is it guaranteed that the solution can be extended indefinitely? One way to answer the question is to require additional conditions which ensure that the solution $x(t)$ will always be in a set where $f(t, x)$ is uniformly Lipschitz in x. This is done in the next theorem by requiring f to satisfy a global Lipschitz condition. The theorem establishes the existence of a unique solution over $[t_0, t_1]$, where t_1 may be arbitrarily large.

Theorem 3.2 (Global Existence and Uniqueness) *Suppose that $f(t, x)$ is piecewise continuous in t and satisfies*

$$\|f(t, x) - f(t, y)\| \leq L\|x - y\|$$

$\forall\, x, y \in R^n$, $\forall\, t \in [t_0, t_1]$. Then, the state equation $\dot{x} = f(t, x)$, with $x(t_0) = x_0$, has a unique solution over $[t_0, t_1]$. $\diamond$

Proof: See Appendix C.1.

Example 3.4 Consider the linear system

$$\dot{x} = A(t)x + g(t) = f(t, x)$$

where $A(t)$ and $g(t)$ are piecewise continuous functions of t. Over any finite interval of time $[t_0, t_1]$, the elements of $A(t)$ are bounded. Hence, $\|A(t)\| \leq a$, where $\|A\|$ is any induced matrix norm. The conditions of Theorem 3.2 are satisfied since

$$\|f(t, x) - f(t, y)\| = \|A(t)(x - y)\| \leq \|A(t)\|\, \|x - y\| \leq a\|x - y\|$$

---

[5]For a proof of this statement, see [81, Section 8.5] or [135, Section 2.3].

for all $x, y \in R^n$ and $t \in [t_0, t_1]$. Therefore, Theorem 3.2 shows that the linear system has a unique solution over $[t_0, t_1]$. Since t_1 can be arbitrarily large, we can also conclude that if $A(t)$ and $g(t)$ are piecewise continuous $\forall\, t \geq t_0$, then the system has a unique solution $\forall\, t \geq t_0$. Hence, the system cannot have a finite escape time.

△

For the linear system of Example 3.4, the global Lipschitz condition of Theorem 3.2 is a reasonable requirement. This may not be the case for nonlinear systems, in general. We should distinguish between the local Lipschitz requirement of Theorem 3.1 and the global Lipschitz requirement of Theorem 3.2. Local Lipschitz property of a function is basically a smoothness requirement. It is implied by continuous differentiability. Except for discontinuous nonlinearities, which are idealizations of physical phenomena, it is reasonable to expect models of physical systems to have locally Lipschitz right-hand side functions. Examples of continuous functions that are not locally Lipschitz are quite exceptional and rarely arise in practice. The global Lipschitz property, on the other hand, is restrictive. Models of many physical systems fail to satisfy it. One can easily construct smooth meaningful examples that do not have the global Lipschitz property, but do have unique global solutions, which is an indication of the conservative nature of Theorem 3.2.

Example 3.5 Consider the scalar system

$$\dot{x} = -x^3 = f(x)$$

The function $f(x)$ does not satisfy a global Lipschitz condition since the Jacobian $\partial f / \partial x = -3x^2$ is not globally bounded. Nevertheless, for any initial state $x(t_0) = x_0$, the equation has the unique solution

$$x(t) = \text{sign}(x_0) \sqrt{\frac{x_0^2}{1 + 2x_0^2(t - t_0)}}$$

which is well defined for all $t \geq t_0$.

△

In view of the conservative nature of the global Lipschitz condition, it would be useful to have a global existence and uniqueness theorem that requires the function f to be only locally Lipschitz. The next theorem achieves that at the expense of having to know more about the solution of the system.

Theorem 3.3 *Let $f(t, x)$ be piecewise continuous in t and locally Lipschitz in x for all $t \geq t_0$ and all x in a domain $D \subset R^n$. Let W be a compact subset of D, $x_0 \in W$, and suppose it is known that every solution of*

$$\dot{x} = f(t, x), \quad x(t_0) = x_0$$

lies entirely in W. Then, there is a unique solution that is defined for all $t \geq t_0$. ◇

Proof: Recall the discussion on extending solutions, preceding Example 3.3. By Theorem 3.1, there is a unique local solution over $[t_0, t_0 + \delta]$. Let $[t_0, T)$ be its maximal interval of existence. We want to show that $T = \infty$. Recall (Exercise 3.26) the fact that if T is finite, then the solution must leave any compact subset of D. Since the solution never leaves the compact set W, we conclude that $T = \infty$. $\square$

The trick in applying Theorem 3.3 is in checking the assumption that every solution lies in a compact set without actually solving the differential equation. We will see in Chapter 4 that Lyapunov's method for studying stability is very valuable in that regard. For now, let us illustrate the application of the theorem by a simple example.

Example 3.6 Consider again the system

$$\dot{x} = -x^3 = f(x)$$

of Example 3.5. The function $f(x)$ is locally Lipschitz on R. If, at any instant of time, $x(t)$ is positive, the derivative $\dot{x}(t)$ will be negative. Similarly, if $x(t)$ is negative, the derivative $\dot{x}(t)$ will be positive. Therefore, starting from any initial condition $x(0) = a$, the solution cannot leave the compact set $\{x \in R \mid |x| \leq |a|\}$. Thus, without calculating the solution, we conclude by Theorem 3.3 that the equation has a unique solution for all $t \geq 0$. $\triangle$

3.2 Continuous Dependence on Initial Conditions and Parameters

For the solution of the state equation (3.1) to be of any interest, it must depend continuously on the initial state x_0, the initial time t_0, and the right-hand side function $f(t, x)$. Continuous dependence on the initial time t_0 is obvious from the integral expression

$$x(t) = x_0 + \int_{t_0}^{t} f(s, x(s)) \, ds$$

Therefore, we leave it as an exercise (Exercise 3.28) and concentrate our attention on continuous dependence on the initial state x_0 and the function f. Let $y(t)$ be a solution of (3.1) that starts at $y(t_0) = y_0$ and is defined on the compact time interval $[t_0, t_1]$. The solution depends continuously on y_0 if solutions starting at nearby points are defined on the same time interval and remain close to each other in that interval. This statement can be made precise with the ε–δ argument: Given $\varepsilon > 0$, there is $\delta > 0$ such that for all z_0 in the ball $\{x \in R^n \mid \|x - y_0\| < \delta\}$, the equation $\dot{x} = f(t, x)$ has a unique solution $z(t)$ defined on $[t_0, t_1]$, with $z(t_0) = z_0$, and satisfies $\|z(t) - y(t)\| < \varepsilon$ for all $t \in [t_0, t_1]$. Continuous dependence on the right-hand side function f is defined similarly, but to state the definition precisely, we need a mathematical representation of the perturbation of f. One possible representation is to replace f by a sequence of functions f_m, which converge uniformly to f as $m \to \infty$. For each function f_m, the solution of $\dot{x} = f_m(t, x)$ with $x(t_0) = x_0$ is denoted by $x_m(t)$. The solution is said to depend continuously on the right-hand side function if $x_m(t) \to x(t)$ as $m \to \infty$. This approach is a little bit involved, and will not be pursued here.[6] A more restrictive, but simpler, mathematical representation is to assume that f depends continuously on a set of constant parameters; that is, $f = f(t, x, \lambda)$, where $\lambda \in R^p$. The constant parameters could represent physical parameters of the system, and the study of perturbation of these parameters accounts for modeling errors or changes in the parameter values due to aging. Let $x(t, \lambda_0)$ be a solution of $\dot{x} = f(t, x, \lambda_0)$ defined on $[t_0, t_1]$, with $x(t_0, \lambda_0) = x_0$. The solution is said to depend continuously on λ if for any $\varepsilon > 0$, there is $\delta > 0$ such that for all λ in the ball $\{\lambda \in R^p \mid \|\lambda - \lambda_0\| < \delta\}$, the equation $\dot{x} = f(t, x, \lambda)$ has a unique solution $x(t, \lambda)$ defined on $[t_0, t_1]$, with $x(t_0, \lambda) = x_0$, and satisfies $\|x(t, \lambda) - x(t, \lambda_0)\| < \varepsilon$ for all $t \in [t_0, t_1]$.

Continuous dependence on initial states and continuous dependence on parameters can be studied simultaneously. We start with a simple result that bypasses the issue of existence and uniqueness and concentrates on the closeness of solutions.

Theorem 3.4 *Let $f(t, x)$ be piecewise continuous in t and Lipschitz in x on $[t_0, t_1] \times W$ with a Lipschitz constant L, where $W \subset R^n$ is an open connected set. Let $y(t)$ and $z(t)$ be solutions of*

$$\dot{y} = f(t, y), \quad y(t_0) = y_0$$

and

$$\dot{z} = f(t, z) + g(t, z), \quad z(t_0) = z_0$$

such that $y(t)$, $z(t) \in W$ for all $t \in [t_0, t_1]$. Suppose that

$$\|g(t, x)\| \leq \mu, \quad \forall \, (t, x) \in [t_0, t_1] \times W$$

for some $\mu > 0$. Then,

$$\|y(t) - z(t)\| \leq \|y_0 - z_0\| \exp[L(t - t_0)] + \frac{\mu}{L} \left\{\exp[L(t - t_0)] - 1\right\}$$

$\forall \, t \in [t_0, t_1]$. $\diamond$

Proof: The solutions $y(t)$ and $z(t)$ are given by

$$y(t) = y_0 + \int_{t_0}^t f(s, y(s)) \, ds$$

$$z(t) = z_0 + \int_{t_0}^t [f(s, z(s)) + g(s, z(s))] \, ds$$

---

[6]See [43, Section 1.3], [75, Section 1.3], or [135, Section 2.5] for results on continuous dependence on parameters using this approach.

Subtracting the two equations and taking norms yield

$$
\begin{aligned}
\|y(t) - z(t)\| \ &\le\ \|y_0 - z_0\| + \int_{t_0}^{t} \|f(s, y(s)) - f(s, z(s))\| \ ds \\
&\quad + \int_{t_0}^{t} \|g(s, z(s))\| \ ds \\
&\le\ \gamma + \mu(t - t_0) + \int_{t_0}^{t} L\|y(s) - z(s)\| \ ds
\end{aligned}
$$

where $\gamma = \|y_0 - z_0\|$. Application of the Gronwall–Bellman inequality (Lemma A.1) to the function $\|y(t) - z(t)\|$ results in

$$
\|y(t) - z(t)\| \le \gamma + \mu(t - t_0) + \int_{t_0}^{t} L[\gamma + \mu(s - t_0)] \exp[L(t - s)] \ ds
$$

Integrating the right-hand side by parts, we obtain

$$
\begin{aligned}
\|y(t) - z(t)\| \ &\le\ \gamma + \mu(t - t_0) - \gamma - \mu(t - t_0) + \gamma \exp[L(t - t_0)] \\
&\quad + \int_{t_0}^{t} \mu \exp[L(t - s)] \ ds \\
&=\ \gamma \exp[L(t - t_0)] + \frac{\mu}{L} \{\exp[L(t - t_0)] - 1\}
\end{aligned}
$$

which completes the proof of the theorem. $\qquad\square$

With Theorem 3.4 in hand, we can prove the next theorem on the continuity of solutions in terms of initial states and parameters.

Theorem 3.5 *Let $f(t, x, \lambda)$ be continuous in (t, x, λ) and locally Lipschitz in x (uniformly in t and λ) on $[t_0, t_1] \times D \times \{\|\lambda - \lambda_0\| \le c\}$, where $D \subset R^n$ is an open connected set. Let $y(t, \lambda_0)$ be a solution of $\dot{x} = f(t, x, \lambda_0)$ with $y(t_0, \lambda_0) = y_0 \in D$. Suppose $y(t, \lambda_0)$ is defined and belongs to D for all $t \in [t_0, t_1]$. Then, given $\varepsilon > 0$, there is $\delta > 0$ such that if*

$$
\|z_0 - y_0\| < \delta \quad \text{and} \quad \|\lambda - \lambda_0\| < \delta
$$

then there is a unique solution $z(t, \lambda)$ of $\dot{x} = f(t, x, \lambda)$ defined on $[t_0, t_1]$, with $z(t_0, \lambda) = z_0$, and $z(t, \lambda)$ satisfies

$$
\|z(t, \lambda) - y(t, \lambda_0)\| < \varepsilon, \quad \forall \ t \in [t_0, t_1]
$$

$\diamond$

Proof: By continuity of $y(t, \lambda_0)$ in t and the compactness of $[t_0, t_1]$, we know that $y(t, \lambda_0)$ is bounded on $[t_0, t_1]$. Define a "tube" U around the solution $y(t, \lambda_0)$ (see Figure 3.1) by

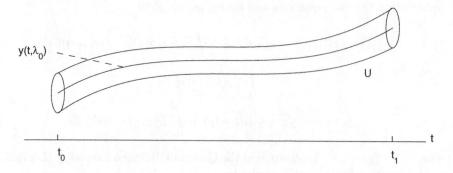

Figure 3.1: A tube constructed around the solution $y(t, \lambda_0)$.

$$U = \{(t, x) \in [t_0, t_1] \times R^n \mid \|x - y(t, \lambda_0)\| \leq \varepsilon\}$$

Suppose that $U \subset [t_0, t_1] \times D$; if not, replace ε by $\varepsilon_1 < \varepsilon$ that is small enough to ensure that $U \subset [t_0, t_1] \times D$ and continue the proof with ε_1. The set U is compact; hence, $f(t, x, \lambda)$ is Lipschitz in x on U with a Lipschitz constant, say, L. By continuity of f in λ, for any $\alpha > 0$, there is $\beta > 0$ (with $\beta < c$) such that

$$\|f(t, x, \lambda) - f(t, x, \lambda_0)\| < \alpha, \ \ \forall \ (t, x) \in U, \ \forall \ \|\lambda - \lambda_0\| < \beta$$

Take $\alpha < \varepsilon$ and $\|z_0 - y_0\| < \alpha$. By the local existence and uniqueness theorem, there is a unique solution $z(t, \lambda)$ on some time interval $[t_0, t_0 + \Delta]$. The solution starts inside the tube U, and as long as it remains in the tube, it can be extended. We will show that, by choosing a small enough α, the solution remains in U for all $t \in [t_0, t_1]$. In particular, we let τ be the first time the solution leaves the tube and show that we can make $\tau > t_1$. On the time interval $[t_0, \tau]$, the conditions of Theorem 3.4 are satisfied with $\mu = \alpha$. Hence,

$$
\begin{aligned}
\|z(t, \lambda) - y(t, \lambda_0)\| \ &< \ \alpha \exp[L(t - t_0)] + \frac{\alpha}{L}\{\exp[L(t - t_0)] - 1\} \\
&< \ \alpha \left(1 + \frac{1}{L}\right) \exp[L(t - t_0)]
\end{aligned}
$$

Choosing $\alpha \leq \varepsilon L \exp[-L(t_1 - t_0)]/(1 + L)$ ensures that the solution $z(t, \lambda)$ cannot leave the tube during the interval $[t_0, t_1]$. Therefore, $z(t, \lambda)$ is defined on $[t_0, t_1]$ and satisfies $\|z(t, \lambda) - y(t, \lambda_0)\| < \varepsilon$. Taking $\delta = \min\{\alpha, \beta\}$ completes the proof of the theorem.   □

3.3 Differentiability of Solutions and Sensitivity Equations

Suppose that $f(t, x, \lambda)$ is continuous in (t, x, λ) and has continuous first partial derivatives with respect to x and λ for all $(t, x, \lambda) \in [t_0, t_1] \times R^n \times R^p$. Let λ_0 be a nominal value of λ, and suppose that the nominal state equation

$$\dot{x} = f(t, x, \lambda_0), \quad \text{with} \quad x(t_0) = x_0$$

has a unique solution $x(t, \lambda_0)$ over $[t_0, t_1]$. From Theorem 3.5, we know that for all λ sufficiently close to λ_0, that is, $\|\lambda - \lambda_0\|$ sufficiently small, the state equation

$$\dot{x} = f(t, x, \lambda), \quad \text{with} \quad x(t_0) = x_0$$

has a unique solution $x(t, \lambda)$ over $[t_0, t_1]$ that is close to the nominal solution $x(t, \lambda_0)$. The continuous differentiability of f with respect to x and λ implies the additional property that the solution $x(t, \lambda)$ is differentiable with respect to λ near λ_0. To see this, write

$$x(t, \lambda) = x_0 + \int_{t_0}^{t} f(s, x(s, \lambda), \lambda) \, ds$$

Taking partial derivatives with respect to λ yields

$$x_\lambda(t, \lambda) = \int_{t_0}^{t} \left[\frac{\partial f}{\partial x}(s, x(s, \lambda), \lambda) \, x_\lambda(s, \lambda) + \frac{\partial f}{\partial \lambda}(s, x(s, \lambda), \lambda) \right] \, ds$$

where $x_\lambda(t, \lambda) = [\partial x(t, \lambda) / \partial \lambda]$ and $[\partial x_0 / \partial \lambda] = 0$, since x_0 is independent of λ. Differentiating with respect to t, it can be seen that $x_\lambda(t, \lambda)$ satisfies the differential equation

$$\frac{\partial}{\partial t} x_\lambda(t, \lambda) = A(t, \lambda) x_\lambda(t, \lambda) + B(t, \lambda), \quad x_\lambda(t_0, \lambda) = 0 \tag{3.4}$$

where

$$A(t, \lambda) = \left. \frac{\partial f(t, x, \lambda)}{\partial x} \right|_{x = x(t, \lambda)}, \quad B(t, \lambda) = \left. \frac{\partial f(t, x, \lambda)}{\partial \lambda} \right|_{x = x(t, \lambda)}$$

For λ sufficiently close to λ_0, the matrices $A(t, \lambda)$ and $B(t, \lambda)$ are defined on $[t_0, t_1]$. Hence, $x_\lambda(t, \lambda)$ is defined on the same interval. At $\lambda = \lambda_0$, the right-hand side of (3.4) depends only on the nominal solution $x(t, \lambda_0)$. Let $S(t) = x_\lambda(t, \lambda_0)$; then $S(t)$ is the unique solution of the equation

$$\dot{S}(t) = A(t, \lambda_0) S(t) + B(t, \lambda_0), \quad S(t_0) = 0 \tag{3.5}$$

The function $S(t)$ is called the *sensitivity function*, and (3.5) is called the *sensitivity equation*. Sensitivity functions provide first-order estimates of the effect of parameter variations on solutions. They can also be used to approximate the solution when λ is sufficiently close to its nominal value λ_0. For small $\|\lambda - \lambda_0\|$, $x(t, \lambda)$ can be expanded in a Taylor series about the nominal solution $x(t, \lambda_0)$ to obtain

$$x(t, \lambda) = x(t, \lambda_0) + S(t)(\lambda - \lambda_0) + \text{ higher-order terms}$$

Neglecting the higher-order terms, the solution $x(t, \lambda)$ can be approximated by

$$x(t, \lambda) \approx x(t, \lambda_0) + S(t)(\lambda - \lambda_0) \tag{3.6}$$

We will not justify this approximation here. It will be justified in Chapter 10 when we study the perturbation theory. The significance of (3.6) is in the fact that knowledge of the nominal solution and the sensitivity function suffices to approximate the solution for all values of λ in a (small) ball centered at λ_0.

The procedure for calculating the sensitivity function $S(t)$ is summarized by the following steps:

- Solve the nominal state equation for the nominal solution $x(t, \lambda_0)$.

- Evaluate the Jacobian matrices

$$A(t, \lambda_0) = \left. \frac{\partial f(t, x, \lambda)}{\partial x} \right|_{x=x(t,\lambda_0), \lambda=\lambda_0} , \quad B(t, \lambda_0) = \left. \frac{\partial f(t, x, \lambda)}{\partial \lambda} \right|_{x=x(t,\lambda_0), \lambda=\lambda_0}$$

- Solve the sensitivity equation (3.5) for $S(t)$.

In this procedure, we need to solve the nonlinear nominal state equation and the linear time-varying sensitivity equation. Except for some trivial cases, we will be forced to solve these equations numerically. An alternative approach for calculating $S(t)$ is to solve for the nominal solution and the sensitivity function simultaneously. This can be done by appending the variational equation (3.4) with the original state equation, then setting $\lambda = \lambda_0$ to obtain the $(n + np)$ augmented equation

$$
\begin{aligned}
\dot{x} &= f(t, x, \lambda_0), & x(t_0) &= x_0 \\
\dot{S} &= \left[\frac{\partial f(t,x,\lambda)}{\partial x} \right]_{\lambda=\lambda_0} S + \left[\frac{\partial f(t,x,\lambda)}{\partial \lambda} \right]_{\lambda=\lambda_0}, & S(t_0) &= 0
\end{aligned}
\tag{3.7}
$$

which is solved numerically. Notice that if the original state equation is autonomous, that is, $f(t, x, \lambda) = f(x, \lambda)$, then the augmented equation (3.7) will be autonomous as well. We illustrate the latter procedure by the next example.

Example 3.7 Consider the phase-locked-loop model

$$
\begin{aligned}
\dot{x}_1 &= x_2 & &= f_1(x_1, x_2) \\
\dot{x}_2 &= -c \sin x_1 - (a + b \cos x_1)x_2 & &= f_2(x_1, x_2)
\end{aligned}
$$

and suppose the parameters a, b, and c have the nominal values $a_0 = 1$, $b_0 = 0$, and $c_0 = 1$. The nominal system is given by

$$
\begin{aligned}
\dot{x}_1 &= x_2 \\
\dot{x}_2 &= -\sin x_1 - x_2
\end{aligned}
$$

The Jacobian matrices $[\partial f / \partial x]$ and $[\partial f / \partial \lambda]$ are given by

$$
\frac{\partial f}{\partial x} = \left[\begin{array}{cc} 0 & 1 \\ -c \cos x_1 + b x_2 \sin x_1 & -(a + b \cos x_1) \end{array} \right]
$$

$$
\frac{\partial f}{\partial \lambda} = \left[\begin{array}{ccc} \dfrac{\partial f}{\partial a} & \dfrac{\partial f}{\partial b} & \dfrac{\partial f}{\partial c} \end{array} \right] = \left[\begin{array}{ccc} 0 & 0 & 0 \\ -x_2 & -x_2 \cos x_1 & -\sin x_1 \end{array} \right]
$$

Evaluate these Jacobian matrices at the nominal parameters $a = 1$, $b = 0$, and $c = 1$ to obtain

$$
\left. \frac{\partial f}{\partial x} \right|_{\text{nominal}} = \left[\begin{array}{cc} 0 & 1 \\ -\cos x_1 & -1 \end{array} \right]
$$

$$
\left. \frac{\partial f}{\partial \lambda} \right|_{\text{nominal}} = \left[\begin{array}{ccc} 0 & 0 & 0 \\ -x_2 & -x_2 \cos x_1 & -\sin x_1 \end{array} \right]
$$

Let

$$
S = \left[\begin{array}{ccc} x_3 & x_5 & x_7 \\ x_4 & x_6 & x_8 \end{array} \right] = \left. \left[\begin{array}{ccc} \dfrac{\partial x_1}{\partial a} & \dfrac{\partial x_1}{\partial b} & \dfrac{\partial x_1}{\partial c} \\[2mm] \dfrac{\partial x_2}{\partial a} & \dfrac{\partial x_2}{\partial b} & \dfrac{\partial x_2}{\partial c} \end{array} \right] \right|_{\text{nominal}}
$$

Then (3.7) is given by

$$
\begin{array}{llll}
\dot{x}_1 &= x_2, & x_1(0) &= x_{10} \\
\dot{x}_2 &= -\sin x_1 - x_2, & x_2(0) &= x_{20} \\
\dot{x}_3 &= x_4, & x_3(0) &= 0 \\
\dot{x}_4 &= -x_3 \cos x_1 - x_4 - x_2, & x_4(0) &= 0 \\
\dot{x}_5 &= x_6, & x_5(0) &= 0 \\
\dot{x}_6 &= -x_5 \cos x_1 - x_6 - x_2 \cos x_1, & x_6(0) &= 0 \\
\dot{x}_7 &= x_8, & x_7(0) &= 0 \\
\dot{x}_8 &= -x_7 \cos x_1 - x_8 - \sin x_1, & x_8(0) &= 0
\end{array}
$$

The solution of this equation was computed for the initial state $x_{10} = x_{20} = 1$. Figure 3.2(a) shows x_3, x_5, and x_7, which are the sensitivities of x_1 with respect to a, b, and c, respectively. Figure 3.2(b) shows the corresponding quantities for x_2. Inspection of these figures shows that the solution is more sensitive to variations in the parameter c than to variations in the parameters a and b. This pattern is consistent when we solve for other initial states. $\triangle$

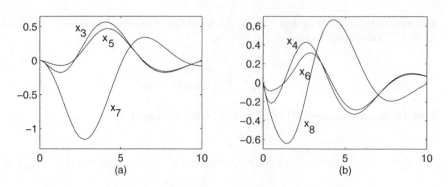

Figure 3.2: Sensitivity function for Example 3.7.

3.4   Comparison Principle

Quite often when we study the state equation $\dot{x} = f(t, x)$ we need to compute bounds on the solution $x(t)$ without computing the solution itself. The Gronwall–Bellman inequality (Lemma A.1) is one tool that can be used toward that goal. Another tool is the comparison lemma. It applies to a situation where the derivative of a scalar differentiable function $v(t)$ satisfies inequality of the form $\dot{v}(t) \leq f(t, v(t))$ for all t in a certain time interval. Such inequality is called a *differential inequality* and a function $v(t)$ satisfying the inequality is called a solution of the differential inequality. The comparison lemma compares the solution of the differential inequality $\dot{v}(t) \leq f(t, v(t))$ with the solution of the differential equation $\dot{u} = f(t, u)$. The lemma applies even when $v(t)$ is not differentiable, but has an upper right-hand derivative $D^+v(t)$, which satisfies a differential inequality. The upper right-hand derivative $D^+v(t)$ is defined in Appendix C.2. For our purposes, it is enough to know two facts:

- If $v(t)$ is differentiable at t, then $D^+v(t) = \dot{v}(t)$.

- If

$$\frac{1}{h}\,|v(t+h) - v(t)| \leq g(t, h), \quad \forall\, h \in (0, b]$$

  and

$$\lim_{h \to 0^+} g(t, h) = g_0(t)$$

  then $D^+v(t) \leq g_0(t)$.

The limit $h \to 0^+$ means that h approaches zero from above.

Lemma 3.4 (Comparison Lemma) *Consider the scalar differential equation*

$$\dot{u} = f(t, u), \quad u(t_0) = u_0$$

where $f(t, u)$ is continuous in t and locally Lipschitz in u, for all $t \geq 0$ and all $u \in J \subset R$. Let $[t_0, T)$ (T could be infinity) be the maximal interval of existence of the solution $u(t)$, and suppose $u(t) \in J$ for all $t \in [t_0, T)$. Let $v(t)$ be a continuous function whose upper right-hand derivative $D^+ v(t)$ satisfies the differential inequality

$$D^+ v(t) \leq f(t, v(t)), \quad v(t_0) \leq u_0$$

with $v(t) \in J$ for all $t \in [t_0, T)$. Then, $v(t) \leq u(t)$ for all $t \in [t_0, T)$. $\diamond$

Proof: See Appendix C.2.

Example 3.8 The scalar differential equation

$$\dot{x} = f(x) = -(1 + x^2)x, \quad x(0) = a$$

has a unique solution on $[0, t_1)$, for some $t_1 > 0$, because $f(x)$ is locally Lipschitz. Let $v(t) = x^2(t)$. The function $v(t)$ is differentiable and its derivative is given by

$$\dot{v}(t) = 2x(t)\dot{x}(t) = -2x^2(t) - 2x^4(t) \leq -2x^2(t)$$

Hence, $v(t)$ satisfies the differential inequality

$$\dot{v}(t) \leq -2v(t), \quad v(0) = a^2$$

Let $u(t)$ be the solution of the differential equation

$$\dot{u} = -2u, \quad u(0) = a^2 \quad \Rightarrow \quad u(t) = a^2 e^{-2t}$$

Then, by the comparison lemma, the solution $x(t)$ is defined for all $t \geq 0$ and satisfies

$$|x(t)| = \sqrt{v(t)} \leq e^{-t}|a|, \quad \forall\, t \geq 0$$

$\triangle$

Example 3.9 The scalar differential equation

$$\dot{x} = f(t, x) = -(1 + x^2)x + e^t, \quad x(0) = a$$

has a unique solution on $[0, t_1)$ for some $t_1 > 0$, because $f(t, x)$ is locally Lipschitz in x. We want to find an upper bound on $|x(t)|$ similar to the one we obtained in the previous example. Let us start with $v(t) = x^2(t)$ as in Example 3.8. The derivative of v is given by

$$\dot{v}(t) = 2x(t)\dot{x}(t) = -2x^2(t) - 2x^4(t) + 2x(t)e^t \leq -2v(t) + 2\sqrt{v(t)}e^t$$

We can apply the comparison lemma to this differential inequality, but the resulting differential equation will not be easy to solve. Instead, we consider a different choice of $v(t)$. Let $v(t) = |x(t)|$. For $x(t) \neq 0$, the function $v(t)$ is differentiable and its derivative is given by

$$\dot{v}(t) = \frac{d}{dt}\sqrt{x^2(t)} = \frac{x(t)\dot{x}(t)}{|x(t)|} = -|x(t)|[1 + x^2(t)] + \frac{x(t)}{|x(t)|}e^t$$

Since $1 + x^2(t) \geq 1$, we have $-|x(t)|[1 + x^2(t)] \leq -|x(t)|$ and $\dot{v}(t) \leq -v(t) + e^t$. On the other hand, when $x(t) = 0$, we have

$$
\frac{|v(t+h) - v(t)|}{h} = \frac{|x(t+h)|}{h} = \frac{1}{h}\left| \int_t^{t+h} f(\tau, x(\tau))\, d\tau \right|
$$

$$
= \left| f(t, 0) + \frac{1}{h}\int_t^{t+h} [f(\tau, x(\tau)) - f(t, x(t))]\, d\tau \right|
$$

$$
\leq |f(t, 0)| + \frac{1}{h}\int_t^{t+h} |f(\tau, x(\tau)) - f(t, x(t))|\, d\tau
$$

Since $f(t, x(t))$ is a continuous function of t, given any $\varepsilon > 0$ there is $\delta > 0$ such that for all $|\tau - t| < \delta$, $|f(\tau, x(\tau)) - f(t, x(t))| < \varepsilon$. Hence, for all $h < \delta$,

$$\frac{1}{h}\int_t^{t+h} |f(\tau, x(\tau)) - f(t, x(t))|\, d\tau < \varepsilon$$

which shows that

$$\lim_{h \to 0^+} \frac{1}{h}\int_t^{t+h} |f(\tau, x(\tau)) - f(t, x(t))|\, d\tau = 0$$

Thus, $D^+ v(t) \leq |f(t, 0)| = e^t$ whenever $x(t) = 0$. Hence, for all $t \in [0, t_1)$, we have

$$D^+ v(t) \leq -v(t) + e^t, \quad v(0) = |a|$$

Letting $u(t)$ be the solution of the linear differential equation

$$\dot{u} = -u + e^t, \quad u(0) = |a|$$

we conclude by the comparison lemma that

$$v(t) \leq u(t) = e^{-t}|a| + \tfrac{1}{2}\left[e^t - e^{-t}\right], \quad \forall\, t \in [0, t_1)$$

The upper bound on $v(t)$ is finite for every finite t_1 and approaches infinity only as $t_1 \to \infty$. Therefore, the solution $x(t)$ is defined for all $t \geq 0$ and satisfies

$$|x(t)| \leq e^{-t}|a| + \tfrac{1}{2}\left[e^t - e^{-t}\right], \quad \forall\, t \geq 0$$

$\triangle$

3.5 Exercises

3.1 For each of the functions $f(x)$ given next, find whether f is (a) continuously differentiable; (b) locally Lipschitz; (c) continuous; (d) globally Lipschitz.

(1) $f(x) = x^2 + |x|$. **(2)** $f(x) = x + \text{sgn}(x)$.
(3) $f(x) = \sin(x)\,\text{sgn}(x)$. **(4)** $f(x) = -x + a\sin(x)$.
(5) $f(x) = -x + 2|x|$. **(6)** $f(x) = \tan(x)$.

(7) $f(x) = \begin{bmatrix} ax_1 + \tanh(bx_1) - \tanh(bx_2) \\ ax_2 + \tanh(bx_1) + \tanh(bx_2) \end{bmatrix}$.

(8) $f(x) = \begin{bmatrix} -x_1 + a|x_2| \\ -(a+b)x_1 + bx_1^2 - x_1 x_2 \end{bmatrix}$.

3.2 Let $D_r = \{x \in R^n \mid \|x\| < r\}$. For each of the following systems, represented as $\dot{x} = f(t,x)$, find whether (a) f is locally Lipschitz in x on D_r, for sufficiently small r; (b) f is locally Lipschitz in x on D_r, for any finite $r > 0$; (c) f is globally Lipschitz in x:

(1) The pendulum equation with friction and constant input torque (Section 1.2.1).

(2) The tunnel-diode circuit (Example 2.1).

(3) The mass–spring equation with linear spring, linear viscous damping, Coulomb friction, and zero external force (Section 1.2.3).

(4) The Van der Pol oscillator (Example 2.6).

(5) The closed-loop equation of a third-order adaptive control system (Section 1.2.5).

(6) The system $\dot{x} = Ax - B\psi(Cx)$, where A, B, and C are $n \times n$, $n \times 1$, and $1 \times n$ matrices, respectively, and $\psi(\cdot)$ is the dead-zone nonlinearity of Figure 1.10(c).

3.3 Show that if $f_1 : R \to R$ and $f_2 : R \to R$ are locally Lipschitz, then $f_1 + f_2$, $f_1 f_2$ and $f_2 \circ f_1$ are locally Lipschitz.

3.4 Let $f : R^n \to R^n$ be defined by

$$f(x) = \begin{cases} \dfrac{1}{\|Kx\|}Kx, & \text{if } g(x)\|Kx\| \ge \mu > 0 \\[2mm] \dfrac{g(x)}{\mu}Kx, & \text{if } g(x)\|Kx\| < \mu \end{cases}$$

where $g : R^n \to R$ is locally Lipschitz and nonnegative, and K is a constant matrix. Show that $f(x)$ is Lipschitz on any compact subset of R^n.

3.5 Let $\| \cdot \|_\alpha$ and $\| \cdot \|_\beta$ be two different p-norms on R^n. Show that $f : R^n \to R^m$ is Lipschitz in $\| \cdot \|_\alpha$ if and only if it is Lipschitz in $\| \cdot \|_\beta$.

3.6 Let $f(t,x)$ be piecewise continuous in t, locally Lipschitz in x, and

$$\|f(t,x)\| \le k_1 + k_2\|x\|, \quad \forall\, (t,x) \in [t_0,\infty) \times R^n$$

(a) Show that the solution of (3.1) satisfies

$$\|x(t)\| \le \|x_0\| \exp[k_2(t-t_0)] + \frac{k_1}{k_2}\{\exp[k_2(t-t_0)] - 1\}$$

for all $t \ge t_0$ for which the solution exists.

(b) Can the solution have a finite escape time?

3.7 Let $g : R^n \to R^n$ be continuously differentiable for all $x \in R^n$ and define $f(x)$ by

$$f(x) = \frac{1}{1 + g^T(x)g(x)} g(x)$$

Show that $\dot{x} = f(x)$, with $x(0) = x_0$, has a unique solution defined for all $t \ge 0$.

3.8 Show that the state equation

$$\begin{aligned}
\dot{x}_1 &= -x_1 + \frac{2x_2}{1+x_2^2}, \quad x_1(0) = a \\
\dot{x}_2 &= -x_2 + \frac{2x_1}{1+x_1^2}, \quad x_2(0) = b
\end{aligned}$$

has a unique solution defined for all $t \ge 0$.

3.9 Suppose that the second-order system $\dot{x} = f(x)$, with a locally Lipschitz $f(x)$, has a limit cycle. Show that any solution that starts in the region enclosed by the limit cycle cannot have a finite escape time.

3.10 Derive the sensitivity equations for the tunnel-diode circuit of Example 2.1 as L and C vary from their nominal values.

3.11 Derive the sensitivity equations for the Van der Pol oscillator of Example 2.6 as ε varies from its nominal value. Use the state equation in the x-coordinates.

3.12 Repeat the previous exercise by using the state equation in the z-coordinates.

3.13 Derive the sensitivity equations for the system

$$\dot{x}_1 = \tan^{-1}(ax_1) - x_1 x_2, \qquad \dot{x}_2 = bx_1^2 - cx_2$$

as the parameters a, b, c vary from their nominal values $a_0 = 1$, $b_0 = 0$, and $c_0 = 1$.

3.14 Consider the system

$$\dot{x}_1 = -\frac{1}{\tau}x_1 + \tanh(\lambda x_1) - \tanh(\lambda x_2)$$

$$\dot{x}_2 = -\frac{1}{\tau}x_2 + \tanh(\lambda x_1) + \tanh(\lambda x_2)$$

where λ and τ are positive constants.

(a) Derive the sensitivity equations as λ and τ vary from their nominal values λ_0 and τ_0.

(b) Show that $r = \sqrt{x_1^2 + x_2^2}$ satisfies the differential inequality

$$\dot{r} \leq -\frac{1}{\tau}r + 2\sqrt{2}$$

(c) Using the comparison lemma, show that the solution of the state equation satisfies the inequality

$$\|x(t)\|_2 \leq e^{-t/\tau}\|x(0)\|_2 + 2\sqrt{2}\tau(1 - e^{-t/\tau})$$

3.15 Using the comparison lemma, show that the solution of the state equation

$$\dot{x}_1 = -x_1 + \frac{2x_2}{1 + x_2^2}, \qquad \dot{x}_2 = -x_2 + \frac{2x_1}{1 + x_1^2}$$

satisfies the inequality

$$\|x(t)\|_2 \leq e^{-t}\|x(0)\|_2 + \sqrt{2}\left(1 - e^{-t}\right)$$

3.16 Using the comparison lemma, find an upper bound on the solution of the scalar equation

$$\dot{x} = -x + \frac{\sin t}{1 + x^2}, \quad x(0) = 2$$

3.17 Consider the initial-value problem (3.1) and let $D \subset R^n$ be a domain that contains $x = 0$. Suppose $x(t)$, the solution of (3.1), belongs to D for all $t \geq t_0$ and $\|f(t, x)\|_2 \leq L\|x\|_2$ on $[t_0, \infty) \times D$. Show that

(a)

$$\left|\frac{d}{dt}\left[x^T(t)x(t)\right]\right| \leq 2L\|x(t)\|_2^2$$

(b)

$$\|x_0\|_2 \exp[-L(t - t_0)] \leq \|x(t)\|_2 \leq \|x_0\|_2 \exp[L(t - t_0)]$$

3.18 Let $y(t)$ be a nonnegative scalar function that satisfies the inequality

$$y(t) \leq k_1 e^{-\alpha(t-t_0)} + \int_{t_0}^{t} e^{-\alpha(t-\tau)} [k_2 y(\tau) + k_3] \, d\tau$$

where k_1, k_2, and k_3 are nonnegative constants and α is a positive constant that satisfies $\alpha > k_2$. Using the Gronwall–Bellman inequality, show that

$$y(t) \leq k_1 e^{-(\alpha-k_2)(t-t_0)} + \frac{k_3}{\alpha - k_2} \left[1 - e^{-(\alpha-k_2)(t-t_0)} \right]$$

Hint: Take $z(t) = y(t) e^{\alpha(t-t_0)}$ and find the inequality satisfied by z.

3.19 Let $f : R^n \to R^n$ be locally Lipschitz in a domain $D \subset R^n$. Let $S \subset D$ be a compact set. Show that there is a positive constant L such that for all $x, y \in S$,

$$\|f(x) - f(y)\| \leq L \|x - y\|$$

Hint: The set S can be covered by a finite number of neighborhoods; that is,

$$S \subset N(a_1, r_1) \cup N(a_2, r_2) \cup \cdots \cup N(a_k, r_k)$$

Consider the following two cases separately:

- $x, y \in S \cap N(a_i, r_i)$ for some i.

- $x, y \notin S \cap N(a_i, r_i)$ for any i; in this case, $\|x - y\| \geq \min_i r_i$.

In the second case, use the fact that $f(x)$ is uniformly bounded on S.

3.20 Show that if $f : R^n \to R^n$ is Lipschitz on $W \subset R^n$, then $f(x)$ is uniformly continuous on W.

3.21 For any $x \in R^n - \{0\}$ and any $p \in [1, \infty)$, define $y \in R^n$ by

$$y_i = \frac{x_i^{p-1}}{\|x\|_p^{p-1}} \, \text{sign}(x_i^p)$$

Show that $y^T x = \|x\|_p$ and $\|y\|_q = 1$, where $q \in (1, \infty]$ is determined from $1/p + 1/q = 1$. For $p = \infty$, find a vector y such that $y^T x = \|x\|_\infty$ and $\|y\|_1 = 1$.

3.22 Prove Lemma 3.3.

3.23 Let $f(x)$ be a continuously differentiable function that maps a convex domain $D \subset R^n$ into R^n. Suppose D contains the origin $x = 0$ and $f(0) = 0$. Show that

$$f(x) = \int_0^1 \frac{\partial f}{\partial x}(\sigma x) \, d\sigma \, x, \quad \forall \, x \in D$$

Hint: Set $g(\sigma) = f(\sigma x)$ for $0 \leq \sigma \leq 1$ and use the fact that $g(1) - g(0) = \int_0^1 g'(\sigma) \, d\sigma$.

3.24 Let $V : R \times R^n \to R$ be continuously differentiable. Suppose that $V(t, 0) = 0$ for all $t \geq 0$ and

$$V(t, x) \geq c_1 \|x\|^2; \quad \left\| \frac{\partial V}{\partial x}(t, x) \right\| \leq c_4 \|x\|, \quad \forall \ (t, x) \in [0, \infty) \times D$$

where c_1 and c_4 are positive constants and $D \subset R^n$ is a convex domain that contains the origin $x = 0$.

(a) Show that $V(t, x) \leq \frac{1}{2} c_4 \|x\|^2$ for all $x \in D$.

Hint: Use the representation $V(t, x) = \int_0^1 \frac{\partial V}{\partial x}(t, \sigma x) \, d\sigma \ x$.

(b) Show that the constants c_1 and c_4 must satisfy $2c_1 \leq c_4$.

(c) Show that $W(t, x) = \sqrt{V(t, x)}$ satisfies the Lipschitz condition

$$|W(t, x_2) - W(t, x_1)| \leq \frac{c_4}{2\sqrt{c_1}} \|x_2 - x_1\|, \quad \forall \ t \geq 0, \ \forall \ x_1, x_2 \in D$$

3.25 Let $f(t, x)$ be piecewise continuous in t and locally Lipschitz in x on $[t_0, t_1] \times D$, for some domain $D \subset R^n$. Let W be a compact subset of D. Let $x(t)$ be the solution of $\dot{x} = f(t, x)$ starting at $x(t_0) = x_0 \in W$. Suppose that $x(t)$ is defined and $x(t) \in W$ for all $t \in [t_0, T)$, $T < t_1$.

(a) Show that $x(t)$ is uniformly continuous on $[t_0, T)$.

(b) Show that $x(T)$ is defined and belongs to W and $x(t)$ is a solution on $[t_0, T]$.

(c) Show that there is $\delta > 0$ such that the solution can be extended to $[t_0, T + \delta]$.

3.26 Let $f(t, x)$ be piecewise continuous in t and locally Lipschitz in x on $[t_0, t_1] \times D$, for some domain $D \subset R^n$. Let $y(t)$ be a solution of (3.1) on a maximal open interval $[t_0, T) \subset [t_0, t_1]$ with $T < \infty$. Let W be any compact subset of D. Show that there is some $t \in [t_0, T)$ with $y(t) \notin W$.
Hint: Use the previous exercise.

3.27 ([43]) Let $x_1 : R \to R^n$ and $x_2 : R \to R^n$ be differentiable functions such that
$$\|x_1(a) - x_2(a)\| \leq \gamma, \quad \|\dot{x}_i(t) - f((t, x_i(t))\| \leq \mu_i, \text{ for } i = 1, 2$$

for $a \leq t \leq b$. If f satisfies the Lipschitz condition (3.2), show that

$$\|x_1(t) - x_2(t)\| \leq \gamma e^{L(t-a)} + (\mu_1 + \mu_2) \left[\frac{e^{L(t-a)} - 1}{L} \right], \quad \text{for } a \leq t \leq b$$

3.28 Show, under the assumptions of Theorem 3.5, that the solution of (3.1) depends continuously on the initial time t_0.

3.29 Let $f(t, x)$ and its partial derivatives with respect to x be continuous in (t, x) for all $(t, x) \in [t_0, t_1] \times R^n$. Let $x(t, \eta)$ be the solution of (3.1) that starts at $x(t_0) = \eta$ and suppose $x(t, \eta)$ is defined on $[t_0, t_1]$. Show that $x(t, \eta)$ is continuously differentiable with respect to η and find the variational equation satisfied by $[\partial x / \partial \eta]$. Hint: Put $y = x - \eta$ to transform (3.1) into

$$\dot{y} = f(t, y + \eta), \quad y(t_0) = 0$$

with η as a parameter.

3.30 Let $f(t, x)$ and its partial derivative with respect to x be continuous in (t, x) for all $(t, x) \in R \times R^n$. Let $x(t, a, \eta)$ be the solution of (3.1) that starts at $x(a) = \eta$ and suppose that $x(t, a, \eta)$ is defined on $[a, t_1]$. Show that $x(t, a, \eta)$ is continuously differentiable with respect to a and η and let $x_a(t)$ and $x_\eta(t)$ denote $[\partial x / \partial a]$ and $[\partial x / \partial \eta]$, respectively. Show that $x_a(t)$ and $x_\eta(t)$ satisfy the identity

$$x_a(t) + x_\eta(t) f(a, \eta) \equiv 0, \quad \forall\, t \in [a, t_1]$$

3.31 ([43]) Let $f : R \times R \to R$ be a continuous function. Suppose that $f(t, x)$ is locally Lipschitz and nondecreasing in x for each fixed value of t. Let $x(t)$ be a solution of $\dot{x} = f(t, x)$ on an interval $[a, b]$. If a continuous function $y(t)$ satisfies the integral inequality

$$y(t) \leq x(a) + \int_a^t f(s, y(s))\, ds$$

for $a \leq t \leq b$, show that $y(t) \leq x(t)$ throughout this interval.

Chapter 4

Lyapunov Stability

Stability theory plays a central role in systems theory and engineering. There are different kinds of stability problems that arise in the study of dynamical systems. This chapter is concerned mainly with stability of equilibrium points. In later chapters, we shall see other kinds of stability, such as input–output stability and stability of periodic orbits. Stability of equilibrium points is usually characterized in the sense of Lyapunov, a Russian mathematician and engineer who laid the foundation of the theory, which now carries his name. An equilibrium point is stable if all solutions starting at nearby points stay nearby; otherwise, it is unstable. It is asymptotically stable if all solutions starting at nearby points not only stay nearby, but also tend to the equilibrium point as time approaches infinity. These notions are made precise in Section 4.1, where the basic theorems of Lyapunov's method for autonomous systems are given. An extension of the basic theory, due to LaSalle, is given in Section 4.2. For a linear time-invariant system $\dot{x}(t) = Ax(t)$, the stability of the equilibrium point $x = 0$ can be completely characterized by the location of the eigenvalues of A. This is discussed in Section 4.3. In the same section, it is shown when and how the stability of an equilibrium point can be determined by linearization about that point. In Section 4.4, we introduce class $\mathcal{K}$ and class $\mathcal{KL}$ functions, which are used extensively in the rest of the chapter, and indeed the rest of the book. In Sections 4.5 and 4.6, we extend Lyapunov's method to nonautonomous systems. In Section 4.5, we define the concepts of uniform stability, uniform asymptotic stability, and exponential stability for nonautonomous systems, and give Lyapunov's method for testing them. In Section 4.6, we study linear time-varying systems and linearization.

Lyapunov stability theorems give sufficient conditions for stability, asymptotic stability, and so on. They do not say whether the given conditions are also necessary. There are theorems which establish, at least conceptually, that for many of Lyapunov stability theorems, the given conditions are indeed necessary. Such theorems are usually called converse theorems. We present three converse theorems in Section 4.7. Moreover, we use the converse theorem for exponential stability to show that an equilibrium point of a nonlinear system is exponentially stable if and only if the linearization of the system about that point has an exponentially stable equilibrium at the origin.

Lyapunov stability analysis can be used to show boundedness of the solution, even when the system has no equilibrium points. This is shown in Section 4.8 where the notions of uniform boundedness and ultimate boundedness are introduced. Finally, in Section 4.9, we introduce the notion of input-to-state stability, which provides a natural extension of Lyapunov stability to systems with inputs.

4.1   Autonomous Systems

Consider the autonomous system

$$\dot{x} = f(x) \tag{4.1}$$

where $f : D \to R^n$ is a locally Lipschitz map from a domain $D \subset R^n$ into R^n. Suppose $\bar{x} \in D$ is an equilibrium point of (4.1); that is, $f(\bar{x}) = 0$. Our goal is to characterize and study the stability of $\bar{x}$. For convenience, we state all definitions and theorems for the case when the equilibrium point is at the origin of R^n; that is, $\bar{x} = 0$. There is no loss of generality in doing so because any equilibrium point can be shifted to the origin via a change of variables. Suppose $\bar{x} \neq 0$ and consider the change of variables $y = x - \bar{x}$. The derivative of y is given by

$$\dot{y} = \dot{x} = f(x) = f(y + \bar{x}) \stackrel{\text{def}}{=} g(y), \quad \text{where } g(0) = 0$$

In the new variable y, the system has equilibrium at the origin. Therefore, without loss of generality, we will always assume that $f(x)$ satisfies $f(0) = 0$ and study the stability of the origin $x = 0$.

Definition 4.1 *The equilibrium point $x = 0$ of* (4.1) *is*

- *stable if, for each $\varepsilon > 0$, there is $\delta = \delta(\varepsilon) > 0$ such that*

$$\|x(0)\| < \delta \Rightarrow \|x(t)\| < \varepsilon, \quad \forall\, t \geq 0$$

- *unstable if it is not stable.*

- *asymptotically stable if it is stable and δ can be chosen such that*

$$\|x(0)\| < \delta \Rightarrow \lim_{t \to \infty} x(t) = 0$$

The ε–δ requirement for stability takes a challenge-answer form. To demonstrate that the origin is stable, then, for any value of ε that a challenger may care to designate, we must produce a value of δ, possibly dependent on ε, such that a trajectory starting in a δ neighborhood of the origin will never leave the ε neighborhood. The three types of stability properties can be illustrated by the pendulum example of Section 1.2.1. The pendulum equation

$$\dot{x}_1 = x_2$$
$$\dot{x}_2 = -a\sin x_1 - bx_2$$

has two equilibrium points at $(x_1 = 0,\ x_2 = 0)$ and $(x_1 = \pi,\ x_2 = 0)$. Neglecting friction, by setting $b = 0$, we have seen in Chapter 2 (Figure 2.2) that trajectories in the neighborhood of the first equilibrium are closed orbits. Therefore, by starting sufficiently close to the equilibrium point, trajectories can be guaranteed to stay within any specified ball centered at the equilibrium point. Hence, the ε–δ requirement for stability is satisfied. The equilibrium point, however, is not asymptotically stable since trajectories starting off the equilibrium point do not tend to it eventually. Instead, they remain in their closed orbits. When friction is taken into consideration ($b > 0$), the equilibrium point at the origin becomes a stable focus. Inspection of the phase portrait of a stable focus shows that the ε–δ requirement for stability is satisfied. In addition, trajectories starting close to the equilibrium point tend to it as t tends to ∞. The second equilibrium point at $x_1 = \pi$ is a saddle point. Clearly the ε–δ requirement cannot be satisfied since, for any $\varepsilon > 0$, there is always a trajectory that will leave the ball $\{x \in R^n \mid \|x - \bar{x}\| \le \varepsilon\}$ even when $x(0)$ is arbitrarily close to the equilibrium point $\bar{x}$.

Implicit in Definition 4.1 is a requirement that solutions of (4.1) be defined for all $t \ge 0$.[1] Such global existence of the solution is not guaranteed by the local Lipschitz property of f. It will be shown, however, that the additional conditions needed in Lyapunov's theorem will ensure global existence of the solution. This will come as an application of Theorem 3.3.

Having defined stability and asymptotic stability of equilibrium points, our task now is to find ways to determine stability. The approach we used in the pendulum example relied on our knowledge of the phase portrait of the pendulum equation. Trying to generalize that approach amounts to actually finding all solutions of (4.1), which may be difficult or even impossible. However, the conclusions we reached about the stable equilibrium point of the pendulum can also be reached by using energy concepts. Let us define the energy of the pendulum $E(x)$ as the sum of its potential and kinetic energies, with the reference of the potential energy chosen such that $E(0) = 0$; that is,

$$E(x) = \int_0^{x_1} a\sin y\ dy + \tfrac{1}{2}x_2^2 = a(1 - \cos x_1) + \tfrac{1}{2}x_2^2$$

When friction is neglected ($b = 0$), the system is conservative; that is, there is no dissipation of energy. Hence, $E = $ constant during the motion of the system or, in

---

[1]It is possible to change the definition to alleviate the implication of global existence of the solution. In [154], stability is defined on the maximal interval of existence $[0, t_1)$, without assuming that $t_1 = \infty$.

other words, $dE/dt = 0$ along the trajectories of the system. Since $E(x) = c$ forms a closed contour around $x = 0$ for small c, we can again arrive at the conclusion that $x = 0$ is a stable equilibrium point. When friction is accounted for $(b > 0)$, energy will dissipate during the motion of the system, that is, $dE/dt \leq 0$ along the trajectories of the system. Due to friction, E cannot remain constant indefinitely while the system is in motion. Hence, it keeps decreasing until it eventually reaches zero, showing that the trajectory tends to $x = 0$ as t tends to ∞. Thus, by examining the derivative of E along the trajectories of the system, it is possible to determine the stability of the equilibrium point. In 1892, Lyapunov showed that certain other functions could be used instead of energy to determine stability of an equilibrium point. Let $V : D \to R$ be a continuously differentiable function defined in a domain $D \subset R^n$ that contains the origin. The derivative of V along the trajectories of (4.1), denoted by $\dot{V}(x)$, is given by

$$
\begin{aligned}
\dot{V}(x) &= \sum_{i=1}^{n} \frac{\partial V}{\partial x_i} \dot{x}_i = \sum_{i=1}^{n} \frac{\partial V}{\partial x_i} f_i(x) \\
&= \begin{bmatrix} \frac{\partial V}{\partial x_1}, & \frac{\partial V}{\partial x_2}, & \cdots, & \frac{\partial V}{\partial x_n} \end{bmatrix} \begin{bmatrix} f_1(x) \\ f_2(x) \\ \vdots \\ f_n(x) \end{bmatrix} = \frac{\partial V}{\partial x} f(x)
\end{aligned}
$$

The derivative of V along the trajectories of a system is dependent on the system's equation. Hence, $\dot{V}(x)$ will be different for different systems. If $\phi(t; x)$ is the solution of (4.1) that starts at initial state x at time $t = 0$, then

$$
\dot{V}(x) = \frac{d}{dt} V(\phi(t; x)) \Big|_{t=0}
$$

Therefore, if $\dot{V}(x)$ is negative, V will decrease along the solution of (4.1). We are now ready to state Lyapunov's stability theorem.

Theorem 4.1 *Let $x = 0$ be an equilibrium point for (4.1) and $D \subset R^n$ be a domain containing $x = 0$. Let $V : D \to R$ be a continuously differentiable function such that*

$$
V(0) = 0 \quad \text{and} \quad V(x) > 0 \text{ in } D - \{0\} \tag{4.2}
$$

$$
\dot{V}(x) \leq 0 \text{ in } D \tag{4.3}
$$

Then, $x = 0$ is stable. Moreover, if

$$
\dot{V}(x) < 0 \text{ in } D - \{0\} \tag{4.4}
$$

then $x = 0$ is asymptotically stable. $\diamond$

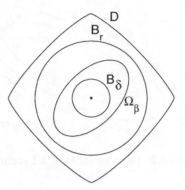

Figure 4.1: Geometric representation of sets in the proof of Theorem 4.1.

Proof: Given $\varepsilon > 0$, choose $r \in (0, \varepsilon]$ such that

$$B_r = \{x \in R^n \mid \|x\| \leq r\} \subset D$$

Let $\alpha = \min_{\|x\|=r} V(x)$. Then, $\alpha > 0$ by (4.2). Take $\beta \in (0, \alpha)$ and let

$$\Omega_\beta = \{x \in B_r \mid V(x) \leq \beta\}$$

Then, Ω_β is in the interior of B_r.[2] (See Figure 4.1.) The set Ω_β has the property that any trajectory starting in Ω_β at $t = 0$ stays in Ω_β for all $t \geq 0$. This follows from (4.3) since

$$\dot{V}(x(t)) \leq 0 \;\Rightarrow\; V(x(t)) \leq V(x(0)) \leq \beta, \; \forall\, t \geq 0$$

Because Ω_β is a compact set,[3] we conclude from Theorem 3.3 that (4.1) has a unique solution defined for all $t \geq 0$ whenever $x(0) \in \Omega_\beta$. As $V(x)$ is continuous and $V(0) = 0$, there is $\delta > 0$ such that

$$\|x\| \leq \delta \;\Rightarrow\; V(x) < \beta$$

Then,

$$B_\delta \subset \Omega_\beta \subset B_r$$

and

$$x(0) \in B_\delta \Rightarrow x(0) \in \Omega_\beta \Rightarrow x(t) \in \Omega_\beta \Rightarrow x(t) \in B_r$$

Therefore,

$$\|x(0)\| < \delta \Rightarrow \|x(t)\| < r \leq \varepsilon, \;\; \forall\, t \geq 0$$

---

[2]This fact can be shown by contradiction. Suppose Ω_β is not in the interior of B_r, then there is a point $p \in \Omega_\beta$ that lies on the boundary of B_r. At this point, $V(p) \geq \alpha > \beta$, but for all $x \in \Omega_\beta$, $V(x) \leq \beta$, which is a contradiction.

[3]Ω_β is closed by definition and bounded, since it is contained in B_r.

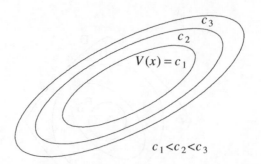

Figure 4.2: Level surfaces of a Lyapunov function.

which shows that the equilibrium point $x = 0$ is stable. Now, assume that (4.4) holds as well. To show asymptotic stability, we need to show that $x(t) \to 0$ as $t \to \infty$; that is, for every $a > 0$, there is $T > 0$ such that $\|x(t)\| < a$, for all $t > T$. By repetition of previous arguments, we know that for every $a > 0$, we can choose $b > 0$ such that $\Omega_b \subset B_a$. Therefore, it is sufficient to show that $V(x(t)) \to 0$ as $t \to \infty$. Since $V(x(t))$ is monotonically decreasing and bounded from below by zero,

$$V(x(t)) \to c \geq 0 \quad \text{as} \quad t \to \infty$$

To show that $c = 0$, we use a contradiction argument. Suppose $c > 0$. By continuity of $V(x)$, there is $d > 0$ such that $B_d \subset \Omega_c$. The limit $V(x(t)) \to c > 0$ implies that the trajectory $x(t)$ lies outside the ball B_d for all $t \geq 0$. Let $-\gamma = \max_{d \leq \|x\| \leq r} \dot{V}(x)$, which exists because the continuous function $\dot{V}(x)$ has a maximum over the compact set $\{d \leq \|x\| \leq r\}$.[4] By (4.4), $-\gamma < 0$. It follows that

$$V(x(t)) = V(x(0)) + \int_0^t \dot{V}(x(\tau)) \, d\tau \leq V(x(0)) - \gamma t$$

Since the right-hand side will eventually become negative, the inequality contradicts the assumption that $c > 0$. □

A continuously differentiable function $V(x)$ satisfying (4.2) and (4.3) is called a *Lyapunov function*. The surface $V(x) = c$, for some $c > 0$, is called a *Lyapunov surface* or a *level surface*. Using Lyapunov surfaces, we notice that Figure 4.2 makes the theorem intuitively clear. It shows Lyapunov surfaces for increasing values of c. The condition $\dot{V} \leq 0$ implies that when a trajectory crosses a Lyapunov surface $V(x) = c$, it moves inside the set $\Omega_c = \{x \in R^n \mid V(x) \leq c\}$ and can never come out again. When $\dot{V} < 0$, the trajectory moves from one Lyapunov surface to an inner Lyapunov surface with a smaller c. As c decreases, the Lyapunov surface $V(x) = c$ shrinks to the origin, showing that the trajectory approaches the origin as

---

[4]See [10, Theorem 4-20].

time progresses. If we only know that $\dot{V} \leq 0$, we cannot be sure that the trajectory will approach the origin,[5] but we can conclude that the origin is stable since the trajectory can be contained inside any ball B_ε by requiring the initial state $x(0)$ to lie inside a Lyapunov surface contained in that ball.

A function $V(x)$ satisfying condition (4.2)—that is, $V(0) = 0$ and $V(x) > 0$ for $x \neq 0$—is said to be *positive definite*. If it satisfies the weaker condition $V(x) \geq 0$ for $x \neq 0$, it is said to be *positive semidefinite*. A function $V(x)$ is said to be *negative definite* or *negative semidefinite* if $-V(x)$ is positive definite or positive semidefinite, respectively. If $V(x)$ does not have a definite sign as per one of these four cases, it is said to be *indefinite*. With this terminology, we can rephrase Lyapunov's theorem to say that *the origin is stable if there is a continuously differentiable positive definite function $V(x)$ so that $\dot{V}(x)$ is negative semidefinite, and it is asymptotically stable if $\dot{V}(x)$ is negative definite.*

A class of scalar functions for which sign definiteness can be easily checked is the class of functions of the quadratic form

$$V(x) = x^T P x = \sum_{i=1}^{n} \sum_{j=1}^{n} p_{ij} x_i x_j$$

where P is a real symmetric matrix. In this case, $V(x)$ is positive definite (positive semidefinite) if and only if all the eigenvalues of P are positive (nonnegative), which is true if and only if all the leading principal minors of P are positive (all principal minors of P are nonnegative).[6] If $V(x) = x^T P x$ is positive definite (positive semidefinite), we say that the matrix P is positive definite (positive semidefinite) and write $P > 0$ $(P \geq 0)$.

Example 4.1 Consider

$$
\begin{aligned}
V(x) &= ax_1^2 + 2x_1 x_3 + ax_2^2 + 4x_2 x_3 + ax_3^2 \\
&= [x_1 \ x_2 \ x_3] \begin{bmatrix} a & 0 & 1 \\ 0 & a & 2 \\ 1 & 2 & a \end{bmatrix} \begin{bmatrix} x_1 \\ x_2 \\ x_3 \end{bmatrix} = x^T P x
\end{aligned}
$$

The leading principal minors of P are a, a^2, and $a(a^2-5)$. Therefore, $V(x)$ is positive definite if $a > \sqrt{5}$. For negative definiteness, the leading principal minors of $-P$ should be positive; that is, the leading principal minors of P should have alternating signs, with the odd-numbered minors being negative and the even-numbered minors being positive. Consequently, $V(x)$ is negative definite if $a < -\sqrt{5}$. By calculating all principal minors, it can be seen that $V(x)$ is positive semidefinite if $a \geq \sqrt{5}$ and negative semidefinite if $a \leq -\sqrt{5}$. For $a \in (-\sqrt{5}, \sqrt{5})$, $V(x)$ is indefinite. $\triangle$

Lyapunov's theorem can be applied without solving the differential equation (4.1). On the other hand, there is no systematic method for finding Lyapunov

---

[5]See, however, LaSalle's theorem in Section 4.2

[6]This is a well-known fact in matrix theory. Its proof can be found in [21] or [63].

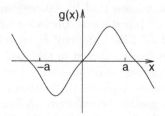

Figure 4.3: A possible nonlinearity in Example 4.2.

functions. In some cases, there are natural Lyapunov function candidates like energy functions in electrical or mechanical systems. In other cases, it is basically a matter of trial and error. The situation, however, is not as bad as it might seem. As we go over various examples and applications throughout the book, some ideas and approaches for searching for Lyapunov functions will be delineated.

Example 4.2 Consider the first-order differential equation

$$\dot{x} = -g(x)$$

where $g(x)$ is locally Lipschitz on $(-a, a)$ and satisfies

$$g(0) = 0; \quad xg(x) > 0, \quad \forall\, x \neq 0 \ \text{ and } \ x \in (-a, a)$$

A sketch of a possible $g(x)$ is shown in Figure 4.3. The system has an isolated equilibrium point at the origin. It is not difficult in this simple example to see that the origin is asymptotically stable, because solutions starting on either side of the origin will have to move toward the origin due to the sign of the derivative $\dot{x}$. To arrive at the same conclusion using Lyapunov's theorem, consider the function

$$V(x) = \int_0^x g(y)\ dy$$

Over the domain $D = (-a, a)$, $V(x)$ is continuously differentiable, $V(0) = 0$, and $V(x) > 0$ for all $x \neq 0$. Thus, $V(x)$ is a valid Lyapunov function candidate. To see whether or not $V(x)$ is indeed a Lyapunov function, we calculate its derivative along the trajectories of the system.

$$\dot{V}(x) = \frac{\partial V}{\partial x}[-g(x)] = -g^2(x) < 0, \ \forall\, x \in D - \{0\}$$

Hence, by Theorem 4.1 we conclude that the origin is asymptotically stable. $\triangle$

Example 4.3 Consider the pendulum equation without friction, namely,

$$
\begin{aligned}
\dot{x}_1 &= x_2 \\
\dot{x}_2 &= -a \sin x_1
\end{aligned}
$$

and let us study the stability of the equilibrium point at the origin. A natural Lyapunov function candidate is the energy function

$$V(x) = a(1 - \cos x_1) + \tfrac{1}{2}x_2^2$$

Clearly, $V(0) = 0$ and $V(x)$ is positive definite over the domain $-2\pi < x_1 < 2\pi$. The derivative of $V(x)$ along the trajectories of the system is given by

$$\dot{V}(x) = a\dot{x}_1 \sin x_1 + x_2\dot{x}_2 = ax_2 \sin x_1 - ax_2 \sin x_1 = 0$$

Thus, conditions (4.2) and (4.3) of Theorem 4.1 are satisfied, and we conclude that the origin is stable. Since $\dot{V}(x) \equiv 0$, we can also conclude that the origin is not asymptotically stable; for trajectories starting on a Lyapunov surface $V(x) = c$ remain on the same surface for all future time. $\triangle$

Example 4.4 Consider again the pendulum equation, but this time with friction, namely,

$$\begin{aligned}
\dot{x}_1 &= x_2 \\
\dot{x}_2 &= -a \sin x_1 - bx_2
\end{aligned}$$

Again, let us try $V(x) = a(1 - \cos x_1) + (1/2)x_2^2$ as a Lyapunov function candidate.

$$\dot{V}(x) = a\dot{x}_1 \sin x_1 + x_2\dot{x}_2 = -bx_2^2$$

The derivative $\dot{V}(x)$ is negative semidefinite. It is not negative definite because $\dot{V}(x) = 0$ for $x_2 = 0$ irrespective of the value of x_1; that is, $\dot{V}(x) = 0$ along the x_1-axis. Therefore, we can only conclude that the origin is stable. However, using the phase portrait of the pendulum equation, we have seen that when $b > 0$, the origin is asymptotically stable. The energy Lyapunov function fails to show this fact. We will see later in Section 4.2 that LaSalle's theorem will enable us to arrive at a different conclusion. For now, let us look for a Lyapunov function $V(x)$ that would have a negative definite $\dot{V}(x)$. Starting from the energy Lyapunov function, let us replace the term $(1/2)x_2^2$ by the more general quadratic form $(1/2)x^T P x$ for some 2×2 positive definite matrix P:

$$\begin{aligned}
V(x) &= \tfrac{1}{2}x^T P x + a(1 - \cos x_1) \\
&= \tfrac{1}{2}[x_1\ x_2] \begin{bmatrix} p_{11} & p_{12} \\ p_{12} & p_{22} \end{bmatrix} \begin{bmatrix} x_1 \\ x_2 \end{bmatrix} + a(1 - \cos x_1)
\end{aligned}$$

For the quadratic form $(1/2)x^T P x$ to be positive definite, the elements of the matrix P must satisfy

$$p_{11} > 0, \qquad p_{11}p_{22} - p_{12}^2 > 0$$

The derivative $\dot{V}(x)$ is given by

$$\begin{aligned}
\dot{V}(x) &= (p_{11}x_1 + p_{12}x_2 + a \sin x_1)\, x_2 + (p_{12}x_1 + p_{22}x_2)\, (-a \sin x_1 - bx_2) \\
&= a(1 - p_{22})x_2 \sin x_1 - ap_{12}x_1 \sin x_1 + (p_{11} - p_{12}b)\, x_1x_2 + (p_{12} - p_{22}b)\, x_2^2
\end{aligned}$$

Now we want to choose p_{11}, p_{12}, and p_{22} such that $\dot{V}(x)$ is negative definite. Since the cross product terms $x_2 \sin x_1$ and $x_1 x_2$ are sign indefinite, we will cancel them by taking $p_{22} = 1$ and $p_{11} = b p_{12}$. With these choices, p_{12} must satisfy $0 < p_{12} < b$ for $V(x)$ to be positive definite. Let us take $p_{12} = b/2$. Then, $\dot{V}(x)$ is given by

$$\dot{V}(x) = -\tfrac{1}{2} a b x_1 \sin x_1 - \tfrac{1}{2} b x_2^2$$

The term $x_1 \sin x_1 > 0$ for all $0 < |x_1| < \pi$. Taking $D = \{x \in R^2 \mid |x_1| < \pi\}$, we see that $V(x)$ is positive definite and $\dot{V}(x)$ is negative definite over D. Thus, by Theorem 4.1, we conclude that the origin is asymptotically stable. $\triangle$

This example emphasizes an important feature of Lyapunov's stability theorem; namely, *the theorem's conditions are only sufficient.* Failure of a Lyapunov function candidate to satisfy the conditions for stability or asymptotic stability does not mean that the equilibrium is not stable or asymptotically stable. It only means that such stability property cannot be established by using this Lyapunov function candidate. Whether the equilibrium point is stable (asymptotically stable) or not can be determined only by further investigation.

In searching for a Lyapunov function in Example 4.4, we approached the problem in a backward manner. We investigated an expression for the derivative $\dot{V}(x)$ and went back to choose the parameters of $V(x)$ so as to make $\dot{V}(x)$ negative definite. This is a useful idea in searching for a Lyapunov function. A procedure that exploits this idea is known as the *variable gradient method.* To describe the procedure, let $V(x)$ be a scalar function of x and $g(x) = \nabla V = (\partial V / \partial x)^T$. The derivative $\dot{V}(x)$ along the trajectories of (4.1) is given by

$$\dot{V}(x) = \frac{\partial V}{\partial x} f(x) = g^T(x) f(x)$$

The idea now is to try to choose $g(x)$ such that it would be the gradient of a positive definite function $V(x)$ and, at the same time, $\dot{V}(x)$ would be negative definite. It is not difficult (Exercise 4.5) to verify that $g(x)$ is the gradient of a scalar function if and only if the Jacobian matrix $[\partial g / \partial x]$ is symmetric; that is,

$$\frac{\partial g_i}{\partial x_j} = \frac{\partial g_j}{\partial x_i}, \quad \forall \, i, j = 1, \ldots, n$$

Under this constraint, we start by choosing $g(x)$ such that $g^T(x) f(x)$ is negative definite. The function $V(x)$ is then computed from the integral

$$V(x) = \int_0^x g^T(y) \, dy = \int_0^x \sum_{i=1}^n g_i(y) \, dy_i$$

The integration is taken over any path joining the origin to x.[7] Usually, this is done along the axes; that is,

$$V(x) \;\; = \;\; \int_0^{x_1} g_1(y_1, 0, \ldots, 0) \, dy_1 + \int_0^{x_2} g_2(x_1, y_2, 0, \ldots, 0) \, dy_2$$

---

[7]The line integral of a gradient vector is independent of the path. (See [10, Theorem 10-37].)

$$+ \cdots + \int_0^{x_n} g_n(x_1, x_2, \ldots, x_{n-1}, y_n) \, dy_n$$

By leaving some parameters of $g(x)$ undetermined, one would try to choose them to ensure that $V(x)$ is positive definite. The variable gradient method can be used to arrive at the Lyapunov function of Example 4.4. Instead of repeating the example, we illustrate the method on a slightly more general system.

Example 4.5 Consider the second-order system

$$\dot{x}_1 = x_2$$
$$\dot{x}_2 = -h(x_1) - ax_2$$

where $a > 0$, $h(\cdot)$ is locally Lipschitz, $h(0) = 0$, and $yh(y) > 0$ for all $y \neq 0$, $y \in (-b, c)$ for some positive constants b and c. The pendulum equation is a special case of this system. To apply the variable gradient method, we want to choose a second-order vector $g(x)$ that satisfies

$$\frac{\partial g_1}{\partial x_2} = \frac{\partial g_2}{\partial x_1}$$

$$\dot{V}(x) = g_1(x)x_2 - g_2(x)[h(x_1) + ax_2] < 0, \quad \text{for } x \neq 0$$

and

$$V(x) = \int_0^x g^T(y) \, dy > 0, \quad \text{for } x \neq 0$$

Let us try

$$g(x) = \begin{bmatrix} \alpha(x)x_1 + \beta(x)x_2 \\ \gamma(x)x_1 + \delta(x)x_2 \end{bmatrix}$$

where the scalar functions $\alpha(\cdot)$, $\beta(\cdot)$, $\gamma(\cdot)$, and $\delta(\cdot)$ are to be determined. To satisfy the symmetry requirement, we must have

$$\beta(x) + \frac{\partial \alpha}{\partial x_2}x_1 + \frac{\partial \beta}{\partial x_2}x_2 = \gamma(x) + \frac{\partial \gamma}{\partial x_1}x_1 + \frac{\partial \delta}{\partial x_1}x_2$$

The derivative $\dot{V}(x)$ is given by

$$\dot{V}(x) = \alpha(x)x_1x_2 + \beta(x)x_2^2 - a\gamma(x)x_1x_2 - a\delta(x)x_2^2 - \delta(x)x_2h(x_1) - \gamma(x)x_1h(x_1)$$

To cancel the cross-product terms, we choose

$$\alpha(x)x_1 - a\gamma(x)x_1 - \delta(x)h(x_1) = 0$$

so that

$$\dot{V}(x) = -[a\delta(x) - \beta(x)]x_2^2 - \gamma(x)x_1h(x_1)$$

To simplify our choices, let us take $\delta(x) = \delta = $ constant, $\gamma(x) = \gamma = $ constant, and $\beta(x) = \beta = $ constant. Then, $\alpha(x)$ depends only on x_1, and the symmetry requirement is satisfied by choosing $\beta = \gamma$. The expression for $g(x)$ reduces to

$$g(x) = \left[\begin{array}{c} a\gamma x_1 + \delta h(x_1) + \gamma x_2 \\ \gamma x_1 + \delta x_2 \end{array} \right]$$

By integration, we obtain

$$
\begin{aligned}
V(x) &= \int_0^{x_1} [a\gamma y_1 + \delta h(y_1)]\, dy_1 + \int_0^{x_2} (\gamma x_1 + \delta y_2)\, dy_2 \\
&= \tfrac{1}{2} a\gamma x_1^2 + \delta \int_0^{x_1} h(y)\, dy + \gamma x_1 x_2 + \tfrac{1}{2}\delta x_2^2 \;=\; \tfrac{1}{2} x^T P x + \delta \int_0^{x_1} h(y)\, dy
\end{aligned}
$$

where

$$P = \left[\begin{array}{cc} a\gamma & \gamma \\ \gamma & \delta \end{array} \right]$$

Choosing $\delta > 0$ and $0 < \gamma < a\delta$ ensures that $V(x)$ is positive definite and $\dot{V}(x)$ is negative definite. For example, taking $\gamma = ak\delta$ for $0 < k < 1$ yields the Lyapunov function

$$V(x) = \frac{\delta}{2} x^T \left[\begin{array}{cc} ka^2 & ka \\ ka & 1 \end{array} \right] x + \delta \int_0^{x_1} h(y)\, dy$$

which satisfies conditions (4.2) and (4.4) of Theorem 4.1 over the domain $D = \{x \in R^2 \mid -b < x_1 < c\}$. Therefore, the origin is asymptotically stable. $\triangle$

When the origin $x = 0$ is asymptotically stable, we are often interested in determining how far from the origin the trajectory can be and still converge to the origin as t approaches ∞. This gives rise to the definition of the *region of attraction* (also called *region of asymptotic stability*, *domain of attraction*, or *basin*). Let $\phi(t; x)$ be the solution of (4.1) that starts at initial state x at time $t = 0$. Then, the region of attraction is defined as the set of all points x such that $\phi(t; x)$ is defined for all $t \geq 0$ and $\lim_{t \to \infty} \phi(t; x) = 0$. Finding the exact region of attraction analytically might be difficult or even impossible. However, Lyapunov functions can be used to estimate the region of attraction, that is, to find sets contained in the region of attraction. From the proof of Theorem 4.1, we see that if there is a Lyapunov function that satisfies the conditions of asymptotic stability over a domain D and, if $\Omega_c = \{x \in R^n \mid V(x) \leq c\}$ is bounded and contained in D, then every trajectory starting in Ω_c remains in Ω_c and approaches the origin as $t \to \infty$. Thus, Ω_c is an estimate of the region of attraction. The estimate, however, may be conservative; that is, it may be much smaller than the actual region of attraction. In Section 8.2, we will solve examples on estimating the region of attraction and see some ideas to enlarge the estimates. Here, we want to pursue another question: Under what conditions will the region of attraction be the whole space R^n? It will be the case if we can show that for any initial state x, the trajectory $\phi(t; x)$ approaches the origin

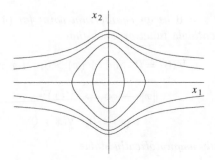

Figure 4.4: Lyapunov surfaces for $V(x) = x_1^2/(1 + x_1^2) + x_2^2$.

as $t \to \infty$, no matter how large $\|x\|$ is. If an asymptotically stable equilibrium point at the origin has this property, it is said to be *globally asymptotically stable*. Recalling again the proof of Theorem 4.1, we can see that global asymptotic stability can be established if any point $x \in R^n$ can be included in the interior of a bounded set Ω_c. It is obvious that for this condition to hold, the conditions of the theorem must hold globally, that is, $D = R^n$; but, is that enough? It turns out that we need more conditions to ensure that any point in R^n can be included in a bounded set Ω_c. The problem is that for large c, the set Ω_c need not be bounded. Consider, for example, the function

$$V(x) = \frac{x_1^2}{1 + x_1^2} + x_2^2$$

Figure 4.4 shows the surfaces $V(x) = c$ for various positive values of c. For small c, the surface $V(x) = c$ is closed; hence, Ω_c is bounded since it is contained in a closed ball B_r for some $r > 0$. This is a consequence of the continuity and positive definiteness of $V(x)$. As c increases, a value is reached after which the surface $V(x) = c$ is open and Ω_c is unbounded. For Ω_c to be in the interior of a ball B_r, c must satisfy $c < \inf_{\|x\| \geq r} V(x)$. If

$$l = \lim_{r \to \infty} \inf_{\|x\| \geq r} V(x) < \infty$$

then Ω_c will be bounded if $c < l$. In the preceding example,

$$l = \lim_{r \to \infty} \min_{\|x\| = r} \left[\frac{x_1^2}{1 + x_1^2} + x_2^2 \right] = \lim_{|x_1| \to \infty} \frac{x_1^2}{1 + x_1^2} = 1$$

Thus, Ω_c is bounded only for $c < 1$. An extra condition that ensures that Ω_c is bounded for all values of $c > 0$ is

$$V(x) \to \infty \quad \text{as} \quad \|x\| \to \infty$$

A function satisfying this condition is said to be *radially unbounded*.

Theorem 4.2 *Let $x = 0$ be an equilibrium point for (4.1). Let $V : R^n \to R$ be a continuously differentiable function such that*

$$V(0) = 0 \;\; \text{and} \;\; V(x) > 0, \;\; \forall\, x \neq 0 \tag{4.5}$$

$$\|x\| \to \infty \;\Rightarrow\; V(x) \to \infty \tag{4.6}$$

$$\dot{V}(x) < 0, \;\; \forall\, x \neq 0 \tag{4.7}$$

then $x = 0$ is globally asymptotically stable. ◇

Proof: Given any point $p \in R^n$, let $c = V(p)$. Condition (4.6) implies that for any $c > 0$, there is $r > 0$ such that $V(x) > c$ whenever $\|x\| > r$. Thus, $\Omega_c \subset B_r$, which implies that Ω_c is bounded. The rest of the proof is similar to that of Theorem 4.1. ☐

Theorem 4.2 is known as Barbashin–Krasovskii theorem. Exercise 4.8 gives a counterexample to show that the radial unboundedness condition of the theorem is indeed needed.

Example 4.6 Consider again the system of Example 4.5, but this time, assume that the condition $yh(y) > 0$ holds for all $y \neq 0$. The Lyapunov function

$$V(x) = \frac{\delta}{2}x^T \begin{bmatrix} ka^2 & ka \\ ka & 1 \end{bmatrix} x + \delta \int_0^{x_1} h(y)\, dy$$

is positive definite for all $x \in R^2$ and radially unbounded. The derivative

$$\dot{V}(x) = -a\delta(1-k)x_2^2 - a\delta k x_1 h(x_1)$$

is negative definite for all $x \in R^2$ since $0 < k < 1$. Therefore, the origin is globally asymptotically stable. △

If the origin $x = 0$ is a globally asymptotically stable equilibrium point of a system, then it must be the unique equilibrium point of the system. For if there were another equilibrium point $\bar{x}$, the trajectory starting at $\bar{x}$ would remain at $\bar{x}$ for all $t \geq 0$; hence, it would not approach the origin, which contradicts the claim that the origin is globally asymptotically stable. Therefore, global asymptotic stability is not studied for multiple equilibria systems like the pendulum equation.

Theorems 4.1 and 4.2 are concerned with establishing the stability or asymptotic stability of an equilibrium point. There are also instability theorems for establishing that an equilibrium point is unstable. The most powerful of these theorems is Chetaev's theorem, which will be stated as Theorem 4.3. Before we state the theorem, let us introduce some terminology that will be used in the theorem's statement. Let $V : D \to R$ be a continuously differentiable function on a domain $D \subset R^n$ that contains the origin $x = 0$. Suppose $V(0) = 0$ and there is a point x_0

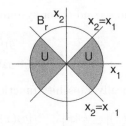

Figure 4.5: The set U for $V(x) = \frac{1}{2}(x_1^2 - x_2^2)$.

arbitrarily close to the origin such that $V(x_0) > 0$. Choose $r > 0$ such that the ball $B_r = \{x \in R^n \mid \|x\| \le r\}$ is contained in D, and let

$$U = \{x \in B_r \mid V(x) > 0\} \qquad (4.8)$$

The set U is a nonempty set contained in B_r. Its boundary is the surface $V(x) = 0$ and the sphere $\|x\| = r$. Since $V(0) = 0$, the origin lies on the boundary of U inside B_r. Notice that U may contain more than one component. For example, Figure 4.5 shows the set U for $V(x) = (x_1^2 - x_2^2)/2$. The set U can be always constructed provided that $V(0) = 0$ and $V(x_0) > 0$ for some x_0 arbitrarily close to the origin.

Theorem 4.3 *Let $x = 0$ be an equilibrium point for (4.1). Let $V : D \to R$ be a continuously differentiable function such that $V(0) = 0$ and $V(x_0) > 0$ for some x_0 with arbitrarily small $\|x_0\|$. Define a set U as in (4.8) and suppose that $\dot{V}(x) > 0$ in U. Then, $x = 0$ is unstable.* $\diamond$

Proof: The point x_0 is in the interior of U and $V(x_0) = a > 0$. The trajectory $x(t)$ starting at $x(0) = x_0$ must leave the set U. To see this point, notice that as long as $x(t)$ is inside U, $V(x(t)) \ge a$, since $\dot{V}(x) > 0$ in U. Let

$$\gamma = \min\{\dot{V}(x) \mid x \in U \text{ and } V(x) \ge a\}$$

which exists since the continuous function $\dot{V}(x)$ has a minimum over the compact set $\{x \in U \text{ and } V(x) \ge a\} = \{x \in B_r \text{ and } V(x) \ge a\}$.[8] Then, $\gamma > 0$ and

$$V(x(t)) = V(x_0) + \int_0^t \dot{V}(x(s)) \, ds \ge a + \int_0^t \gamma \, ds = a + \gamma t$$

This inequality shows that $x(t)$ cannot stay forever in U because $V(x)$ is bounded on U. Now, $x(t)$ cannot leave U through the surface $V(x) = 0$ since $V(x(t)) \ge a$. Hence, it must leave U through the sphere $\|x\| = r$. Because this can happen for an arbitrarily small $\|x_0\|$, the origin is unstable. $\square$

There are other instability theorems that were proved before Chetaev's theorem, but they are corollaries of the theorem. (See Exercises 4.11 and 4.12.)

---

[8]See [10, Theorem 4-20].

Example 4.7 Consider the second-order system

$$\begin{aligned}
\dot{x}_1 &= x_1 + g_1(x) \\
\dot{x}_2 &= -x_2 + g_2(x)
\end{aligned}$$

where $g_1(\cdot)$ and $g_2(\cdot)$ are locally Lipschitz functions that satisfy the inequalities

$$|g_1(x)| \le k\|x\|_2^2, \quad |g_2(x)| \le k\|x\|_2^2$$

in a neighborhood D of the origin. These inequalities imply that $g_1(0) = g_2(0) = 0$. Hence, the origin is an equilibrium point. Consider the function

$$V(x) = \tfrac{1}{2}(x_1^2 - x_2^2)$$

On the line $x_2 = 0$, $V(x) > 0$ at points arbitrarily close to the origin. The set U is shown in Figure 4.5. The derivative of $V(x)$ along the trajectories of the system is given by

$$\dot{V}(x) = x_1^2 + x_2^2 + x_1 g_1(x) - x_2 g_2(x)$$

The magnitude of the term $x_1 g_1(x) - x_2 g_2(x)$ satisfies the inequality

$$|x_1 g_1(x) - x_2 g_2(x)| \le \sum_{i=1}^{2} |x_i| \cdot |g_i(x)| \le 2k\|x\|_2^3$$

Hence,

$$\dot{V}(x) \ge \|x\|_2^2 - 2k\|x\|_2^3 = \|x\|_2^2(1 - 2k\|x\|_2)$$

Choosing r such that $B_r \subset D$ and $r < 1/(2k)$, it is seen that all the conditions of Theorem 4.3 are satisfied. Therefore, the origin is unstable. $\triangle$

4.2   The Invariance Principle

In our study of the pendulum equation with friction (Example 4.4), we saw that the energy Lyapunov function fails to satisfy the asymptotic stability condition of Theorem 4.1 because $\dot{V}(x) = -bx_2^2$ is only negative semidefinite. Notice, however, that $\dot{V}(x)$ is negative everywhere, except on the line $x_2 = 0$, where $\dot{V}(x) = 0$. For the system to maintain the $\dot{V}(x) = 0$ condition, the trajectory of the system must be confined to the line $x_2 = 0$. Unless $x_1 = 0$, this is impossible because from the pendulum equation

$$x_2(t) \equiv 0 \;\Rightarrow\; \dot{x}_2(t) \equiv 0 \;\Rightarrow\; \sin x_1(t) \equiv 0$$

Hence, on the segment $-\pi < x_1 < \pi$ of the $x_2 = 0$ line, the system can maintain the $\dot{V}(x) = 0$ condition only at the origin $x = 0$. Therefore, $V(x(t))$ must decrease toward 0 and, consequently, $x(t) \to 0$ as $t \to \infty$, which is consistent with the fact that, due to friction, energy cannot remain constant while the system is in motion.

The foregoing argument shows, formally, that if in a domain about the origin we can find a Lyapunov function whose derivative along the trajectories of the system is negative semidefinite, and if we can establish that no trajectory can stay identically at points where $\dot{V}(x) = 0$, except at the origin, then the origin is asymptotically stable. This idea follows from LaSalle's *invariance principle*, which is the subject of this section. To state and prove LaSalle's invariance theorem, we need to introduce a few definitions. Let $x(t)$ be a solution of (4.1). A point p is said to be a *positive limit point* of $x(t)$ if there is a sequence $\{t_n\}$, with $t_n \to \infty$ as $n \to \infty$, such that $x(t_n) \to p$ as $n \to \infty$. The set of all positive limit points of $x(t)$ is called the *positive limit set* of $x(t)$. A set M is said to be an *invariant set* with respect to (4.1) if

$$x(0) \in M \Rightarrow x(t) \in M, \quad \forall\, t \in R$$

That is, if a solution belongs to M at some time instant, then it belongs to M for all future and past time. A set M is said to be a *positively invariant set* if

$$x(0) \in M \Rightarrow x(t) \in M, \quad \forall\, t \geq 0$$

We also say that $x(t)$ approaches a set M as t approaches infinity, if for each $\varepsilon > 0$ there is $T > 0$ such that

$$\text{dist}(x(t), M) < \varepsilon, \quad \forall\, t > T$$

where $\text{dist}(p, M)$ denotes the distance from a point p to a set M, that is, the smallest distance from p to any point in M. More precisely,

$$\text{dist}(p, M) = \inf_{x \in M} \|p - x\|$$

These few concepts can be illustrated by examining an asymptotically stable equilibrium point and a stable limit cycle in the plane. The asymptotically stable equilibrium is the positive limit set of every solution starting sufficiently near the equilibrium point. The stable limit cycle is the positive limit set of every solution starting sufficiently near the limit cycle. The solution approaches the limit cycle as $t \to \infty$. Notice, however, that the solution does not approach any specific point on the limit cycle. In other words, the statement $x(t)$ approaches M as $t \to \infty$ does not imply that $\lim_{t\to\infty} x(t)$ exists. The equilibrium point and the limit cycle are invariant sets, since any solution starting in either set remains in the set for all $t \in R$. The set $\Omega_c = \{x \in R^n \mid V(x) \leq c\}$ with $\dot{V}(x) \leq 0$ for all $x \in \Omega_c$ is a positively invariant set since, as we saw in the proof of Theorem 4.1, a solution starting in Ω_c remains in Ω_c for all $t \geq 0$.

A fundamental property of limit sets is stated in the next lemma, whose proof is given in Appendix C.3.

Lemma 4.1 *If a solution $x(t)$ of (4.1) is bounded and belongs to D for $t \geq 0$, then its positive limit set L^+ is a nonempty, compact, invariant set. Moreover, $x(t)$ approaches L^+ as $t \to \infty$.* $\diamond$

We are now ready to state LaSalle's theorem.

Theorem 4.4 *Let $\Omega \subset D$ be a compact set that is positively invariant with respect to (4.1). Let $V : D \to R$ be a continuously differentiable function such that $\dot{V}(x) \leq 0$ in Ω. Let E be the set of all points in Ω where $\dot{V}(x) = 0$. Let M be the largest invariant set in E. Then every solution starting in Ω approaches M as $t \to \infty$.* $\diamond$

Proof: Let $x(t)$ be a solution of (4.1) starting in Ω. Since $\dot{V}(x) \leq 0$ in Ω, $V(x(t))$ is a decreasing function of t. Since $V(x)$ is continuous on the compact set Ω, it is bounded from below on Ω. Therefore, $V(x(t))$ has a limit a as $t \to \infty$. Note also that the positive limit set L^+ is in Ω because Ω is a closed set. For any $p \in L^+$, there is a sequence t_n with $t_n \to \infty$ and $x(t_n) \to p$ as $n \to \infty$. By continuity of $V(x)$, $V(p) = \lim_{n \to \infty} V(x(t_n)) = a$. Hence, $V(x) = a$ on L^+. Since (by Lemma 4.1) L^+ is an invariant set, $\dot{V}(x) = 0$ on L^+. Thus,

$$L^+ \subset M \subset E \subset \Omega$$

Since $x(t)$ is bounded, $x(t)$ approaches L^+ as $t \to \infty$ (by Lemma 4.1). Hence, $x(t)$ approaches M as $t \to \infty$. $\square$

Unlike Lyapunov's theorem, Theorem 4.4 does not require the function $V(x)$ to be positive definite. Note also that the construction of the set Ω does not have to be tied in with the construction of the function $V(x)$. However, in many applications the construction of $V(x)$ will itself guarantee the existence of a set Ω. In particular, if $\Omega_c = \{x \in R^n \mid V(x) \leq c\}$ is bounded and $\dot{V}(x) \leq 0$ in Ω_c, then we can take $\Omega = \Omega_c$. When $V(x)$ is positive definite, Ω_c is bounded for sufficiently small $c > 0$. This is not necessarily true when $V(x)$ is not positive definite. For example, if $V(x) = (x_1 - x_2)^2$, the set Ω_c is not bounded no matter how small c is. If $V(x)$ is radially unbounded—that is, $V(x) \to \infty$ as $\|x\| \to \infty$—the set Ω_c is bounded for all values of c. This is true whether or not $V(x)$ is positive definite.

When our interest is in showing that $x(t) \to 0$ as $t \to \infty$, we need to establish that the largest invariant set in E is the origin. This is done by showing that no solution can stay identically in E, other than the trivial solution $x(t) \equiv 0$. Specializing Theorem 4.4 to this case and taking $V(x)$ to be positive definite, we obtain the following two corollaries that extend Theorems 4.1 and 4.2.[9]

Corollary 4.1 *Let $x = 0$ be an equilibrium point for (4.1). Let $V : D \to R$ be a continuously differentiable positive definite function on a domain D containing the origin $x = 0$, such that $\dot{V}(x) \leq 0$ in D. Let $S = \{x \in D \mid \dot{V}(x) = 0\}$ and suppose that no solution can stay identically in S, other than the trivial solution $x(t) \equiv 0$. Then, the origin is asymptotically stable.* $\diamond$

---

[9]Corollaries 4.1 and 4.2 are known as the theorems of Barbashin and Krasovskii, who proved them before the introduction of LaSalle's invariance principle.

Corollary 4.2 *Let $x = 0$ be an equilibrium point for (4.1). Let $V : R^n \to R$ be a continuously differentiable, radially unbounded, positive definite function such that $\dot{V}(x) \leq 0$ for all $x \in R^n$. Let $S = \{x \in R^n \mid \dot{V}(x) = 0\}$ and suppose that no solution can stay identically in S, other than the trivial solution $x(t) \equiv 0$. Then, the origin is globally asymptotically stable.* ◇

When $\dot{V}(x)$ is negative definite, $S = \{0\}$. Then, Corollaries 4.1 and 4.2 coincide with Theorems 4.1 and 4.2, respectively.

Example 4.8 Consider the system

$$\begin{aligned} \dot{x}_1 &= x_2 \\ \dot{x}_2 &= -h_1(x_1) - h_2(x_2) \end{aligned}$$

where $h_1(\cdot)$ and $h_2(\cdot)$ are locally Lipschitz and satisfy

$$h_i(0) = 0, \quad yh_i(y) > 0, \quad \forall \, y \neq 0 \text{ and } y \in (-a, a)$$

The system has an isolated equilibrium point at the origin. Depending upon the functions $h_1(\cdot)$ and $h_2(\cdot)$, it might have other equilibrium points. The system can be viewed as a generalized pendulum with $h_2(x_2)$ as the friction term. Therefore, a Lyapunov function candidate may be taken as the energy-like function

$$V(x) = \int_0^{x_1} h_1(y) \, dy \; + \; \tfrac{1}{2}x_2^2$$

Let $D = \{x \in R^2 \mid -a < x_i < a\}$; $V(x)$ is positive definite in D and

$$\dot{V}(x) = h_1(x_1)x_2 + x_2[-h_1(x_1) - h_2(x_2)] = -x_2h_2(x_2) \leq 0$$

is negative semidefinite. To find $S = \{x \in D \mid \dot{V}(x) = 0\}$, note that

$$\dot{V}(x) = 0 \; \Rightarrow \; x_2h_2(x_2) = 0 \; \Rightarrow \; x_2 = 0, \; \text{ since } -a < x_2 < a$$

Hence, $S = \{x \in D \mid x_2 = 0\}$. Let $x(t)$ be a solution that belongs identically to S:

$$x_2(t) \equiv 0 \Rightarrow \dot{x}_2(t) \equiv 0 \Rightarrow h_1(x_1(t)) \equiv 0 \Rightarrow x_1(t) \equiv 0$$

Therefore, the only solution that can stay identically in S is the trivial solution $x(t) \equiv 0$. Thus, the origin is asymptotically stable. △

Example 4.9 Consider again the system of Example 4.8, but this time let $a = \infty$ and assume that $h_1(\cdot)$ satisfies the additional condition:

$$\int_0^y h_1(z) \, dz \; \to \; \infty \text{ as } |y| \to \infty$$

The Lyapunov function $V(x) = \int_0^{x_1} h_1(y) \, dy + (1/2)x_2^2$ is radially unbounded. Similar to the previous example, it can be shown that $\dot{V}(x) \leq 0$ in R^2, and the set

$$S = \{x \in R^2 \mid \dot{V}(x) = 0\} = \{x \in R^2 \mid x_2 = 0\}$$

contains no solutions other than the trivial solution. Hence, the origin is globally asymptotically stable.   △

Not only does LaSalle's theorem relax the negative definiteness requirement of Lyapunov's theorem, but it also extends Lyapunov's theorem in three different directions. First, it gives an estimate of the region of attraction, which is not necessarily of the form $\Omega_c = \{x \in R^n \mid V(x) \leq c\}$. The set Ω of Theorem 4.4 can be any compact positively invariant set. We will use this feature in Section 8.2 to obtain less conservative estimates of the region of attraction. Second, LaSalle's theorem can be used in cases where the system has an equilibrium set, rather than an isolated equilibrium point. This will be illustrated by an application to a simple adaptive control example from Section 1.2.6. Third, the function $V(x)$ does not have to be positive definite. The utility of this feature will be illustrated by an application to the neural network example of Section 1.2.5.

Example 4.10 Consider the first-order system

$$\dot{y} = ay + u$$

together with the adaptive control law

$$u = -ky, \qquad \dot{k} = \gamma y^2, \quad \gamma > 0$$

Taking $x_1 = y$ and $x_2 = k$, the closed-loop system is represented by

$$\begin{aligned} \dot{x}_1 &= -(x_2 - a)x_1 \\ \dot{x}_2 &= \gamma x_1^2 \end{aligned}$$

The line $x_1 = 0$ is an equilibrium set. We want to show that the trajectories approach this equilibrium set as $t \to \infty$, which means that the adaptive controller regulates y to zero. Consider the Lyapunov function candidate

$$V(x) = \tfrac{1}{2}x_1^2 + \frac{1}{2\gamma}(x_2 - b)^2$$

where $b > a$. The derivative of V along the trajectories of the system is given by

$$\dot{V}(x) = x_1\dot{x}_1 + \frac{1}{\gamma}(x_2 - b)\dot{x}_2 = -x_1^2(x_2 - a) + x_1^2(x_2 - b) = -x_1^2(b - a) \leq 0$$

Hence, $\dot{V}(x) \leq 0$. Since $V(x)$ is radially unbounded, the set $\Omega_c = \{x \in R^2 \mid V(x) \leq c\}$ is a compact, positively invariant set. Thus, taking $\Omega = \Omega_c$, all the conditions of Theorem 4.4 are satisfied. The set E is given by $E = \{x \in \Omega_c \mid x_1 = 0\}$. Because any point on the line $x_1 = 0$ is an equilibrium point, E is an invariant set. Therefore, in this example, $M = E$. From Theorem 4.4, we conclude that every trajectory starting in Ω_c approaches E as $t \to \infty$; that is, $x_1(t) \to 0$ as $t \to \infty$. Moreover, since $V(x)$ is radially unbounded, the conclusion is global; that is, it holds for all initial conditions $x(0)$ because for any $x(0)$, the constant c can be chosen large enough that $x(0) \in \Omega_c$. $\triangle$

Note that the Lyapunov function in Example 4.10 is dependent on a constant b, which is required to satisfy $b > a$. Since in the adaptive control problem the constant a is not known, we may not know the constant b explicitly, but we know that it always exists. This highlights another feature of Lyapunov's method, which we have not seen before; namely, in some situations, we may be able to assert the existence of a Lyapunov function that satisfies the conditions of a certain theorem even though we may not explicitly know that function. In Example 4.10, we can determine the Lyapunov function explicitly if we know some bound on a. For example, if we know that $|a| \le \alpha$, where the bound α is known, we can choose $b > \alpha$.

Example 4.11 The neural network of Section 1.2.5 is represented by

$$\dot{x}_i = \frac{1}{C_i} h_i(x_i) \left[\sum_j T_{ij} x_j - \frac{1}{R_i} g_i^{-1}(x_i) + I_i \right]$$

for $i = 1, 2, \ldots, n$, where the state variables x_i are the voltages at the amplifier outputs. They can only take values in the set

$$H = \{x \in R^n \mid -V_M < x_i < V_M\}$$

The functions $g_i : R \to (-V_M, V_M)$ are sigmoid functions,

$$h_i(x_i) = \left. \frac{dg_i}{du_i} \right|_{u_i = g_i^{-1}(x_i)} > 0, \quad \forall\, x_i \in (-V_M, V_M)$$

I_i are constant current inputs, $R_i > 0$, and $C_i > 0$. Assume that the symmetry condition $T_{ij} = T_{ji}$ is satisfied. The system may have several equilibrium points in H. We assume that all equilibrium points in H are isolated. Due to the symmetry property $T_{ij} = T_{ji}$, the vector whose ith component is

$$-\left[\sum_j T_{ij} x_j - \frac{1}{R_i} g_i^{-1}(x_i) + I_i \right]$$

is a gradient vector of a scalar function. By integration, similar to what we have done in the variable gradient method, it can be shown that this scalar function is given by

$$V(x) = -\frac{1}{2}\sum_i\sum_j T_{ij}x_ix_j + \sum_i \frac{1}{R_i}\int_0^{x_i} g_i^{-1}(y)\,dy - \sum_i I_ix_i$$

This function is continuously differentiable, but (typically) not positive definite. We rewrite the state equations as

$$\dot{x}_i = -\frac{1}{C_i}h_i(x_i)\frac{\partial V}{\partial x_i}$$

Let us now apply Theorem 4.4 with $V(x)$ as a candidate function. The derivative of $V(x)$ along the trajectories of the system is given by

$$\dot{V}(x) = \sum_{i=1}^n \frac{\partial V}{\partial x_i}\dot{x}_i = -\sum_{i=1}^n \frac{1}{C_i}h_i(x_i)\left(\frac{\partial V}{\partial x_i}\right)^2 \leq 0$$

Moreover,

$$\dot{V}(x) = 0 \Rightarrow \frac{\partial V}{\partial x_i} = 0 \Rightarrow \dot{x}_i = 0, \ \ \forall\, i$$

Hence, $\dot{V}(x) = 0$ only at equilibrium points. To apply Theorem 4.4, we need to construct a set Ω. Let

$$\Omega(\varepsilon) = \{x \in R^n \mid -(V_M - \varepsilon) \leq x_i \leq (V_M - \varepsilon)\}$$

where $\varepsilon > 0$ is arbitrarily small. The set $\Omega(\varepsilon)$ is closed and bounded, and $\dot{V}(x) \leq 0$ in $\Omega(\varepsilon)$. It remains to show that $\Omega(\varepsilon)$ is a positively invariant set; that is, every trajectory starting in $\Omega(\varepsilon)$ stays for all future time in $\Omega(\varepsilon)$. To simplify the task, we assume a specific form for the sigmoid function $g_i(\cdot)$. Let

$$g_i(u_i) = \frac{2V_M}{\pi}\tan^{-1}\left(\frac{\lambda\pi u_i}{2V_M}\right), \ \ \lambda > 0$$

Then,

$$\dot{x}_i = \frac{1}{C_i}h_i(x_i)\left[\sum_j T_{ij}x_j - \frac{2V_M}{\lambda\pi R_i}\tan\left(\frac{\pi x_i}{2V_M}\right) + I_i\right]$$

For $|x_i| \geq V_M - \varepsilon$,

$$\left|\tan\left(\frac{\pi x_i}{2V_M}\right)\right| \geq \tan\left(\frac{\pi(V_M - \varepsilon)}{2V_M}\right) \to \infty \text{ as } \varepsilon \to 0$$

Since x_i and I_i are bounded, ε can be chosen small enough to ensure that

$$x_i\sum_j T_{ij}x_j - \frac{2V_Mx_i}{\lambda\pi R_i}\tan\left(\frac{\pi x_i}{2V_M}\right) + x_iI_i < 0, \ \ \text{for } V_M - \varepsilon \leq |x_i| < V_M$$

Hence,

$$\frac{d}{dt}\left(x_i^2\right) = 2x_i\dot{x}_i < 0, \quad \text{for } V_M - \varepsilon \leq |x_i| < V_M, \ \forall\, i$$

Consequently, trajectories starting in $\Omega(\varepsilon)$ will stay in $\Omega(\varepsilon)$ for all future time. In fact, trajectories starting in $H - \Omega(\varepsilon)$ will converge to $\Omega(\varepsilon)$, implying that all equilibrium points lie in the compact set $\Omega(\varepsilon)$. Hence, there can be only a finite number of isolated equilibrium points. In $\Omega(\varepsilon)$, $E = M =$ the set of equilibrium points inside $\Omega(\varepsilon)$. By Theorem 4.4, we know that every trajectory in $\Omega(\varepsilon)$ approaches M as $t \to \infty$. Since M consists of isolated equilibrium points, it can be shown (Exercise 4.20) that a trajectory approaching M must approach one of these equilibria. Hence, the system will not oscillate. $\triangle$

4.3 Linear Systems and Linearization

The linear time-invariant system

$$\dot{x} = Ax \tag{4.9}$$

has an equilibrium point at the origin. The equilibrium point is isolated if and only if $\det(A) \neq 0$. If $\det(A) = 0$, the matrix A has a nontrivial null space. Every point in the null space of A is an equilibrium point for the system (4.9). In other words, if $\det(A) = 0$, the system has an equilibrium subspace. Notice that a linear system cannot have multiple isolated equilibrium points. For, if $\bar{x}_1$ and $\bar{x}_2$ are two equilibrium points for (4.9), then by linearity, every point on the line connecting $\bar{x}_1$ and $\bar{x}_2$ is an equilibrium point for the system. Stability properties of the origin can be characterized by the locations of the eigenvalues of the matrix A. Recall from linear system theory[10] that the solution of (4.9) for a given initial state $x(0)$ is given by

$$x(t) = \exp(At)x(0) \tag{4.10}$$

and that for any matrix A there is a nonsingular matrix P (possibly complex) that transforms A into its Jordan form; that is,

$$P^{-1}AP = J = \text{block diag}[J_1, J_2, \dots, J_r]$$

where J_i is a Jordan block associated with the eigenvalue λ_i of A. A Jordan block of order one takes the form $J_i = \lambda_i$, while a Jordan block of order $m > 1$ takes the form

$$J_i = \begin{bmatrix} \lambda_i & 1 & 0 & \dots & \dots & 0 \\ 0 & \lambda_i & 1 & 0 & \dots & 0 \\ \vdots & & \ddots & & & \vdots \\ \vdots & & & \ddots & & 0 \\ \vdots & & & & \ddots & 1 \\ 0 & \dots & \dots & \dots & 0 & \lambda_i \end{bmatrix}_{m \times m}$$

---

[10]See, for example, [9], [35], [81], [94], or [158].

Therefore,

$$\exp(At) = P\exp(Jt)P^{-1} = \sum_{i=1}^{r}\sum_{k=1}^{m_i} t^{k-1}\exp(\lambda_i t)R_{ik} \qquad (4.11)$$

where m_i is the order of the Jordan block J_i. If an $n \times n$ matrix A has a repeated eigenvalue λ_i of algebraic multiplicity q_i,[11] then the Jordan blocks associated with λ_i have order one if and only if $\text{rank}(A - \lambda_i I) = n - q_i$. The next theorem characterizes the stability properties of the origin.

Theorem 4.5 *The equilibrium point $x = 0$ of $\dot{x} = Ax$ is stable if and only if all eigenvalues of A satisfy $\text{Re}\lambda_i \leq 0$ and for every eigenvalue with $\text{Re}\lambda_i = 0$ and algebraic multiplicity $q_i \geq 2$, $\text{rank}(A - \lambda_i I) = n - q_i$, where n is the dimension of x. The equilibrium point $x = 0$ is (globally) asymptotically stable if and only if all eigenvalues of A satisfy $\text{Re}\lambda_i < 0$.* ◇

Proof: From (4.10), we can see that the origin is stable if and only if $\exp(At)$ is a bounded function of t for all $t \geq 0$. If one of the eigenvalues of A is in the open right-half complex plane, the corresponding exponential term $\exp(\lambda_i t)$ in (4.11) will grow unbounded as $t \to \infty$. Therefore, we must restrict the eigenvalues to be in the closed left-half complex plane. However, those eigenvalues on the imaginary axis (if any) could give rise to unbounded terms if the order of an associated Jordan block is higher than one, due to the term t^{k-1} in (4.11). Therefore, we must restrict eigenvalues on the imaginary axis to have Jordan blocks of order one, which is equivalent to the rank condition $\text{rank}(A - \lambda_i I) = n - q_i$. Thus, we conclude that the condition for stability is a necessary one. It is clear that the condition is also sufficient to ensure that $\exp(At)$ is bounded. For asymptotic stability of the origin, $\exp(At)$ must approach 0 as $t \to \infty$. From (4.11), this is the case if and only if $\text{Re}\lambda_i < 0$, $\forall\ i$. Since $x(t)$ depends linearly on the initial state $x(0)$, asymptotic stability of the origin is global. □

The proof shows, mathematically, why repeated eigenvalues on the imaginary axis must satisfy the rank condition $\text{rank}(A - \lambda_i I) = n - q_i$. The next example may shed some light on the physical meaning of this requirement.

Example 4.12 Figure 4.6 shows a series connection and a parallel connection of two identical systems. Each system is represented by the state model

$$\begin{aligned}
\dot{x} &= \begin{bmatrix} 0 & 1 \\ -1 & 0 \end{bmatrix}x + \begin{bmatrix} 0 \\ 1 \end{bmatrix}u \\
y &= \begin{bmatrix} 1 & 0 \end{bmatrix}x
\end{aligned}$$

where u and y are the input and output, respectively. Let A_s and A_p be the matrices of the series and parallel connections, when modeled in the form (4.9) (no driving

---

[11]Equivalently, q_i is the multiplicity of λ_i as a zero of $\det(\lambda I - A)$.

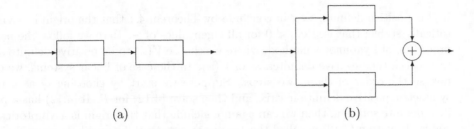

Figure 4.6: (a) Series connection; (b) parallel connection.

inputs). Then

$$A_p = \begin{bmatrix} 0 & 1 & 0 & 0 \\ -1 & 0 & 0 & 0 \\ 0 & 0 & 0 & 1 \\ 0 & 0 & -1 & 0 \end{bmatrix} \quad \text{and} \quad A_s = \begin{bmatrix} 0 & 1 & 0 & 0 \\ -1 & 0 & 0 & 0 \\ 0 & 0 & 0 & 1 \\ 1 & 0 & -1 & 0 \end{bmatrix}$$

The matrices A_p and A_s have the same eigenvalues on the imaginary axis, $\pm j$ with algebraic multiplicity $q_i = 2$, where $j = \sqrt{-1}$. It can be easily checked that $\text{rank}(A_p - jI) = 2 = n - q_i$, while $\text{rank}(A_s - jI) = 3 \neq n - q_i$. Thus, by Theorem 4.5, the origin of the parallel connection is stable, while the origin of the series connection is unstable. To physically see the difference between the two cases, notice that in the parallel connection, nonzero initial conditions produce sinusoidal oscillations of frequency 1 rad/sec, which are bounded functions of time. The sum of these sinusoidal signals remains bounded. On the other hand, nonzero initial conditions in the first component of the series connection produce a sinusoidal oscillation of frequency 1 rad/sec, which acts as a driving input for the second component. Since the second component has an undamped natural frequency of 1 rad/sec, the driving input causes "resonance" and the response grows unbounded. $\triangle$

When all eigenvalues of A satisfy $\text{Re}\lambda_i < 0$, A is called a *Hurwitz matrix* or a *stability matrix*. The origin of (4.9) is asymptotically stable if and only if A is Hurwitz. Asymptotic stability of the origin can be also investigated by using Lyapunov's method. Consider a quadratic Lyapunov function candidate

$$V(x) = x^T P x$$

where P is a real symmetric positive definite matrix. The derivative of V along the trajectories of the linear system (4.9) is given by

$$\dot{V}(x) = x^T P \dot{x} + \dot{x}^T P x = x^T (PA + A^T P)x = -x^T Q x$$

where Q is a symmetric matrix defined by

$$PA + A^T P = -Q \tag{4.12}$$

If Q is positive definite, we can conclude by Theorem 4.1 that the origin is asymptotically stable; that is, $\mathrm{Re}\lambda_i < 0$ for all eigenvalues of A. Here we follow the usual procedure of Lyapunov's method, where we choose $V(x)$ to be positive definite and then check the negative definiteness of $\dot{V}(x)$. In the case of linear systems, we can reverse the order of these two steps. Suppose we start by choosing Q as a real symmetric positive definite matrix, and then solve (4.12) for P. If (4.12) has a positive definite solution, then we can again conclude that the origin is asymptotically stable. Equation (4.12) is called the *Lyapunov equation*. The next theorem characterizes asymptotic stability of the origin in terms of the solution of the Lyapunov equation.

Theorem 4.6 *A matrix A is Hurwitz; that is, $\mathrm{Re}\lambda_i < 0$ for all eigenvalues of A, if and only if for any given positive definite symmetric matrix Q there exists a positive definite symmetric matrix P that satisfies the Lyapunov equation (4.12). Moreover, if A is Hurwitz, then P is the unique solution of (4.12).* ◇

Proof: Sufficiency follows from Theorem 4.1 with the Lyapunov function $V(x) = x^T P x$, as we have already shown. To prove necessity, assume that all eigenvalues of A satisfy $\mathrm{Re}\lambda_i < 0$ and consider the matrix P, defined by

$$P = \int_0^\infty \exp(A^T t) Q \exp(At) \, dt \tag{4.13}$$

The integrand is a sum of terms of the form $t^{k-1}\exp(\lambda_i t)$, where $\mathrm{Re}\lambda_i < 0$. Therefore, the integral exists. The matrix P is symmetric and positive definite. The fact that it is positive definite can be shown as follows: Supposing it is not so, there is a vector $x \neq 0$ such that $x^T P x = 0$. However,

$$x^T P x = 0 \quad \Rightarrow \quad \int_0^\infty x^T \exp(A^T t) Q \exp(At) x \, dt = 0$$
$$\Rightarrow \quad \exp(At)x \equiv 0, \ \forall \, t \geq 0 \ \Rightarrow \ x = 0$$

since $\exp(At)$ is nonsingular for all t. This contradiction shows that P is positive definite. Now, substituting (4.13) in the left-hand side of (4.12) yields

$$PA + A^T P = \int_0^\infty \exp(A^T t) Q \exp(At) A \, dt + \int_0^\infty A^T \exp(A^T t) Q \exp(At) \, dt$$
$$= \int_0^\infty \frac{d}{dt} \exp(A^T t) Q \exp(At) \, dt = \exp(A^T t) Q \exp(At)\Big|_0^\infty = -Q$$

which shows that P is indeed a solution of (4.12). To show that it is the unique solution, suppose there is another solution $\tilde{P} \neq P$. Then,

$$(P - \tilde{P})A + A^T(P - \tilde{P}) = 0$$

Premultiplying by $\exp(A^T t)$ and postmultiplying by $\exp(At)$, we obtain

$$0 = \exp(A^T t)[(P - \tilde{P})A + A^T(P - \tilde{P})]\exp(At) = \frac{d}{dt}\left\{\exp(A^T t)(P - \tilde{P})\exp(At)\right\}$$

Hence,

$$\exp(A^T t)(P - \tilde{P})\exp(At) \equiv \text{a constant } \forall\, t$$

In particular, since $\exp(A0) = I$, we have

$$(P - \tilde{P}) = \exp(A^T t)(P - \tilde{P})\exp(At) \to 0 \text{ as } t \to \infty$$

Therefore, $\tilde{P} = P$. □

The positive definiteness requirement on Q can be relaxed. It is left to the reader (Exercise 4.22) to verify that Q can be taken as a positive semidefinite matrix of the form $Q = C^T C$, where the pair (A, C) is observable.

Equation (4.12) is a linear algebraic equation that can be solved by rearranging it in the form $Mx = y$, where x and y are defined by stacking the elements of P and Q in vectors, as will be illustrated in the next example. There are numerically efficient methods for solving such equations.[12]

Example 4.13 Let

$$A = \begin{bmatrix} 0 & -1 \\ 1 & -1 \end{bmatrix}, \quad Q = \begin{bmatrix} 1 & 0 \\ 0 & 1 \end{bmatrix}, \text{ and } P = \begin{bmatrix} p_{11} & p_{12} \\ p_{12} & p_{22} \end{bmatrix}$$

where, due to symmetry, $p_{12} = p_{21}$. The Lyapunov equation (4.12) can be rewritten as

$$\begin{bmatrix} 0 & 2 & 0 \\ -1 & -1 & 1 \\ 0 & -2 & -2 \end{bmatrix} \begin{bmatrix} p_{11} \\ p_{12} \\ p_{22} \end{bmatrix} = \begin{bmatrix} -1 \\ 0 \\ -1 \end{bmatrix}$$

The unique solution of this equation is given by

$$\begin{bmatrix} p_{11} \\ p_{12} \\ p_{22} \end{bmatrix} = \begin{bmatrix} 1.5 \\ -0.5 \\ 1.0 \end{bmatrix} \quad \Rightarrow \quad P = \begin{bmatrix} 1.5 & -0.5 \\ -0.5 & 1.0 \end{bmatrix}$$

The matrix P is positive definite since its leading principal minors (1.5 and 1.25) are positive. Hence, all eigenvalues of A are in the open left-half complex plane. △

The Lyapunov equation can be used to test whether or not a matrix A is Hurwitz, as an alternative to calculating the eigenvalues of A. One starts by choosing a positive definite matrix Q (for example, $Q = I$) and solves the Lyapunov equation (4.12) for P. If the equation has a positive definite solution, we conclude that A is Hurwitz; otherwise, it is not so. However, there is no computational advantage

---

[12]Consult [67] on numerical methods for solving linear algebraic equations. The Lyapunov equation can also be solved by viewing it as a special case of the Sylvester equation $PA + BP + C = 0$, which is treated in [67]. Almost all commercial software programs for control systems include commands for solving the Lyapunov equation.

in solving the Lyapunov equation over calculating the eigenvalues of A.[13] Besides, the eigenvalues provide more direct information about the response of the linear system. The interest in the Lyapunov equation is not in its use as a stability test for linear systems;[14] rather, it is in the fact that it provides a procedure for finding a Lyapunov function for any linear system $\dot{x} = Ax$ when A is Hurwitz. The mere existence of a Lyapunov function will allow us to draw conclusions about the system when the right-hand side Ax is perturbed, whether such perturbation is a linear perturbation in the coefficients of A or a nonlinear perturbation. This advantage will unfold as we continue our study of Lyapunov's method.

Let us go back to the nonlinear system

$$\dot{x} = f(x) \tag{4.14}$$

where $f : D \to R^n$ is a continuously differentiable map from a domain $D \subset R^n$ into R^n. Suppose the origin $x = 0$ is in D and is an equilibrium point for the system; that is, $f(0) = 0$. By the mean value theorem,

$$f_i(x) = f_i(0) + \frac{\partial f_i}{\partial x}(z_i)\, x$$

where z_i is a point on the line segment connecting x to the origin. The foregoing equality is valid for any point $x \in D$ such that the line segment connecting x to the origin lies entirely in D. Since $f(0) = 0$, we can write

$$f_i(x) = \frac{\partial f_i}{\partial x}(z_i)x = \frac{\partial f_i}{\partial x}(0)x + \left[\frac{\partial f_i}{\partial x}(z_i) - \frac{\partial f_i}{\partial x}(0)\right] x$$

Hence,

$$f(x) = Ax + g(x)$$

where

$$A = \frac{\partial f}{\partial x}(0) \quad \text{and} \quad g_i(x) = \left[\frac{\partial f_i}{\partial x}(z_i) - \frac{\partial f_i}{\partial x}(0)\right] x$$

The function $g_i(x)$ satisfies

$$|g_i(x)| \leq \left\|\frac{\partial f_i}{\partial x}(z_i) - \frac{\partial f_i}{\partial x}(0)\right\| \|x\|$$

By continuity of $[\partial f / \partial x]$, we see that

$$\frac{\|g(x)\|}{\|x\|} \to 0 \quad \text{as} \quad \|x\| \to 0$$

---

[13]A typical procedure for solving the Lyapunov equation, the Bartels–Stewart algorithm [67], starts by transforming A into its real Schur form, which gives the eigenvalues of A. Hence, the computational effort for solving the Lyapunov equation is more than calculating the eigenvalues of A. Other algorithms for solving the Lyapunov equation take an amount of computations comparable to the Bartels–Stewart algorithm.

[14]It might be of interest, however, to know that one can use the Lyapunov equation to derive the classical Routh–Hurwitz criterion. (See [35, pp. 417–419].)

This suggests that in a small neighborhood of the origin we can approximate the nonlinear system (4.14) by its linearization about the origin

$$\dot{x} = Ax, \quad \text{where} \quad A = \frac{\partial f}{\partial x}(0)$$

The next theorem spells out conditions under which we can draw conclusions about the stability of the origin as an equilibrium point for the nonlinear system by investigating its stability as an equilibrium point for the linear system. The theorem is known as *Lyapunov's indirect method*.

Theorem 4.7 *Let $x = 0$ be an equilibrium point for the nonlinear system*

$$\dot{x} = f(x)$$

where $f : D \to R^n$ is continuously differentiable and D is a neighborhood of the origin. Let

$$A = \left. \frac{\partial f}{\partial x}(x) \right|_{x=0}$$

Then,

1. *The origin is asymptotically stable if $\text{Re}\lambda_i < 0$ for all eigenvalues of A.*

2. *The origin is unstable if $\text{Re}\lambda_i > 0$ for one or more of the eigenvalues of A.*

$\diamond$

Proof: To prove the first part, let A be a Hurwitz matrix. Then, by Theorem 4.6, we know that for any positive definite symmetric matrix Q, the solution P of the Lyapunov equation (4.12) is positive definite. We use $V(x) = x^T P x$ as a Lyapunov function candidate for the nonlinear system. The derivative of $V(x)$ along the trajectories of the system is given by

$$
\begin{aligned}
\dot{V}(x) &= x^T P f(x) + f^T(x) P x \\
&= x^T P [Ax + g(x)] + [x^T A^T + g^T(x)] P x \\
&= x^T (PA + A^T P) x + 2 x^T P g(x) \\
&= -x^T Q x + 2 x^T P g(x)
\end{aligned}
$$

The first term on the right-hand side is negative definite, while the second term is (in general) indefinite. The function $g(x)$ satisfies

$$\frac{\|g(x)\|_2}{\|x\|_2} \to 0 \quad \text{as} \quad \|x\|_2 \to 0$$

Therefore, for any $\gamma > 0$, there exists $r > 0$ such that

$$\|g(x)\|_2 < \gamma \|x\|_2, \quad \forall \, \|x\|_2 < r$$

Hence,

$$\dot{V}(x) < -x^T Q x + 2\gamma \|P\|_2 \|x\|_2^2, \quad \forall \, \|x\|_2 < r$$

But

$$x^T Q x \geq \lambda_{\min}(Q) \|x\|_2^2$$

where $\lambda_{\min}(\cdot)$ denotes the minimum eigenvalue of a matrix. Note that $\lambda_{\min}(Q)$ is real and positive since Q is symmetric and positive definite. Thus,

$$\dot{V}(x) < -[\lambda_{\min}(Q) - 2\gamma \|P\|_2] \|x\|_2^2, \quad \forall \, \|x\|_2 < r$$

Choosing $\gamma < (1/2)\lambda_{\min}(Q)/\|P\|_2$ ensures that $\dot{V}(x)$ is negative definite. By Theorem 4.1, we conclude that the origin is asymptotically stable. To prove the second part of the theorem, let us consider first the special case when A has no eigenvalues on the imaginary axis. If the eigenvalues of A cluster into a group of eigenvalues in the open right-half plane and a group of eigenvalues in the open left-half plane, then there is a nonsingular matrix T such that[15]

$$TAT^{-1} = \begin{bmatrix} -A_1 & 0 \\ 0 & A_2 \end{bmatrix}$$

where A_1 and A_2 are Hurwitz matrices. Let

$$z = Tx = \begin{bmatrix} z_1 \\ z_2 \end{bmatrix}$$

where the partition of z is compatible with the dimensions of A_1 and A_2. The change of variables $z = Tx$ transforms the system

$$\dot{x} = Ax + g(x)$$

into the form

$$\begin{aligned} \dot{z}_1 &= -A_1 z_1 + g_1(z) \\ \dot{z}_2 &= A_2 z_2 + g_2(z) \end{aligned}$$

where the functions $g_i(z)$ have the property that for any $\gamma > 0$, there exists $r > 0$ such that

$$\|g_i(z)\|_2 < \gamma \|z\|_2, \quad \forall \, \|z\|_2 \leq r, \; i = 1, 2$$

The origin $z = 0$ is an equilibrium point for the system in the z-coordinates. Clearly, any conclusion we arrive at concerning the stability properties of $z = 0$ carries over to the equilibrium point $x = 0$ in the x-coordinates, since T is nonsingular.[16] To show that the origin is unstable, we apply Theorem 4.3. The construction of a

---

[15]There are several methods for finding the matrix T, one of which is to transform the matrix A into its real Jordan form [67].

[16]See Exercise 4.26 for a general discussion of stability preserving maps.

function $V(z)$ will be done basically as in Example 4.7, except for working with vectors, instead of scalars. Let Q_1 and Q_2 be positive definite symmetric matrices of the dimensions of A_1 and A_2, respectively. Since A_1 and A_2 are Hurwitz, we know from Theorem 4.6 that the Lyapunov equations

$$P_i A_i + A_i^T P_i = -Q_i, \quad i = 1, 2$$

have unique positive definite solutions P_1 and P_2. Let

$$V(z) = z_1^T P_1 z_1 - z_2^T P_2 z_2 = z^T \begin{bmatrix} P_1 & 0 \\ 0 & -P_2 \end{bmatrix} z$$

In the subspace $z_2 = 0$, $V(z) > 0$ at points arbitrarily close to the origin. Let

$$U = \{ z \in R^n \mid \|z\|_2 \le r \text{ and } V(z) > 0 \}$$

In U,

$$\begin{aligned} \dot{V}(z) &= -z_1^T (P_1 A_1 + A_1^T P_1) z_1 + 2 z_1^T P_1 g_1(z) \\ &\quad - z_2^T (P_2 A_2 + A_2^T P_2) z_2 - 2 z_2^T P_2 g_2(z) \\ &= z_1^T Q_1 z_1 + z_2^T Q_2 z_2 + 2 z^T \begin{bmatrix} P_1 g_1(z) \\ -P_2 g_2(z) \end{bmatrix} \\ &\ge \lambda_{\min}(Q_1)\|z_1\|_2^2 + \lambda_{\min}(Q_2)\|z_2\|_2^2 \\ &\quad - 2\|z\|_2 \sqrt{\|P_1\|_2^2 \|g_1(z)\|_2^2 + \|P_2\|_2^2 \|g_2(z)\|_2^2} \\ &> (\alpha - 2\sqrt{2}\beta\gamma)\|z\|_2^2 \end{aligned}$$

where

$$\alpha = \min\{\lambda_{\min}(Q_1), \lambda_{\min}(Q_2)\} \quad \text{and} \quad \beta = \max\{\|P_1\|_2, \|P_2\|_2\}$$

Thus, choosing $\gamma < \alpha/(2\sqrt{2}\beta)$ ensures that $\dot{V}(z) > 0$ in U. Therefore, by Theorem 4.3, the origin is unstable. Notice that we could have applied Theorem 4.3 in the original coordinates by defining the matrices

$$P = T^T \begin{bmatrix} P_1 & 0 \\ 0 & -P_2 \end{bmatrix} T; \quad Q = T^T \begin{bmatrix} Q_1 & 0 \\ 0 & Q_2 \end{bmatrix} T$$

which satisfy the equation

$$PA + A^T P = Q$$

The matrix Q is positive definite, and $V(x) = x^T P x$ is positive for points arbitrarily close to the origin $x = 0$. Let us consider now the general case when A may have eigenvalues on the imaginary axis, in addition to eigenvalues in the open right-half complex plane. We can reduce this case to the special case we have just studied by a simple trick of shifting the imaginary axis. Suppose A has m eigenvalues with

$\text{Re}\lambda_i > \delta > 0$. Then, the matrix $[A - (\delta/2)I]$ has m eigenvalues in the open right-half plane, but no eigenvalues on the imaginary axis. By previous arguments, there exist matrices $P = P^T$ and $Q = Q^T > 0$ such that

$$P\left[A - \frac{\delta}{2}I\right] + \left[A - \frac{\delta}{2}I\right]^T P = Q$$

where $V(x) = x^T P x$ is positive for points arbitrarily close to the origin. The derivative of $V(x)$ along the trajectories of the system is given by

$$
\begin{aligned}
\dot{V}(x) &= x^T(PA + A^T P)x + 2x^T P g(x) \\
&= x^T\left[P\left(A - \frac{\delta}{2}I\right) + \left(A - \frac{\delta}{2}I\right)^T P\right]x + \delta x^T P x + 2x^T P g(x) \\
&= x^T Q x + \delta V(x) + 2x^T P g(x)
\end{aligned}
$$

In the set

$$\{x \in R^n \mid \|x\|_2 \le r \text{ and } V(x) > 0\}$$

where r is chosen such that $\|g(x)\|_2 \le \gamma\|x\|_2$ for $\|x\|_2 < r$, $\dot{V}(x)$ satisfies

$$\dot{V}(x) \ge \lambda_{\min}(Q)\|x\|_2^2 - 2\|P\|_2\|x\|_2\|g(x)\|_2 \ge (\lambda_{\min}(Q) - 2\gamma\|P\|_2)\,\|x\|_2^2$$

which is positive for $\gamma < (1/2)\lambda_{\min}(Q)/\|P\|_2$. Applying Theorem 4.3 concludes the proof. $\square$

Theorem 4.7 provides us with a simple procedure for determining the stability of an equilibrium point at the origin. We calculate the *Jacobian matrix*

$$A = \left.\frac{\partial f}{\partial x}\right|_{x=0}$$

and test its eigenvalues. If $\text{Re}\lambda_i < 0$ for all i or $\text{Re}\lambda_i > 0$ for some i, we conclude that the origin is asymptotically stable or unstable, respectively. Moreover, the proof of the theorem shows that when $\text{Re}\lambda_i < 0$ for all i, we can also find a Lyapunov function for the system that will work locally in some neighborhood of the origin. The Lyapunov function is the quadratic form $V(x) = x^T P x$, where P is the solution of the Lyapunov equation (4.12) for any positive definite symmetric matrix Q. Note that Theorem 4.7 does not say anything about the case when $\text{Re}\lambda_i \le 0$ for all i, with $\text{Re}\lambda_i = 0$ for some i. In this case, linearization fails to determine the stability of the equilibrium point.[17]

Example 4.14 Consider the scalar system

$$\dot{x} = ax^3$$

---

[17]See Section 8.1 for further investigation of the critical case when linearization fails.

Linearizing the system about the origin $x = 0$ yields

$$A = \frac{\partial f}{\partial x}\bigg|_{x=0} = 3ax^2\big|_{x=0} = 0$$

There is one eigenvalue that lies on the imaginary axis. Hence, linearization fails to determine the stability of the origin. This failure is genuine in the sense that the origin could be asymptotically stable, stable, or unstable, depending on the value of the parameter a. If $a < 0$, the origin is asymptotically stable as can be seen from the Lyapunov function $V(x) = x^4$, whose derivative $\dot{V}(x) = 4ax^6 < 0$ for $x \neq 0$. If $a = 0$, the system is linear and the origin is stable according to Theorem 4.5. If $a > 0$, the origin is unstable as can be seen from Theorem 4.3 and the function $V(x) = x^4$, whose derivative $\dot{V}(x) = 4ax^6 > 0$ for $x \neq 0$. $\triangle$

Example 4.15 The pendulum equation

$$\begin{aligned}
\dot{x}_1 &= x_2 \\
\dot{x}_2 &= -a\sin x_1 - bx_2
\end{aligned}$$

has two equilibrium points at $(x_1 = 0, \ x_2 = 0)$ and $(x_1 = \pi, \ x_2 = 0)$. Let us investigate stability of both points by using linearization. The Jacobian matrix is given by

$$\frac{\partial f}{\partial x} = \begin{bmatrix} \frac{\partial f_1}{\partial x_1} & \frac{\partial f_1}{\partial x_2} \\ \frac{\partial f_2}{\partial x_1} & \frac{\partial f_2}{\partial x_2} \end{bmatrix} = \begin{bmatrix} 0 & 1 \\ -a\cos x_1 & -b \end{bmatrix}$$

To determine the stability of the origin, we evaluate the Jacobian at $x = 0$:

$$A = \frac{\partial f}{\partial x}\bigg|_{x=0} = \begin{bmatrix} 0 & 1 \\ -a & -b \end{bmatrix}$$

The eigenvalues of A are

$$\lambda_{1,2} = -\tfrac{1}{2}b \pm \tfrac{1}{2}\sqrt{b^2 - 4a}$$

For all $a, \ b > 0$, the eigenvalues satisfy $\text{Re}\lambda_i < 0$. Consequently, the equilibrium point at the origin is asymptotically stable. In the absence of friction ($b = 0$), both eigenvalues are on the imaginary axis. Thus, we cannot determine the stability of the origin through linearization. We have seen in Example 4.3 that, in this case, the origin is a stable equilibrium point as determined by an energy Lyapunov function. To determine the stability of the equilibrium point at $(x_1 = \pi, \ x_2 = 0)$, we evaluate the Jacobian at that point. This is equivalent to performing a change of variables $z_1 = x_1 - \pi$, $z_2 = x_2$ to shift the equilibrium point to the origin, and evaluating the Jacobian $[\partial f/\partial z]$ at $z = 0$:

$$\tilde{A} = \frac{\partial f}{\partial x}\bigg|_{x_1=\pi, x_2=0} = \begin{bmatrix} 0 & 1 \\ a & -b \end{bmatrix}$$

The eigenvalues of $\tilde{A}$ are

$$\lambda_{1,2} = -\tfrac{1}{2}b \pm \tfrac{1}{2}\sqrt{b^2 + 4a}$$

For all $a > 0$ and $b \geq 0$, there is one eigenvalue in the open right-half plane. Hence, the equilibrium point at $(x_1 = \pi,\ x_2 = 0)$ is unstable. $\triangle$

4.4 Comparison Functions

As we move from autonomous to nonautonomous systems, one degree of difficulty will arise from the fact that the solution of the nonautonomous system $\dot{x} = f(t, x)$, starting at $x(t_0) = x_0$, depends on both t and t_0. To cope with this new situation, we will refine the definitions of stability and asymptotic stability so that they hold uniformly in the initial time t_0. While we can refine Definition 4.1 to achieve the required uniformity, it turns out that there are more transparent definitions which use special comparison functions, known as class $\mathcal{K}$ and class $\mathcal{KL}$ functions.

Definition 4.2 *A continuous function* $\alpha : [0, a) \to [0, \infty)$ *is said to belong to class* $\mathcal{K}$ *if it is strictly increasing and* $\alpha(0) = 0$. *It is said to belong to class* $\mathcal{K}_\infty$ *if* $a = \infty$ *and* $\alpha(r) \to \infty$ *as* $r \to \infty$.

Definition 4.3 *A continuous function* $\beta : [0, a) \times [0, \infty) \to [0, \infty)$ *is said to belong to class* $\mathcal{KL}$ *if, for each fixed* s, *the mapping* $\beta(r, s)$ *belongs to class* $\mathcal{K}$ *with respect to* r *and, for each fixed* r, *the mapping* $\beta(r, s)$ *is decreasing with respect to* s *and* $\beta(r, s) \to 0$ *as* $s \to \infty$.

Example 4.16

- $\alpha(r) = \tan^{-1}(r)$ is strictly increasing since $\alpha'(r) = 1/(1 + r^2) > 0$. It belongs to class $\mathcal{K}$, but not to class $\mathcal{K}_\infty$ since $\lim_{r \to \infty} \alpha(r) = \pi/2 < \infty$.

- $\alpha(r) = r^c$, for any positive real number c, is strictly increasing since $\alpha'(r) = cr^{c-1} > 0$. Moreover, $\lim_{r \to \infty} \alpha(r) = \infty$; thus, it belongs to class $\mathcal{K}_\infty$.

- $\alpha(r) = \min\{r, r^2\}$ is continuous, strictly increasing, and $\lim_{r \to \infty} \alpha(r) = \infty$. Hence, it belongs to class $\mathcal{K}_\infty$. Notice that $\alpha(r)$ is not continuously differentiable at $r = 1$. Continuous differentiability is not required for a class $\mathcal{K}$ function.

- $\beta(r, s) = r/(ksr + 1)$, for any positive real number k, is strictly increasing in r since
$$\frac{\partial \beta}{\partial r} = \frac{1}{(ksr + 1)^2} > 0$$
and strictly decreasing in s since
$$\frac{\partial \beta}{\partial s} = \frac{-kr^2}{(ksr + 1)^2} < 0$$

Moreover, $\beta(r,s) \to 0$ as $s \to \infty$. Therefore, it belongs to class $\mathcal{KL}$.

- $\beta(r,s) = r^c e^{-s}$, for any positive real number c, belongs to class $\mathcal{KL}$. $\triangle$

The next lemma states some useful properties of class $\mathcal{K}$ and class $\mathcal{KL}$ functions, which will be needed later on. The proof of the lemma is left as an exercise for the reader (Exercise 4.34).

Lemma 4.2 *Let α_1 and α_2 be class $\mathcal{K}$ functions on $[0,a)$, α_3 and α_4 be class $\mathcal{K}_\infty$ functions, and β be a class $\mathcal{KL}$ function. Denote the inverse of α_i by α_i^{-1}. Then,*

- α_1^{-1} *is defined on $[0, \alpha_1(a))$ and belongs to class $\mathcal{K}$.*

- α_3^{-1} *is defined on $[0, \infty)$ and belongs to class $\mathcal{K}_\infty$.*

- $\alpha_1 \circ \alpha_2$ *belongs to class $\mathcal{K}$.*

- $\alpha_3 \circ \alpha_4$ *belongs to class $\mathcal{K}_\infty$.*

- $\sigma(r,s) = \alpha_1(\beta(\alpha_2(r), s))$ *belongs to class $\mathcal{KL}$.* $\diamond$

Class $\mathcal{K}$ and class $\mathcal{KL}$ functions enter into Lyapunov analysis through the next two lemmas.

Lemma 4.3 *Let $V : D \to R$ be a continuous positive definite function defined on a domain $D \subset R^n$ that contains the origin. Let $B_r \subset D$ for some $r > 0$. Then, there exist class $\mathcal{K}$ functions α_1 and α_2, defined on $[0, r]$, such that*

$$\alpha_1(\|x\|) \leq V(x) \leq \alpha_2(\|x\|)$$

for all $x \in B_r$. If $D = R^n$, the functions α_1 and α_2 will be defined on $[0, \infty)$ and the foregoing inequality will hold for all $x \in R^n$. Moreover, if $V(x)$ is radially unbounded, then α_1 and α_2 can be chosen to belong to class $\mathcal{K}_\infty$. $\diamond$

Proof: See Appendix C.4.

For a quadratic positive definite function $V(x) = x^T P x$, Lemma 4.3 follows from the inequalities

$$\lambda_{\min}(P)\|x\|_2^2 \leq x^T P x \leq \lambda_{\max}(P)\|x\|_2^2$$

Lemma 4.4 *Consider the scalar autonomous differential equation*

$$\dot{y} = -\alpha(y), \quad y(t_0) = y_0$$

where α is a locally Lipschitz class $\mathcal{K}$ function defined on $[0, a)$. For all $0 \leq y_0 < a$, this equation has a unique solution $y(t)$ defined for all $t \geq t_0$. Moreover,

$$y(t) = \sigma(y_0, t - t_0)$$

where σ is a class $\mathcal{KL}$ function defined on $[0, a) \times [0, \infty)$. $\diamond$

Proof: See Appendix C.5.

We can see that the claim of this lemma is true by examining specific examples, where a closed-form solution of the scalar equation can be found. For example, if $\dot{y} = -ky$, $k > 0$, then the solution is

$$y(t) = y_0 \exp[-k(t - t_0)] \;\Rightarrow\; \sigma(r, s) = r \exp(-ks)$$

As another example, if $\dot{y} = -ky^2$, $k > 0$, then the solution is

$$y(t) = \frac{y_0}{ky_0(t - t_0) + 1} \;\Rightarrow\; \sigma(r, s) = \frac{r}{krs + 1}$$

To see how class $\mathcal{K}$ and class $\mathcal{KL}$ functions enter into Lyapunov analysis, let us see how they could have been used in the proof of Theorem 4.1. In the proof, we wanted to choose β and δ such that $B_\delta \subset \Omega_\beta \subset B_r$. Using the fact that a positive definite function $V(x)$ satisfies

$$\alpha_1(\|x\|) \leq V(x) \leq \alpha_2(\|x\|)$$

we can choose $\beta \leq \alpha_1(r)$ and $\delta \leq \alpha_2^{-1}(\beta)$. This is so because

$$V(x) \leq \beta \;\Rightarrow\; \alpha_1(\|x\|) \leq \alpha_1(r) \;\Leftrightarrow\; \|x\| \leq r$$

and

$$\|x\| \leq \delta \;\Rightarrow\; V(x) \leq \alpha_2(\delta) \leq \beta$$

In the same proof, we wanted to show that when $\dot{V}(x)$ is negative definite, the solution $x(t)$ tends to zero as t tends to infinity. Using Lemma 4.3 we see that there is a class $\mathcal{K}$ function α_3 such that $\dot{V}(x) \leq -\alpha_3(\|x\|)$. Hence, V satisfies the differential inequality

$$\dot{V} \leq -\alpha_3(\alpha_2^{-1}(V))$$

The comparison lemma (Lemma 3.4) shows that $V(x(t))$ is bounded by the solution of the scalar differential equation

$$\dot{y} = -\alpha_3(\alpha_2^{-1}(y)), \quad y(0) = V(x(0))$$

Lemma 4.2 shows that $\alpha_3 \circ \alpha_2^{-1}$ is a class $\mathcal{K}$ function and Lemma 4.4 shows that the solution of the scalar equation is $y(t) = \beta(y(0), t)$, where β is a class $\mathcal{KL}$ function. Consequently, $V(x(t))$ satisfies the inequality $V(x(t)) \leq \beta(V(x(0)), t)$, which shows that $V(x(t))$ tends to zero as t tends to infinity. In fact, we can go beyond the proof of Theorem 4.1 to provide estimates of $\|x(t)\|$ that are not provided in that proof. The inequality $V(x(t)) \leq V(x(0))$ implies that

$$\alpha_1(\|x(t)\|) \leq V(x(t)) \leq V(x(0)) \leq \alpha_2(\|x(0)\|)$$

Hence, $\|x(t)\| \leq \alpha_1^{-1}(\alpha_2(\|x(0)\|))$, where $\alpha_1^{-1} \circ \alpha_2$ is a class $\mathcal{K}$ function. Similarly, the inequality $V(x(t)) \leq \beta(V(x(0)), t)$ implies that

$$\alpha_1(\|x(t)\|) \leq V(x(t)) \leq \beta(V(x(0)), t) \leq \beta(\alpha_2(\|x(0)\|), t)$$

Therefore, $\|x(t)\| \leq \alpha_1^{-1}(\beta(\alpha_2(\|x(0)\|), t))$, where $\alpha_1^{-1}(\beta(\alpha_2(r), t))$ is a class $\mathcal{KL}$ function.

4.5 Nonautonomous Systems

Consider the nonautonomous system

$$\dot{x} = f(t, x) \tag{4.15}$$

where $f : [0, \infty) \times D \to R^n$ is piecewise continuous in t and locally Lipschitz in x on $[0, \infty) \times D$, and $D \subset R^n$ is a domain that contains the origin $x = 0$. The origin is an equilibrium point for (4.15) at $t = 0$ if

$$f(t, 0) = 0, \quad \forall\, t \geq 0$$

An equilibrium point at the origin could be a translation of a nonzero equilibrium point or, more generally, a translation of a nonzero solution of the system. To see the latter point, suppose $\bar{y}(\tau)$ is a solution of the system

$$\frac{dy}{d\tau} = g(\tau, y)$$

defined for all $\tau \geq a$. The change of variables

$$x = y - \bar{y}(\tau); \quad t = \tau - a$$

transforms the system into the form

$$\dot{x} = g(\tau, y) - \dot{\bar{y}}(\tau) = g(t + a, x + \bar{y}(t + a)) - \dot{\bar{y}}(t + a) \overset{\text{def}}{=} f(t, x)$$

Since

$$\dot{\bar{y}}(t + a) = g(t + a, \bar{y}(t + a)), \quad \forall\, t \geq 0$$

the origin $x = 0$ is an equilibrium point of the transformed system at $t = 0$. Therefore, by examining the stability behavior of the origin as an equilibrium point for the transformed system, we determine the stability behavior of the solution $\bar{y}(\tau)$ of the original system. Notice that if $\bar{y}(\tau)$ is not constant, the transformed system will be nonautonomous even when the original system is autonomous, that is, even when $g(\tau, y) = g(y)$. This is why studying the stability behavior of solutions in the sense of Lyapunov can be done only in the context of studying the stability behavior of the equilibria of nonautonomous systems.

The notions of stability and asymptotic stability of equilibrium points of nonautonomous systems are basically the same as those introduced in Definition 4.1 for autonomous systems. The new element here is that, while the solution of an autonomous system depends only on $(t - t_0)$, the solution of a nonautonomous system may depend on both t and t_0. Therefore, the stability behavior of the equilibrium point will, in general, be dependent on t_0. The origin $x = 0$ is a stable equilibrium point for (4.15) if, for each $\varepsilon > 0$, and any $t_0 \geq 0$ there is $\delta = \delta(\varepsilon, t_0) > 0$ such that

$$\|x(t_0)\| < \delta \Rightarrow \|x(t)\| < \varepsilon, \ \ \forall \, t \geq t_0$$

The constant δ is, in general, dependent on the initial time t_0. The existence of δ for every t_0 does not necessarily guarantee that there is one constant δ, dependent only on ε, that would work for all t_0, as illustrated by the next example.

Example 4.17 The linear first-order system

$$\dot{x} = (6t \sin t - 2t)x$$

has the solution

$$
\begin{aligned}
x(t) &= x(t_0) \exp \left[\int_{t_0}^{t} (6\tau \sin \tau - 2\tau) \, d\tau \right] \\
&= x(t_0) \exp \left[6 \sin t - 6t \cos t - t^2 - 6 \sin t_0 + 6t_0 \cos t_0 + t_0^2 \right]
\end{aligned}
$$

For any t_0, the term $-t^2$ will eventually dominate, which shows that the exponential term is bounded for all $t \geq t_0$ by a constant $c(t_0)$ dependent on t_0. Hence,

$$|x(t)| < |x(t_0)| c(t_0), \ \ \forall \, t \geq t_0$$

For any $\varepsilon > 0$, the choice $\delta = \varepsilon / c(t_0)$ shows that the origin is stable. Now, suppose t_0 takes on the successive values $t_0 = 2n\pi$, for $n = 0, 1, 2, \ldots$, and $x(t)$ is evaluated π seconds later in each case. Then,

$$x(t_0 + \pi) = x(t_0) \exp \left[(4n + 1)(6 - \pi)\pi \right]$$

which implies that, for $x(t_0) \neq 0$,

$$\frac{x(t_0 + \pi)}{x(t_0)} \to \infty \ \ \text{as} \ \ n \to \infty$$

Thus, given $\varepsilon > 0$, there is no δ independent of t_0 that would satisfy the stability requirement uniformly in t_0. $\triangle$

Nonuniformity with respect to t_0 could also appear in studying asymptotic stability of the origin, as the next example shows.

Example 4.18 The linear first-order system

$$\dot{x} = -\frac{x}{1+t}$$

has the solution

$$x(t) = x(t_0) \exp\left(\int_{t_0}^{t} \frac{-1}{1+\tau} \, d\tau\right) = x(t_0)\frac{1+t_0}{1+t}$$

Since $|x(t)| \leq |x(t_0)|$, $\forall \, t \geq t_0$, the origin is clearly stable. Actually, given any $\varepsilon > 0$, we can choose δ independent of t_0. It is also clear that

$$x(t) \to 0 \quad \text{as} \quad t \to \infty$$

Consequently, according to Definition 4.1, the origin is asymptotically stable. Notice, however, that the convergence of $x(t)$ to the origin is not uniform with respect to the initial time t_0. Recall that convergence of $x(t)$ to the origin is equivalent to saying that, given any $\varepsilon > 0$, there is $T = T(\varepsilon, t_0) > 0$ such that $|x(t)| < \varepsilon$ for all $t \geq t_0 + T$. Although this is true for every t_0, the constant T cannot be chosen independent of t_0. $\triangle$

As a consequence, we need to refine Definition 4.1 to emphasize the dependence of the stability behavior of the origin on the initial time t_0. We are interested in a refinement that defines stability and asymptotic stability of the origin as uniform properties with respect to the initial time.[18]

Definition 4.4 *The equilibrium point $x = 0$ of (4.15) is*

- *stable if, for each $\varepsilon > 0$, there is $\delta = \delta(\varepsilon, t_0) > 0$ such that*

$$\|x(t_0)\| < \delta \Rightarrow \|x(t)\| < \varepsilon, \quad \forall \, t \geq t_0 \geq 0 \tag{4.16}$$

- *uniformly stable if, for each $\varepsilon > 0$, there is $\delta = \delta(\varepsilon) > 0$, independent of t_0, such that (4.16) is satisfied.*

- *unstable if it is not stable.*

- *asymptotically stable if it is stable and there is a positive constant $c = c(t_0)$ such that $x(t) \to 0$ as $t \to \infty$, for all $\|x(t_0)\| < c$.*

---

[18]See [72] or [95] for other refinements of Definition 4.1. It is worthwhile to note that, for autonomous systems, the definition of global uniform asymptotic stability given here is equivalent to global asymptotic stability as defined in Section 4.1. In particular, $\delta(\varepsilon)$ can be always chosen such that $\lim_{\varepsilon \to \infty} \delta(\varepsilon) = \infty$. This is shown in the proof of Theorem 4.17. Lemma C.2 shows that, when the origin of an autonomous system is globally asymptotically stable, its solution $x(t)$ satisfies $\|x(t)\| \leq \beta(\|x(t_0)\|, 0)$ for all $x(t_0)$, where $\beta(r, 0)$ is a class $\mathcal{K}_\infty$ function. The function $\delta(\varepsilon)$ can be taken as $\delta(\varepsilon) = \beta^{-1}(\varepsilon, 0)$.

- *uniformly asymptotically stable if it is uniformly stable and there is a positive constant c, independent of t_0, such that for all $\|x(t_0)\| < c$, $x(t) \to 0$ as $t \to \infty$, uniformly in t_0; that is, for each $\eta > 0$, there is $T = T(\eta) > 0$ such that*

$$\|x(t)\| < \eta, \quad \forall \, t \geq t_0 + T(\eta), \, \forall \, \|x(t_0)\| < c \qquad (4.17)$$

- *globally uniformly asymptotically stable if it is uniformly stable, $\delta(\varepsilon)$ can be chosen to satisfy $\lim_{\varepsilon \to \infty} \delta(\varepsilon) = \infty$, and, for each pair of positive numbers η and c, there is $T = T(\eta, c) > 0$ such that*

$$\|x(t)\| < \eta, \quad \forall \, t \geq t_0 + T(\eta, c), \, \forall \, \|x(t_0)\| < c \qquad (4.18)$$

The next lemma gives equivalent, more transparent, definitions of uniform stability and uniform asymptotic stability by using class $\mathcal{K}$ and class $\mathcal{KL}$ functions.

Lemma 4.5 *The equilibrium point $x = 0$ of (4.15) is*

- *uniformly stable if and only if there exist a class $\mathcal{K}$ function α and a positive constant c, independent of t_0, such that*

$$\|x(t)\| \leq \alpha(\|x(t_0)\|), \quad \forall \, t \geq t_0 \geq 0, \, \forall \, \|x(t_0)\| < c \qquad (4.19)$$

- *uniformly asymptotically stable if and only if there exist a class $\mathcal{KL}$ function β and a positive constant c, independent of t_0, such that*

$$\|x(t)\| \leq \beta(\|x(t_0)\|, t - t_0), \quad \forall \, t \geq t_0 \geq 0, \, \forall \, \|x(t_0)\| < c \qquad (4.20)$$

- *globally uniformly asymptotically stable if and only if inequality (4.20) is satisfied for any initial state $x(t_0)$.* $\diamond$

Proof: See Appendix C.6.

As a consequence of Lemma 4.5, we see that in the case of autonomous systems stability and asymptotic stability per Definition 4.1 imply the existence of class $\mathcal{K}$ and class $\mathcal{KL}$ functions that satisfy inequalities (4.19) and (4.20). This is the case because, for autonomous systems, stability and asymptotic stability of the origin are uniform with respect to the initial time t_0.

A special case of uniform asymptotic stability arises when the class $\mathcal{KL}$ function β in (4.20) takes the form $\beta(r, s) = kre^{-\lambda s}$. This case is very important and will be designated as a distinct stability property of equilibrium points.

Definition 4.5 *The equilibrium point $x = 0$ of (4.15) is exponentially stable if there exist positive constants c, k, and λ such that*

$$\|x(t)\| \leq k\|x(t_0)\|e^{-\lambda(t - t_0)}, \, \forall \, \|x(t_0)\| < c \qquad (4.21)$$

and globally exponentially stable if (4.21) is satisfied for any initial state $x(t_0)$.

Lyapunov theory for autonomous systems can be extended to nonautonomous systems. For each of Theorems 4.1 through 4.4, one can state various extensions to nonautonomous systems. We will not document all these extensions here.[19] Instead, we concentrate on uniform stability and uniform asymptotic stability. These are the cases we encounter in most nonautonomous applications of Lyapunov's method.

Theorem 4.8 *Let $x = 0$ be an equilibrium point for (4.15) and $D \subset R^n$ be a domain containing $x = 0$. Let $V : [0, \infty) \times D \to R$ be a continuously differentiable function such that*

$$W_1(x) \leq V(t, x) \leq W_2(x) \tag{4.22}$$

$$\frac{\partial V}{\partial t} + \frac{\partial V}{\partial x} f(t, x) \leq 0 \tag{4.23}$$

$\forall \ t \geq 0$ and $\forall \ x \in D$, where $W_1(x)$ and $W_2(x)$ are continuous positive definite functions on D. Then, $x = 0$ is uniformly stable. ◇

Proof: The derivative of V along the trajectories of (4.15) is given by

$$\dot{V}(t, x) = \frac{\partial V}{\partial t} + \frac{\partial V}{\partial x} f(t, x) \ \leq \ 0$$

Choose $r > 0$ and $c > 0$ such that $B_r \subset D$ and $c < \min_{\|x\|=r} W_1(x)$. Then, $\{x \in B_r \mid W_1(x) \leq c\}$ is in the interior of B_r. Define a time-dependent set $\Omega_{t,c}$ by

$$\Omega_{t,c} = \{x \in B_r \mid V(t, x) \leq c\}$$

The set $\Omega_{t,c}$ contains $\{x \in B_r \mid W_2(x) \leq c\}$ since

$$W_2(x) \leq c \Rightarrow V(t, x) \leq c$$

On the other hand, $\Omega_{t,c}$ is a subset of $\{x \in B_r \mid W_1(x) \leq c\}$ since

$$V(t, x) \leq c \Rightarrow W_1(x) \leq c$$

Thus,

$$\{x \in B_r \mid W_2(x) \leq c\} \subset \Omega_{t,c} \subset \{x \in B_r \mid W_1(x) \leq c\} \subset B_r \subset D$$

for all $t \geq 0$. These five nested sets are sketched in Figure 4.7. The setup of Figure 4.7 is similar to that of Figure 4.1, except that the surface $V(t, x) = c$ is now dependent on t, and that is why it is surrounded by the time-independent surfaces $W_1(x) = c$ and $W_2(x) = c$.

Since $\dot{V}(t, x) \leq 0$ on D, for any $t_0 \geq 0$ and any $x_0 \in \Omega_{t_0,c}$, the solution starting at (t_0, x_0) stays in $\Omega_{t,c}$ for all $t \geq t_0$. Therefore, any solution starting in $\{x \in$

---

[19]Lyapunov theory for nonautonomous systems is well documented in the literature. Good references on the subject include [72] and [154], while good introductions can be found in [201] and [135].

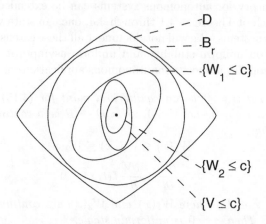

Figure 4.7: Geometric representation of sets in the proof of Theorem 4.8.

$B_r \mid W_2(x) \leq c\}$ stays in $\Omega_{t,c}$, and consequently in $\{x \in B_r \mid W_1(x) \leq c\}$, for all future time. Hence, the solution is bounded and defined for all $t \geq t_0$. Moreover, since $\dot{V} \leq 0$,

$$V(t, x(t)) \leq V(t_0, x(t_0)), \quad \forall \, t \geq t_0$$

By Lemma 4.3, there exist class $\mathcal{K}$ functions α_1 and α_2, defined on $[0, r]$, such that

$$\alpha_1(\|x\|) \leq W_1(x) \leq V(t, x) \leq W_2(x) \leq \alpha_2(\|x\|)$$

Combining the preceding two inequalities, we see that

$$\|x(t)\| \leq \alpha_1^{-1}(V(t, x(t))) \leq \alpha_1^{-1}(V(t_0, x(t_0))) \leq \alpha_1^{-1}(\alpha_2(\|x(t_0)\|))$$

Since $\alpha_1^{-1} \circ \alpha_2$ is a class $\mathcal{K}$ function (by Lemma 4.2), the inequality $\|x(t)\| \leq \alpha_1^{-1}(\alpha_2(\|x(t_0)\|))$ shows that the origin is uniformly stable.   □
.

Theorem 4.9 *Suppose the assumptions of Theorem 4.8 are satisfied with inequality (4.23) strengthened to*

$$\frac{\partial V}{\partial t} + \frac{\partial V}{\partial x} f(t, x) \leq -W_3(x) \tag{4.24}$$

$\forall \, t \geq 0$ *and* $\forall \, x \in D$, *where* $W_3(x)$ *is a continuous positive definite function on* D. *Then,* $x = 0$ *is uniformly asymptotically stable. Moreover, if* r *and* c *are chosen such that* $B_r = \{\|x\| \leq r\} \subset D$ *and* $c < \min_{\|x\|=r} W_1(x)$, *then every trajectory starting in* $\{x \in B_r \mid W_2(x) \leq c\}$ *satisfies*

$$\|x(t)\| \leq \beta(\|x(t_0)\|, t - t_0), \quad \forall \, t \geq t_0 \geq 0$$

for some class $\mathcal{KL}$ *function* β. *Finally, if* $D = R^n$ *and* $W_1(x)$ *is radially unbounded, then* $x = 0$ *is globally uniformly asymptotically stable.*   ◇

Proof: Continuing with the proof of Theorem 4.8, we know that trajectories starting in $\{x \in B_r \mid W_2(x) \le c\}$ stay in $\{x \in B_r \mid W_1(x) \le c\}$ for all $t \ge t_0$. By Lemma 4.3, there exists a class $\mathcal{K}$ function α_3, defined on $[0, r]$, such that

$$\dot{V}(t, x) = \frac{\partial V}{\partial t} + \frac{\partial V}{\partial x} f(t, x) \le -W_3(x) \le -\alpha_3(\|x\|)$$

Using the inequality

$$V \le \alpha_2(\|x\|) \;\Leftrightarrow\; \alpha_2^{-1}(V) \le \|x\| \;\Leftrightarrow\; \alpha_3(\alpha_2^{-1}(V)) \le \alpha_3(\|x\|)$$

we see that V satisfies the differential inequality

$$\dot{V} \le -\alpha_3(\alpha_2^{-1}(V)) \stackrel{\text{def}}{=} -\alpha(V)$$

where $\alpha = \alpha_3 \circ \alpha_2^{-1}$ is a class $\mathcal{K}$ function defined on $[0, r]$. (See Lemma 4.2.) Assume, without loss of generality,[20] that α is locally Lipschitz. Let $y(t)$ satisfy the autonomous first-order differential equation

$$\dot{y} = -\alpha(y), \quad y(t_0) = V(t_0, x(t_0)) \ge 0$$

By (the comparison) Lemma 3.4,

$$V(t, x(t)) \le y(t), \quad \forall \, t \ge t_0$$

By Lemma 4.4, there exists a class $\mathcal{KL}$ function $\sigma(r, s)$ defined on $[0, r] \times [0, \infty)$ such that

$$V(t, x(t)) \le \sigma(V(t_0, x(t_0)), t - t_0), \quad \forall \, V(t_0, x(t_0)) \in [0, c]$$

Therefore, any solution starting in $\{x \in B_r \mid W_2(x) \le c\}$ satisfies the inequality

$$
\begin{aligned}
\|x(t)\| &\le \alpha_1^{-1}(V(t, x(t))) \le \alpha_1^{-1}\left(\sigma(V(t_0, x(t_0)), t - t_0)\right) \\
&\le \alpha_1^{-1}\left(\sigma(\alpha_2(\|x(t_0)\|), t - t_0)\right) \stackrel{\text{def}}{=} \beta(\|x(t_0)\|, t - t_0)
\end{aligned}
$$

Lemma 4.2 shows that β is a class $\mathcal{KL}$ function. Thus, inequality (4.20) is satisfied, which implies that $x = 0$ is uniformly asymptotically stable. If $D = R^n$, the functions α_1, α_2, and α_3 are defined on $[0, \infty)$. Hence, α, and consequently β, are independent of c. As $W_1(x)$ is radially unbounded, c can be chosen arbitrarily large to include any initial state in $\{W_2(x) \le c\}$. Thus, (4.20) holds for any initial state, showing that the origin is globally uniformly asymptotically stable. $\qquad\square$

---

[20]If α is not locally Lipschitz, we can choose a locally Lipschitz class $\mathcal{K}$ function β such that $\alpha(r) \ge \beta(r)$ over the domain of interest. Then, $\dot{V} \le -\beta(V)$, and we can continue the proof with β instead of α. For example, suppose $\alpha(r) = \sqrt{r}$. The function $\sqrt{r}$ is a class $\mathcal{K}$ function, but not locally Lipschitz at $r = 0$. Define β as $\beta(r) = r$, for $r < 1$ and $\beta(r) = \sqrt{r}$, for $r \ge 1$. The function β is class $\mathcal{K}$ and locally Lipschitz. Moreover, $\alpha(r) \ge \beta(r)$ for all $r \ge 0$.

A function $V(t, x)$ is said to be *positive semidefinite* if $V(t, x) \geq 0$. It is said to be *positive definite* if $V(t, x) \geq W_1(x)$ for some positive definite function $W_1(x)$, *radially unbounded* if $W_1(x)$ is so, and *decrescent* if $V(t, x) \leq W_2(x)$. A function $V(t, x)$ is said to be *negative definite (semidefinite)* if $-V(t, x)$ is *positive definite (semidefinite)*. Therefore, Theorems 4.8 and 4.9 say that *the origin is uniformly stable if there is a continuously differentiable, positive definite, decrescent function $V(t, x)$, whose derivative along the trajectories of the system is negative semidefinite. It is uniformly asymptotically stable if the derivative is negative definite, and globally uniformly asymptotically stable if the conditions for uniform asymptotic stability hold globally with a radially unbounded $V(t, x)$.*

Theorem 4.10 *Let $x = 0$ be an equilibrium point for (4.15) and $D \subset R^n$ be a domain containing $x = 0$. Let $V : [0, \infty) \times D \to R$ be a continuously differentiable function such that*

$$k_1 \|x\|^a \leq V(t, x) \leq k_2 \|x\|^a \tag{4.25}$$

$$\frac{\partial V}{\partial t} + \frac{\partial V}{\partial x} f(t, x) \leq -k_3 \|x\|^a \tag{4.26}$$

$\forall\, t \geq 0$ *and* $\forall\, x \in D$, *where k_1, k_2, k_3, and a are positive constants. Then, $x = 0$ is exponentially stable. If the assumptions hold globally, then $x = 0$ is globally exponentially stable.* $\diamond$

Proof: With the help of Figure 4.7, it can be seen that trajectories starting in $\{k_2 \|x\|^a \leq c\}$, for sufficiently small c, remain bounded for all $t \geq t_0$. Inequalities (4.25) and (4.26) show that V satisfies the differential inequality

$$\dot{V} \leq -\frac{k_3}{k_2} V$$

By (the comparison) Lemma 3.4,

$$V(t, x(t)) \leq V(t_0, x(t_0)) e^{-(k_3/k_2)(t-t_0)}$$

Hence,

$$
\begin{aligned}
\|x(t)\| &\leq \left[\frac{V(t, x(t))}{k_1} \right]^{1/a} \leq \left[\frac{V(t_0, x(t_0)) e^{-(k_3/k_2)(t-t_0)}}{k_1} \right]^{1/a} \\
&\leq \left[\frac{k_2 \|x(t_0)\|^a e^{-(k_3/k_2)(t-t_0)}}{k_1} \right]^{1/a} = \left(\frac{k_2}{k_1} \right)^{1/a} \|x(t_0)\| e^{-(k_3/k_2 a)(t-t_0)}
\end{aligned}
$$

Thus, the origin is exponentially stable. If all the assumptions hold globally, c can be chosen arbitrarily large and the foregoing inequality holds for all $x(t_0) \in R^n$. $\square$

Example 4.19 Consider the scalar system

$$\dot{x} = -[1 + g(t)] x^3$$

where $g(t)$ is continuous and $g(t) \geq 0$ for all $t \geq 0$. Using the Lyapunov function candidate $V(x) = x^2/2$, we obtain

$$\dot{V}(t, x) = -[1 + g(t)]x^4 \leq -x^4, \quad \forall\, x \in R, \ \forall\, t \geq 0$$

The assumptions of Theorem 4.9 are satisfied globally with $W_1(x) = W_2(x) = V(x)$ and $W_3(x) = x^4$. Hence, the origin is globally uniformly asymptotically stable. $\triangle$

Example 4.20 Consider the system

$$\begin{aligned}
\dot{x}_1 &= -x_1 - g(t)x_2 \\
\dot{x}_2 &= x_1 - x_2
\end{aligned}$$

where $g(t)$ is continuously differentiable and satisfies

$$0 \leq g(t) \leq k \ \text{ and } \ \dot{g}(t) \leq g(t), \quad \forall\, t \geq 0$$

Taking $V(t, x) = x_1^2 + [1 + g(t)]x_2^2$ as a Lyapunov function candidate, it can be easily seen that

$$x_1^2 + x_2^2 \leq V(t, x) \leq x_1^2 + (1 + k)x_2^2, \quad \forall\, x \in R^2$$

Hence, $V(t, x)$ is positive definite, decrescent, and radially unbounded. The derivative of V along the trajectories of the system is given by

$$\dot{V}(t, x) = -2x_1^2 + 2x_1x_2 - [2 + 2g(t) - \dot{g}(t)]x_2^2$$

Using the inequality

$$2 + 2g(t) - \dot{g}(t) \geq 2 + 2g(t) - g(t) \geq 2$$

we obtain

$$\dot{V}(t, x) \leq -2x_1^2 + 2x_1x_2 - 2x_2^2 = -\begin{bmatrix} x_1 \\ x_2 \end{bmatrix}^T \begin{bmatrix} 2 & -1 \\ -1 & 2 \end{bmatrix} \begin{bmatrix} x_1 \\ x_2 \end{bmatrix} \stackrel{\text{def}}{=} -x^T Q x$$

where Q is positive definite; therefore, $\dot{V}(t, x)$ is negative definite. Thus, all the assumptions of Theorem 4.9 are satisfied globally with positive definite quadratic functions W_1, W_2, and W_3. Recalling that a positive definite quadratic function $x^T P x$ satisfies

$$\lambda_{min}(P)x^T x \leq x^T P x \leq \lambda_{max}(P)x^T x$$

we see that the conditions of Theorem 4.10 are satisfied globally with $a = 2$. Hence, the origin is globally exponentially stable. $\triangle$

Example 4.21 The linear time-varying system

$$\dot{x} = A(t)x \tag{4.27}$$

has an equilibrium point at $x = 0$. Let $A(t)$ be continuous for all $t \geq 0$. Suppose there is a continuously differentiable, symmetric, bounded, positive definite matrix $P(t)$; that is,

$$0 < c_1 I \leq P(t) \leq c_2 I, \quad \forall\, t \geq 0$$

which satisfies the matrix differential equation

$$-\dot{P}(t) = P(t)A(t) + A^T(t)P(t) + Q(t) \tag{4.28}$$

where $Q(t)$ is continuous, symmetric, and positive definite; that is,

$$Q(t) \geq c_3 I > 0, \quad \forall\, t \geq 0$$

The Lyapunov function candidate

$$V(t, x) = x^T P(t) x$$

satisfies

$$c_1 \|x\|_2^2 \leq V(t, x) \leq c_2 \|x\|_2^2$$

and its derivative along the trajectories of the system (4.27) is given by

$$
\begin{aligned}
\dot{V}(t, x) &= x^T \dot{P}(t) x + x^T P(t) \dot{x} + \dot{x}^T P(t) x \\
&= x^T [\dot{P}(t) + P(t)A(t) + A^T(t)P(t)] x = -x^T Q(t) x \leq -c_3 \|x\|_2^2
\end{aligned}
$$

Thus, all the assumptions of Theorem 4.10 are satisfied globally with $a = 2$, and we conclude that the origin is globally exponentially stable. $\triangle$

4.6   Linear Time-Varying Systems and Linearization

The stability behavior of the origin as an equilibrium point for the linear time-varying system

$$\dot{x}(t) = A(t)x \tag{4.29}$$

can be completely characterized in terms of the state transition matrix of the system. From linear system theory,[21] we know that the solution of (4.29) is given by

$$x(t) = \Phi(t, t_0) x(t_0)$$

where $\Phi(t, t_0)$ is the state transition matrix. The next theorem characterizes uniform asymptotic stability in terms of $\Phi(t, t_0)$.

Theorem 4.11 *The equilibrium point $x = 0$ of (4.29) is (globally) uniformly asymptotically stable if and only if the state transition matrix satisfies the inequality*

$$\|\Phi(t, t_0)\| \leq k e^{-\lambda(t - t_0)}, \quad \forall\, t \geq t_0 \geq 0 \tag{4.30}$$

for some positive constants k and λ. $\diamond$

---

[21]See, for example, [9], [35], [94], or [158].

Proof: Due to the linear dependence of $x(t)$ on $x(t_0)$, if the origin is uniformly asymptotically stable, it is globally so. Sufficiency of (4.30) is obvious since

$$\|x(t)\| \leq \|\Phi(t, t_0)\| \, \|x(t_0)\| \leq k\|x(t_0)\|e^{-\lambda(t-t_0)}$$

To prove necessity, suppose the origin is uniformly asymptotically stable. Then, there is a class $\mathcal{KL}$ function β such that

$$\|x(t)\| \leq \beta(\|x(t_0)\|, t - t_0), \quad \forall \, t \geq t_0, \, \forall \, x(t_0) \in R^n$$

From the definition of an induced matrix norm (Appendix A), we have

$$\|\Phi(t, t_0)\| = \max_{\|x\|=1} \|\Phi(t, t_0)x\| \leq \max_{\|x\|=1} \beta(\|x\|, t - t_0) = \beta(1, t - t_0)$$

Since

$$\beta(1, s) \to 0 \quad \text{as} \quad s \to \infty$$

there exists $T > 0$ such that $\beta(1, T) \leq 1/e$. For any $t \geq t_0$, let N be the smallest positive integer such that $t \leq t_0 + NT$. Divide the interval $[t_0, t_0 + (N-1)T]$ into $(N-1)$ equal subintervals of width T each. Using the transition property of $\Phi(t, t_0)$, we can write

$$\Phi(t, t_0) = \Phi(t, t_0 + (N-1)T)\Phi(t_0 + (N-1)T, t_0 + (N-2)T) \cdots \Phi(t_0 + T, t_0)$$

Hence,

$$
\begin{aligned}
\|\Phi(t, t_0)\| &\leq \|\Phi(t, t_0 + (N-1)T)\| \prod_{k=1}^{k=N-1} \|\Phi(t_0 + kT, t_0 + (k-1)T)\| \\
&\leq \beta(1, 0) \prod_{k=1}^{k=N-1} \frac{1}{e} = e\beta(1, 0)e^{-N} \\
&\leq e\beta(1, 0)e^{-(t-t_0)/T} = ke^{-\lambda(t-t_0)}
\end{aligned}
$$

where $k = e\beta(1, 0)$ and $\lambda = 1/T$. $\qquad\qquad\qquad\qquad\qquad\qquad\qquad$ $\square$

Theorem 4.11 shows that, for linear systems, uniform asymptotic stability of the origin is equivalent to exponential stability. Although inequality (4.30) characterizes uniform asymptotic stability of the origin without the need to search for a Lyapunov function, it is not as useful as the eigenvalue criterion we have for linear time-invariant systems, because knowledge of the state transition matrix $\Phi(t, t_0)$ requires solving the state equation (4.29). Note that, for linear time-varying systems, uniform asymptotic stability cannot be characterized by the location of the eigenvalues of the matrix A [22] as the following example shows.

---

[22] There are special cases where uniform asymptotic stability of the origin as an equilibrium point for (4.29) is equivalent to an eigenvalue condition. One case is periodic systems. (See Exercise 4.40 and Example 10.8.) Another case is slowly-varying systems. (See Example 9.9.)

Example 4.22 Consider a second-order linear system with

$$A(t) = \begin{bmatrix} -1 + 1.5\cos^2 t & 1 - 1.5\sin t\cos t \\ -1 - 1.5\sin t\cos t & -1 + 1.5\sin^2 t \end{bmatrix}$$

For each t, the eigenvalues of $A(t)$ are given by $-0.25 \pm 0.25\sqrt{7}j$. Thus, the eigenvalues are independent of t and lie in the open left-half plane. Yet, the origin is unstable. It can be verified that

$$\Phi(t,0) = \begin{bmatrix} e^{0.5t}\cos t & e^{-t}\sin t \\ -e^{0.5t}\sin t & e^{-t}\cos t \end{bmatrix}$$

which shows that there are initial states $x(0)$, arbitrarily close to the origin, for which the solution is unbounded and escapes to infinity. $\triangle$

Although Theorem 4.11 may not be very helpful as a stability test, we will see that it guarantees the existence of a Lyapunov function for the linear system (4.29). We saw in Example 4.21 that if we can find a positive definite, bounded matrix $P(t)$ that satisfies the differential equation (4.28) for some positive definite $Q(t)$, then $V(t,x) = x^T P(t)x$ is a Lyapunov function for the system. If the matrix $Q(t)$ is chosen to be bounded in addition to being positive definite, that is,

$$0 < c_3 I \leq Q(t) \leq c_4 I, \quad \forall\, t \geq 0$$

and if $A(t)$ is continuous and bounded, then it can be shown that when the origin is exponentially stable, there is a solution of (4.28) that possesses the desired properties.

Theorem 4.12 *Let $x = 0$ be the exponentially stable equilibrium point of (4.29). Suppose $A(t)$ is continuous and bounded. Let $Q(t)$ be a continuous, bounded, positive definite, symmetric matrix. Then, there is a continuously differentiable, bounded, positive definite, symmetric matrix $P(t)$ that satisfies (4.28). Hence, $V(t,x) = x^T P(t)x$ is a Lyapunov function for the system that satisfies the conditions of Theorem 4.10.* $\diamond$

Proof: Let

$$P(t) = \int_t^\infty \Phi^T(\tau,t)Q(\tau)\Phi(\tau,t)\, d\tau$$

and $\phi(\tau; t, x)$ be the solution of (4.29) that starts at (t, x). Due to linearity, $\phi(\tau; t, x) = \Phi(\tau,t)x$. In view of the definition of $P(t)$, we have

$$x^T P(t)x = \int_t^\infty \phi^T(\tau; t, x)Q(\tau)\phi(\tau; t, x)\, d\tau$$

The use of (4.30) yields

$$
\begin{aligned}
x^T P(t)x &\leq \int_t^\infty c_4 \|\Phi(\tau,t)\|_2^2 \, \|x\|_2^2 d\tau \\
&\leq \int_t^\infty k^2 e^{-2\lambda(\tau-t)} \, d\tau \, c_4 \|x\|_2^2 \;=\; \frac{k^2 c_4}{2\lambda}\|x\|_2^2 \;\overset{\text{def}}{=}\; c_2\|x\|_2^2
\end{aligned}
$$

On the other hand, since

$$
\|A(t)\|_2 \leq L, \quad \forall \, t \geq 0
$$

the solution $\phi(\tau; t, x)$ satisfies the lower bound[23]

$$
\|\phi(\tau; t, x)\|_2^2 \geq \|x\|_2^2 e^{-2L(\tau-t)}
$$

Hence,

$$
\begin{aligned}
x^T P(t)x &\geq \int_t^\infty c_3 \|\phi(\tau;t,x)\|_2^2 \, d\tau \\
&\geq \int_t^\infty e^{-2L(\tau-t)} \, d\tau \, c_3 \|x\|_2^2 \;=\; \frac{c_3}{2L}\|x\|_2^2 \;\overset{\text{def}}{=}\; c_1\|x\|_2^2
\end{aligned}
$$

Thus,

$$
c_1\|x\|_2^2 \leq x^T P(t)x \leq c_2\|x\|_2^2
$$

which shows that $P(t)$ is positive definite and bounded. The definition of $P(t)$ shows that it is symmetric and continuously differentiable. The fact that $P(t)$ satisfies (4.28) can be shown by differentiating $P(t)$ and using the property

$$
\frac{\partial}{\partial t}\Phi(\tau,t) = -\Phi(\tau,t)A(t)
$$

In particular,

$$
\begin{aligned}
\dot{P}(t) &= \int_t^\infty \Phi^T(\tau,t)Q(\tau)\frac{\partial}{\partial t}\Phi(\tau,t) \, d\tau \\
&\quad + \int_t^\infty \left[\frac{\partial}{\partial t}\Phi^T(\tau,t)\right] Q(\tau)\Phi(\tau,t) \, d\tau \; - \; Q(t) \\
&= -\int_t^\infty \Phi^T(\tau,t)Q(\tau)\Phi(\tau,t) \, d\tau \, A(t) \\
&\quad -A^T(t)\int_t^\infty \Phi^T(\tau,t)Q(\tau)\Phi(\tau,t) \, d\tau \; - \; Q(t) \\
&= -P(t)A(t) - A^T(t)P(t) - Q(t)
\end{aligned}
$$

The fact that $V(t,x) = x^T P(t)x$ is a Lyapunov function is shown in Example 4.21.

$\square$

---

[23]See Exercise 3.17.

When the linear system (4.29) is time invariant, that is, when A is constant, the Lyapunov function $V(t, x)$ of Theorem 4.12 can be chosen to be independent of t. Recall that, for linear time-invariant systems,

$$\Phi(\tau, t) = \exp[(\tau - t)A]$$

which satisfies (4.30) when A is Hurwitz. Choosing Q to be a positive definite, symmetric (constant) matrix, the matrix $P(t)$ is given by

$$P = \int_t^\infty \exp[(\tau - t)A^T]Q \exp[(\tau - t)A] \, d\tau = \int_0^\infty \exp[A^T s]Q \exp[As] \, ds$$

which is independent of t. Comparing this expression for P with (4.13) shows that P is the unique solution of the Lyapunov equation (4.12). Thus, the Lyapunov function of Theorem 4.12 reduces to the one we used in Section 4.3.

The existence of Lyapunov functions for linear systems per Theorem 4.12 will now be used to prove a linearization result that extends Theorem 4.7 to the nonautonomous case. Consider the nonlinear nonautonomous system

$$\dot{x} = f(t, x) \tag{4.31}$$

where $f : [0, \infty) \times D \to R^n$ is continuously differentiable and $D = \{x \in R^n \mid \|x\|_2 < r\}$. Suppose the origin $x = 0$ is an equilibrium point for the system at $t = 0$; that is, $f(t, 0) = 0$ for all $t \geq 0$. Furthermore, suppose the Jacobian matrix $[\partial f / \partial x]$ is bounded and Lipschitz on D, uniformly in t; thus,

$$\left\| \frac{\partial f_i}{\partial x}(t, x_1) - \frac{\partial f_i}{\partial x}(t, x_2) \right\|_2 \leq L_1 \|x_1 - x_2\|_2, \quad \forall \, x_1, x_2 \in D, \, \forall \, t \geq 0$$

for all $1 \leq i \leq n$. By the mean value theorem,

$$f_i(t, x) = f_i(t, 0) + \frac{\partial f_i}{\partial x}(t, z_i) \, x$$

where z_i is a point on the line segment connecting x to the origin. Since $f(t, 0) = 0$, we can write $f_i(t, x)$ as

$$f_i(t, x) = \frac{\partial f_i}{\partial x}(t, z_i) \, x = \frac{\partial f_i}{\partial x}(t, 0) \, x + \left[\frac{\partial f_i}{\partial x}(t, z_i) - \frac{\partial f_i}{\partial x}(t, 0) \right] x$$

Hence,

$$f(t, x) = A(t)x + g(t, x)$$

where

$$A(t) = \frac{\partial f}{\partial x}(t, 0) \quad \text{and} \quad g_i(t, x) = \left[\frac{\partial f_i}{\partial x}(t, z_i) - \frac{\partial f_i}{\partial x}(t, 0) \right] x$$

The function $g(t, x)$ satisfies

$$\|g(t, x)\|_2 \leq \left(\sum_{i=1}^{n} \left\| \frac{\partial f_i}{\partial x}(t, z_i) - \frac{\partial f_i}{\partial x}(t, 0) \right\|_2^2 \right)^{1/2} \|x\|_2 \leq L\|x\|_2^2$$

where $L = \sqrt{n} L_1$. Therefore, in a small neighborhood of the origin, we may approximate the nonlinear system (4.31) by its linearization about the origin. The next theorem states Lyapunov's indirect method for showing exponential stability of the origin in the nonautonomous case.

Theorem 4.13 *Let $x = 0$ be an equilibrium point for the nonlinear system*

$$\dot{x} = f(t, x)$$

where $f : [0, \infty) \times D \to R^n$ is continuously differentiable, $D = \{x \in R^n \mid \|x\|_2 < r\}$, and the Jacobian matrix $[\partial f / \partial x]$ is bounded and Lipschitz on D, uniformly in t. Let

$$A(t) = \frac{\partial f}{\partial x}(t, x) \bigg|_{x=0}$$

Then, the origin is an exponentially stable equilibrium point for the nonlinear system if it is an exponentially stable equilibrium point for the linear system

$$\dot{x} = A(t)x$$

$\diamond$

Proof: Since the linear system has an exponentially stable equilibrium point at the origin and $A(t)$ is continuous and bounded, Theorem 4.12 ensures the existence of a continuously differentiable, bounded, positive definite symmetric matrix $P(t)$ that satisfies (4.28), where $Q(t)$ is continuous, positive definite, and symmetric. We use $V(t, x) = x^T P(t)x$ as a Lyapunov function candidate for the nonlinear system. The derivative of $V(t, x)$ along the trajectories of the system is given by

$$
\begin{aligned}
\dot{V}(t, x) &= x^T P(t)f(t, x) + f^T(t, x)P(t)x + x^T \dot{P}(t)x \\
&= x^T [P(t)A(t) + A^T(t)P(t) + \dot{P}(t)]x + 2x^T P(t)g(t, x) \\
&= -x^T Q(t)x + 2x^T P(t)g(t, x) \\
&\leq -c_3\|x\|_2^2 + 2c_2 L\|x\|_2^3 \\
&\leq -(c_3 - 2c_2 L\rho)\|x\|_2^2, \quad \forall \ \|x\|_2 < \rho
\end{aligned}
$$

Choosing $\rho < \min\{r, c_3/(2c_2 L)\}$ ensures that $\dot{V}(t, x)$ is negative definite in $\|x\|_2 < \rho$. Therefore, all the conditions of Theorem 4.10 are satisfied in $\|x\|_2 < \rho$, and we conclude that the origin is exponentially stable. $\square$

4.7   Converse Theorems

Theorems 4.9 and 4.10 establish uniform asymptotic stability or exponential stability of the origin by requiring the existence of a Lyapunov function $V(t,x)$ that satisfies certain conditions. Requiring the existence of an auxiliary function $V(t,x)$ that satisfies certain conditions is typical in many theorems of Lyapunov's method. The conditions of these theorems cannot be checked directly on the data of the problem. Instead, one has to search for the auxiliary function. Faced with this searching problem, two questions come to mind. First, is there a function that satisfies the conditions of the theorem? Second, how can we search for such a function? In many cases, Lyapunov theory provides an affirmative answer to the first question. The answer takes the form of a converse Lyapunov theorem, which is the inverse of one of Lyapunov's theorems. For example, a converse theorem for uniform asymptotic stability would confirm that if the origin is uniformly asymptotically stable, then there is a Lyapunov function that satisfies the conditions of Theorem 4.9. Most of these converse theorems are proven by actually constructing auxiliary functions that satisfy the conditions of the respective theorems. Unfortunately, this construction almost always assumes the knowledge of the solution of the differential equation. Therefore, the theorems do not help in the practical search for an auxiliary function. The mere knowledge that a function exists is, however, better than nothing. At least, we know that our search is not hopeless. The theorems are also useful in using Lyapunov theory to draw conceptual conclusions about the behavior of dynamical systems. Theorem 4.15 is an example of such use. Other examples will appear in the following chapters. In this section, we give three converse Lyapunov theorems.[24] The first one is a converse Lyapunov theorem when the origin is exponentially stable and, the second, when it is uniformly asymptotically stable. The third theorem applies to autonomous systems and defines the converse Lyapunov function for the whole region of attraction of an asymptotically stable equilibrium point.

The idea of constructing a converse Lyapunov function is not new to us. We have done it for linear systems in the proof of Theorem 4.12. A careful reading of that proof shows that linearity of the system does not play a crucial role in the proof, except for showing that $V(t,x)$ is quadratic in x. This observation leads to the first of our three converse theorems, whose proof is a simple extension of the proof of Theorem 4.12.

Theorem 4.14 *Let $x = 0$ be an equilibrium point for the nonlinear system*

$$\dot{x} = f(t,x)$$

where $f : [0,\infty) \times D \to R^n$ is continuously differentiable, $D = \{x \in R^n \mid \|x\| < r\}$, and the Jacobian matrix $[\partial f/\partial x]$ is bounded on D, uniformly in t. Let k, λ, and r_0

---

[24]See [72] or [107] for a comprehensive treatment of converse Lyapunov theorems and [118] and [193] for more recent results.

be positive constants with $r_0 < r/k$. Let $D_0 = \{x \in R^n \mid \|x\| < r_0\}$. Assume that the trajectories of the system satisfy

$$\|x(t)\| \leq k\|x(t_0)\|e^{-\lambda(t-t_0)}, \quad \forall \, x(t_0) \in D_0, \, \forall \, t \geq t_0 \geq 0$$

Then, there is a function $V : [0, \infty) \times D_0 \to R$ that satisfies the inequalities

$$c_1\|x\|^2 \leq V(t, x) \leq c_2\|x\|^2$$

$$\frac{\partial V}{\partial t} + \frac{\partial V}{\partial x}f(t, x) \leq -c_3\|x\|^2$$

$$\left\|\frac{\partial V}{\partial x}\right\| \leq c_4\|x\|$$

for some positive constants c_1, c_2, c_3, and c_4. Moreover, if $r = \infty$ and the origin is globally exponentially stable, then $V(t, x)$ is defined and satisfies the aforementioned inequalities on R^n. Furthermore, if the system is autonomous, V can be chosen independent of t. ◇

Proof: Due to the equivalence of norms, it is sufficient to prove the theorem for the 2-norm. Let $\phi(\tau; t, x)$ denote the solution of the system that starts at (t, x); that is, $\phi(t; t, x) = x$. For all $x \in D_0$, $\phi(\tau; t, x) \in D$ for all $\tau \geq t$. Let

$$V(t, x) = \int_t^{t+\delta} \phi^T(\tau; t, x)\phi(\tau; t, x) \, d\tau$$

where δ is a positive constant to be chosen. Due to the exponentially decaying bound on the trajectories, we have

$$
\begin{aligned}
V(t, x) &= \int_t^{t+\delta} \|\phi(\tau; t, x)\|_2^2 \, d\tau \\
&\leq \int_t^{t+\delta} k^2 e^{-2\lambda(\tau-t)} \, d\tau \, \|x\|_2^2 = \frac{k^2}{2\lambda}(1 - e^{-2\lambda\delta})\|x\|_2^2
\end{aligned}
$$

On the other hand, the Jacobian matrix $[\partial f/\partial x]$ is bounded on D. Let

$$\left\|\frac{\partial f}{\partial x}(t, x)\right\|_2 \leq L, \quad \forall \, x \in D$$

Then, $\|f(t, x)\|_2 \leq L\|x\|_2$ and $\phi(\tau; t, x)$ satisfies the lower bound[25]

$$\|\phi(\tau; t, x)\|_2^2 \geq \|x\|_2^2 e^{-2L(\tau-t)}$$

Hence,

$$V(t, x) \geq \int_t^{t+\delta} e^{-2L(\tau-t)} \, d\tau \, \|x\|_2^2 = \frac{1}{2L}(1 - e^{-2L\delta})\|x\|_2^2$$

---

[25]See Exercise 3.17.

Thus, $V(t, x)$ satisfies the first inequality of the theorem with

$$c_1 = \frac{(1 - e^{-2L\delta})}{2L} \quad \text{and} \quad c_2 = \frac{k^2(1 - e^{-2\lambda\delta})}{2\lambda}$$

To calculate the derivative of V along the trajectories of the system, define the sensitivity functions

$$\phi_t(\tau; t, x) = \frac{\partial}{\partial t}\phi(\tau; t, x); \quad \phi_x(\tau; t, x) = \frac{\partial}{\partial x}\phi(\tau; t, x)$$

Then,

$$
\begin{aligned}
\frac{\partial V}{\partial t} + \frac{\partial V}{\partial x}f(t, x) &= \phi^T(t + \delta; t, x)\phi(t + \delta; t, x) - \phi^T(t; t, x)\phi(t; t, x) \\
&\quad + \int_t^{t+\delta} 2\phi^T(\tau; t, x)\phi_t(\tau; t, x)\,d\tau \\
&\quad + \int_t^{t+\delta} 2\phi^T(\tau; t, x)\phi_x(\tau; t, x)\,d\tau\,f(t, x) \\
&= \phi^T(t + \delta; t, x)\phi(t + \delta; t, x) - \|x\|_2^2 \\
&\quad + \int_t^{t+\delta} 2\phi^T(\tau; t, x)[\phi_t(\tau; t, x) + \phi_x(\tau; t, x)f(t, x)]\,d\tau
\end{aligned}
$$

It is not difficult to show that[26]

$$\phi_t(\tau; t, x) + \phi_x(\tau; t, x)f(t, x) \equiv 0, \quad \forall\, \tau \geq t$$

Therefore,

$$
\begin{aligned}
\frac{\partial V}{\partial t} + \frac{\partial V}{\partial x}f(t, x) &= \phi^T(t + \delta; t, x)\phi(t + \delta; t, x) - \|x\|_2^2 \\
&\leq -(1 - k^2 e^{-2\lambda\delta})\|x\|_2^2
\end{aligned}
$$

By choosing $\delta = \ln(2k^2)/(2\lambda)$, the second inequality of the theorem is satisfied with $c_3 = 1/2$. To show the last inequality, let us note that $\phi_x(\tau; t, x)$ satisfies the sensitivity equation

$$\frac{\partial}{\partial \tau}\phi_x = \frac{\partial f}{\partial x}(\tau, \phi(\tau; t, x))\,\phi_x, \quad \phi_x(t; t, x) = I$$

Since

$$\left\| \frac{\partial f}{\partial x}(t, x) \right\|_2 \leq L$$

---

[26]See Exercise 3.30.

on D, ϕ_x satisfies the bound[27]

$$\|\phi_x(\tau; t, x)\|_2 \leq e^{L(\tau - t)}$$

Therefore,

$$
\begin{aligned}
\left\|\frac{\partial V}{\partial x}\right\|_2 &= \left\|\int_t^{t+\delta} 2\phi^T(\tau; t, x)\phi_x(\tau; t, x)\, d\tau\right\|_2 \\
&\leq \int_t^{t+\delta} 2\|\phi(\tau; t, x)\|_2\, \|\phi_x(\tau; t, x)\|_2\, d\tau \\
&\leq \int_t^{t+\delta} 2k e^{-\lambda(\tau - t)}\, e^{L(\tau - t)}\, d\tau\, \|x\|_2 \\
&= \frac{2k}{(\lambda - L)}[1 - e^{-(\lambda - L)\delta}]\|x\|_2
\end{aligned}
$$

Thus, the last inequality of the theorem is satisfied with

$$c_4 = \frac{2k}{(\lambda - L)}[1 - e^{-(\lambda - L)\delta}]$$

If all the assumptions hold globally, then clearly r_0 can be chosen arbitrarily large. If the system is autonomous, then $\phi(\tau; t, x)$ depends only on $(\tau - t)$; that is,

$$\phi(\tau; t, x) = \psi(\tau - t; x)$$

Then,

$$V(t, x) = \int_t^{t+\delta} \psi^T(\tau - t; x)\psi(\tau - t; x)\, d\tau = \int_0^\delta \psi^T(s; x)\psi(s; x)\, ds$$

which is independent of t. $\qquad\square$

In Theorem 4.13, we saw that if the linearization of a nonlinear system about the origin has an exponentially stable equilibrium point, then the origin is an exponentially stable equilibrium point for the nonlinear system. We will use Theorem 4.14 to prove that exponential stability of the linearization is a necessary and sufficient condition for exponential stability of the origin.

Theorem 4.15 *Let $x = 0$ be an equilibrium point for the nonlinear system*

$$\dot{x} = f(t, x)$$

where $f : [0, \infty) \times D \to R^n$ is continuously differentiable, $D = \{x \in R^n \mid \|x\|_2 < r\}$, and the Jacobian matrix $[\partial f/\partial x]$ is bounded and Lipschitz on D, uniformly in t. Let

$$A(t) = \frac{\partial f}{\partial x}(t, x)\bigg|_{x=0}$$

---

[27]See Exercise 3.17.

Then, $x = 0$ is an exponentially stable equilibrium point for the nonlinear system if and only if it is an exponentially stable equilibrium point for the linear system

$$\dot{x} = A(t)x$$

$\diamond$

Proof: The "if" part follows from Theorem 4.13. To prove the "only if" part, write the linear system as

$$\dot{x} = f(t,x) - [f(t,x) - A(t)x] = f(t,x) - g(t,x)$$

Recalling the argument preceding Theorem 4.13, we know that

$$\|g(t,x)\|_2 \le L\|x\|_2^2, \quad \forall\, x \in D,\ \forall\, t \ge 0$$

Since the origin is an exponentially stable equilibrium of the nonlinear system, there are positive constants k, λ, and c such that

$$\|x(t)\|_2 \le k\|x(t_0)\|_2 e^{-\lambda(t-t_0)}, \quad \forall\, t \ge t_0 \ge 0,\ \forall\, \|x(t_0)\|_2 < c$$

Choosing $r_0 < \min\{c, r/k\}$, all the conditions of Theorem 4.14 are satisfied. Let $V(t,x)$ be the function provided by Theorem 4.14 and use it as a Lyapunov function candidate for the linear system. Then,

$$
\begin{aligned}
\frac{\partial V}{\partial t} + \frac{\partial V}{\partial x}A(t)x &= \frac{\partial V}{\partial t} + \frac{\partial V}{\partial x}f(t,x) - \frac{\partial V}{\partial x}g(t,x) \\
&\le -c_3\|x\|_2^2 + c_4 L\|x\|_2^3 \\
&< -(c_3 - c_4 L\rho)\|x\|_2^2, \quad \forall\, \|x\|_2 < \rho
\end{aligned}
$$

The choice $\rho < \min\{r_0, c_3/(c_4 L)\}$ ensures that $\dot{V}(t,x)$ is negative definite in $\|x\|_2 < \rho$. Consequently, all the conditions of Theorem 4.10 are satisfied in $\|x\|_2 < \rho$, and we conclude that the origin is an exponentially stable equilibrium point for the linear system. $\qquad\square$

Corollary 4.3 *Let $x = 0$ be an equilibrium point of the nonlinear system $\dot{x} = f(x)$, where $f(x)$ is continuously differentiable in some neighborhood of $x = 0$. Let $A = [\partial f/\partial x](0)$. Then, $x = 0$ is an exponentially stable equilibrium point for the nonlinear system if and only if A is Hurwitz.* $\diamond$

Example 4.23 Consider the first-order system $\dot{x} = -x^3$. We saw in Example 4.14 that the origin is asymptotically stable, but linearization about the origin results in the linear system $\dot{x} = 0$, whose A matrix is not Hurwitz. Using Corollary 4.3, we conclude that the origin is not exponentially stable. $\triangle$

The following converse Lyapunov theorems (Theorem 4.16 and 4.17) extend Theorem 4.15 in two different directions, but their proofs are more involved. Theorem 4.16 applies to the more general case of uniform asymptotic stability.[28] Theorem 4.17 applies to autonomous systems and produces a Lyapunov function that is defined on the whole region of attraction.

Theorem 4.16 *Let $x = 0$ be an equilibrium point for the nonlinear system*

$$\dot{x} = f(t, x)$$

where $f : [0, \infty) \times D \to R^n$ is continuously differentiable, $D = \{x \in R^n \mid \|x\| < r\}$, and the Jacobian matrix $[\partial f / \partial x]$ is bounded on D, uniformly in t. Let β be a class $\mathcal{KL}$ function and r_0 be a positive constant such that $\beta(r_0, 0) < r$. Let $D_0 = \{x \in R^n \mid \|x\| < r_0\}$. Assume that the trajectory of the system satisfies

$$\|x(t)\| \leq \beta(\|x(t_0)\|, t - t_0), \quad \forall \, x(t_0) \in D_0, \; \forall \, t \geq t_0 \geq 0$$

Then, there is a continuously differentiable function $V : [0, \infty) \times D_0 \to R$ that satisfies the inequalities

$$\alpha_1(\|x\|) \leq V(t, x) \leq \alpha_2(\|x\|)$$

$$\frac{\partial V}{\partial t} + \frac{\partial V}{\partial x} f(t, x) \leq -\alpha_3(\|x\|)$$

$$\left\| \frac{\partial V}{\partial x} \right\| \leq \alpha_4(\|x\|)$$

where α_1, α_2, α_3, and α_4 are class $\mathcal{K}$ functions defined on $[0, r_0]$. If the system is autonomous, V can be chosen independent of t. $\diamond$

Proof: See Appendix C.7.

Theorem 4.17 *Let $x = 0$ be an asymptotically stable equilibrium point for the nonlinear system*

$$\dot{x} = f(x)$$

where $f : D \to R^n$ is locally Lipschitz and $D \subset R^n$ is a domain that contains the origin. Let $R_A \subset D$ be the region of attraction of $x = 0$. Then, there is a smooth, positive definite function $V(x)$ and a continuous, positive definite function $W(x)$, both defined for all $x \in R_A$, such that

$$V(x) \to \infty \text{ as } x \to \partial R_A$$

$$\frac{\partial V}{\partial x} f(x) \leq -W(x), \quad \forall \, x \in R_A$$

and for any $c > 0$, $\{V(x) \leq c\}$ is a compact subset of R_A. When $R_A = R^n$, $V(x)$ is radially unbounded. $\diamond$

---

[28]Theorem 4.16 can be stated for a function $f(t, x)$ that is only locally Lipschitz, rather than continuously differentiable [125, Theorem 14]. It is also possible to state the theorem for the case of global uniform asymptotic stability [125, Theorem 23]

Proof: See Appendix C.8.

An interesting feature of Theorem 4.17 is that any bounded subset S of the region of attraction can be included in a compact set of the form $\{V(x) \le c\}$ for some constant $c > 0$. This feature is useful because quite often we have to limit our analysis to a positively invariant, compact set of the form $\{V(x) \le c\}$. With the property $S \subset \{V(x) \le c\}$, our analysis will be valid for the whole set S. If, on the other hand, all we know is the existence of a Lyapunov function $V_1(x)$ on S, we will have to choose a constant c_1 such that $\{V_1(x) \le c_1\}$ is compact and included in S; then our analysis will be limited to $\{V_1(x) \le c_1\}$, which is only a subset of S.

4.8   Boundedness and Ultimate Boundedness

Lyapunov analysis can be used to show boundedness of the solution of the state equation, even when there is no equilibrium point at the origin. To motivate the idea, consider the scalar equation

$$\dot{x} = -x + \delta \sin t, \quad x(t_0) = a, \quad a > \delta > 0$$

which has no equilibrium points and whose solution is given by

$$x(t) = e^{-(t-t_0)}a + \delta \int_{t_0}^{t} e^{-(t-\tau)} \sin \tau \, d\tau$$

The solution satisfies the bound

$$
\begin{aligned}
|x(t)| &\le e^{-(t-t_0)}a + \delta \int_{t_0}^{t} e^{-(t-\tau)} \, d\tau = e^{-(t-t_0)}a + \delta \left[1 - e^{-(t-t_0)} \right] \\
&\le a, \quad \forall \, t \ge t_0
\end{aligned}
$$

which shows that the solution is bounded for all $t \ge t_0$, uniformly in t_0, that is, with a bound independent of t_0. While this bound is valid for all $t \ge t_0$, it becomes a conservative estimate of the solution as time progresses, because it does not take into consideration the exponentially decaying term. If, on the other hand, we pick any number b such that $\delta < b < a$, it can be easily seen that

$$|x(t)| \le b, \quad \forall \, t \ge t_0 + \ln \left(\frac{a - \delta}{b - \delta} \right)$$

The bound b, which again is independent of t_0, gives a better estimate of the solution after a transient period has passed. In this case, the solution is said to be uniformly ultimately bounded and b is called the ultimate bound. Showing that the solution of $\dot{x} = -x + \delta \sin t$ has the uniform boundedness and ultimate boundedness properties can be done via Lyapunov analysis without using the explicit solution of the state equation. Starting with $V(x) = x^2/2$, we calculate the derivative of V along the trajectories of the system, to obtain

$$\dot{V} = x\dot{x} = -x^2 + x\delta \sin t \leq -x^2 + \delta|x|$$

The right-hand side of the foregoing inequality is not negative definite because, near the origin, the positive linear term $\delta|x|$ dominates the negative quadratic term $-x^2$. However, $\dot{V}$ is negative outside the set $\{|x| \leq \delta\}$. With $c > \delta^2/2$, solutions starting in the set $\{V(x) \leq c\}$ will remain therein for all future time since $\dot{V}$ is negative on the boundary $V = c$. Hence, the solutions are uniformly bounded. Moreover, if we pick any number ε such that $(\delta^2/2) < \varepsilon < c$, then $\dot{V}$ will be negative in the set $\{\varepsilon \leq V \leq c\}$, which shows that, in this set, V will decrease monotonically until the solution enters the set $\{V \leq \varepsilon\}$. From that time on, the solution cannot leave the set $\{V \leq \varepsilon\}$ because $\dot{V}$ is negative on the boundary $V = \varepsilon$. Thus, we can conclude that the solution is uniformly ultimately bounded with the ultimate bound $|x| \leq \sqrt{2\varepsilon}$.

The purpose of this section is to show how Lyapunov analysis can be used to draw similar conclusions for the system

$$\dot{x} = f(t, x) \tag{4.32}$$

where $f : [0, \infty) \times D \rightarrow R^n$ is piecewise continuous in t and locally Lipschitz in x on $[0, \infty) \times D$, and $D \subset R^n$ is a domain that contains the origin.

Definition 4.6 *The solutions of* (4.32) *are*

- *uniformly bounded if there exists a positive constant c, independent of $t_0 \geq 0$, and for every $a \in (0, c)$, there is $\beta = \beta(a) > 0$, independent of t_0, such that*

$$\|x(t_0)\| \leq a \implies \|x(t)\| \leq \beta, \quad \forall\, t \geq t_0 \tag{4.33}$$

- *globally uniformly bounded if* (4.33) *holds for arbitrarily large a.*

- *uniformly ultimately bounded with ultimate bound b if there exist positive constants b and c, independent of $t_0 \geq 0$, and for every $a \in (0, c)$, there is $T = T(a, b) \geq 0$, independent of t_0, such that*

$$\|x(t_0)\| \leq a \implies \|x(t)\| \leq b, \quad \forall\, t \geq t_0 + T \tag{4.34}$$

- *globally uniformly ultimately bounded if* (4.34) *holds for arbitrarily large a.*

In the case of autonomous systems, we may drop the word "uniformly" since the solution depends only on $t - t_0$.

To see how Lyapunov analysis can be used to study boundedness and ultimate boundedness, consider a continuously differentiable, positive definite function $V(x)$ and suppose that the set $\{V(x) \leq c\}$ is compact, for some $c > 0$. Let

$$\Lambda = \{\varepsilon \leq V(x) \leq c\}$$

for some positive constant $\varepsilon < c$. Suppose the derivative of V along the trajectories of the system $\dot{x} = f(t, x)$ satisfies

$$\dot{V}(t, x) \leq -W_3(x), \quad \forall\, x \in \Lambda,\ \forall\, t \geq t_0 \tag{4.35}$$

where $W_3(x)$ is a continuous positive definite function. Inequality (4.35) implies that the sets $\Omega_c = \{V(x) \leq c\}$ and $\Omega_\varepsilon = \{V(x) \leq \varepsilon\}$ are positively invariant since on the boundaries $\partial\Omega_c$ and $\partial\Omega_\varepsilon$, the derivative $\dot{V}$ is negative. A sketch of the sets Λ, Ω_c, and Ω_ε is shown in Figure 4.8. Since $\dot{V}$ is negative in Λ, a trajectory starting in Λ must move in a direction of decreasing $V(x(t))$. In fact, while in Λ, V satisfies inequalities (4.22) and (4.24) of Theorem 4.9. Therefore, the trajectory behaves as if the origin was uniformly asymptotically stable and satisfies an inequality of the form

$$\|x(t)\| \leq \beta(\|x(t_0)\|, t - t_0)$$

for some class $\mathcal{KL}$ function β. The function $V(x(t))$ will continue decreasing until the trajectory enters the set Ω_ε in finite time and stays therein for all future time. The fact that the trajectory enters Ω_ε in finite time can be shown as follows: Let $k = \min_{x \in \Lambda} W_3(x) > 0$. The minimum exists because $W_3(x)$ is continuous and Λ is compact. It is positive since $W_3(x)$ is positive definite. Hence,

$$W_3(x) \geq k, \quad \forall\, x \in \Lambda \tag{4.36}$$

Inequalities (4.35) and (4.36) imply that

$$\dot{V}(t, x) \leq -k, \quad \forall\, x \in \Lambda,\ \forall\, t \geq t_0$$

Therefore,

$$V(x(t)) \leq V(x(t_0)) - k(t - t_0) \leq c - k(t - t_0)$$

which shows that $V(x(t))$ reduces to ε within the time interval $[t_0, t_0 + (c - \varepsilon)/k]$.

In many problems, the inequality $\dot{V} \leq -W_3$ is obtained by using norm inequalities. In such cases, it is more likely that we arrive at

$$\dot{V}(t, x) \leq -W_3(x), \quad \forall\, \mu \leq \|x\| \leq r,\ \forall\, t \geq t_0 \tag{4.37}$$

If r is sufficiently larger than μ, we can choose c and ε such that the set Λ is nonempty and contained in $\{\mu \leq \|x\| \leq r\}$. In particular, let α_1 and α_2 be class $\mathcal{K}$ functions such that [29]

$$\alpha_1(\|x\|) \leq V(x) \leq \alpha_2(\|x\|) \tag{4.38}$$

From the left inequality of (4.38), we have

$$V(x) \leq c \implies \alpha_1(\|x\|) \leq c \iff \|x\| \leq \alpha_1^{-1}(c)$$

---

[29] By Lemma 4.3, it is always possible to find such class $\mathcal{K}$ functions.

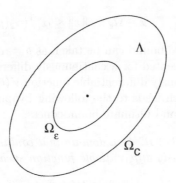

Figure 4.8: Representation of the set Λ, Ω_ε and Ω_c.

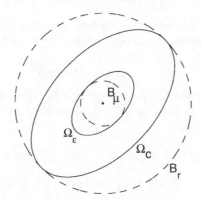

Figure 4.9: Representation of the sets Ω_ε, Ω_c (solid) and B_μ, B_r (dashed).

Therefore, taking $c = \alpha_1(r)$ ensures that $\Omega_c \subset B_r$. On the other hand, from the right inequality of (4.38), we have

$$\|x\| \leq \mu \;\Rightarrow\; V(x) \leq \alpha_2(\mu)$$

Consequently, taking $\varepsilon = \alpha_2(\mu)$ ensures that $B_\mu \subset \Omega_\varepsilon$. To obtain $\varepsilon < c$, we must have $\mu < \alpha_2^{-1}(\alpha_1(r))$. A sketch of the sets Ω_c, Ω_ε, B_r, and B_μ is shown in Figure 4.9.

The foregoing argument shows that all trajectories starting in Ω_c enter Ω_ε within a finite time T.[30] To calculate the ultimate bound on $x(t)$, we use the left inequality of (4.38) to write

$$V(x) \leq \varepsilon \Rightarrow \alpha_1(\|x\|) \leq \varepsilon \Leftrightarrow \|x\| \leq \alpha_1^{-1}(\varepsilon)$$

---

[30] If the trajectory starts in Ω_ε, $T = 0$.

Recalling that $\varepsilon = \alpha_2(\mu)$, we see that

$$x \in \Omega_\varepsilon \Rightarrow \|x\| \leq \alpha_1^{-1}(\alpha_2(\mu))$$

Therefore, the ultimate bound can be taken as $b = \alpha_1^{-1}(\alpha_2(\mu))$.

The ideas just presented for a continuously differentiable function $V(x)$ can be extended to a continuously differentiable function $V(t, x)$, as long as $V(t, x)$ satisfies inequality (4.38), which leads to the following Lyapunov-like theorem for showing uniform boundedness and ultimate boundedness.

Theorem 4.18 *Let $D \subset R^n$ be a domain that contains the origin and $V : [0, \infty) \times D \to R$ be a continuously differentiable function such that*

$$\alpha_1(\|x\|) \leq V(t, x) \leq \alpha_2(\|x\|) \tag{4.39}$$

$$\frac{\partial V}{\partial t} + \frac{\partial V}{\partial x} f(t, x) \leq -W_3(x), \quad \forall \, \|x\| \geq \mu > 0 \tag{4.40}$$

$\forall \, t \geq 0$ and $\forall \, x \in D$, where α_1 and α_2 are class $\mathcal{K}$ functions and $W_3(x)$ is a continuous positive definite function. Take $r > 0$ such that $B_r \subset D$ and suppose that

$$\mu < \alpha_2^{-1}(\alpha_1(r)) \tag{4.41}$$

Then, there exists a class $\mathcal{KL}$ function β and for every initial state $x(t_0)$, satisfying $\|x(t_0)\| \leq \alpha_2^{-1}(\alpha_1(r))$, there is $T \geq 0$ (dependent on $x(t_0)$ and μ) such that the solution of (4.32) satisfies

$$\|x(t)\| \leq \beta(\|x(t_0)\|, t - t_0), \quad \forall \, t_0 \leq t \leq t_0 + T \tag{4.42}$$

$$\|x(t)\| \leq \alpha_1^{-1}(\alpha_2(\mu)), \quad \forall \, t \geq t_0 + T \tag{4.43}$$

Moreover, if $D = R^n$ and α_1 belongs to class $\mathcal{K}_\infty$, then (4.42) and (4.43) hold for any initial state $x(t_0)$, with no restriction on how large μ is. $\diamond$

Proof: See Appendix C.9.

Inequalities (4.42) and (4.43) show that $x(t)$ is uniformly bounded for all $t \geq t_0$ and uniformly ultimately bounded with the ultimate bound $\alpha_1^{-1}(\alpha_2(\mu))$. The ultimate bound is a class $\mathcal{K}$ function of μ; hence, the smaller the value of μ, the smaller the ultimate bound. As $\mu \to 0$, the ultimate bound approaches zero.

The main application of Theorem 4.18 arises in studying the stability of perturbed systems.[31] The next example illustrates the basic idea of that application.

Example 4.24 In Section 1.2.3, we saw that a mass–spring system with a hardening spring, linear viscous damping, and a periodic external force can be represented by the Duffing's equation

$$m\ddot{y} + c\dot{y} + ky + ka^2 y^3 = A \cos \omega t$$

---

[31]See Section 9.2.

Taking $x_1 = y$, $x_2 = \dot{y}$ and assuming certain numerical values for the various constants, the system is represented by the state model

$$
\begin{aligned}
\dot{x}_1 &= x_2 \\
\dot{x}_2 &= -(1 + x_1^2)x_1 - x_2 + M\cos\omega t
\end{aligned}
$$

where $M \geq 0$ is proportional to the amplitude of the periodic external force. When $M = 0$, the system has an equilibrium point at the origin. It is shown in Example 4.6 that the origin is globally asymptotically stable and a Lyapunov function can be taken as[32]

$$
\begin{aligned}
V(x) &= x^T \begin{bmatrix} \frac{1}{2} & \frac{1}{2} \\ \frac{1}{2} & 1 \end{bmatrix} x + 2\int_0^{x_1} (y + y^3)\, dy = x^T \begin{bmatrix} \frac{1}{2} & \frac{1}{2} \\ \frac{1}{2} & 1 \end{bmatrix} x + x_1^2 + \tfrac{1}{2}x_1^4 \\
&= x^T \begin{bmatrix} \frac{3}{2} & \frac{1}{2} \\ \frac{1}{2} & 1 \end{bmatrix} x + \tfrac{1}{2}x_1^4 \stackrel{\text{def}}{=} x^T P x + \tfrac{1}{2}x_1^4
\end{aligned}
$$

When $M > 0$, we apply Theorem 4.18 with $V(x)$ as a candidate function. The function $V(x)$ is positive definite and radially unbounded; hence, by Lemma 4.3, there exist class $\mathcal{K}_\infty$ functions α_1 and α_2 that satisfy (4.39) globally. The derivative of V along the trajectories of the system is given by

$$
\dot{V} = -x_1^2 - x_1^4 - x_2^2 + (x_1 + 2x_2)M\cos\omega t \leq -\|x\|_2^2 - x_1^4 + M\sqrt{5}\|x\|_2
$$

where we wrote $(x_1 + 2x_2)$ as $y^T x$ and used the inequality $y^T x \leq \|x\|_2\|y\|_2$. To satisfy (4.40), we want to use part of $-\|x\|_2^2$ to dominate $M\sqrt{5}\|x\|_2$ for large $\|x\|$. Towards that end, we rewrite the foregoing inequality as

$$
\dot{V} \leq -(1-\theta)\|x\|_2^2 - x_1^4 - \theta\|x\|_2^2 + M\sqrt{5}\|x\|_2
$$

where $0 < \theta < 1$. Then,

$$
\dot{V} \leq -(1-\theta)\|x\|_2^2 - x_1^4, \quad \forall\, \|x\|_2 \geq \frac{M\sqrt{5}}{\theta}
$$

which shows that inequality (4.40) is satisfied globally with $\mu = M\sqrt{5}/\theta$. We conclude that the solutions are globally uniformly ultimately bounded. Suppose we want to go the extra step of calculating the ultimate bound. In this case, we have to find the functions α_1 and α_2. From the inequalities

$$
V(x) \geq x^T P x \geq \lambda_{min}(P)\|x\|_2^2
$$

$$
V(x) \leq x^T P x + \tfrac{1}{2}\|x\|_2^4 \leq \lambda_{max}(P)\|x\|_2^2 + \tfrac{1}{2}\|x\|_2^4
$$

---

[32]The constants δ and k of Example 4.6 are taken as $\delta = 2$ and $k = 1/2$.

we see that α_1 and α_2 can be taken as

$$\alpha_1(r) = \lambda_{min}(P)r^2 \quad \text{and} \quad \alpha_2(r) = \lambda_{max}(P)r^2 + \tfrac{1}{2}r^4$$

Thus, the ultimate bound is given by

$$b = \alpha_1^{-1}(\alpha_2(\mu)) = \sqrt{\frac{\alpha_2(\mu)}{\lambda_{min}(P)}} = \sqrt{\frac{\lambda_{max}(P)\mu^2 + \mu^4/2}{\lambda_{min}(P)}}$$

$\triangle$

4.9   Input-to-State Stability

Consider the system

$$\dot{x} = f(t, x, u) \tag{4.44}$$

where $f : [0, \infty) \times R^n \times R^m \to R^n$ is piecewise continuous in t and locally Lipschitz in x and u. The input $u(t)$ is a piecewise continuous, bounded function of t for all $t \geq 0$. Suppose the unforced system

$$\dot{x} = f(t, x, 0) \tag{4.45}$$

has a globally uniformly asymptotically stable equilibrium point at the origin $x = 0$. What can we say about the behavior of the system (4.44) in the presence of a bounded input $u(t)$? For the linear time-invariant system

$$\dot{x} = Ax + Bu$$

with a Hurwitz matrix A, we can write the solution as

$$x(t) = e^{(t-t_0)A}x(t_0) + \int_{t_0}^{t} e^{(t-\tau)A}Bu(\tau)\,d\tau$$

and use the bound $\|e^{(t-t_0)A}\| \leq ke^{-\lambda(t-t_0)}$ to estimate the solution by

$$\begin{aligned}
\|x(t)\| &\leq ke^{-\lambda(t-t_0)}\|x(t_0)\| + \int_{t_0}^{t} ke^{-\lambda(t-\tau)}\|B\|\|u(\tau)\|\,d\tau \\
&\leq ke^{-\lambda(t-t_0)}\|x(t_0)\| + \frac{k\|B\|}{\lambda}\sup_{t_0 \leq \tau \leq t}\|u(\tau)\|
\end{aligned}$$

This estimate shows that the zero-input response decays to zero exponentially fast, while the zero-state response is bounded for every bounded input. In fact, the estimate shows more than a bounded-input–bounded-state property. It shows that the bound on the zero-state response is proportional to the bound on the input. How much of this behavior should we expect for the nonlinear system (4.44)? For a general nonlinear system, it should not be surprising that these properties may not hold even when the origin of the unforced system is globally uniformly asymptotically stable. Consider, for example, the scalar system

$$\dot{x} = -3x + (1 + 2x^2)u$$

which has a globally exponentially stable origin when $u = 0$. Yet, when $x(0) = 2$ and $u(t) \equiv 1$, the solution $x(t) = (3 - e^t)/(3 - 2e^t)$ is unbounded; it even has a finite escape time.

Let us view the system (4.44) as a perturbation of the unforced system (4.45). Suppose we have a Lyapunov function $V(t, x)$ for the unforced system and let us calculate the derivative of V in the presence of u. Due to the boundedness of u, it is plausible that in some cases it should be possible to show that $\dot{V}$ is negative outside a ball of radius μ, where μ depends on $\sup \|u\|$. This would be expected, for example, when the function $f(t, x, u)$ satisfies the Lipschitz condition

$$\|f(t, x, u) - f(t, x, 0)\| \leq L\|u\| \tag{4.46}$$

Showing that $\dot{V}$ is negative outside a ball of radius μ would enable us to apply Theorem 4.18 of the previous section to show that $x(t)$ satisfies (4.42) and (4.43). These inequalities show that $\|x(t)\|$ is bounded by a class $\mathcal{KL}$ function $\beta(\|x(t_0)\|, t - t_0)$ over $[t_0, t_0 + T]$ and by a class $\mathcal{K}$ function $\alpha_1^{-1}(\alpha_2(\mu))$ for $t \geq t_0 + T$. Consequently,

$$\|x(t)\| \leq \beta(\|x(t_0)\|, t - t_0) + \alpha_1^{-1}(\alpha_2(\mu))$$

is valid for all $t \geq t_0$, which motivates the next definition of *input-to-state stability*.

Definition 4.7 *The system (4.44) is said to be input-to-state stable if there exist a class $\mathcal{KL}$ function β and a class $\mathcal{K}$ function γ such that for any initial state $x(t_0)$ and any bounded input $u(t)$, the solution $x(t)$ exists for all $t \geq t_0$ and satisfies*

$$\|x(t)\| \leq \beta(\|x(t_0)\|, t - t_0) + \gamma \left(\sup_{t_0 \leq \tau \leq t} \|u(\tau)\| \right) \tag{4.47}$$

Inequality (4.47) guarantees that for any bounded input $u(t)$, the state $x(t)$ will be bounded. Furthermore, as t increases, the state $x(t)$ will be ultimately bounded by a class $\mathcal{K}$ function of $\sup_{t \geq t_0} \|u(t)\|$. We leave it to the reader (Exercise 4.58) to use inequality (4.47) to show that if $u(t)$ converges to zero as $t \to \infty$, so does $x(t)$.[33] Since, with $u(t) \equiv 0$, (4.47) reduces to

$$\|x(t)\| \leq \beta(\|x(t_0)\|, t - t_0)$$

input-to-state stability implies that the origin of the unforced system (4.45) is globally uniformly asymptotically stable. The notion of input-to-state stability is defined

---

[33]Another interesting use of inequality (4.47) will be given shortly in Lemma 4.7.

for the global case where the initial state and the input can be arbitrarily large. A local version of this notion is presented in Exercise 4.60.

The Lyapunov-like theorem that follows gives a sufficient condition for input-to-state stability.[34]

Theorem 4.19 *Let* $V : [0, \infty) \times R^n \to R$ *be a continuously differentiable function such that*

$$\alpha_1(\|x\|) \leq V(t, x) \leq \alpha_2(\|x\|) \tag{4.48}$$

$$\frac{\partial V}{\partial t} + \frac{\partial V}{\partial x} f(t, x, u) \leq -W_3(x), \quad \forall \|x\| \geq \rho(\|u\|) > 0 \tag{4.49}$$

$\forall (t, x, u) \in [0, \infty) \times R^n \times R^m$, *where* α_1, α_2 *are class* $\mathcal{K}_\infty$ *functions,* ρ *is a class* $\mathcal{K}$ *function, and* $W_3(x)$ *is a continuous positive definite function on* R^n. *Then, the system* (4.44) *is input-to-state stable with* $\gamma = \alpha_1^{-1} \circ \alpha_2 \circ \rho$. $\diamond$

Proof: By applying the global version of Theorem 4.18, we find that the solution $x(t)$ exists and satisfies

$$\|x(t)\| \leq \beta(\|x(t_0)\|, t - t_0) + \gamma \left(\sup_{\tau \geq t_0} \|u(\tau)\| \right), \quad \forall\, t \geq t_0 \tag{4.50}$$

Since $x(t)$ depends only on $u(\tau)$ for $t_0 \leq \tau \leq t$, the supremum on the right-hand side of (4.50) can be taken over $[t_0, t]$, which yields (4.47).[35] $\square$

The next lemma is an immediate consequences of the converse Lyapunov theorem for global exponential stability (Theorem 4.14).

Lemma 4.6 *Suppose* $f(t, x, u)$ *is continuously differentiable and globally Lipschitz in* (x, u), *uniformly in* t. *If the unforced system* (4.45) *has a globally exponentially stable equilibrium point at the origin* $x = 0$, *then the system* (4.44) *is input-to-state stable.* $\diamond$

Proof: View the system (4.44) as a perturbation of the unforced system (4.45). (The converse Lyapunov) Theorem 4.14 shows that the unforced system (4.45) has a Lyapunov function $V(t, x)$ that satisfies (4.10) through (4.12) globally. Due to the uniform global Lipschitz property of f, the perturbation term satisfies (4.46) for all $t \geq t_0$ and all (x, u). The derivative of V with respect to (4.44) satisfies

$$\begin{aligned} \dot{V} &= \frac{\partial V}{\partial t} + \frac{\partial V}{\partial x} f(t, x, 0) + \frac{\partial V}{\partial x}[f(t, x, u) - f(t, x, 0)] \\ &\leq -c_3\|x\|^2 + c_4\|x\|L\|u\| \end{aligned}$$

---

[34]For autonomous systems, it is shown in [183] that the conditions of Theorem 4.19 are also necessary. In the literature, it is common to abbreviate input-to-state stability as ISS and to call the function V of Theorem 4.19 an ISS-Lyapunov function.

[35]In particular, repeat the aforementioned argument over the period $[0, T]$ to show that

$$\|x(\sigma)\| \leq \beta(\|x(t_0)\|, \sigma - t_0) + \gamma \left(\sup_{t_0 \leq \tau \leq T} \|u(\tau)\| \right), \quad \forall\, t_0 \leq \sigma \leq T$$

Then, set $\sigma = T = t$.

To use the term $-c_3\|x\|^2$ to dominate $c_4 L\|x\|\|u\|$ for large $\|x\|$, we rewrite the foregoing inequality as

$$\dot{V} \le -c_3(1-\theta)\|x\|^2 - c_3\theta\|x\|^2 + c_4 L\|x\|\|u\|$$

where $0 < \theta < 1$. Then,

$$\dot{V} \le -c_3(1-\theta)\|x\|^2, \quad \forall \, \|x\| \ge \frac{c_4 L\|u\|}{c_3\theta}$$

for all (t, x, u). Hence, the conditions of Theorem 4.19 are satisfied with $\alpha_1(r) = c_1 r^2$, $\alpha_2(r) = c_2 r^2$, and $\rho(r) = (c_4 L/c_3\theta)r$, and we conclude that the system is input-to-state stable with $\gamma(r) = \sqrt{c_2/c_1}(c_4 L/c_3\theta)r$. □

Lemma 4.6 requires a globally Lipschitz function f and global exponential stability of the origin of the unforced system to conclude input-to-state stability. It is easy to construct examples where the lemma does not hold in the absence of one of these two conditions. The system $\dot{x} = -3x + (1 + x^2)u$, which we discussed earlier in the section, does not satisfy the global Lipschitz condition. The system

$$\dot{x} = -\frac{x}{1 + x^2} + u \stackrel{\text{def}}{=} f(x, u)$$

has a globally Lipschitz f since the partial derivatives of f with respect to x and u are globally bounded. The origin of $\dot{x} = -x/(1 + x^2)$ is globally asymptotically stable, as it can be seen by the Lyapunov function $V(x) = x^2/2$, whose derivative $\dot{V}(x) = -x^2/(1 + x^2)$ is negative definite for all x. It is locally exponentially stable because the linearization at the origin is $\dot{x} = -x$. However, it is not globally exponentially stable. This is easiest seen through the fact that the system is not input-to-state stable. Notice that with $u(t) \equiv 1$, $f(x, u) \ge 1/2$. Hence, $x(t) \ge x(t_0) + t/2$ for all $t \ge 0$, which shows that the solution is unbounded.

In the absence of global exponential stability or globally Lipschitz functions, we may still be able to show input-to-state stability by applying Theorem 4.19. This process is illustrated by the three examples that follow.

Example 4.25 The system

$$\dot{x} = -x^3 + u$$

has a globally asymptotically stable origin when $u = 0$. Taking $V = x^2/2$, the derivative of V along the trajectories of the system is given by

$$\dot{V} = -x^4 + xu = -(1-\theta)x^4 - \theta x^4 + xu \le -(1-\theta)x^4, \quad \forall \, |x| \ge \left(\frac{|u|}{\theta}\right)^{1/3}$$

where $0 < \theta < 1$. Thus, the system is input-to-state stable with $\gamma(r) = (r/\theta)^{1/3}$. △

Example 4.26 The system

$$\dot{x} = f(x, u) = -x - 2x^3 + (1 + x^2)u^2$$

has a globally exponentially stable origin when $u = 0$, but Lemma 4.6 does not apply since f is not globally Lipschitz. Taking $V = x^2/2$, we obtain

$$\dot{V} = -x^2 - 2x^4 + x(1 + x^2)u^2 \leq -x^4, \ \forall \ |x| \geq u^2$$

Thus, the system is input-to-state stable with $\gamma(r) = r^2$. $\qquad\qquad\qquad \triangle$

In Examples 4.25 and 4.26, the function $V(x) = x^2/2$ satisfies (4.48) with $\alpha_1(r) = \alpha_2(r) = r^2/2$. Hence, $\alpha_1^{-1}(\alpha_2(r)) = r$ and $\gamma(r)$ reduces to $\rho(r)$. In higher-dimensional systems, the calculation of γ is more involved.

Example 4.27 Consider the system

$$\begin{aligned} \dot{x}_1 &= -x_1 + x_2^2 \\ \dot{x}_2 &= -x_2 + u \end{aligned}$$

We start by setting $u = 0$ and investigate global asymptotic stability of the origin of the unforced system. Using

$$V(x) = \frac{1}{2}x_1^2 + \frac{1}{4}ax_2^4, \quad a > 0$$

as a Lyapunov function candidate, we obtain

$$\dot{V} = -x_1^2 + x_1x_2^2 - ax_2^4 = -\left(x_1 - \frac{1}{2}x_2^2\right)^2 - \left(a - \frac{1}{4}\right)x_2^4$$

Choosing $a > 1/4$ shows that the origin is globally asymptotically stable. Now we allow $u \neq 0$ and use $V(x)$ with $a = 1$ as a candidate function for Theorem 4.19. The derivative $\dot{V}$ is given by

$$\dot{V} = -\frac{1}{2}(x_1 - x_2^2)^2 - \frac{1}{2}(x_1^2 + x_2^4) + x_2^3u \leq -\frac{1}{2}(x_1^2 + x_2^4) + |x_2|^3|u|$$

To use the term $-(x_1^2 + x_2^4)/2$ to dominate $|x_2|^3|u|$, we rewrite the foregoing inequality as

$$\dot{V} \leq -\frac{1}{2}(1 - \theta)(x_1^2 + x_2^4) - \frac{1}{2}\theta(x_1^2 + x_2^4) + |x_2|^3|u|$$

where $0 < \theta < 1$. The term

$$-\frac{1}{2}\theta(x_1^2 + x_2^4) + |x_2|^3|u|$$

will be ≤ 0 if $|x_2| \geq 2|u|/\theta$ or $|x_2| \leq 2|u|/\theta$ and $|x_1| \geq (2|u|/\theta)^2$. This condition is implied by

$$\max\{|x_1|, |x_2|\} \geq \max\left\{\frac{2|u|}{\theta}, \left(\frac{2|u|}{\theta}\right)^2\right\}$$

Using the norm $\|x\|_\infty = \max\{|x_1|, |x_2|\}$ and defining the class $\mathcal{K}$ function ρ by

$$\rho(r) = \max\left\{\frac{2r}{\theta}, \left(\frac{2r}{\theta}\right)^2\right\}$$

we see that inequality (4.49) is satisfied as

$$\dot{V} \leq -\tfrac{1}{2}(1-\theta)(x_1^2 + x_2^4), \quad \forall \, \|x\|_\infty \geq \rho(|u|)$$

Inequality (4.48) follows from Lemma 4.3 since $V(x)$ is positive definite and radially unbounded. Hence, the system is input-to-state stable. Suppose we want to find the class $\mathcal{K}$ function γ. In this case, we need to find α_1 and α_2. It is not hard to see that

$$V(x) = \tfrac{1}{2}x_1^2 + \tfrac{1}{4}x_2^4 \leq \tfrac{1}{2}\|x\|_\infty^2 + \tfrac{1}{4}\|x\|_\infty^4$$

$$V(x) = \tfrac{1}{2}x_1^2 + \tfrac{1}{4}x_2^4 \geq \begin{cases} \tfrac{1}{2}|x_1|^2 = \tfrac{1}{2}\|x\|_\infty^2, & \text{if } |x_2| \leq |x_1| \\[2mm] \tfrac{1}{4}|x_2|^4 = \tfrac{1}{4}\|x\|_\infty^4, & \text{if } |x_2| \geq |x_1| \end{cases}$$

Inequality (4.48) is satisfied with the class $\mathcal{K}_\infty$ functions

$$\alpha_1(r) = \min\left\{\tfrac{1}{2}r^2, \tfrac{1}{4}r^4\right\} \quad \text{and} \quad \alpha_2(r) = \tfrac{1}{2}r^2 + \tfrac{1}{4}r^4$$

Thus, $\gamma(r) = \alpha_1^{-1}(\alpha_2(\rho(r)))$, where

$$\alpha_1^{-1}(s) = \begin{cases} (4s)^{\frac{1}{4}}, & \text{if } s \leq 1 \\[2mm] \sqrt{2s}, & \text{if } s \geq 1 \end{cases}$$

The function γ depends on the choice of $\|x\|$. Had we chosen another p-norm, we could have ended up with a different γ. $\qquad\qquad \triangle$

An interesting application of the concept of input-to-state stability arises in the stability analysis of the cascade system

$$\dot{x}_1 = f_1(t, x_1, x_2) \tag{4.51}$$
$$\dot{x}_2 = f_2(t, x_2) \tag{4.52}$$

where $f_1 : [0, \infty) \times R^{n_1} \times R^{n_2} \to R^{n_1}$ and $f_2 : [0, \infty) \times R^{n_2} \to R^{n_2}$ are piecewise continuous in t and locally Lipschitz in $x = \begin{bmatrix} x_1 \\ x_2 \end{bmatrix}$. Suppose both

$$\dot{x}_1 = f_1(t, x_1, 0)$$

and (4.52) have globally uniformly asymptotically stable equilibrium points at their respective origins. Under what condition will the origin $x = 0$ of the cascade system possess the same property? The next lemma shows that this will be the case if (4.51), with x_2 viewed as input, is input-to-state stable.

Lemma 4.7 *Under the stated assumptions, if the system* (4.51), *with x_2 as input, is input-to-state stable and the origin of* (4.52) *is globally uniformly asymptotically stable, then the origin of the cascade system* (4.51) *and* (4.52) *is globally uniformly asymptotically stable.* $\diamond$

Proof: Let $t_0 \geq 0$ be the initial time. The solutions of (4.51) and (4.52) satisfy

$$\|x_1(t)\| \leq \beta_1(\|x_1(s)\|, t - s) + \gamma_1\left(\sup_{s \leq \tau \leq t} \|x_2(\tau)\|\right) \tag{4.53}$$

$$\|x_2(t)\| \leq \beta_2(\|x_2(s)\|, t - s) \tag{4.54}$$

globally, where $t \geq s \geq t_0$, β_1, β_2 are class $\mathcal{KL}$ functions and γ_1 is a class $\mathcal{K}$ function. Apply (4.53) with $s = (t + t_0)/2$ to obtain

$$\|x_1(t)\| \leq \beta_1\left(\left\|x_1\left(\frac{t + t_0}{2}\right)\right\|, \frac{t - t_0}{2}\right) + \gamma_1\left(\sup_{\frac{t+t_0}{2} \leq \tau \leq t} \|x_2(\tau)\|\right) \tag{4.55}$$

To estimate $x_1((t + t_0)/2)$, apply (4.53) with $s = t_0$ and t replaced by $(t + t_0)/2$ to obtain

$$\left\|x_1\left(\frac{t + t_0}{2}\right)\right\| \leq \beta_1\left(\|x_1(t_0)\|, \frac{t - t_0}{2}\right) + \gamma_1\left(\sup_{t_0 \leq \tau \leq \frac{t+t_0}{2}} \|x_2(\tau)\|\right) \tag{4.56}$$

Using (4.54), we obtain

$$\sup_{t_0 \leq \tau \leq \frac{t+t_0}{2}} \|x_2(\tau)\| \leq \beta_2(\|x_2(t_0)\|, 0) \tag{4.57}$$

$$\sup_{\frac{t+t_0}{2} \leq \tau \leq t} \|x_2(\tau)\| \leq \beta_2\left(\|x_2(t_0)\|, \frac{t - t_0}{2}\right) \tag{4.58}$$

Substituting (4.56) through (4.58) into (4.55) and using the inequalities

$$\|x_1(t_0)\| \leq \|x(t_0)\|, \quad \|x_2(t_0)\| \leq \|x(t_0)\|, \quad \|x(t)\| \leq \|x_1(t)\| + \|x_2(t)\|$$

yield

$$\|x(t)\| \leq \beta(\|x(t_0)\|, t - t_0)$$

where

$$\beta(r, s) = \beta_1\left(\beta_1\left(r, \frac{s}{2}\right) + \gamma_1(\beta_2(r, 0)), \frac{s}{2}\right) + \gamma_1\left(\beta_2\left(r, \frac{s}{2}\right)\right) + \beta_2(r, s)$$

It can be easily verified that β is a class $\mathcal{KL}$ function for all $r \geq 0$. Hence, the origin of (4.51) and (4.52) is globally uniformly asymptotically stable. $\square$

4.10   Exercises

4.1 Consider a second-order autonomous system. For each of the following types of equilibrium points, classify whether the equilibrium point is stable, unstable, or asymptotically stable:

   (1) stable node   **(2)** unstable node   **(3)** stable focus
   (4) unstable focus   **(5)** center   **(6)** saddle

Justify your answer using phase portraits.

4.2 Consider the scalar system $\dot{x} = ax^p + g(x)$, where p is a positive integer and $g(x)$ satisfies $|g(x)| \le k|x|^{p+1}$ in some neighborhood of the origin $x = 0$. Show that the origin is asymptotically stable if p is odd and $a < 0$. Show that it is unstable if p is odd and $a > 0$ or p is even and $a \ne 0$.

4.3 For each of the following systems, use a quadratic Lyapunov function candidate to show that the origin is asymptotically stable:

$$\textbf{(1)} \quad \dot{x}_1 = -x_1 + x_1 x_2, \qquad\qquad \dot{x}_2 = -x_2$$

$$\textbf{(2)} \quad \dot{x}_1 = -x_2 - x_1(1 - x_1^2 - x_2^2), \qquad \dot{x}_2 = x_1 - x_2(1 - x_1^2 - x_2^2)$$

$$\textbf{(3)} \quad \dot{x}_1 = x_2(1 - x_1^2), \qquad\qquad \dot{x}_2 = -(x_1 + x_2)(1 - x_1^2)$$

$$\textbf{(4)} \quad \dot{x}_1 = -x_1 - x_2, \qquad\qquad \dot{x}_2 = 2x_1 - x_2^3$$

Investigate whether the origin is globally asymptotically stable.

4.4 (**[151]**) Euler equations for a rotating rigid spacecraft are given by

$$\begin{aligned}
J_1 \dot{\omega}_1 &= (J_2 - J_3)\omega_2\omega_3 + u_1 \\
J_2 \dot{\omega}_2 &= (J_3 - J_1)\omega_3\omega_1 + u_2 \\
J_3 \dot{\omega}_3 &= (J_1 - J_2)\omega_1\omega_2 + u_3
\end{aligned}$$

where ω_1 to ω_3 are the components of the angular velocity vector ω along the principal axes, u_1 to u_3 are the torque inputs applied about the principal axes, and J_1 to J_3 are the principal moments of inertia.

(a) Show that with $u_1 = u_2 = u_3 = 0$ the origin $\omega = 0$ is stable. Is it asymptotically stable?

(b) Suppose the torque inputs apply the feedback control $u_i = -k_i\omega_i$, where k_1 to k_3 are positive constants. Show that the origin of the closed-loop system is globally asymptotically stable.

4.5 Let $g(x)$ be a map from R^n into R^n. Show that $g(x)$ is the gradient vector of a scalar function $V : R^n \to R$ if and only if

$$\frac{\partial g_i}{\partial x_j} = \frac{\partial g_j}{\partial x_i}, \quad \forall\, i, j = 1, 2, \dots, n$$

4.6 Consider the system

$$\dot{x}_1 = x_2, \qquad \dot{x}_2 = -(x_1 + x_2) - h(x_1 + x_2)$$

where h is continuously differentiable and $zh(z) > 0$ for all $z \in R$. Using the variable gradient method, find a Lyapunov function that shows that the origin is globally asymptotically stable.

4.7 Consider the system $\dot{x} = -Q\phi(x)$, where Q is a symmetric positive definite matrix and $\phi(x)$ is a continuously differentiable function for which the ith component ϕ_i depends only on x_i, that is, $\phi_i(x) = \phi_i(x_i)$. Assume that $\phi_i(0) = 0$ and $y\phi_i(y) > 0$ in some neighborhood of $y = 0$, for all $1 \le i \le n$.

(a) Using the variable gradient method, find a Lyapunov function that shows that the origin is asymptotically stable.

(b) Under what conditions will it be globally asymptotically stable?

(c) Apply to the case

$$n = 2, \ \phi_1(x_1) = x_1 - x_1^2, \ \phi_2(x_2) = x_2 + x_2^3, \ Q = \begin{bmatrix} 2 & 1 \\ 1 & 1 \end{bmatrix}$$

4.8 ([72]) Consider the second-order system

$$\dot{x}_1 = \frac{-6x_1}{u^2} + 2x_2, \qquad \dot{x}_2 = \frac{-2(x_1 + x_2)}{u^2}$$

where $u = 1 + x_1^2$. Let $V(x) = x_1^2/(1 + x_1^2) + x_2^2$.

(a) Show that $V(x) > 0$ and $\dot{V}(x) < 0$ for all $x \in R^2 - \{0\}$.

(b) Consider the hyperbola $x_2 = 2/(x_1 - \sqrt{2})$. Show, by investigating the vector field on the boundary of this hyperbola, that trajectories to the right of the branch in the first quadrant cannot cross that branch.

(c) Show that the origin is not globally asymptotically stable.

Hint: In part (b), show that $\dot{x}_2/\dot{x}_1 = -1/(1 + 2\sqrt{2}x_1 + 2x_1^2)$ on the hyperbola, and compare with the slope of the tangents to the hyperbola.

4.9 In checking radial unboundedness of a positive definite function $V(x)$, it may appear that it is sufficient to examine $V(x)$ as $\|x\| \to \infty$ along the principal axes. This is not true, as shown by the function

$$V(x) = \frac{(x_1 + x_2)^2}{1 + (x_1 + x_2)^2} + (x_1 - x_2)^2$$

(a) Show that $V(x) \to \infty$ as $\|x\| \to \infty$ along the lines $x_1 = 0$ or $x_2 = 0$.

(b) Show that $V(x)$ is not radially unbounded.

4.10 (Krasovskii's Method) Consider the system $\dot{x} = f(x)$ with $f(0) = 0$. Assume that $f(x)$ is continuously differentiable and its Jacobian $[\partial f / \partial x]$ satisfies

$$P \left[\frac{\partial f}{\partial x}(x) \right] + \left[\frac{\partial f}{\partial x}(x) \right]^T P \le -I, \quad \forall \, x \in R^n, \quad \text{where } P = P^T > 0$$

(a) Using the representation $f(x) = \int_0^1 \frac{\partial f}{\partial x}(\sigma x) x \, d\sigma$, show that

$$x^T P f(x) + f^T(x) P x \le -x^T x, \quad \forall \, x \in R^n$$

(b) Show that $V(x) = f^T(x) P f(x)$ is positive definite for all $x \in R^n$ and radially unbounded.

(c) Show that the origin is globally asymptotically stable.

4.11 Using Theorem 4.3, prove Lyapunov's first instability theorem:
For the system (4.1), if a continuously differentiable function $V_1(x)$ can be found in a neighborhood of the origin such that $V_1(0) = 0$, and $\dot{V}_1$ along the trajectories of the system is positive definite, but V_1 itself is not negative definite or negative semidefinite arbitrarily near the origin, then the origin is unstable.

4.12 Using Theorem 4.3, prove Lyapunov's second instability theorem:
For the system (4.1), if in a neighborhood D of the origin, a continuously differentiable function $V_1(x)$ exists such that $V_1(0) = 0$ and $\dot{V}_1$ along the trajectories of the system is of the form $\dot{V}_1 = \lambda V_1 + W(x)$ where $\lambda > 0$ and $W(x) \ge 0$ in D, and if $V_1(x)$ is not negative definite or negative semidefinite arbitrarily near the origin, then the origin is unstable.

4.13 For each of the following systems, show that the origin is unstable:

$$\textbf{(1)} \quad \dot{x}_1 = x_1^3 + x_1^2 x_2, \qquad \dot{x}_2 = -x_2 + x_2^2 + x_1 x_2 - x_1^3$$

$$\textbf{(2)} \quad \dot{x}_1 = -x_1^3 + x_2, \qquad \dot{x}_2 = x_1^6 - x_2^3$$

Hint: In part (2), show that $\Gamma = \{0 \le x_1 \le 1\} \cap \{x_2 \ge x_1^3\} \cap \{x_2 \le x_1^2\}$ is a nonempty positively invariant set, and investigate the behavior of the trajectories inside Γ.

4.14 Consider the system

$$\dot{x}_1 = x_2, \qquad \dot{x}_2 = -g(x_1)(x_1 + x_2)$$

where g is locally Lipschitz and $g(y) \ge 1$ for all $y \in R$. Verify that $V(x) = \int_0^{x_1} y g(y) \, dy + x_1 x_2 + x_2^2$ is positive definite for all $x \in R^2$ and radially unbounded, and use it to show that the equilibrium point $x = 0$ is globally asymptotically stable.

4.15 Consider the system

$$\dot{x}_1 = x_2, \quad \dot{x}_2 = -h_1(x_1) - x_2 - h_2(x_3), \quad \dot{x}_3 = x_2 - x_3$$

where h_1 and h_2 are locally Lipschitz functions that satisfy $h_i(0) = 0$ and $yh_i(y) > 0$ for all $y \neq 0$.

(a) Show that the system has a unique equilibrium point at the origin.

(b) Show that $V(x) = \int_0^{x_1} h_1(y) \, dy + x_2^2/2 + \int_0^{x_3} h_2(y) \, dy$ is positive definite for all $x \in R^3$.

(c) Show that the origin is asymptotically stable.

(d) Under what conditions on h_1 and h_2, can you show that the origin is globally asymptotically stable?

4.16 Show that the origin of

$$\dot{x}_1 = x_2, \quad \dot{x}_2 = -x_1^3 - x_2^3$$

is globally asymptotically stable.

4.17 ([77]) Consider Liénard's equation

$$\ddot{y} + h(y)\dot{y} + g(y) = 0$$

where g and h are continuously differentiable.

(a) Using $x_1 = y$ and $x_2 = \dot{y}$, write the state equation and find conditions on g and h to ensure that the origin is an isolated equilibrium point.

(b) Using $V(x) = \int_0^{x_1} g(y) \, dy + (1/2)x_2^2$ as a Lyapunov function candidate, find conditions on g and h to ensure that the origin is asymptotically stable.

(c) Repeat part (b) using $V(x) = (1/2) \left[x_2 + \int_0^{x_1} h(y) \, dy \right]^2 + \int_0^{x_1} g(y) \, dy$.

4.18 The mass–spring system of Exercise 1.12 is modeled by

$$M\ddot{y} = Mg - ky - c_1\dot{y} - c_2\dot{y}|\dot{y}|$$

Show that the system has a globally asymptotically stable equilibrium point.

4.19 Consider the equations of motion of an m-link robot, described in Exercise 1.4. Assume that $P(q)$ is a positive definite function of q and $g(q) = 0$ has an isolated roots at $q = 0$.

(a) With $u = 0$, use the total energy $V(q, \dot{q}) = \frac{1}{2}\dot{q}^T M(q)\dot{q} + P(q)$ as a Lyapunov function candidate to show that the origin $(q = 0, \dot{q} = 0)$ is stable.

(b) With $u = -K_d \dot{q}$, where K_d is a positive diagonal matrix, show that the origin is asymptotically stable.

(c) With $u = g(q) - K_p(q - q^*) - K_d \dot{q}$, where K_p and K_d are positive diagonal matrices and q^* is a desired robot position in R^m, show that the point $(q = q^*,\ \dot{q} = 0)$ is an asymptotically stable equilibrium point.

4.20 Suppose the set M in LaSalle's theorem consists of a finite number of isolated points. Show that $\lim_{t \to \infty} x(t)$ exists and equals one of these points.

4.21 ([81]) A gradient system is a dynamical system of the form $\dot{x} = -\nabla V(x)$, where $\nabla V(x) = [\partial V / \partial x]^T$ and $V : D \subset R^n \to R$ is twice continuously differentiable.

(a) Show that $\dot{V}(x) \leq 0$ for all $x \in D$, and $\dot{V}(x) = 0$ if and only if x is an equilibrium point.

(b) Suppose the set $\Omega_c = \{x \in R^n \mid V(x) \leq c\}$ is compact for every $c \in R$. Show that every solution of the system is defined for all $t \geq 0$.

(c) Continuing with part (b), suppose $\nabla V(x) \neq 0$, except for a finite number of points $p_1, \ldots, p_r$. Show that for every solution $x(t)$, $\lim_{t \to \infty} x(t)$ exists and equals one of the points $p_1, \ldots, p_r$.

4.22 Consider the Lyapunov equation $PA + A^T P = -C^T C$, where the pair (A, C) is observable. Show that A is Hurwitz if and only if there exists $P = P^T > 0$ that satisfies the equation. Furthermore, show that if A is Hurwitz, the Lyapunov equation will have a unique solution.
Hint: Apply LaSalle's theorem and recall that for an observable pair (A, C), the vector $C \exp(At)x \equiv 0 \ \forall \ t$ if and only if $x = 0$.

4.23 Consider the linear system $\dot{x} = (A - BR^{-1}B^T P)x$, where $P = P^T > 0$ satisfies the Riccati equation

$$PA + A^T P + Q - PBR^{-1}B^T P = 0$$

$R = R^T > 0$, and $Q = Q^T \geq 0$. Using $V(x) = x^T P x$ as a Lyapunov function candidate, show that the origin is globally asymptotically stable when

(1) $Q > 0$.

(2) $Q = C^T C$ and (A, C) is observable; see the hint of Exercise 4.22.

4.24 Consider the system[36]

$$\dot{x} = f(x) - kG(x)R^{-1}(x)G^T(x) \left(\frac{\partial V}{\partial x} \right)^T$$

---

[36]This is a closed-loop system under optimal stabilizing control. See [172].

where $V(x)$ is a continuously differentiable, positive definite function that satisfies the Hamilton–Jacobi–Bellman equation

$$\frac{\partial V}{\partial x} f(x) + q(x) - \frac{1}{4} \frac{\partial V}{\partial x} G(x) R^{-1}(x) G^T(x) \left(\frac{\partial V}{\partial x} \right)^T = 0$$

$q(x)$ is a positive semidefinite function, $R(x)$ is a nonsingular matrix, and k is a positive constant. Using $V(x)$ as a Lyapunov function candidate, show that the origin is asymptotically stable when

(1) $q(x)$ is positive definite and $k \geq 1/4$.

(2) $q(x)$ is positive semidefinite, $k > 1/4$, and the only solution of $\dot{x} = f(x)$ that can stay identically in the set $\{q(x) = 0\}$ is the trivial solution $x(t) \equiv 0$.

When will the origin be globally asymptotically stable?

4.25 Consider the linear system $\dot{x} = Ax + Bu$, where (A, B) is controllable. Let $W = \int_0^\tau e^{-At} B B^T e^{-A^T t} \, dt$ for some $\tau > 0$. Show that W is positive definite and let $K = B^T W^{-1}$. Use $V(x) = x^T W^{-1} x$ as a Lyapunov function candidate for the system $\dot{x} = (A - BK)x$ to show that $(A - BK)$ is Hurwitz.

4.26 Let $\dot{x} = f(x)$, where $f : R^n \to R^n$. Consider the change of variables $z = T(x)$, where $T(0) = 0$ and $T : R^n \to R^n$ is a diffeomorphism in the neighborhood of the origin; that is, the inverse map $T^{-1}(\cdot)$ exists, and both $T(\cdot)$ and $T^{-1}(\cdot)$ are continuously differentiable. The transformed system is

$$\dot{z} = \hat{f}(z), \quad \text{where } \hat{f}(z) = \left. \frac{\partial T}{\partial x} f(x) \right|_{x = T^{-1}(z)}$$

(a) Show that $x = 0$ is an isolated equilibrium point of $\dot{x} = f(x)$ if and only if $z = 0$ is an isolated equilibrium point of $\dot{z} = \hat{f}(z)$.

(b) Show that $x = 0$ is stable (asymptotically stable or unstable) if and only if $z = 0$ is stable (asymptotically stable or unstable).

4.27 Consider the system

$$\dot{x}_1 = -x_2 x_3 + 1, \qquad \dot{x}_2 = x_1 x_3 - x_2, \qquad \dot{x}_3 = x_3^2(1 - x_3)$$

(a) Show that the system has a unique equilibrium point.

(b) Using linearization, show that the equilibrium point asymptotically stable. Is it globally asymptotically stable?

4.28 Consider the system

$$\dot{x}_1 = -x_1, \qquad \dot{x}_2 = (x_1 x_2 - 1)x_2^3 + (x_1 x_2 - 1 + x_1^2)x_2$$

(a) Show that $x = 0$ is the unique equilibrium point.

(b) Show, by using linearization, that $x = 0$ is asymptotically stable.

(c) Show that $\Gamma = \{x \in R^2 \mid x_1 x_2 \geq 2\}$ is a positively invariant set.

(d) Is $x = 0$ globally asymptotically stable?

4.29 Consider the system

$$\dot{x}_1 = x_1 - x_1^3 + x_2, \qquad \dot{x}_2 = 3x_1 - x_2$$

(a) Find all equilibrium point of the system.

(b) Using linearization, study the stability of each equilibrium point.

(c) Using quadratic Lyapunov functions, estimate the region of attraction of each asymptotically stable equilibrium point. Try to make your estimate as large as possible.

(d) Construct the phase portrait of the system and show on it the exact regions of attraction as well as your estimates.

4.30 Repeat the previous exercise for the system

$$\dot{x}_1 = -\tfrac{1}{2}\tan\left(\frac{\pi x_1}{2}\right) + x_2, \qquad \dot{x}_2 = x_1 - \tfrac{1}{2}\tan\left(\frac{\pi x_2}{2}\right)$$

4.31 For each of the systems of Exercise 4.3, use linearization to show that the origin is asymptotically stable.

4.32 For each for the following systems, investigate whether the origin is stable, asymptotically stable, or unstable:

(1)
$$\begin{aligned}
\dot{x}_1 &= -x_1 + x_1^2 \\
\dot{x}_2 &= -x_2 + x_3^2 \\
\dot{x}_3 &= x_3 - x_1^2
\end{aligned}$$

(2)
$$\begin{aligned}
\dot{x}_1 &= x_2 \\
\dot{x}_2 &= -\sin x_3 + x_1[-2x_3 - \mathrm{sat}(y)]^2 \\
\dot{x}_3 &= -2x_3 - \mathrm{sat}(y) \\
&\text{where } y = -2x_1 - 5x_2 + 2x_3
\end{aligned}$$

(3)
$$\begin{aligned}
\dot{x}_1 &= -2x_1 + x_1^3 \\
\dot{x}_2 &= -x_2 + x_1^2 \\
\dot{x}_3 &= -x_3
\end{aligned}$$

(4)
$$\begin{aligned}
\dot{x}_1 &= -x_1 \\
\dot{x}_2 &= -x_1 - x_2 - x_3 - x_1 x_3 \\
\dot{x}_3 &= (x_1 + 1)x_2
\end{aligned}$$

4.33 Consider the second-order system $\dot{x} = f(x)$, where $f(0) = 0$ and $f(x)$ is twice continuously differentiable in some neighborhood of the origin. Suppose $[\partial f/\partial x](0) = -B$, where B be Hurwitz. Let P be the positive definite solution of the Lyapunov equation $PB + B^T P = -I$ and take $V(x) = x^T P x$. Show that there exists $c^* > 0$ such that, for every $0 < c < c^*$, the surface $V(x) = c$ is closed and $[\partial V/\partial x]f(x) > 0$ for all $x \in \{V(x) = c\}$.

4.34 Prove Lemma 4.2.

4.35 Let α be a class $\mathcal{K}$ function on $[0, a)$. Show that

$$\alpha(r_1 + r_2) \leq \alpha(2r_1) + \alpha(2r_2), \quad \forall\, r_1, r_2 \in [0, a)$$

4.36 Is the origin of the scalar system $\dot{x} = -x/(t+1)$, $t \geq 0$, uniformly asymptotically stable?

4.37 For each of the following linear systems, use a quadratic Lyapunov function to show that the origin is exponentially stable:

(1) $\dot{x} = \begin{bmatrix} -1 & \alpha(t) \\ \alpha(t) & -2 \end{bmatrix} x$, $|\alpha(t)| \leq 1$ $\qquad$ **(2)** $\dot{x} = \begin{bmatrix} -1 & \alpha(t) \\ -\alpha(t) & -2 \end{bmatrix} x$

(3) $\dot{x} = \begin{bmatrix} 0 & 1 \\ -1 & -\alpha(t) \end{bmatrix} x$, $\alpha(t) \geq 2$ $\qquad$ **(4)** $\dot{x} = \begin{bmatrix} -1 & 0 \\ \alpha(t) & -2 \end{bmatrix} x$

In all cases, $\alpha(t)$ is continuous and bounded for all $t \geq 0$.

4.38 ([95]) An RLC circuit with time-varying elements is represented by

$$\dot{x}_1 = \frac{1}{L(t)} x_2, \qquad \dot{x}_2 = -\frac{1}{C(t)} x_1 - \frac{R(t)}{L(t)} x_2$$

Suppose that $L(t)$, $C(t)$, and $R(t)$ are continuously differentiable and satisfy the inequalities $k_1 \leq L(t) \leq k_2$, $k_3 \leq C(t) \leq k_4$, and $k_5 \leq R(t) \leq k_6$ for all $t \geq 0$, where k_1, k_3, and k_5 are positive. Consider a Lyapunov function candidate

$$V(t, x) = \left[R(t) + \frac{2L(t)}{R(t)C(t)} \right] x_1^2 + 2x_1 x_2 + \frac{2}{R(t)} x_2^2$$

(a) Show that $V(t, x)$ is positive definite and decrescent.

(b) Find conditions on $\dot{L}(t)$, $\dot{C}(t)$, and $\dot{R}(t)$ that will ensure exponential stability of the origin.

4.39 ([154]) A pendulum with time-varying friction is represented by

$$\dot{x}_1 = x_2, \qquad \dot{x}_2 = -\sin x_1 - g(t)x_2$$

Suppose that $g(t)$ is continuously differentiable and satisfies

$$0 < a < \alpha \leq g(t) \leq \beta < \infty \quad \text{and} \quad \dot{g}(t) \leq \gamma < 2$$

for all $t \geq 0$. Consider the Lyapunov function candidate

$$V(t, x) = \tfrac{1}{2}(a \sin x_1 + x_2)^2 + [1 + ag(t) - a^2](1 - \cos x_1)$$

(a) Show that $V(t,x)$ is positive definite and decrescent.

(b) Show that $\dot{V} \le -(\alpha - a)x_2^2 - a(2 - \gamma)(1 - \cos x_1) + O(\|x\|^3)$, where $O(\|x\|^3)$ is a term bounded by $k\|x\|^3$ in some neighborhood of the origin.

(c) Show that the origin is uniformly asymptotically stable.

4.40 (Floquet theory) Consider the linear system $\dot{x} = A(t)x$, where $A(t) = A(t+T)$.[37] Let $\Phi(\cdot,\cdot)$ be the state transition matrix. Define a constant matrix B via the equation $\exp(BT) = \Phi(T,0)$, and let $P(t) = \exp(Bt)\Phi(0,t)$. Show that

(a) $P(t+T) = P(t)$.

(b) $\Phi(t,\tau) = P^{-1}(t)\exp[(t - \tau)B]P(\tau)$.

(c) the origin of $\dot{x} = A(t)x$ is exponentially stable if and only if B is Hurwitz.

4.41 Consider the system

$$\dot{x}_1 = x_2, \qquad \dot{x}_2 = 2x_1 x_2 + 3t + 2 - 3x_1 - 2(t+1)x_2$$

(a) Verify that $x_1(t) = t$, $x_2(t) = 1$ is a solution.

(b) Show that if $x(0)$ is sufficiently close to $\begin{bmatrix} 0 \\ 1 \end{bmatrix}$, then $x(t)$ approaches $\begin{bmatrix} t \\ 1 \end{bmatrix}$ as $t \to \infty$.

4.42 Consider the system

$$\dot{x} = -a[I_n + S(x) + xx^T]x$$

where a is a positive constant, I_n is the $n \times n$ identity matrix, and $S(x)$ is an x-dependent skew symmetric matrix. Show that the origin is globally exponentially stable.

4.43 Consider the system $\dot{x} = f(x) + G(x)u$. Suppose there exist a positive definite symmetric matrix P, a positive semidefinite function $W(x)$, and positive constants γ and σ such that

$$2x^T P f(x) + \gamma x^T P x + W(x) - 2\sigma x^T P G(x)G^T(x)Px \le 0, \quad \forall\, x \in R^n$$

Show that with $u = -\sigma G^T(x)Px$ the closed-loop system has a globally exponentially stable equilibrium point at the origin.

4.44 Consider the system

$$\dot{x}_1 = -x_1 + x_2 + (x_1^2 + x_2^2)\sin t, \qquad \dot{x}_2 = -x_1 - x_2 + (x_1^2 + x_2^2)\cos t$$

Show that the origin is exponentially stable and estimate the region of attraction.

---

[37]See [158] for a comprehensive treatment of Floquet theory.

4.45 Consider the system

$$\dot{x}_1 = h(t)x_2 - g(t)x_1^3, \qquad \dot{x}_2 = -h(t)x_1 - g(t)x_2^3$$

where $h(t)$ and $g(t)$ are bounded, continuously differentiable functions and $g(t) \geq k > 0$, for all $t \geq 0$.

(a) Is the equilibrium point $x = 0$ uniformly asymptotically stable?

(b) Is it exponentially stable?

(c) Is it globally uniformly asymptotically stable?

(d) Is it globally exponentially stable?

4.46 Show that the origin of the system

$$\dot{x}_1 = -x_2 - x_1(1 - x_1^2 - x_2^2), \qquad \dot{x}_2 = x_1 - x_2(1 - x_1^2 - x_2^2)$$

is asymptotically stable. Is it exponentially stable?

4.47 Consider the system

$$\dot{x}_1 = -\phi(t)x_1 + a\phi(t)x_2, \qquad \dot{x}_2 = b\phi(t)x_1 - ab\phi(t)x_2 - c\psi(t)x_2^3$$

where a, b, and c are positive constants and $\phi(t)$ and $\psi(t)$ are nonnegative, continuous, bounded functions that satisfy

$$\phi(t) \geq \phi_0 > 0, \quad \psi(t) \geq \psi_0 > 0, \quad \forall\, t \geq 0$$

Show that the origin is globally uniformly asymptotically stable. Is it exponentially stable?

4.48 Consider two systems represented by $\dot{x} = f(x)$ and $\dot{x} = h(x)f(x)$ where $f : R^n \to R^n$ and $h : R^n \to R$ are continuously differentiable, $f(0) = 0$, and $h(0) > 0$. Show that the origin of the first system is exponentially stable if and only if the origin of the second system is exponentially stable.

4.49 Show that the system

$$\dot{x}_1 = -ax_1 + b, \qquad \dot{x}_2 = -cx_2 + x_1(\alpha - \beta x_1 x_2)$$

where all coefficients are positive, has a globally exponentially stable equilibrium point.

Hint: Shift the equilibrium point to the origin and use V of the form $V = k_1 Y_1^2 + k_2 y_2^2 + k_3 y_1^4$, where (y_1, y_2) are the new coordinates.

4.50 Consider the system

$$\dot{x} = f(t, x); \quad f(t, 0) = 0$$

where $[\partial f / \partial x]$ is bounded and Lipschitz in x in a neighborhood of the origin, uniformly in t for all $t \geq t_0 \geq 0$. Suppose that the origin of the linearization at $x = 0$ is exponentially stable, and the solutions of the system satisfy

$$\|x(t)\| \leq \beta(\|x(t_0)\|, t - t_0), \quad \forall\, t \geq t_0 \geq 0, \quad \forall\, \|x(t_0)\| < c \qquad (4.59)$$

for some class $\mathcal{KL}$ function β and some positive constant c.

(a) Show that there is a class $\mathcal{K}$ function α and a positive constant γ such that

$$\|x(t)\| \leq \alpha(\|x(t_0)\|) \exp[-\gamma(t - t_0)], \quad \forall\, t \geq t_0, \quad \forall\, \|x(t_0)\| < c$$

(b) Show that there is a positive constant M, possibly dependent on c, such that

$$\|x(t)\| \leq M\|x(t_0)\| \exp[-\gamma(t - t_0)], \quad \forall\, t \geq t_0, \quad \forall\, \|x(t_0)\| < c \qquad (4.60)$$

(c) If inequality (4.59) holds globally, can you state inequality (4.60) globally?

4.51 Suppose the assumptions of Theorem 4.18 are satisfied with $\alpha_1(r) = k_1 r^a$, $\alpha_2(r) = k_2 r^a$, and $W(x) \geq k_3 \|x\|^a$, for some positive constants k_1, k_2, k_3, and a. Show that (4.42) and (4.43) are satisfied with $\beta(r, s) = kr \exp(-\gamma s)$ and $\alpha_1^{-1}(\alpha_2(\mu)) = k\mu$, where $k = (k_2/k_1)^{1/a}$ and $\gamma = k_3/(k_2 a)$.

4.52 Consider Theorem 4.18 when $V(t, x) = V(x)$ and suppose inequality (4.40) is replaced by

$$\frac{\partial V}{\partial x} f(t, x) \leq -W_3(x), \quad \forall\, W_4(x) \geq \mu > 0$$

for some continuous positive definite functions $W_3(x)$ and $W_4(x)$. Show that (4.42) and (4.43) hold for every initial state $x(t_0) \in \{V(x) \leq c\} \subset D$, provided $\{V(x) \leq c\}$ is compact and $\max_{W_4(x) \leq \mu} V(x) < c$.

4.53 ([72]) Consider the system $\dot{x} = f(t, x)$ and suppose there is a function $V(t, x)$ that satisfies

$$W_1(x) \leq V(t, x) \leq W_2(x), \quad \forall\, \|x\| \geq r > 0$$

$$\frac{\partial V}{\partial t} + \frac{\partial V}{\partial x} f(t, x) < 0, \quad \forall\, \|x\| \geq r_1 \geq r$$

where $W_1(x)$ and $W_2(x)$ are continuous, positive definite functions. Show that the solutions of the system are uniformly bounded.
Hint: Notice that $V(t, x)$ is not necessarily positive definite.

4.54 For each of the following scalar systems, investigate input-to-state stability:

$$(\textbf{1}) \quad \dot{x} = -(1+u)x^3 \qquad\qquad (\textbf{2}) \quad \dot{x} = -(1+u)x^3 - x^5$$

$$(\textbf{3}) \quad \dot{x} = -x + x^2 u \qquad\qquad (\textbf{4}) \quad \dot{x} = x - x^3 + u$$

4.55 For each of the following systems, investigate input-to-state stability:

$$(\textbf{1}) \qquad \dot{x}_1 \;=\; -x_1 + x_1^2 x_2, \qquad\qquad \dot{x}_2 \;=\; -x_1^3 - x_2 + u$$

$$(\textbf{2}) \qquad \dot{x}_1 \;=\; -x_1 + x_2, \qquad\qquad \dot{x}_2 \;=\; -x_1^3 - x_2 + u$$

$$(\textbf{3}) \qquad \dot{x}_1 \;=\; x_2, \qquad\qquad \dot{x}_2 \;=\; -x_1^3 - x_2 + u$$

$$(\textbf{4}) \qquad \dot{x}_1 \;=\; (x_1 - x_2 + u)(x_1^2 - 1), \qquad\qquad \dot{x}_2 \;=\; (x_1 + x_2 + u)(x_1^2 - 1)$$

$$(\textbf{5}) \qquad \dot{x}_1 \;=\; -x_1 + x_1^2 x_2, \qquad\qquad \dot{x}_2 \;=\; -x_2 + x_1 + u$$

$$(\textbf{6}) \qquad \dot{x}_1 \;=\; -x_1 - x_2 + u_1, \qquad\qquad \dot{x}_2 \;=\; x_1 - x_2^3 + u_2$$

$$(\textbf{7}) \qquad \dot{x}_1 \;=\; -x_1 + x_2, \qquad\qquad \dot{x}_2 \;=\; -x_1 - \sigma(x_1) - x_2 + u$$

where σ is a locally Lipschitz function, $\sigma(0) = 0$, and $y\sigma(y) \geq 0$ for all $y \neq 0$.

4.56 Using Lemma 4.7, show that the origin of the system

$$\dot{x}_1 = -x_1^3 + x_2, \qquad \dot{x}_2 = -x_2^3$$

is globally asymptotically stable.

4.57 Prove another version of Theorem 4.19, where all the assumptions are the same except that inequality (4.49) is replaced by

$$\frac{\partial V}{\partial t} + \frac{\partial V}{\partial x} f(t, x, u) \leq -\alpha_3(\|x\|) + \psi(u)$$

where α_3 is a class $\mathcal{K}_\infty$ function and $\psi(u)$ is a continuous function of u with $\psi(0) = 0$.

4.58 Use inequality (4.47) to show that if $u(t)$ converges to zero as $t \to \infty$, so does $x(t)$.

4.59 Consider the scalar system $\dot{x} = -x^3 + e^{-t}$. Show that $x(t) \to 0$ as $t \to \infty$.

4.60 Suppose the assumptions of Theorem 4.19 are satisfied for $\|x\| < r$ and $\|u\| < r_u$ with class $\mathcal{K}$ functions α_1 and α_2 that are not necessarily class $\mathcal{K}_\infty$. Show that there exist positive constants k_1 and k_2 such that inequality (4.47) is satisfied for $\|x(t_0)\| < k_1$ and $\sup_{t \geq t_0} \|u(t)\| < k_2$. In this case, the system is said to be *locally input-to-state stable*.

4.61 Consider the system

$$\dot{x}_1 = x_1 \left\{ \left[\sin\left(\frac{\pi x_2}{2}\right) \right]^2 - 1 \right\}, \quad \dot{x}_2 = -x_2 + u$$

(a) With $u = 0$, show that the origin is globally asymptotically stable.

(b) Show that for any bounded input $u(t)$, the state $x(t)$ is bounded.

(c) With $u(t) \equiv 1$, $x_1(0) = a$, and $x_2(0) = 1$, show that the solution is $x_1(t) \equiv a$, $x_2(t) \equiv 1$.

(d) Is the system input-to-state stable?

In the next seven exercises, we deal with the discrete-time dynamical system[38]

$$x(k+1) = f(x(k)), \quad f(0) = 0 \qquad (4.61)$$

The rate of change of a scalar function $V(x)$ along the motion of (4.61) is defined by

$$\Delta V(x) = V(f(x)) - V(x)$$

4.62 Restate Definition 4.1 for the origin of the discrete-time system (4.61).

4.63 Show that the origin of (4.61) is stable if, in a neighborhood of the origin, there is a continuous positive definite function $V(x)$ so that $\Delta V(x)$ is negative semidefinite. Show that it is asymptotically stable if, in addition, $\Delta V(x)$ is negative definite. Finally, show that the origin is globally asymptotically stable if the conditions for asymptotic stability hold globally and $V(x)$ is radially unbounded.

4.64 Show that the origin of (4.61) is exponentially stable if, in a neighborhood of the origin, there is a continuous positive definite function $V(x)$ such that

$$c_1 \|x\|^2 \le V(x) \le c_2 \|x\|^2, \qquad \Delta V(x) \le -c_3 \|x\|^2$$

for some positive constants c_1, c_2, and c_3.
Hint: For discrete-time systems, exponential stability is defined by the inequality $\|x(k)\| \le \alpha \|x(0)\| \gamma^k$ for all $k \ge 0$, where $\alpha \ge 1$ and $0 < \gamma < 1$.

4.65 Show that the origin of (4.61) is asymptotically stable if, in a neighborhood of the origin, there is a continuous positive definite function $V(x)$ so that $\Delta V(x)$ is negative semidefinite and $\Delta V(x)$ does not vanish identically for any $x \ne 0$.

4.66 Consider the linear system $x(k+1) = Ax(k)$. Show that the following statements are equivalent:

---

[38] See [95] for a detailed treatment of Lyapunov stability for discrete-time dynamical systems.

(1) $x = 0$ is asymptotically stable.

(2) $|\lambda_i| < 1$ for all eigenvalues of A.

(3) Given any $Q = Q^T > 0$, there exists $P = P^T > 0$, which is the unique solution of the linear equation $A^T P A - P = -Q$.

4.67 Let A be the linearization of (4.61) at the origin; that is, $A = [\partial f / \partial x](0)$. Show that the origin is asymptotically stable if all the eigenvalues of A have magnitudes less than one.

4.68 Let $x = 0$ be an equilibrium point for the nonlinear discrete-time system $x(k+1) = f(x(k))$, where $f : D \to R^n$ is continuously differentiable and $D = \{x \in R^n \mid \|x\| < r\}$. Let C, $\gamma < 1$, and r_0 be positive constants with $r_0 < r/C$. Let $D_0 = \{x \in R^n \mid \|x\| < r_0\}$. Assume that the solutions of the system satisfy

$$\|x(k)\| \leq C\|x(0)\|\gamma^k, \quad \forall\, x(0) \in D_0, \ \forall\, k \geq 0$$

Show that there is a function $V : D_0 \to R$ that satisfies

$$c_1\|x\|^2 \leq V(x) \leq c_2\|x\|^2$$

$$\Delta V(x) = V(f(x)) - V(x) \leq -c_3\|x\|^2$$

$$|V(x) - V(y)| \leq c_4\|x - y\| \left(\|x\| + \|y\|\right)$$

for all $x, y \in D_0$ for some positive constants c_1, c_2, c_3, and c_4.

Chapter 5

Input–Output Stability

In most of this book, we use the state–space approach to model nonlinear dynamical systems and place a lot of emphasis on the behavior of the state variables. An alternative approach to the mathematical modeling of dynamical systems is the input–output approach.[1] An input–output model relates the output of the system directly to the input, with no knowledge of the internal structure that is represented by the state equation. The system is viewed as a black box that can be accessed only through its input and output terminals. In Section 5.1, we introduce input–output mathematical models and define $\mathcal{L}$ stability, a concept of stability in the input–output sense. In Section 5.2, we study $\mathcal{L}$ stability of nonlinear systems represented by state models. In Section 5.3, we discuss the calculation of the $\mathcal{L}_2$ gain for a class of time-invariant systems. Finally, in Section 5.4, we present a version of the small-gain theorem.

5.1 $\mathcal{L}$ Stability

We consider a system whose input–output relation is represented by

$$y = Hu$$

where H is some mapping or operator that specifies y in terms of u. The input u belongs to a space of signals that map the time interval $[0, \infty)$ into the Euclidean space R^m; that is, $u : [0, \infty) \to R^m$. Examples are the space of piecewise continuous, bounded functions; that is, $\sup_{t \geq 0} \|u(t)\| < \infty$, and the space of piecewise

---

[1]In this chapter, we give just enough of a glimpse of the input–output approach to enable the reader to understand the relationship of Lyapunov stability to input–output stability and to introduce the terminology needed to state the small-gain theorem. For a comprehensive treatment of the subject, the reader may consult [53], [208], or [162]. The foundation of the input–output approach to nonlinear systems can be found in the 1960's work of Sandberg and Zames. (See, for example, [164], [217], and [218].)

continuous, square-integrable functions; that is, $\int_0^\infty u^T(t)u(t)\ dt < \infty$. To measure the size of a signal, we introduce the norm function $\|u\|$, which satisfies three properties:

- The norm of a signal is zero if and only if the signal is identically zero and is strictly positive otherwise.

- Scaling a signal results in a corresponding scaling of the norm; that is, $\|au\| = a\|u\|$ for any positive constant a and every signal u.

- The norm satisfies the triangle inequality $\|u_1 + u_2\| \le \|u_1\| + \|u_2\|$ for any signals u_1 and u_2.

For the space of piecewise continuous, bounded functions, the norm is defined as

$$\|u\|_{\mathcal{L}_\infty} = \sup_{t \ge 0} \|u(t)\| < \infty$$

and the space is denoted by $\mathcal{L}_\infty^m$. For the space of piecewise continuous, square-integrable functions, the norm is defined by

$$\|u\|_{\mathcal{L}_2} = \sqrt{\int_0^\infty u^T(t)u(t)\ dt} < \infty$$

and the space is denoted by $\mathcal{L}_2^m$. More generally, the space $\mathcal{L}_p^m$ for $1 \le p < \infty$ is defined as the set of all piecewise continuous functions $u : [0, \infty) \to R^m$ such that

$$\|u\|_{\mathcal{L}_p} = \left(\int_0^\infty \|u(t)\|^p\ dt \right)^{1/p} < \infty$$

The subscript p in $\mathcal{L}_p^m$ refers to the type of p-norm used to define the space, while the superscript m is the dimension of the signal u. If they are clear from the context, we may drop one or both of them and refer to the space simply as $\mathcal{L}_p$, $\mathcal{L}^m$, or $\mathcal{L}$. To distinguish the norm of u as a vector in the space $\mathcal{L}$ from the norm of $u(t)$ as a vector in R^m, we write the first norm as $\| \cdot \|_{\mathcal{L}}$.[2]

If we think of $u \in \mathcal{L}^m$ as a "well-behaved" input, the question to ask is whether the output y will be "well behaved" in the sense that $y \in \mathcal{L}^q$, where $\mathcal{L}^q$ is the same space as $\mathcal{L}^m$, except that the number of output variables q is, in general, different from the number of input variables m. A system having the property that any "well-behaved" input will generate a "well-behaved" output will be defined as a stable system. However, we cannot define H as a mapping from $\mathcal{L}^m$ to $\mathcal{L}^q$, because we have to deal with systems which are unstable, in that an input $u \in \mathcal{L}^m$ may

---

[2]Note that the norm $\| \cdot \|$ used in the definition of $\| \cdot \|_{\mathcal{L}_p}$, for any $p \in [1, \infty]$, can be any p-norm in R^m; the number p is not necessarily the same in the two norms. For example, we may define the $\mathcal{L}_\infty$ space with $\|u\|_{\mathcal{L}_\infty} = \sup_{t \ge 0} \|u(t)\|_1$, $\|u\|_{\mathcal{L}_\infty} = \sup_{t \ge 0} \|u(t)\|_2$, or $\|u\|_{\mathcal{L}_\infty} = \sup_{t \ge 0} \|u(t)\|_\infty$. However, it is common to define the $\mathcal{L}_2$ space with the 2-norm in R^m.

generate an output y that does not belong to $\mathcal{L}^q$. Therefore, H is usually defined as a mapping from an extended space $\mathcal{L}_e^m$ to an extended space $\mathcal{L}_e^q$, where $\mathcal{L}_e^m$ is defined by

$$\mathcal{L}_e^m = \{u \mid u_\tau \in \mathcal{L}^m, \forall\, \tau \in [0, \infty)\}$$

and u_τ is a truncation of u defined by

$$u_\tau(t) = \left\{ \begin{array}{ll} u(t), & 0 \leq t \leq \tau \\ 0, & t > \tau \end{array} \right.$$

The extended space $\mathcal{L}_e^m$ is a linear space that contains the unextended space $\mathcal{L}^m$ as a subset. It allows us to deal with unbounded "ever-growing" signals. For example, the signal $u(t) = t$ does not belong to the space $\mathcal{L}_\infty$, but its truncation

$$u_\tau(t) = \left\{ \begin{array}{ll} t, & 0 \leq t \leq \tau \\ 0, & t > \tau \end{array} \right.$$

belongs to $\mathcal{L}_\infty$ for every finite τ. Hence, $u(t) = t$ belongs to the extended space $\mathcal{L}_{\infty e}$.

A mapping $H : \mathcal{L}_e^m \to \mathcal{L}_e^q$ is said to be causal if the value of the output $(Hu)(t)$ at any time t depends only on the values of the input up to time t. This is equivalent to

$$(Hu)_\tau = (Hu_\tau)_\tau$$

Causality is an intrinsic property of dynamical systems represented by state models.

With the space of input and output signals defined, we can now define input–output stability.

Definition 5.1 *A mapping* $H : \mathcal{L}_e^m \to \mathcal{L}_e^q$ *is* $\mathcal{L}$ *stable if there exist a class* $\mathcal{K}$ *function* α, *defined on* $[0, \infty)$, *and a nonnegative constant* β *such that*

$$\|(Hu)_\tau\|_{\mathcal{L}} \leq \alpha\left(\|u_\tau\|_{\mathcal{L}}\right) + \beta \tag{5.1}$$

for all $u \in \mathcal{L}_e^m$ *and* $\tau \in [0, \infty)$. *It is finite-gain* $\mathcal{L}$ *stable if there exist nonnegative constants* γ *and* β *such that*

$$\|(Hu)_\tau\|_{\mathcal{L}} \leq \gamma\|u_\tau\|_{\mathcal{L}} + \beta \tag{5.2}$$

for all $u \in \mathcal{L}_e^m$ *and* $\tau \in [0, \infty)$.

The constant β in (5.1) or (5.2) is called the bias term. It is included in the definition to allow for systems where Hu does not vanish at $u = 0$.[3] When inequality (5.2) is satisfied, we are usually interested in the smallest possible γ for which there is β such that (5.2) is satisfied. When this value of γ is well defined, we will call it the gain of the system. When inequality (5.2) is satisfied with some $\gamma \geq 0$, we say that the system has an $\mathcal{L}$ gain less than or equal to γ.

---

[3]See Exercise 5.3 for a different role of the bias term.

For causal, $\mathcal{L}$ stable systems, it can be shown by a simple argument that

$$u \in \mathcal{L}^m \Rightarrow Hu \in \mathcal{L}^q$$

and

$$\|Hu\|_{\mathcal{L}} \le \alpha\left(\|u\|_{\mathcal{L}}\right) + \beta, \quad \forall\, u \in \mathcal{L}^m$$

For causal, finite-gain $\mathcal{L}$ stable systems, the foregoing inequality takes the form

$$\|Hu\|_{\mathcal{L}} \le \gamma\|u_\tau\|_{\mathcal{L}} + \beta, \quad \forall\, u \in \mathcal{L}^m$$

The definition of $\mathcal{L}_\infty$ stability is the familiar notion of bounded-input–bounded-output stability; namely, if the system is $\mathcal{L}_\infty$ stable, then for every bounded input $u(t)$, the output $Hu(t)$ is bounded.

Example 5.1 A memoryless, possibly time-varying, function $h : [0, \infty) \times R \to R$ can be viewed as an operator H that assigns to every input signal $u(t)$ the output signal $y(t) = h(t, u(t))$. We use this simple operator to illustrate the definition of $\mathcal{L}$ stability. Let

$$h(u) = a + b\tanh cu = a + b\,\frac{e^{cu} - e^{-cu}}{e^{cu} + e^{-cu}}$$

for some nonnegative constants a, b, and c. Using the fact

$$h'(u) = \frac{4bc}{\left(e^{cu} + e^{-cu}\right)^2} \le bc, \quad \forall\, u \in R$$

we have

$$|h(u)| \le a + bc|u|, \quad \forall\, u \in R$$

Hence, H is finite-gain $\mathcal{L}_\infty$ stable with $\gamma = bc$ and $\beta = a$. Furthermore, if $a = 0$, then for each $p \in [1, \infty)$,

$$\int_0^\infty |h(u(t))|^p \, dt \le (bc)^p \int_0^\infty |u(t)|^p \, dt$$

Thus, for each $p \in [1, \infty]$, the operator H is finite-gain $\mathcal{L}_p$ stable with zero bias and $\gamma = bc$. Let h be a time-varying function that satisfies

$$|h(t, u)| \le a|u|, \quad \forall\, t \ge 0, \ \forall\, u \in R$$

for some positive constant a. For each $p \in [1, \infty]$, the operator H is finite-gain $\mathcal{L}_p$ stable with zero bias and $\gamma = a$. Finally, let

$$h(u) = u^2$$

Since

$$\sup_{t \ge 0} |h(u(t))| \le \left(\sup_{t \ge 0} |u(t)|\right)^2$$

H is $\mathcal{L}_\infty$ stable with zero bias and $\alpha(r) = r^2$. It is not finite-gain $\mathcal{L}_\infty$ stable because the function $h(u) = u^2$ cannot be bounded by a straight line of the form $|h(u)| \le \gamma|u| + \beta$, for all $u \in R$. $\triangle$

Example 5.2 Consider a single-input–single-output system defined by the causal convolution operator

$$y(t) = \int_0^t h(t-\sigma)u(\sigma)\, d\sigma$$

where $h(t) = 0$ for $t < 0$. Suppose $h \in \mathcal{L}_{1e}$; that is, for every $\tau \in [0, \infty)$,

$$\|h_\tau\|_{\mathcal{L}_1} = \int_0^\infty |h_\tau(\sigma)|\, d\sigma = \int_0^\tau |h(\sigma)|\, d\sigma < \infty$$

If $u \in \mathcal{L}_{\infty e}$ and $\tau \geq t$, then

$$
\begin{aligned}
|y(t)| &\leq \int_0^t |h(t-\sigma)|\, |u(\sigma)|\, d\sigma \\
&\leq \int_0^t |h(t-\sigma)|\, d\sigma \sup_{0 \leq \sigma \leq \tau} |u(\sigma)| = \int_0^t |h(s)|\, ds \sup_{0 \leq \sigma \leq \tau} |u(\sigma)|
\end{aligned}
$$

Consequently,

$$\|y_\tau\|_{\mathcal{L}_\infty} \leq \|h_\tau\|_{\mathcal{L}_1} \|u_\tau\|_{\mathcal{L}_\infty}, \quad \forall\, \tau \in [0, \infty)$$

This inequality resembles (5.2), but it is not the same as (5.2) because the constant γ in (5.2) is required to be independent of τ. While $\|h_\tau\|_{\mathcal{L}_1}$ is finite for every finite τ, it may not be bounded uniformly in τ. For example, $h(t) = e^t$ has $\|h_\tau\|_{\mathcal{L}_1} = (e^\tau - 1)$, which is finite for all $\tau \in [0, \infty)$ but not uniformly bounded in τ. Inequality (5.2) will be satisfied if $h \in \mathcal{L}_1$; that is,

$$\|h\|_{\mathcal{L}_1} = \int_0^\infty |h(\sigma)|\, d\sigma < \infty$$

Then, the inequality

$$\|y_\tau\|_{\mathcal{L}_\infty} \leq \|h\|_{\mathcal{L}_1} \|u_\tau\|_{\mathcal{L}_\infty}, \quad \forall\, \tau \in [0, \infty)$$

shows that the system is finite-gain $\mathcal{L}_\infty$ stable. The condition $\|h\|_{\mathcal{L}_1} < \infty$ actually guarantees finite-gain $\mathcal{L}_p$ stability for each $p \in [1, \infty]$. Consider first the case $p = 1$. For $t \leq \tau < \infty$, we have

$$\int_0^\tau |y(t)|\, dt = \int_0^\tau \left| \int_0^t h(t-\sigma)u(\sigma)\, d\sigma \right|\, dt \leq \int_0^\tau \int_0^t |h(t-\sigma)|\, |u(\sigma)|\, d\sigma\, dt$$

Reversing the order of integration yields

$$\int_0^\tau |y(t)|\, dt \leq \int_0^\tau |u(\sigma)| \int_\sigma^\tau |h(t-\sigma)|\, dt\, d\sigma \leq \int_0^\tau |u(\sigma)|\, \|h\|_{\mathcal{L}_1}\, d\sigma \leq \|h\|_{\mathcal{L}_1} \|u_\tau\|_{\mathcal{L}_1}$$

Thus,

$$\|y_\tau\|_{\mathcal{L}_1} \leq \|h\|_{\mathcal{L}_1} \|u_\tau\|_{\mathcal{L}_1}, \quad \forall\, \tau \in [0, \infty)$$

Consider now the case $p \in (1, \infty)$ and let $q \in (1, \infty)$ be defined by $1/p + 1/q = 1$. For $t \leq \tau < \infty$, we have

$$
\begin{aligned}
|y(t)| &\leq \int_0^t |h(t-\sigma)| \, |u(\sigma)| \, d\sigma \\
&= \int_0^t |h(t-\sigma)|^{1/q} |h(t-\sigma)|^{1/p} |u(\sigma)| \, d\sigma \\
&\leq \left(\int_0^t |h(t-\sigma)| \, d\sigma \right)^{1/q} \left(\int_0^t |h(t-\sigma)| \, |u(\sigma)|^p \, d\sigma \right)^{1/p} \\
&\leq (\|h_\tau\|_{\mathcal{L}_1})^{1/q} \left(\int_0^t |h(t-\sigma)| \, |u(\sigma)|^p \, d\sigma \right)^{1/p}
\end{aligned}
$$

where the second inequality is obtained by applying Hölder's inequality.[4] Thus,

$$
\begin{aligned}
\left(\|y_\tau\|_{\mathcal{L}_p} \right)^p &= \int_0^\tau |y(t)|^p \, dt \\
&\leq \int_0^\tau (\|h_\tau\|_{\mathcal{L}_1})^{p/q} \left(\int_0^t |h(t-\sigma)| \, |u(\sigma)|^p \, d\sigma \right) dt \\
&= (\|h_\tau\|_{\mathcal{L}_1})^{p/q} \int_0^\tau \int_0^t |h(t-\sigma)| \, |u(\sigma)|^p \, d\sigma \, dt
\end{aligned}
$$

By reversing the order of integration, we obtain

$$
\begin{aligned}
\left(\|y_\tau\|_{\mathcal{L}_p} \right)^p &\leq (\|h_\tau\|_{\mathcal{L}_1})^{p/q} \int_0^\tau |u(\sigma)|^p \int_\sigma^\tau |h(t-\sigma)| \, dt \, d\sigma \\
&\leq (\|h_\tau\|_{\mathcal{L}_1})^{p/q} \|h_\tau\|_{\mathcal{L}_1} \left(\|u_\tau\|_{\mathcal{L}_p} \right)^p = (\|h_\tau\|_{\mathcal{L}_1})^p \left(\|u_\tau\|_{\mathcal{L}_p} \right)^p
\end{aligned}
$$

Hence,

$$
\|y_\tau\|_{\mathcal{L}_p} \leq \|h\|_{\mathcal{L}_1} \|u_\tau\|_{\mathcal{L}_p}
$$

In summary, if $\|h\|_{\mathcal{L}_1} < \infty$, then for each $p \in [1, \infty]$, the causal convolution operator is finite-gain $\mathcal{L}_p$ stable and (5.2) is satisfied with $\gamma = \|h\|_{\mathcal{L}_1}$ and $\beta = 0$. $\qquad \triangle$

One drawback of Definition 5.1 is the implicit requirement that inequality (5.1) or inequality (5.2) be satisfied for all signals in the input space $\mathcal{L}^m$. This excludes systems where the input–output relation may be defined only for a subset of the input space. The next example explores the point and motivates the definition of small-signal $\mathcal{L}$ stability that follows the example.

---

[4]Hölder's inequality states that if $f \in \mathcal{L}_{pe}$ and $g \in \mathcal{L}_{qe}$, where $p \in (1, \infty)$ and $1/p + 1/q = 1$, then

$$
\int_0^\tau |f(t)g(t)| \, dt \leq \left(\int_0^\tau |f(t)|^p \, dt \right)^{1/p} \left(\int_0^\tau |g(t)|^q \, dt \right)^{1/q}
$$

for every $\tau \in [0, \infty)$. (See [14].)

Example 5.3 Consider a single-input–single-output system defined by the nonlinearity

$$y = \tan u$$

The output $y(t)$ is defined only when the input signal is restricted to

$$|u(t)| < \frac{\pi}{2}, \quad \forall\, t \geq 0$$

Thus, the system is not $\mathcal{L}_\infty$ stable in the sense of Definition 5.1. However, if we restrict $u(t)$ to the set

$$|u| \leq r < \frac{\pi}{2}$$

then

$$|y| \leq \left(\frac{\tan r}{r}\right)|u|$$

and the system will satisfy the inequality

$$\|y\|_{\mathcal{L}_p} \leq \left(\frac{\tan r}{r}\right)\|u\|_{\mathcal{L}_p}$$

for every $u \in \mathcal{L}_p$ such that $|u(t)| \leq r$ for all $t \geq 0$, where p could be any number in $[1, \infty]$. In the space $\mathcal{L}_\infty$, the requirement $|u(t)| \leq r$ implies that $\|u\|_{\mathcal{L}_\infty} \leq r$, showing that the foregoing inequality holds only for input signals of small norm. However, for other $\mathcal{L}_p$ spaces with $p < \infty$ the instantaneous bound on $|u(t)|$ does not necessarily restrict the norm of the input signal. For example, the signal

$$u(t) = re^{-rt/a}, \quad a > 0$$

which belongs to $\mathcal{L}_p$ for each $p \in [1, \infty]$, satisfies the instantaneous bound $|u(t)| \leq r$ while its $\mathcal{L}_p$ norm

$$\|u\|_{\mathcal{L}_p} = r\left(\frac{a}{rp}\right)^{1/p}, \quad 1 \leq p < \infty$$

can be arbitrarily large. $\triangle$

Definition 5.2 *A mapping $H : \mathcal{L}_e^m \to \mathcal{L}_e^q$ is small-signal $\mathcal{L}$ stable (respectively, small-signal finite-gain $\mathcal{L}$ stable) if there is a positive constant r such that inequality (5.1) [respectively, inequality (5.2)] is satisfied for all $u \in \mathcal{L}_e^m$ with $\sup_{0 \leq t \leq \tau} \|u(t)\| \leq r$.*

5.2 $\mathcal{L}$ Stability of State Models

The notion of input–output stability is intuitively appealing. This is probably why most of us were introduced to dynamical system stability in the framework of bounded-input–bounded-output stability. Since, in Lyapunov stability, we put a lot of emphasis on studying the stability of equilibrium points and the asymptotic behavior of state variables, one may wonder: What can we see about input–output stability starting from the formalism of Lyapunov stability? In this section, we show how Lyapunov stability tools can be used to establish $\mathcal{L}$ stability of nonlinear systems represented by state models.

Consider the system

$$\dot{x} = f(t, x, u), \quad x(0) = x_0 \tag{5.3}$$
$$y = h(t, x, u) \tag{5.4}$$

where $x \in R^n$, $u \in R^m$, $y \in R^q$, $f : [0, \infty) \times D \times D_u \to R^n$ is piecewise continuous in t and locally Lipschitz in (x, u), $h : [0, \infty) \times D \times D_u \to R^q$ is piecewise continuous in t and continuous in (x, u), $D \subset R^n$ is a domain that contains $x = 0$, and $D_u \subset R^m$ is a domain that contains $u = 0$. For each fixed $x_0 \in D$, the state model given by (5.3) and (5.4) defines an operator H that assigns to each input signal $u(t)$ the corresponding output signal $y(t)$. Suppose $x = 0$ is an equilibrium point of the unforced system

$$\dot{x} = f(t, x, 0) \tag{5.5}$$

The theme of this section is that if the origin of (5.5) is uniformly asymptotically stable (or exponentially stable), then, under some assumptions on f and h, the system (5.3) and (5.4) will be $\mathcal{L}$ stable or small-signal $\mathcal{L}$ stable for a certain signal space $\mathcal{L}$. We pursue this idea first in the case of exponentially stability, and then for the more general case of uniform asymptotic stability.

Theorem 5.1 *Consider the system* (5.3)–(5.4) *and take* $r > 0$ *and* $r_u > 0$ *such that* $\{\|x\| \le r\} \subset D$ *and* $\{\|u\| \le r_u\} \subset D_u$. *Suppose that*

- $x = 0$ *is an exponentially stable equilibrium point of* (5.5), *and there is a Lyapunov function* $V(t,x)$ *that satisfies*

$$c_1\|x\|^2 \le V(t, x) \le c_2\|x\|^2 \tag{5.6}$$

$$\frac{\partial V}{\partial t} + \frac{\partial V}{\partial x} f(t, x, 0) \le -c_3\|x\|^2 \tag{5.7}$$

$$\left\|\frac{\partial V}{\partial x}\right\| \le c_4\|x\| \tag{5.8}$$

for all $(t, x) \in [0, \infty) \times D$ *for some positive constants* c_1, c_2, c_3, *and* c_4.

- f *and* h *satisfy the inequalities*

$$\|f(t, x, u) - f(t, x, 0)\| \le L\|u\| \tag{5.9}$$

$$\|h(t, x, u)\| \le \eta_1\|x\| + \eta_2\|u\| \tag{5.10}$$

for all $(t, x, u) \in [0, \infty) \times D \times D_u$ *for some nonnegative constants* L, η_1, *and* η_2.

Then, for each x_0 with $\|x_0\| \leq r\sqrt{c_1/c_2}$, the system (5.3)–(5.4) is small-signal finite-gain $\mathcal{L}_p$ stable for each $p \in [1, \infty]$. In particular, for each $u \in \mathcal{L}_{pe}$ with $\sup_{0 \leq t \leq \tau} \|u(t)\| \leq \min\{r_u, c_1 c_3 r/(c_2 c_4 L)\}$, the output $y(t)$ satisfies

$$\|y_\tau\|_{\mathcal{L}_p} \leq \gamma \|u_\tau\|_{\mathcal{L}_p} + \beta \tag{5.11}$$

for all $\tau \in [0, \infty)$, with

$$\gamma = \eta_2 + \frac{\eta_1 c_2 c_4 L}{c_1 c_3}, \quad \beta = \eta_1 \|x_0\| \sqrt{\frac{c_2}{c_1}} \rho, \text{ where } \rho = \begin{cases} 1, & \text{if } p = \infty \\ \left(\frac{2 c_2}{c_3 p}\right)^{1/p}, & \text{if } p \in [1, \infty) \end{cases}$$

Furthermore, if the origin is globally exponentially stable and all the assumptions hold globally (with $D = R^n$ and $D_u = R^m$), then, for each $x_0 \in R^n$, the system (5.3)–(5.4) is finite-gain $\mathcal{L}_p$ stable for each $p \in [1, \infty]$. $\diamond$

Proof: The derivative of V along the trajectories of (5.3) satisfies

$$\dot{V}(t, x, u) = \frac{\partial V}{\partial t} + \frac{\partial V}{\partial x} f(t, x, 0) + \frac{\partial V}{\partial x}[f(t, x, u) - f(t, x, 0)]$$
$$\leq -c_3 \|x\|^2 + c_4 L \|x\| \|u\|$$

Take $W(t) = \sqrt{V(t, x(t))}$. When $V(t, x(t)) \neq 0$, use $\dot{W} = \dot{V}/(2\sqrt{V})$ and (5.6) to obtain

$$\dot{W} \leq -\frac{1}{2}\left(\frac{c_3}{c_2}\right) W + \frac{c_4 L}{2\sqrt{c_1}} \|u(t)\|$$

When $V(t, x(t)) = 0$, it can be verified[5] that

$$D^+ W(t) \leq \frac{c_4 L}{2\sqrt{c_1}} \|u(t)\| \tag{5.12}$$

Hence,

$$D^+ W(t) \leq -\frac{1}{2}\left(\frac{c_3}{c_2}\right) W + \frac{c_4 L}{2\sqrt{c_1}} \|u(t)\|$$

for all values of $V(t, x(t))$. By (the comparison) Lemma 3.4, $W(t)$ satisfies the inequality

$$W(t) \leq e^{-t c_3/2 c_2} W(0) + \frac{c_4 L}{2\sqrt{c_1}} \int_0^t e^{-(t-\tau) c_3/2 c_2} \|u(\tau)\| \, d\tau$$

Using (5.6), we obtain

$$\|x(t)\| \leq \sqrt{\frac{c_2}{c_1}} \|x_0\| e^{-t c_3/2 c_2} + \frac{c_4 L}{2 c_1} \int_0^t e^{-(t-\tau) c_3/2 c_2} \|u(\tau)\| \, d\tau$$

---

[5]See Exercise 5.6.

It can be easily verified that

$$\|x_0\| \le r\sqrt{\frac{c_1}{c_2}} \quad \text{and} \quad \sup_{0 \le \sigma \le t} \|u(\sigma)\| \le \frac{c_1 c_3 r}{c_2 c_4 L}$$

ensure that $\|x(t)\| \le r$; hence, $x(t)$ stays within the domain of validity of the assumptions. Using (5.10), we have

$$\|y(t)\| \le k_1 e^{-at} + k_2 \int_0^t e^{-a(t-\tau)} \|u(\tau)\| \, d\tau + k_3 \|u(t)\| \tag{5.13}$$

where

$$k_1 = \sqrt{\frac{c_2}{c_1}} \|x_0\| \eta_1, \quad k_2 = \frac{c_4 L \eta_1}{2c_1}, \quad k_3 = \eta_2, \quad a = \frac{c_3}{2c_2}$$

Set

$$y_1(t) = k_1 e^{-at}, \quad y_2(t) = k_2 \int_0^t e^{-a(t-\tau)} \|u(\tau)\| \, d\tau, \quad y_3(t) = k_3 \|u(t)\|$$

Suppose now that $u \in \mathcal{L}_{pe}^m$ for some $p \in [1, \infty]$. Using the results of Example 5.2, it can be easily verified that

$$\|y_{2\tau}\|_{\mathcal{L}_p} \le \frac{k_2}{a} \|u_\tau\|_{\mathcal{L}_p}$$

It is also straightforward to see that

$$\|y_{3\tau}\|_{\mathcal{L}_p} \le k_3 \|u_\tau\|_{\mathcal{L}_p}$$

As for the first term, $y_1(t)$, it can be verified that

$$\|y_{1\tau}\|_{\mathcal{L}_p} \le k_1 \rho, \quad \text{where} \quad \rho = \begin{cases} 1, & \text{if } p = \infty \\ \left(\frac{1}{ap}\right)^{1/p}, & \text{if } p \in [1, \infty) \end{cases}$$

Thus, by the triangle inequality, (5.11) is satisfied with

$$\gamma = k_3 + \frac{k_2}{a}, \quad \beta = k_1 \rho$$

When all the assumptions hold globally, there is no need to restrict $\|x_0\|$ or the instantaneous values of $\|u(t)\|$. Therefore, (5.11) is satisfied for each $x_0 \in R^n$ and $u \in \mathcal{L}_{pe}$. $\qquad \square$

The use of (the converse Lyapunov) Theorem 4.14 shows the existence of a Lyapunov function satisfying (5.6) through (5.8). Consequently, we have the following corollary.

Corollary 5.1 *Suppose that, in some neighborhood of $(x = 0, u = 0)$, the function $f(t, x, u)$ is continuously differentiable, the Jacobian matrices $[\partial f/\partial x]$ and $[\partial f/\partial u]$ are bounded, uniformly in t, and $h(t, x, u)$ satisfies (5.10). If the origin $x = 0$ is an exponentially stable equilibrium point of (5.5), then there is a constant $r_0 > 0$ such that for each x_0 with $\|x_0\| < r_0$, the system (5.3)–(5.4) is small-signal finite-gain $\mathcal{L}_p$ stable for each $p \in [1, \infty]$. Furthermore, if all the assumptions hold globally and the origin $x = 0$ is a globally exponentially stable equilibrium point of (5.5), then for each $x_0 \in R^n$, the system (5.3)–(5.4) is finite-gain $\mathcal{L}_p$ stable for each $p \in [1, \infty]$.* $\diamond$

For the linear time-invariant system

$$\dot{x} = Ax + Bu, \tag{5.14}$$

$$y = Cx + Du \tag{5.15}$$

the global exponential stability condition of Theorem 5.1 is equivalent to the condition that A is Hurwitz. Thus, we have the following result for linear systems:

Corollary 5.2 *The linear time-invariant system (5.14)–(5.15) is finite-gain $\mathcal{L}_p$ stable for each $p \in [1, \infty]$ if A is Hurwitz. Moreover, (5.11) is satisfied with*

$$\gamma = \|D\|_2 + \frac{2\lambda_{max}^2(P)\|B\|_2\|C\|_2}{\lambda_{min}(P)}, \quad \beta = \rho\|C\|_2\|x_0\|\sqrt{\frac{\lambda_{max}(P)}{\lambda_{min}(P)}}$$

where

$$\rho = \begin{cases} 1, & \text{if } p = \infty \\[2ex] \left(\frac{2\lambda_{max}(P)}{p}\right)^{1/p}, & \text{if } p \in [1, \infty) \end{cases}$$

and P is the solution of the Lyapunov equation $PA + A^T P = -I$. $\diamond$

We leave it for the reader to derive the foregoing expressions for γ and β.

Example 5.4 Consider the single-input–single-output, first-order system

$$\dot{x} = -x - x^3 + u, \quad x(0) = x_0$$

$$y = \tanh x + u$$

The origin of $\dot{x} = -x - x^3$ is globally exponentially stable, as can be seen by the Lyapunov function $V(x) = x^2/2$. The function V satisfies (5.6) through (5.8) globally with $c_1 = c_2 = 1/2$, $c_3 = c_4 = 1$. The functions f and h satisfy (5.9) and (5.10) globally with $L = \eta_1 = \eta_2 = 1$. Hence, for each $x_0 \in R$ and each $p \in [1, \infty]$, the system is finite-gain $\mathcal{L}_p$ stable. $\triangle$

Example 5.5 Consider the single-input–single-output second-order system

$$\dot{x}_1 = x_2$$
$$\dot{x}_2 = -x_1 - x_2 - a\tanh x_1 + u$$
$$y = x_1$$

where a is a nonnegative constant. Use

$$V(x) = x^T P x = p_{11}x_1^2 + 2p_{12}x_1x_2 + p_{22}x_2^2$$

as a Lyapunov function candidate for the unforced system:

$$\dot{V} = -2p_{12}(x_1^2 + ax_1\tanh x_1) + 2(p_{11} - p_{12} - p_{22})x_1x_2 - 2ap_{22}x_2\tanh x_1 - 2(p_{22} - p_{12})x_2^2$$

Choose $p_{11} = p_{12} + p_{22}$ to cancel the cross-product term x_1x_2. Then, taking $p_{22} = 2p_{12} = 1$ makes P positive definite and results in

$$\dot{V} = -x_1^2 - x_2^2 - ax_1\tanh x_1 - 2ax_2\tanh x_1$$

Using the fact that $x_1\tanh x_1 \geq 0$ for all $x_1 \in R$, we obtain

$$\dot{V} \leq -\|x\|_2^2 + 2a|x_1|\,|x_2| \leq -(1-a)\|x\|_2^2$$

Thus, for all $a < 1$, V satisfies (5.6) through (5.8) globally with $c_1 = \lambda_{\min}(P)$, $c_2 = \lambda_{\max}(P)$, $c_3 = 1 - a$, and $c_4 = 2\|P\|_2 = 2\lambda_{\max}(P)$. The functions f and h satisfy (5.9) and (5.10) globally with $L = \eta_1 = 1$, $\eta_2 = 0$. Hence, for each $x_0 \in R$ and each $p \in [1, \infty]$, the system is finite-gain $\mathcal{L}_p$ stable.   △

We turn now to the more general case when the origin of (5.5) is uniformly asymptotically stable and restrict our attention to the study of $\mathcal{L}_\infty$ stability. The next two theorems give conditions for small-signal $\mathcal{L}_\infty$ stability and $\mathcal{L}_\infty$ stability, respectively

Theorem 5.2 *Consider the system* (5.3)–(5.4) *and take* $r > 0$ *such that* $\{\|x\| \leq r\} \subset D$. *Suppose that*

- $x = 0$ *is a uniformly asymptotically stable equilibrium point of* (5.5), *and there is a Lyapunov function* $V(t,x)$ *that satisfies*

$$\alpha_1(\|x\|) \leq V(t,x) \leq \alpha_2(\|x\|) \tag{5.16}$$

$$\frac{\partial V}{\partial t} + \frac{\partial V}{\partial x}f(t,x,0) \leq -\alpha_3(\|x\|) \tag{5.17}$$

$$\left\|\frac{\partial V}{\partial x}\right\| \leq \alpha_4(\|x\|) \tag{5.18}$$

for all $(t,x) \in [0,\infty) \times D$ *for some class* $\mathcal{K}$ *functions* α_1 *to* α_4.

- f and h satisfy the inequalities

$$\|f(t, x, u) - f(t, x, 0)\| \leq \alpha_5(\|u\|) \tag{5.19}$$

$$\|h(t, x, u)\| \leq \alpha_6(\|x\|) + \alpha_7(\|u\|) + \eta \tag{5.20}$$

for all $(t, x, u) \in [0, \infty) \times D \times D_u$ for some class $\mathcal{K}$ functions α_5 to α_7, and a nonnegative constant η.

Then, for each x_0 with $\|x_0\| \leq \alpha_2^{-1}(\alpha_1(r))$, the system (5.3)–(5.4) is small-signal $\mathcal{L}_\infty$ stable. $\diamond$

Proof: The derivative of V along the trajectories of (5.3) satisfies

$$
\begin{aligned}
\dot{V}(t, x, u) &= \frac{\partial V}{\partial t} + \frac{\partial V}{\partial x} f(t, x, 0) + \frac{\partial V}{\partial x}[f(t, x, u) - f(t, x, 0)] \\
&\leq -\alpha_3(\|x\|) + \alpha_4(\|x\|)\alpha_5(\|u\|) \\
&\leq -(1 - \theta)\alpha_3(\|x\|) - \theta\alpha_3(\|x\|) + \alpha_4(r)\alpha_5\left(\sup_{0 \leq t \leq \tau} \|u(t)\|\right)
\end{aligned}
$$

where $0 < \theta < 1$. Set

$$\mu = \alpha_3^{-1}\left(\frac{\alpha_4(r)\alpha_5\left(\sup_{0 \leq t \leq \tau} \|u(t)\|\right)}{\theta}\right)$$

and choose $r_u > 0$ small enough that $\{\|u\| \leq r_u\} \subset D_u$ and $\mu < \alpha_2^{-1}(\alpha_1(r))$ for $\sup_{0 \leq t \leq \tau} \|u(t)\| \leq r_u$. Then,

$$\dot{V} \leq -(1 - \theta)\alpha_3(\|x\|), \quad \forall \|x\| \geq \mu$$

By applying Theorem 4.18, we conclude from (4.42) and (4.43) that $\|x(t)\|$ satisfies the inequality

$$\|x(t)\| \leq \beta(\|x_0\|, t) + \gamma\left(\sup_{0 \leq t \leq \tau} \|u(t)\|\right) \tag{5.21}$$

for all $0 \leq t \leq \tau$, where β and γ are class $\mathcal{KL}$ and class $\mathcal{K}$ functions, respectively. Using (5.20), we obtain

$$
\begin{aligned}
\|y(t)\| &\leq \alpha_6\left(\beta(\|x_0\|, t) + \gamma\left(\sup_{0 \leq t \leq \tau} \|u(t)\|\right)\right) + \alpha_7(\|u(t)\|) + \eta \\
&\leq \alpha_6\left(2\beta(\|x_0\|, t)\right) + \alpha_6\left(2\gamma\left(\sup_{0 \leq t \leq \tau} \|u(t)\|\right)\right) + \alpha_7(\|u(t)\|) + \eta
\end{aligned}
$$

where we used the general property of class $\mathcal{K}$ functions [6]

$$\alpha(a + b) \leq \alpha(2a) + \alpha(2b)$$

---

[6]See Exercise 4.35.

Thus,

$$\|y_\tau\|_{\mathcal{L}_\infty} \leq \gamma_0 \left(\|u_\tau\|_{\mathcal{L}_\infty}\right) + \beta_0 \tag{5.22}$$

where

$$\gamma_0 = \alpha_6 \circ 2\gamma + \alpha_7 \quad \text{and} \quad \beta_0 = \alpha_6(2\beta(\|x_0\|, 0)) + \eta$$

$\square$

The use of (the converse Lyapunov) Theorem 4.16 shows the existence of a Lyapunov function satisfying (5.16) through (5.18). Consequently, we have the following corollary:

Corollary 5.3 *Suppose that, in some neighborhood of $(x = 0, u = 0)$, the function $f(t, x, u)$ is continuously differentiable, the Jacobian matrices $[\partial f/\partial x]$ and $[\partial f/\partial u]$ are bounded, uniformly in t, and $h(t, x, u)$ satisfies (5.20). If the unforced system (5.5) has a uniformly asymptotically stable equilibrium point at the origin $x = 0$, then the system (5.3)–(5.4) is small-signal $\mathcal{L}_\infty$ stable.* $\diamond$

To extend the proof of Theorem 5.2 to show $\mathcal{L}_\infty$ stability, we need to demonstrate that (5.21) holds for any initial state $x_0 \in R^n$ and any bounded input. As we discussed in Section 4.9, such inequality will not automatically hold when the conditions of Theorem 5.2 are satisfied globally, even when the origin of (5.5) is globally uniformly asymptotically stable. However, it will follow from input-to-state stability of the system (5.3), which can be checked using Theorem 4.19.

Theorem 5.3 *Consider the system (5.3)–(5.4) with $D = R^n$ and $D_u = R^m$. Suppose that*

- *The system (5.3) is input-to-state stable.*

- *h satisfies the inequality*

$$\|h(t, x, u)\| \leq \alpha_1(\|x\|) + \alpha_2(\|u\|) + \eta \tag{5.23}$$

for all $(t, x, u) \in [0, \infty) \times R^n \times R^m$ for some class $\mathcal{K}$ functions α_1, α_2, and a nonnegative constant η.

Then, for each $x_0 \in R^n$, the system (5.3)–(5.4) is $\mathcal{L}_\infty$ stable. $\diamond$

Proof: Input-to-state stability shows that an inequality similar to (5.21) holds for any $x_0 \in R^n$ and any $u \in \mathcal{L}_{\infty e}$. The rest of the proof is the same as that of Theorem 5.2. $\square$

Example 5.6 Consider the single-input–single-output first-order system

$$\begin{aligned} \dot{x} &= -x - 2x^3 + (1 + x^2)u^2 \\ y &= x^2 + u \end{aligned}$$

We saw in Example 4.26 that the state equation is input-to-state stable. The output function h satisfies (5.23) globally with $\alpha_1(r) = r^2$, $\alpha_2(r) = r$, and $\eta = 0$. Thus, the system is $\mathcal{L}_\infty$ stable. $\triangle$

Example 5.7 Consider the single-input–single-output second-order system

$$\dot{x}_1 = -x_1^3 + g(t)x_2$$
$$\dot{x}_2 = -g(t)x_1 - x_2^3 + u$$
$$y = x_1 + x_2$$

where $g(t)$ is continuous and bounded for all $t \geq 0$. Taking $V = (x_1^2 + x_2^2)$, we have

$$\dot{V} = -2x_1^4 - 2x_2^4 + 2x_2 u$$

Using

$$x_1^4 + x_2^4 \geq \tfrac{1}{2}\|x\|_2^4$$

yields

$$
\begin{aligned}
\dot{V} &\leq -\|x\|_2^4 + 2\|x\|_2|u| \\
&= -(1-\theta)\|x\|_2^4 - \theta\|x\|_2^4 + 2\|x\|_2|u|, \quad 0 < \theta < 1 \\
&\leq -(1-\theta)\|x\|_2^4, \quad \forall\ \|x\|_2 \geq \left(\frac{2|u|}{\theta}\right)^{1/3}
\end{aligned}
$$

Thus, V satisfies inequalities (4.48) and (4.49) of Theorem 4.19 globally, with $\alpha_1(r) = \alpha_2(r) = r^2$, $W_3(x) = -(1-\theta)\|x\|_2^4$, and $\rho(r) = (2r/\theta)^{1/3}$. Hence, the state equation is input-to-state stable. Furthermore, the function $h = x_1 + x_2$ satisfies (5.23) globally with $\alpha_1(r) = \sqrt{2}r$, $\alpha_2 = 0$, and $\eta = 0$. Thus, the system is $\mathcal{L}_\infty$ stable. $\triangle$

5.3 $\mathcal{L}_2$ Gain

$\mathcal{L}_2$ stability plays a special role in systems analysis. It is natural to work with square-integrable signals, which can be viewed as finite-energy signals.[7] In many control problems,[8] the system is represented as an input–output map, from a disturbance input u to a controlled output y, which is required to be small. With $\mathcal{L}_2$ input signals, the control system is designed to make the input–output map finite-gain $\mathcal{L}_2$ stable and to minimize the $\mathcal{L}_2$ gain. In such problems, it is important not only to be able to find out that the system is finite-gain $\mathcal{L}_2$ stable, but also to calculate the $\mathcal{L}_2$ gain or an upper bound on it. In this section, we show how to calculate the $\mathcal{L}_2$ gain for a special class of time-invariant systems. We start with linear systems.

---

[7]If you think of $u(t)$ as current or voltage, then $u^T(t)u(t)$ is proportional to the instantaneous power of the signal, and its integral over all time is a measure of the energy content of the signal.

[8]See the literature on H_∞ control; for example, [20], [54], [61], [90], [199], or [219].

Theorem 5.4 *Consider the linear time-invariant system*

$$\dot{x} = Ax + Bu \qquad\qquad (5.24)$$
$$y = Cx + Du \qquad\qquad (5.25)$$

where A is Hurwitz. Let $G(s) = C(sI - A)^{-1}B + D$. Then, the $\mathcal{L}_2$ gain of the system is $\sup_{\omega \in R} \|G(j\omega)\|_2$.[9]   ◇

Proof: Due to linearity, we set $x(0) = 0$. From Fourier transform theory,[10] we know that for a causal signal $y \in \mathcal{L}_2$, the Fourier transform $Y(j\omega)$ is given by

$$Y(j\omega) = \int_0^\infty y(t)e^{-j\omega t} \, dt$$

and

$$Y(j\omega) = G(j\omega)U(j\omega)$$

Using Parseval's theorem,[11] we can write

$$
\begin{aligned}
\|y\|_{\mathcal{L}_2}^2 &= \int_0^\infty y^T(t)y(t) \, dt = \frac{1}{2\pi} \int_{-\infty}^\infty Y^*(j\omega)Y(j\omega) \, d\omega \\
&= \frac{1}{2\pi} \int_{-\infty}^\infty U^*(j\omega)G^T(-j\omega)G(j\omega)U(j\omega) \, d\omega \\
&\leq \left(\sup_{\omega \in R} \|G(j\omega)\|_2 \right)^2 \frac{1}{2\pi} \int_{-\infty}^\infty U^*(j\omega)U(j\omega) \, d\omega \\
&= \left(\sup_{\omega \in R} \|G(j\omega)\|_2 \right)^2 \|u\|_{\mathcal{L}_2}^2
\end{aligned}
$$

which shows that the $\mathcal{L}_2$ gain is less than or equal to $\sup_{\omega \in R} \|G(j\omega)\|_2$. Showing that the $\mathcal{L}_2$ gain is equal to $\sup_{\omega \in R} \|G(j\omega)\|_2$ is done by a contradiction argument that is given in Appendix C.10.   □

The case of linear time-invariant systems is exceptional in that we can actually find the exact $\mathcal{L}_2$ gain. In more general cases, like the case of the next theorem, we can only find an upper bound on the $\mathcal{L}_2$ gain.

---

[9]This is the induced 2-norm of the complex matrix $G(j\omega)$, which is equal to $\sqrt{\lambda_{\max}[G^T(-j\omega)G(j\omega)]} = \sigma_{\max}[G(j\omega)]$. This quantity is known as the H_∞ norm of $G(j\omega)$, when $G(j\omega)$ is viewed as an element of the Hardy space H_∞. (See [61].)

[10]See [53].

[11]Parseval's theorem [53] states that for a causal signal $y \in \mathcal{L}_2$,

$$\int_0^\infty y^T(t)y(t) \, dt = \frac{1}{2\pi} \int_{-\infty}^\infty Y^*(j\omega)Y(j\omega) \, d\omega$$

Theorem 5.5 *Consider the time-invariant nonlinear system*

$$\dot{x} = f(x) + G(x)u, \quad x(0) = x_0 \tag{5.26}$$

$$y = h(x) \tag{5.27}$$

where $f(x)$ is locally Lipschitz, and $G(x)$, $h(x)$ are continuous over R^n. The matrix G is $n \times m$ and $h : R^n \to R^q$. The functions f and h vanish at the origin; that is, $f(0) = 0$ and $h(0) = 0$. Let γ be a positive number and suppose there is a continuously differentiable, positive semidefinite function $V(x)$ that satisfies the inequality

$$\mathcal{H}(V, f, G, h, \gamma) \stackrel{\text{def}}{=} \frac{\partial V}{\partial x} f(x) + \frac{1}{2\gamma^2} \frac{\partial V}{\partial x} G(x) G^T(x) \left(\frac{\partial V}{\partial x} \right)^T + \frac{1}{2} h^T(x) h(x) \leq 0 \tag{5.28}$$

for all $x \in R^n$. Then, for each $x_0 \in R^n$, the system (5.26)–(5.27) is finite-gain $\mathcal{L}_2$ stable and its $\mathcal{L}_2$ gain is less than or equal to γ. $\diamond$

Proof: By completing the squares, we have

$$\frac{\partial V}{\partial x} f(x) + \frac{\partial V}{\partial x} G(x) u = -\frac{1}{2} \gamma^2 \left\| u - \frac{1}{\gamma^2} G^T(x) \left(\frac{\partial V}{\partial x} \right)^T \right\|_2^2 + \frac{\partial V}{\partial x} f(x)$$

$$+ \frac{1}{2\gamma^2} \frac{\partial V}{\partial x} G(x) G^T(x) \left(\frac{\partial V}{\partial x} \right)^T + \frac{1}{2} \gamma^2 \|u\|_2^2$$

Substituting (5.28) yields

$$\frac{\partial V}{\partial x} f(x) + \frac{\partial V}{\partial x} G(x) u \leq \frac{1}{2} \gamma^2 \|u\|_2^2 - \frac{1}{2} \|y\|_2^2 - \frac{1}{2} \gamma^2 \left\| u - \frac{1}{\gamma^2} G^T(x) \left(\frac{\partial V}{\partial x} \right)^T \right\|_2^2$$

Hence,

$$\frac{\partial V}{\partial x} f(x) + \frac{\partial V}{\partial x} G(x) u \leq \frac{1}{2} \gamma^2 \|u\|_2^2 - \frac{1}{2} \|y\|_2^2 \tag{5.29}$$

Note that the left-hand side of (5.29) is the derivative of V along the trajectories of the system (5.26). Integrating (5.29) yields

$$V(x(\tau)) - V(x_0) \leq \frac{1}{2} \gamma^2 \int_0^\tau \|u(t)\|_2^2 \, dt - \frac{1}{2} \int_0^\tau \|y(t)\|_2^2 \, dt$$

where $x(t)$ is the solution of (5.26) for a given $u \in \mathcal{L}_{2e}$. Using $V(x) \geq 0$, we obtain

$$\int_0^\tau \|y(t)\|_2^2 \, dt \leq \gamma^2 \int_0^\tau \|u(t)\|_2^2 \, dt + 2V(x_0)$$

Taking the square roots and using the inequality $\sqrt{a^2 + b^2} \leq a + b$ for nonnegative numbers a and b, we obtain

$$\|y_\tau\|_{\mathcal{L}_2} \leq \gamma \|u_\tau\|_{\mathcal{L}_2} + \sqrt{2V(x_0)} \tag{5.30}$$

which completes the proof.   □

Inequality (5.28) is known as the *Hamilton–Jacobi inequality* (or the *Hamilton–Jacobi equation* when $\leq$ is replaced by =). The search for a function $V(x)$ that satisfies (5.28) requires basically the solution of a partial differential equation, which might be difficult to solve. If we succeed in finding $V(x)$, we obtain a finite-gain $\mathcal{L}_2$ stability result, which, unlike Theorem 5.1, does not require the origin of the unforced system to be exponentially stable. This point is illustrated by the next example.

Example 5.8 Consider the single-input–single-output system

$$
\begin{aligned}
\dot{x}_1 &= x_2 \\
\dot{x}_2 &= -ax_1^3 - kx_2 + u \\
y &= x_2
\end{aligned}
$$

where a and k are positive constants. The unforced system is a special case of the class of systems treated in Example 4.9. In that example, we used the energy-like Lyapunov function $V(x) = ax_1^4/4 + x_2^2/2$ to show that the origin is globally asymptotically stable. Using $V(x) = \alpha(ax_1^4/4 + x_2^2/2)$ with $\alpha > 0$ as a candidate for the solution of the Hamilton–Jacobi inequality (5.28), it can be shown that

$$
\mathcal{H}(V, f, G, h, \gamma) = \left(-\alpha k + \frac{\alpha^2}{2\gamma^2} + \frac{1}{2} \right) x_2^2
$$

To satisfy (5.28), we need to choose $\alpha > 0$ and $\gamma > 0$ such that

$$
-\alpha k + \frac{\alpha^2}{2\gamma^2} + \frac{1}{2} \leq 0 \tag{5.31}
$$

By simple algebraic manipulation, we can rewrite this inequality as

$$
\gamma^2 \geq \frac{\alpha^2}{2\alpha k - 1}
$$

Since we are interested in the smallest possible γ, we choose α to minimize the right-hand side of the preceding inequality. The minimum value $1/k^2$ is achieved at $\alpha = 1/k$. Thus, choosing $\gamma = 1/k$, we conclude that the system is finite-gain $\mathcal{L}_2$ stable and its $\mathcal{L}_2$ gain is less than or equal to $1/k$. We note that the conditions of Theorem 5.1 are not satisfied in this example because the origin of the unforced system is not exponentially stable. Linearization at the origin yields the matrix

$$
\begin{bmatrix} 0 & 1 \\ 0 & -k \end{bmatrix}
$$

which is not Hurwitz.   △

The idea of the preceding example is generalized in the next one.

Example 5.9 Consider the nonlinear system (5.26)–(5.27), with $m = q$, and suppose there is a continuously differentiable positive semidefinite function $W(x)$ that satisfies[12]

$$\frac{\partial W}{\partial x} f(x) \leq -kh^T(x)h(x), \quad k > 0 \tag{5.32}$$

$$\frac{\partial W}{\partial x} G(x) = h^T(x) \tag{5.33}$$

for all $x \in R^n$. Using $V(x) = \alpha W(x)$ with $\alpha > 0$ as a candidate for the solution of the Hamilton–Jacobi inequality (5.28), it can be shown that

$$\mathcal{H}(V, f, G, h, \gamma) = \left(-\alpha k + \frac{\alpha^2}{2\gamma^2} + \frac{1}{2} \right) h^T(x)h(x)$$

To satisfy (5.28), we need to choose $\alpha > 0$ and $\gamma > 0$ such that

$$-\alpha k + \frac{\alpha^2}{2\gamma^2} + \frac{1}{2} \leq 0$$

This inequality is the same as inequality (5.31) of Example 5.8. By repeating the argument used there, it can be shown that the system is finite-gain $\mathcal{L}_2$ stable and its $\mathcal{L}_2$ gain is less than or equal to $1/k$. $\triangle$

Example 5.10 Consider the nonlinear system (5.26)–(5.27), with $m = q$, and suppose there is a continuously differentiable positive semidefinite function $W(x)$ that satisfies[13]

$$\frac{\partial W}{\partial x} f(x) \leq 0 \tag{5.34}$$

$$\frac{\partial W}{\partial x} G(x) = h^T(x) \tag{5.35}$$

for all $x \in R^n$. The output feedback control

$$u = -ky + v, \quad k > 0$$

results in the closed-loop system

$$\dot{x} = f(x) - kG(x)G^T(x) \left(\frac{\partial W}{\partial x} \right)^T + G(x)v \overset{\text{def}}{=} f_c(x) + G(x)v$$

$$y = h(x) = G^T(x) \left(\frac{\partial W}{\partial x} \right)^T$$

---

[12]A system satisfying (5.32) and (5.33) will be defined in the next chapter as an output strictly passive system.

[13]A system satisfying (5.34) and (5.35) will be defined in the next chapter as a passive system. We will come back to this example in Section 6.5 and look at it as a feedback connection of two passive systems.

It can be easily verified that, for the closed-loop system, $W(x)$ satisfies (5.32) and (5.33) of the previous example. Hence, the input–output map from v to y is finite-gain $\mathcal{L}_2$ stable and its $\mathcal{L}_2$ gain is less than or equal to $1/k$. This shows, in essence, that the $\mathcal{L}_2$ gain can be made arbitrarily small by choosing the feedback gain k sufficiently large. $\triangle$

Example 5.11 Consider the linear time-invariant system

$$
\begin{aligned}
\dot{x} &= Ax + Bu \\
y &= Cx
\end{aligned}
$$

Suppose there is a positive semidefinite solution P of the Riccati equation

$$
PA + A^T P + \frac{1}{\gamma^2} PBB^T P + C^T C = 0 \tag{5.36}
$$

for some $\gamma > 0$. Taking $V(x) = (1/2)x^T P x$ and using the expression $[\partial V/\partial x] = x^T P$, it can be easily seen that $V(x)$ satisfies the Hamilton–Jacobi equation

$$
\mathcal{H}(V, Ax, B, Cx) = x^T PAx + \frac{1}{2\gamma^2} x^T PB^T BPx + \frac{1}{2} x^T C^T Cx = 0
$$

Hence, the system is finite-gain $\mathcal{L}_2$ stable and its $\mathcal{L}_2$ gain is less than or equal to γ. This result gives an alternative method for computing an upper bound on the $\mathcal{L}_2$ gain, as opposed to the frequency-domain calculation of Theorem 5.4. It is interesting to note that the existence of a positive semidefinite solution of (5.36) is a necessary and sufficient condition for the $\mathcal{L}_2$ gain to be less than or equal to γ.[14] $\triangle$

In Theorem 5.5, we assumed that the assumptions hold globally. It is clear from the proof of the theorem that if the assumptions hold only on a finite domain D, we will still arrive at inequality (5.30) as long as the solution of (5.26) stays in D.

Corollary 5.4 *Suppose the assumptions of Theorem 5.5 are satisfied on a domain $D \subset R^n$ that contains the origin. Then, for any $x_0 \in D$ and any $u \in \mathcal{L}_{2e}$ for which the solution of (5.26) satisfies $x(t) \in D$ for all $t \in [0, \tau]$, we have*

$$
\|y_\tau\|_{\mathcal{L}_2} \leq \gamma \|u_\tau\|_{\mathcal{L}_2} + \sqrt{2V(x_0)}
$$

$\diamond$

Ensuring that the solution $x(t)$ of (5.26) remains in some neighborhood of the origin, when both $\|x_0\|$ and $sup_{0 \leq t \leq \tau} \|u(t)\|$ are sufficiently small, follows from asymptotic stability of the origin of $\dot{x} = f(x)$. This fact is used to show small-signal $\mathcal{L}_2$ stability in the next lemma.

---

[14]See [54] for the proof of necessity.

Lemma 5.1 *Suppose the assumptions of Theorem 5.5 are satisfied on a domain $D \subset R^n$ that contains the origin, $f(x)$ is continuously differentiable, and $x = 0$ is an asymptotically stable equilibrium point of $\dot{x} = f(x)$. Then, there is $k_1 > 0$ such that for each x_0 with $\|x_0\| \leq k_1$, the system (5.26)–(5.27) is small-signal finite-gain $\mathcal{L}_2$ stable with $\mathcal{L}_2$ gain less than or equal to γ.* $\diamond$

Proof: Take $r > 0$ such that $\{\|x\| \leq r\} \subset D$. By (the converse Lyapunov) Theorem 4.16, there exist $r_0 > 0$ and a continuously differentiable Lyapunov function $W(x)$ that satisfies

$$\alpha_1(\|x\|) \leq W(x) \leq \alpha_2(\|x\|)$$

$$\frac{\partial W}{\partial x} f(x) \leq -\alpha_3(\|x\|)$$

for all $\|x\| < r_0$, for some class $\mathcal{K}$ functions α_1 to α_3. The derivative of W along the trajectories of (5.26) satisfies

$$
\begin{aligned}
\dot{W}(x,u) &= \frac{\partial W}{\partial x} f(x,0) + \frac{\partial W}{\partial x}[f(x,u) - f(x,0)] \leq -\alpha_3(\|x\|) + kL\|u\| \\
&\leq -(1-\theta)\alpha_3(\|x\|) - \theta\alpha_3(\|x\|) + kL \sup_{0 \leq t \leq \tau} \|u(t)\| \\
&\leq -(1-\theta)\alpha_3(\|x\|), \quad \forall \|x\| \geq \alpha_3^{-1}\left(kL \sup_{0 \leq t \leq \tau} \|u(t)\|/\theta\right)
\end{aligned}
$$

where k is an upper bound on $\|\partial W/\partial x\|$, L is a Lipschitz constant of f with respect to u, and $0 < \theta < 1$. Similar to the proof of Theorem 5.2, we can apply Theorem 4.18 to show that there exist a class $\mathcal{KL}$ function β, a class $\mathcal{K}$ function γ_0, and positive constants k_1 and k_2 such that, for any initial state x_0 with $\|x_0\| \leq k_1$ and any input $u(t)$ with $\sup_{0 \leq t \leq \tau} \|u(t)\| \leq k_2$, the solution $x(t)$ satisfies

$$\|x(t)\| \leq \beta(\|x_0\|, t) + \gamma_0\left(\sup_{0 \leq t \leq \tau} \|u(t)\|\right)$$

for all $0 \leq t \leq \tau$. Thus, by choosing k_1 and k_2 small enough, we can be sure that $\|x(t)\| \leq r$ for all $0 \leq t \leq \tau$. The lemma follows then from Corollary 5.4. $\square$

To apply Lemma 5.1, we need to check asymptotic stability of the origin of $\dot{x} = f(x)$. This task can be done by using linearization or searching for a Lyapunov function. The next lemma shows that, under certain conditions, we can use the same function V that satisfies the Hamilton–Jacobi inequality (5.28) as a Lyapunov function for showing asymptotic stability.

Lemma 5.2 *Suppose the assumptions of Theorem 5.5 are satisfied on a domain $D \subset R^n$ that contains the origin, $f(x)$ is continuously differentiable, and no solution of $\dot{x} = f(x)$ can stay identically in $S = \{x \in D \mid h(x) = 0\}$ other than the trivial solution $x(t) \equiv 0$. Then, the origin of $\dot{x} = f(x)$ is asymptotically stable and there is $k_1 > 0$ such that for each x_0 with $\|x_0\| \leq k_1$, the system (5.26)–(5.27) is small-signal finite-gain $\mathcal{L}_2$ stable with $\mathcal{L}_2$ gain less than or equal to γ.* $\diamond$

Proof: Take $u(t) \equiv 0$. By (5.28), we have

$$\dot{V}(x) = \frac{\partial V}{\partial x} f(x) \leq -\tfrac{1}{2} h^T(x) h(x), \quad \forall\, x \in D \qquad (5.37)$$

Take $r > 0$ such that $B_r = \{\|x\| \leq r\} \subset D$. We will show that $V(x)$ is positive definite in B_r. Toward that end, let $\phi(t; x)$ be the solution of $\dot{x} = f(x)$ that starts at $\phi(0; x) = x \in B_r$. By existence and uniqueness of solutions (Theorem 3.1) and continuous dependence of the solution on initial states (Theorem 3.4), there exists $\delta > 0$ such that for each $x \in B_r$ the solution $\phi(t; x)$ stays in D for all $t \in [0, \delta]$. Integrating (5.37) over $[0, \tau]$ for $\tau \leq \delta$, we obtain

$$V(\phi(\tau; x)) - V(x) \leq -\tfrac{1}{2} \int_0^\tau \|h(\phi(t; x))\|_2^2 \, dt$$

Using $V(\phi(\tau; x)) \geq 0$, we obtain

$$V(x) \geq \tfrac{1}{2} \int_0^\tau \|h(\phi(t; x))\|_2^2 \, dt$$

Suppose now that there is $\bar{x} \neq 0$ such that $V(\bar{x}) = 0$. The foregoing inequality implies that

$$\int_0^\tau \|h(\phi(t; \bar{x}))\|_2^2 \, dt = 0, \quad \forall\, \tau \in [0, \delta] \;\Rightarrow\; h(\phi(t; \bar{x})) \equiv 0, \quad \forall\, t \in [0, \delta]$$

Since during this interval the solution stays in S and, by assumption, the only solution that can stay identically in S is the trivial solution, we conclude that $\phi(t; \bar{x}) \equiv 0 \Rightarrow \bar{x} = 0$. Thus, $V(x)$ is positive definite in B_r. Using $V(x)$ as a Lyapunov function candidate for $\dot{x} = f(x)$, we conclude from (5.37) and LaSalle's invariance principle (Corollary 4.1) that the origin of $\dot{x} = f(x)$ is asymptotically stable. Application of Lemma 5.1 completes the proof. □

Example 5.12 As a variation on the theme of Examples 5.8 and 5.9, consider the system

$$
\begin{aligned}
\dot{x}_1 &= x_2 \\
\dot{x}_2 &= -a(x_1 - \tfrac{1}{3} x_1^3) - k x_2 + u \\
y &= x_2
\end{aligned}
$$

where a, $k > 0$. The function $V(x) = \alpha \left[a \left(x_1^2/2 - x_1^4/12 \right) + x_2^2/2 \right]$, with $\alpha > 0$, is positive semidefinite in the set $\{|x_1| \leq \sqrt{6}\}$. Using $V(x)$ as a candidate for the solution of the Hamilton–Jacobi inequality (5.28), it can be shown that

$$\mathcal{H}(V, f, G, h, \gamma) = \left(-\alpha k + \frac{\alpha^2}{2\gamma^2} + \frac{1}{2} \right) x_2^2$$

Repeating the argument used in Example 5.8, it can be easily seen that by choosing $\alpha = \gamma = 1/k$, inequality (5.28) is satisfied for all $x \in R^2$. Since the conditions of Theorem 5.5 are not satisfied globally, we investigate small-signal finite-gain stability by using Lemma 5.1. We need to show that the origin of the unforced system is asymptotically stable. This can be shown by linearization at the origin, which results in a Hurwitz matrix. Alternatively, we can apply Lemma 5.2, whose conditions are satisfied in the domain $D = \{|x_1| < \sqrt{3}\}$, because

$$x_2(t) \equiv 0 \Rightarrow x_1(t)[3 - x_1^2(t)] \equiv 0 \Rightarrow x_1(t) \equiv 0$$

Thus, we conclude that the system is small-signal finite-gain $\mathcal{L}_2$ stable and its $\mathcal{L}_2$ gain is less than or equal to $1/k$. $\triangle$

5.4   Feedback Systems: The Small-Gain Theorem

The formalism of input–output stability is particularly useful in studying stability of interconnected systems, since the gain of a system allows us to track how the norm of a signal increases or decreases as it passes through the system. This is particularly so for the feedback connection of Figure 5.1. Here, we have two systems $H_1 : \mathcal{L}_e^m \to \mathcal{L}_e^q$ and $H_2 : \mathcal{L}_e^q \to \mathcal{L}_e^m$. Suppose both systems are finite-gain $\mathcal{L}$ stable;[15] that is,

$$\|y_{1\tau}\|_{\mathcal{L}} \leq \gamma_1 \|e_{1\tau}\|_{\mathcal{L}} + \beta_1, \quad \forall\, e_1 \in \mathcal{L}_e^m, \ \forall\, \tau \in [0, \infty) \tag{5.38}$$

$$\|y_{2\tau}\|_{\mathcal{L}} \leq \gamma_2 \|e_{2\tau}\|_{\mathcal{L}} + \beta_2, \quad \forall\, e_2 \in \mathcal{L}_e^q, \ \forall\, \tau \in [0, \infty) \tag{5.39}$$

Suppose further that the feedback system is *well defined* in the sense that for every pair of inputs $u_1 \in \mathcal{L}_e^m$ and $u_2 \in \mathcal{L}_e^q$, there exist unique outputs $e_1, y_2 \in \mathcal{L}_e^m$ and $e_2, y_1 \in \mathcal{L}_e^q$.[16] Define

$$u = \begin{bmatrix} u_1 \\ u_2 \end{bmatrix}, \quad y = \begin{bmatrix} y_1 \\ y_2 \end{bmatrix}, \quad e = \begin{bmatrix} e_1 \\ e_2 \end{bmatrix}$$

The question of interest is whether the feedback connection, when viewed as a mapping from the input u to the output e or a mapping from input u to the output y, is finite-gain $\mathcal{L}$ stable.[17] It is not hard to see (Exercise 5.21) that the mapping from u to e is finite-gain $\mathcal{L}$ stable if and only if the mapping from u to y is finite-gain $\mathcal{L}$ stable. Therefore, we can simply say that the feedback connection is finite-gain

---

[15]In this section, we present a version of the classical small-gain theorem that applies to finite-gain $\mathcal{L}$ stability. For more general versions which apply to $\mathcal{L}$ stability, see [93] and [123].

[16]Sufficient conditions for existence and uniqueness of solutions are available in the literature. The most common approach uses the contraction mapping principle. (See, for example, [53, Theorem III.3.1].) A more recent approach that makes use of existence and uniqueness of the solution of state equations can be found in [93].

[17]See Exercise 5.20 for an explanation of why we have to consider both inputs and outputs in studying the stability of the feedback connection.

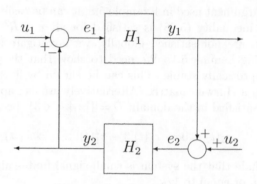

Figure 5.1: Feedback connection.

$\mathcal{L}$ stable if either mapping is finite-gain $\mathcal{L}$ stable. The following theorem, known as *the small-gain theorem*, gives a sufficient condition for finite-gain $\mathcal{L}$ stability of the feedback connection.

Theorem 5.6 *Under the preceding assumptions, the feedback connection is finite-gain $\mathcal{L}$ stable if $\gamma_1\gamma_2 < 1$.* $\diamond$

Proof: Assuming existence of the solution, we can write

$$e_{1\tau} = u_{1\tau} - (H_2 e_2)_\tau, \qquad e_{2\tau} = u_{2\tau} + (H_1 e_1)_\tau$$

Then,

$$
\begin{aligned}
\|e_{1\tau}\|_{\mathcal{L}} &\leq \|u_{1\tau}\|_{\mathcal{L}} + \|(H_2 e_2)_\tau\|_{\mathcal{L}} \leq \|u_{1\tau}\|_{\mathcal{L}} + \gamma_2\|e_{2\tau}\|_{\mathcal{L}} + \beta_2 \\
&\leq \|u_{1\tau}\|_{\mathcal{L}} + \gamma_2\left(\|u_{2\tau}\|_{\mathcal{L}} + \gamma_1\|e_{1\tau}\|_{\mathcal{L}} + \beta_1\right) + \beta_2 \\
&= \gamma_1\gamma_2\|e_{1\tau}\|_{\mathcal{L}} + \left(\|u_{1\tau}\|_{\mathcal{L}} + \gamma_2\|u_{2\tau}\|_{\mathcal{L}} + \beta_2 + \gamma_2\beta_1\right)
\end{aligned}
$$

Since $\gamma_1\gamma_2 < 1$,

$$\|e_{1\tau}\|_{\mathcal{L}} \leq \frac{1}{1 - \gamma_1\gamma_2}\left(\|u_{1\tau}\|_{\mathcal{L}} + \gamma_2\|u_{2\tau}\|_{\mathcal{L}} + \beta_2 + \gamma_2\beta_1\right) \tag{5.40}$$

for all $\tau \in [0, \infty)$. Similarly,

$$\|e_{2\tau}\|_{\mathcal{L}} \leq \frac{1}{1 - \gamma_1\gamma_2}\left(\|u_{2\tau}\|_{\mathcal{L}} + \gamma_1\|u_{1\tau}\|_{\mathcal{L}} + \beta_1 + \gamma_1\beta_2\right) \tag{5.41}$$

for all $\tau \in [0, \infty)$. The proof is competed by noting that $\|e\|_{\mathcal{L}} \leq \|e_1\|_{\mathcal{L}} + \|e_2\|_{\mathcal{L}}$, which follows from the triangle inequality. $\Box$

The feedback connection of Figure 5.1 provides a convenient setup for studying robustness issues in dynamical systems. Quite often, dynamical systems subject to model uncertainties can be represented in the form of a feedback connection with H_1, say, as a stable nominal system and H_2 as a stable perturbation. Then, the requirement $\gamma_1 \gamma_2 < 1$ is satisfied whenever γ_2 is small enough. Therefore, the small-gain theorem provides a conceptual framework for understanding many of the robustness results that arise in the study of dynamical systems, especially when feedback is used. Many of the robustness results that we can derive by using Lyapunov stability techniques can be interpreted as special cases of the small-gain theorem.

Example 5.13 Consider the feedback connection of Figure 5.1. Let H_1 be a linear time-invariant system with a Hurwitz square transfer function matrix $G(s) = C(sI - A)^{-1}B$. Let H_2 be a memoryless function $e_2 = \psi(t, y_2)$ that satisfies

$$\|\psi(t,y)\|_2 \leq \gamma_2 \|y\|_2, \quad \forall\, t \geq 0, \ \forall\, y \in R^m$$

From Theorem 5.4, we know that H_1 is finite-gain $\mathcal{L}_2$ stable and its $\mathcal{L}_2$ gain is given by

$$\gamma_1 = \sup_{w \in R} \|G(j\omega)\|_2$$

We have seen in Example 5.1 that H_2 is finite-gain $\mathcal{L}_2$ stable and its $\mathcal{L}_2$ gain is less than or equal to γ_2. Assuming the feedback connection is well defined, we conclude by the small-gain theorem that it will be finite-gain $\mathcal{L}_2$ stable if $\gamma_1 \gamma_2 < 1$. $\triangle$

Example 5.14 Consider the system

$$
\begin{aligned}
\dot{x} &= f(t, x, v + d_1(t)) \\
\varepsilon \dot{z} &= Az + B[u + d_2(t)] \\
v &= Cz
\end{aligned}
$$

where f is a smooth function of its arguments, A is a Hurwitz matrix, $-CA^{-1}B = I$, ε is a small positive parameter, and d_1, d_2 are disturbance signals. The linear part of this model represents actuator dynamics that are, typically, much faster than the plant dynamics represented here by the nonlinear equation $\dot{x} = f$. The disturbance signals d_1 and d_2 enter the system at the input of the plant and the input of the actuator, respectively. Suppose the disturbance signals d_1 and d_2 belong to a signal space $\mathcal{L}$, where $\mathcal{L}$ could be any $\mathcal{L}_p$ space, and the control goal is to attenuate the effect of this disturbance on the state x. This goal can be met if feedback control can be designed so that the closed-loop input–output map from (d_1, d_2) to x is finite-gain $\mathcal{L}$ stable and the $\mathcal{L}$ gain is less than some given tolerance $\delta > 0$. To simplify the design problem, it is common to neglect the actuator dynamics by setting $\varepsilon = 0$ and substituting $v = -CA^{-1}B(u + d_2) = u + d_2$ in the plant equation to obtain the reduced-order model

$$\dot{x} = f(t, x, u + d)$$

where $d = d_1 + d_2$. Assuming that the state variables are available for measurement, we use this model to design a state feedback control law $u = \gamma(t, x)$ to meet the design objective. Suppose we have succeeded in designing a smooth state feedback control $u = \gamma(t, x)$ such that

$$\|x\|_{\mathcal{L}} \leq \gamma\|d\|_{\mathcal{L}} + \beta \tag{5.42}$$

for some $\gamma < \delta$. Will the control meet the design objective when applied to the actual system with the actuator dynamics included? This is a question of robustness of the controller with respect to the unmodeled actuator dynamics.[18] When the control is applied to the actual system, the closed-loop equation is given by

$$\begin{aligned}
\dot{x} &= f(t, x, Cz + d_1(t)) \\
\varepsilon\dot{z} &= Az + B[\gamma(t, x) + d_2(t)]
\end{aligned}$$

Let us assume that $d_2(t)$ is differentiable and $\dot{d}_2 \in \mathcal{L}$. The change of variables

$$\eta = z + A^{-1}B[\gamma(t, x) + d_2(t)]$$

brings the closed-loop system into the form

$$\begin{aligned}
\dot{x} &= f(t, x, \gamma(t, x) + d(t) + C\eta) \\
\varepsilon\dot{\eta} &= A\eta + \varepsilon A^{-1}B[\dot{\gamma} + \dot{d}_2(t)]
\end{aligned}$$

where

$$\dot{\gamma} = \frac{\partial \gamma}{\partial t} + \frac{\partial \gamma}{\partial x}f(t, x, \gamma(t, x) + d(t) + C\eta)$$

It is not difficult to see that the closed-loop system can be represented in the form of Figure 5.1 with H_1 defined by

$$\begin{aligned}
\dot{x} &= f(t, x, \gamma(t, x) + e_1) \\
y_1 &= \dot{\gamma} = \frac{\partial \gamma}{\partial t} + \frac{\partial \gamma}{\partial x}f(t, x, \gamma(t, x) + e_1)
\end{aligned}$$

H_2 defined by

$$\begin{aligned}
\dot{\eta} &= \frac{1}{\varepsilon}A\eta + A^{-1}Be_2 \\
y_2 &= -C\eta
\end{aligned}$$

and

$$u_1 = d_1 + d_2 = d, \quad u_2 = \dot{d}_2$$

In this representation, the system H_1 is the nominal reduced-order closed-loop system, while H_2 represents the effect of the unmodeled dynamics. Setting $\varepsilon = 0$

---

[18]In Example 11.14, we investigate a similar robustness problem, in the context of stabilization, using singular perturbation theory.

opens the loop and the overall closed-loop system reduces to the nominal one. Let us assume that the feedback function $\gamma(t, x)$ satisfies the inequality

$$\left\| \frac{\partial \gamma}{\partial t} + \frac{\partial \gamma}{\partial x} f(t, x, \gamma(t, x) + e_1) \right\| \le c_1 \|x\| + c_2 \|e_1\| \tag{5.43}$$

for all (t, x, e_1), where c_1 and c_2 are nonnegative constants. Using (5.42) and (5.43), it can be shown that

$$\|y_1\|_{\mathcal{L}} \le \gamma_1 \|e_1\|_{\mathcal{L}} + \beta_1$$

where

$$\gamma_1 = c_1 \gamma + c_2, \quad \beta_1 = c_1 \beta$$

Since H_2 is a linear time-invariant system and A is Hurwitz, we apply Corollary 5.2 to show that H_2 is finite-gain $\mathcal{L}_p$ stable for any $p \in [1, \infty]$ and

$$\|y_2\|_{\mathcal{L}} \le \gamma_2 \|e_2\|_{\mathcal{L}} + \beta_2 \overset{\text{def}}{=} \varepsilon \gamma_f \|e_2\|_{\mathcal{L}} + \beta_2$$

where

$$\gamma_f = \frac{2\lambda_{max}^2(Q) \|A^{-1}B\|_2 \|C\|_2}{\lambda_{min}(Q)}, \quad \beta_2 = \rho \|C\|_2 \|\eta(0)\| \sqrt{\frac{\lambda_{max}(Q)}{\lambda_{min}(Q)}}$$

$$\rho = \begin{cases} 1, & \text{if } p = \infty \\ \left(\frac{2\varepsilon \lambda_{max}(Q)}{p} \right)^{1/p}, & \text{if } p \in [1, \infty) \end{cases}$$

and Q is the solution of the Lyapunov equation $QA + A^T Q = -I$.[19] Thus, assuming the feedback connection is well defined, we conclude from the small-gain theorem that the input–output map from u to e is $\mathcal{L}$ stable. From (5.40), we have

$$\|e_1\|_{\mathcal{L}} \le \frac{1}{1 - \varepsilon \gamma_1 \gamma_f} \left[\|u_1\|_{\mathcal{L}} + \varepsilon \gamma_f \|u_2\|_{\mathcal{L}} + \varepsilon \gamma_f \beta_1 + \beta_2 \right]$$

Using

$$\|x\|_{\mathcal{L}} \le \gamma \|e_1\|_{\mathcal{L}} + \beta$$

which follows from (5.42), and the definition of u_1 and u_2, we obtain

$$\|x\|_{\mathcal{L}} \le \frac{\gamma}{1 - \varepsilon \gamma_1 \gamma_f} \left[\|d\|_{\mathcal{L}} + \varepsilon \gamma_f \|\dot{d}_2\|_{\mathcal{L}} + \varepsilon \gamma_f \beta_1 + \beta_2 \right] + \beta \tag{5.44}$$

It is interesting to note that the right-hand side of (5.44) approaches

$$\gamma \|d\|_{\mathcal{L}} + \beta + \gamma \beta_2$$

as $\varepsilon \to 0$, which shows that for sufficiently small ε the upper bound on the $\mathcal{L}$ gain of the map from d to x, under the actual closed-loop system, will be close to the corresponding quantity under the nominal closed-loop system. $\quad \triangle$

---

[19] P of Corollary 5.2 is taken as εQ so that $(\varepsilon Q)(A/\varepsilon) + (A/\varepsilon)^T (\varepsilon Q) = -I$.

5.5 Exercises

5.1 Show that the series connection of two $\mathcal{L}$ stable (respectively, finite-gain $\mathcal{L}$ stable) systems is $\mathcal{L}$ stable (respectively, finite-gain $\mathcal{L}$ stable).

5.2 Show that the parallel connection of two $\mathcal{L}$ stable (respectively, finite-gain $\mathcal{L}$ stable) systems is $\mathcal{L}$ stable (respectively, finite-gain $\mathcal{L}$ stable).

5.3 Consider a system defined by the memoryless function $y = u^{1/3}$.

(a) Show that the system is $\mathcal{L}_\infty$ stable with zero bias.

(b) For any positive constant a, show that the system is finite-gain $\mathcal{L}_\infty$ stable with $\gamma = a$ and $\beta = (1/a)^{1/2}$.

(c) Compare the two statements.

5.4 Consider a system defined by the memoryless function by $y = h(u)$, where $h : R^m \to R^q$ is globally Lipschitz. Investigate $\mathcal{L}_p$ stability for each $p \in [1, \infty]$ when

$$(1)\ h(0) = 0. \qquad (2)\ h(0) \neq 0.$$

5.5 For each of the relay characteristices shown in Figure 5.2, investigate $\mathcal{L}_\infty$ and $\mathcal{L}_2$ stability.

5.6 Verify that $D^+W(t)$ satisfies (5.12) when $V(t, x(t)) = 0$.
Hint: Using Exercise 3.24, show that $V(t + h, x(t + h)) \leq c_4 h^2 L^2 \|u\|^2/2 + h\, o(h)$, where $o(h)/h \to 0$ as $h \to 0$. Then, use the fact that $c_4 \geq 2c_1$.

5.7 Suppose the assumptions of Theorem 5.1 are satisfied, except (5.10), which is replaced by

$$\|h(t, x, u)\| \leq \eta_1\|x\| + \eta_2\|u\| + \eta_3, \quad \eta_3 > 0$$

Show that the system is small-signal finite-gain $\mathcal{L}_\infty$ stable (or finite-gain $\mathcal{L}_\infty$ stable, if the assumptions hold globally) and find the constants γ and β in (5.11).

5.8 Suppose the assumptions of Theorem 5.1 are satisfied, except (5.10), which is replaced by (5.20). Show that the system is small-signal $\mathcal{L}_\infty$ stable (or $\mathcal{L}_\infty$ stable, if the assumptions hold globally).

5.9 Derive a result similar to Corollary 5.2 for linear time-varying systems.

5.10 For each of the following systems, investigate $\mathcal{L}_\infty$ and finite-gain $\mathcal{L}_\infty$ stability:

$$
(1) \quad
\begin{aligned}
\dot{x} &= -(1 + u)x^3 \\
y &= x
\end{aligned}
\qquad\qquad
(2) \quad
\begin{aligned}
\dot{x} &= -(1 + u)x^3 - x^5 \\
y &= x + u
\end{aligned}
$$

$$
(3) \quad
\begin{aligned}
\dot{x} &= -x/(1 + x^2) + u \\
y &= x/(1 + x^2)
\end{aligned}
\qquad\qquad
(4) \quad
\begin{aligned}
\dot{x} &= -x - x^3 + x^2 u \\
y &= x \sin u
\end{aligned}
$$

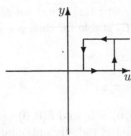

(a) On–off with hysteresis

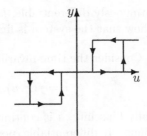

(b) On–off with dead zone and hysteresis

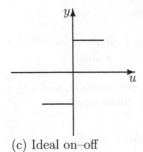

(c) Ideal on–off

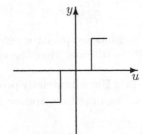

(d) On–off with dead zone

Figure 5.2: Relay characteristics

5.11 For each of the following systems, investigate $\mathcal{L}_\infty$ and finite-gain $\mathcal{L}_\infty$ stability:

(**1**) $\dot{x}_1 = -x_1 + x_1^2 x_2,$ $\qquad$ $\dot{x}_2 = -x_1^3 - x_2 + u,$ $\qquad$ $y = x_1$

(**2**) $\dot{x}_1 = -x_1 + x_2,$ $\qquad$ $\dot{x}_2 = -x_1^3 - x_2 + u,$ $\qquad$ $y = x_2$

(**3**) $\dot{x}_1 = (x_1 + u)(\|x\|_2^2 - 1),$ $\qquad$ $\dot{x}_2 = x_2(\|x\|_2^2 - 1),$ $\qquad$ $y = x_1$

(**4**) $\dot{x}_1 = -x_1 - x_2 + u_1,$ $\qquad$ $\dot{x}_2 = x_1 - x_2^3 + u_2,$ $\qquad$ $y = x_1(x_2 + u_1)$

(**5**) $\dot{x}_1 = -x_1 + x_1^2 x_2,$ $\qquad$ $\dot{x}_2 = x_1 - x_2 + u,$ $\qquad$ $y = x_1 + u$

(**6**) $\dot{x}_1 = x_2,$ $\qquad$ $\dot{x}_2 = -x_1^3 - x_2 + u,$ $\qquad$ $y = x_2$

(**7**) $\dot{x}_1 = -x_1 - x_2,$ $\qquad$ $\dot{x}_2 = x_1 - x_3 + u,$ $\qquad$ $y(t) = x_1(t - T)$

where $T > 0$.

5.12 Consider the system

$$\dot{x}_1 = x_2, \qquad \dot{x}_2 = -y - h(y) + u, \qquad y = x_1 + x_2$$

where h is continuously differentiable, $h(0) = 0$, and $zh(z) > az^2$ for all $z \in R$, for some $a > 0$. Show that the system is finite-gain $\mathcal{L}_p$ stable for each $p \in [1, \infty]$.

5.13 ([192]) Consider the time-invariant system

$$\dot{x} = f(x, u), \qquad y = h(x, u)$$

where f is locally Lipschitz, h is continuous, $f(0,0) = 0$, and $h(0,0) = 0$. Suppose there is a continuously differentiable, positive definite, radially unbounded function $V(x)$ such that

$$\frac{\partial V}{\partial x} f(x, u) \le -W(x) + \psi(u), \quad \forall \ (x, u)$$

where $W(x)$ is continuous, positive definite, and radially unbounded, $\psi(u)$ is continuous, and $\psi(0) = 0$. Show that the system is $\mathcal{L}_\infty$ stable.

5.14 Let $H(s)$ be a Hurwitz strictly proper transfer function, and $h(t) = \mathcal{L}^{-1}\{H(s)\}$ be the corresponding impulse response function. Show that

$$\sup_{\omega \in R} |H(j\omega)| \le \int_0^\infty |h(t)| \, dt$$

5.15 For each of the following systems, show that the system is finite-gain (or small-signal finite-gain) $\mathcal{L}_2$ stable and find an upper bound on the $\mathcal{L}_2$ gain:

(1)
$$\begin{aligned}
\dot{x}_1 &= x_2 \\
\dot{x}_2 &= -a \sin x_1 - k x_2 + u \\
y &= x_2 \\
a &> 0, \ k > 0
\end{aligned}$$

(2)
$$\begin{aligned}
\dot{x}_1 &= -x_2 \\
\dot{x}_2 &= x_1 - x_2 \operatorname{sat}(x_2^2 - x_3^2) + x_2 u \\
\dot{x}_3 &= x_3 \operatorname{sat}(x_2^2 - x_3^2) - x_3 u \\
y &= x_2^2 - x_3^2
\end{aligned}$$

(3)
$$\begin{aligned}
\dot{x}_1 &= x_2 \\
\dot{x}_2 &= x_1 - \operatorname{sat}(2x_1 + x_2) + u \\
y &= x_1
\end{aligned}$$

(4)
$$\begin{aligned}
\dot{x}_1 &= x_2 \\
\dot{x}_2 &= -(1 + x_1^2)x_2 - x_1^3 + x_1 u \\
y &= x_1 x_2
\end{aligned}$$

5.16 Consider the system

$$\dot{x}_1 = -x_1 + x_2, \qquad \dot{x}_2 = -x_1 - \sigma(x_1) - x_2 + u, \qquad y = x_2$$

where σ is locally Lipschitz, $\sigma(0) = 0$, and $z\sigma(z) \ge 0$ for all $z \in R$.

(a) Is the system finite-gain $\mathcal{L}_\infty$ stable?

(b) Is it finite-gain $\mathcal{L}_2$ stable? If yes, find an upper bound on the $\mathcal{L}_2$ gain.

5.17 ([77]) Consider the system

$$\dot{x} = f(x) + G(x)u, \qquad y = h(x) + J(x)u$$

where f, G, h, and J are smooth functions of x. Suppose there is a positive constant γ such that $\gamma^2 I - J^T(x)J(x) > 0$ and

$$\mathcal{H} = \frac{\partial V}{\partial x} f + \frac{1}{2} \left[h^T J + \frac{\partial V}{\partial x} G \right] \left(\gamma^2 I - J^T J \right)^{-1} \left[h^T J + \frac{\partial V}{\partial x} G \right]^T + \frac{1}{2} h^T h \le 0$$

$\forall\, x$. Show that the system is finite-gain $\mathcal{L}_2$ stable with $\mathcal{L}_2$ gain less than or equal to γ.

Hint: Set

$$\gamma^2 I - J^T(x)J(x) = W^T(x)W(x), \quad L(x) = -\left[W^T(x) \right]^{-1} \left[h^T(x)J(x) + \frac{\partial V}{\partial x} G(x) \right]^T$$

and show that the following inequality holds $\forall\, u$

$$\frac{\partial V}{\partial x} f + \frac{\partial V}{\partial x} Gu = -\frac{1}{2}[L + Wu]^T[L + Wu] + \frac{\gamma^2}{2} u^T u - \frac{1}{2} y^T y + \mathcal{H}$$

5.18 ([199]) Consider the system

$$\dot{x} = f(x) + G(x)u + K(x)w, \qquad y = h(x)$$

where u is a control input and w is a disturbance input. The functions f, G, K, and h are smooth, and $f(0) = 0$, $h(0) = 0$. Let $\gamma > 0$. Suppose there is a smooth positive semidefinite function $V(x)$ that satisfies

$$\frac{\partial V}{\partial x} f(x) + \frac{1}{2} \frac{\partial V}{\partial x} \left[\frac{1}{\gamma^2} K(x)K^T(x) - G(x)G^T(x) \right] \left(\frac{\partial V}{\partial x} \right)^T + \frac{1}{2} h^T(x)h(x) \le 0$$

$\forall\, x$. Show that with the feedback control $u = -G^T(x)(\partial V / \partial x)^T$ the closed-loop map from w to $\begin{bmatrix} y \\ u \end{bmatrix}$ is finite-gain $\mathcal{L}_2$ stable with $\mathcal{L}_2$ gain less than or equal to γ.

5.19 ([200]) The purpose of this exercise is to show that the $\mathcal{L}_2$ gain of a linear time-invariant system of the form (5.24)–(5.25), with a Hurwitz matrix A, is the same, whether the space of functions is defined on $R_+ = [0, \infty)$ or on the whole real line $R = (-\infty, \infty)$. Let $\mathcal{L}_2$ be the space of square integrable functions on R_+ with the norm $\|u\|_{\mathcal{L}_2}^2 = \int_0^\infty u^T(t)u(t)\, dt$ and $\mathcal{L}_{2R}$ be the space of square integrable functions on R with the norm $\|u\|_{\mathcal{L}_{2R}}^2 = \int_{-\infty}^\infty u^T(t)u(t)\, dt$. Let γ_2 and γ_{2R} be the $\mathcal{L}_2$ gains on $\mathcal{L}_2$ and $\mathcal{L}_{2R}$, respectively. Since $\mathcal{L}_2$ is a subset of $\mathcal{L}_{2R}$, it is clear that $\gamma_2 \le \gamma_{2R}$. We will show that $\gamma_2 = \gamma_{2R}$ by showing that, for every $\varepsilon > 0$, there is a signal $u \in \mathcal{L}_2$ such that $y \in \mathcal{L}_2$ and $\|y\|_{\mathcal{L}_2} \ge (1 - \varepsilon)\gamma_{2R}\|u\|_{\mathcal{L}_2}$.

(a) Given $\varepsilon > 0$ show that we can always choose $0 < \delta < 1$ such that

$$\frac{1 - \varepsilon/2 - \sqrt{\delta}}{\sqrt{1 - \delta}} \geq 1 - \varepsilon$$

(b) Show that we can always select $u \in \mathcal{L}_{2R}$ and time $t_1 < \infty$ such that

$$\|u\|_{\mathcal{L}_{2R}} = 1, \quad \|y\|_{\mathcal{L}_{2R}} \geq \gamma_{2R} \left(1 - \frac{\varepsilon}{2}\right), \quad \int_{-\infty}^{t_1} u^T(t)u(t)\ dt = \delta$$

(c) Let $u(t) = u_1(t) + u_2(t)$, where u_1 vanishes for $t < t_1$ and u_2 vanishes for $t > t_1$. Let $y_1(t)$ be the output corresponding to the input $u_1(t)$. Show that

$$\frac{\|y_1\|_{\mathcal{L}_{2R}}}{\|u_1\|_{\mathcal{L}_{2R}}} \geq \frac{1 - \varepsilon/2 - \sqrt{\delta}}{\sqrt{1 - \delta}}\gamma_{2R} \geq (1 - \varepsilon)\gamma_{2R}$$

(d) For all $t \geq 0$, define $u(t)$ and $y(t)$ by $u(t) = u_1(t + t_1)$ and $y(t) = y_1(t + t_1)$. Show that both u and y belong to $\mathcal{L}_2$, $y(t)$ is the output corresponding to $u(t)$, and $\|y\|_{\mathcal{L}_2} \geq (1 - \varepsilon)\gamma_{2R}\|u\|_{\mathcal{L}_2}$.

5.20 Consider the feedback connection of Figure 5.1, where H_1 and H_2 are linear time-invariant systems represented by the transfer functions $H_1(s) = (s-1)/(s+1)$ and $H_2(s) = 1/(s-1)$. Find the closed-loop transfer functions from (u_1, u_2) to (y_1, y_2) and from (u_1, u_2) to (e_1, e_2). Use these transfer functions to discuss why we have to consider both inputs (u_1, u_2) and both outputs (e_1, e_2) (or (y_1, y_2)) in studying the stability of the feedback connection.

5.21 Consider the feedback connection of Figure 5.1. Show that the mapping from (u_1, u_2) to (y_1, y_2) is finite-gain $\mathcal{L}$ stable if and only if the mapping from (u_1, u_2) to (e_1, e_2) is finite-gain $\mathcal{L}$ stable.

5.22 Let $d_2(t) = a \sin \omega t$ in Example 5.14, where a and ω are positive constants.

(a) Show that, for sufficiently small ε, the state of the closed-loop system is uniformly bounded.

(b) Investigate the effect of increasing ω.

5.23 Consider the feedback connection of Figure 5.1, where H_1 and H_2 are given by

$$H_1 : \begin{cases} \dot{x}_1 &= -x_1 + x_2 \\ \dot{x}_2 &= -x_1^3 - x_2 + e_1 \\ y_1 &= x_2 \end{cases} \quad \text{and} \quad H_2 : \begin{cases} \dot{x}_3 &= -x_3^3 + e_2 \\ y_2 &= (1/2)x_3^3 \end{cases}$$

Let $u_2 = 0$, $u = u_1$ be the input, and $y = y_1$ be the output.

(a) Using $x = [x_1,\ x_2,\ x_3]^T$ as the state vector, find the state model of the system.

(b) Is the system $\mathcal{L}_2$ stable?

Chapter 6

Passivity

Passivity provides us with a useful tool for the analysis of nonlinear systems, which relates nicely to Lyapunov and $\mathcal{L}_2$ stability. We start in Section 6.1 by defining passivity of memoryless nonlinearities. We extend the definition to dynamical systems, represented by state models, in Section 6.2. In both cases, we use electrical networks to motivate the definitions. In Section 6.3, we study positive real and strictly positive real transfer functions and show that they represent passive and strictly passive systems, respectively. The connection between passivity and both Lyapunov and $\mathcal{L}_2$ stability is established in Section 6.4. These four sections prepare us to address the main results of the chapter, namely, the passivity theorems of Section 6.5. The main passivity theorem states that *the (negative) feedback connection of two passive systems is passive.* Under additional observability conditions, the feedback connection is also asymptotically stable. The passivity theorems of Section 6.5 and the small-gain theorem of Section 5.4 provide a conceptually important generalization of the fact that the feedback connection of two stable linear systems will be stable if the loop gain is less than one or the loop phase is less than 180 degrees. The connection between passivity and the phase of a transfer function comes from the frequency-domain characterization of positive real transfer functions, given in Section 6.3. There we know that the phase of a positive real transfer function cannot exceed 90 degree. Hence, the loop phase cannot exceed 180 degrees. If one of the two transfer functions is strictly positive real, the loop phase will be strictly less than 180 degrees. Section 6.5 discusses also loop transformations, which allow us, in certain cases, to transform the feedback connection of two systems that may not be passive into the feedback connection of two passive systems, hence extending the utility of the passivity theorems.

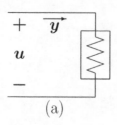
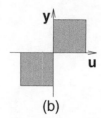

Figure 6.1: (a) A passive resistor; (b) u–y characteristic lies in the first–third quadrant.

6.1   Memoryless Functions

Our goal in this section is to define passivity of the memoryless function $y = h(t, u)$, where $h : [0, \infty) \times R^p \to R^p$. We use electric networks to motivate the definition. Figure 6.1(a) shows a one-port resistive element with voltage u and current y. We view this element as a system with input u and output y. The resistive element is passive if the inflow of power is always nonnegative; that is, if $uy \geq 0$ for all points (u, y) on its u–y characteristic. Geometrically, this means that the u–y curve must lie in the first and third quadrants, as shown in Figure 6.1(b). The simplest such resistive element is a linear resistor that obeys Ohm's law $u = Ry$ or $y = Gu$, where R is the resistance and $G = 1/R$ is the conductance. For positive resistance, the u–y characteristic is a straight line of slope G and the product $uy = Gy^2$ is always nonnegative. In fact, it is always positive except at the origin point $(0, 0)$. Nonlinear passive resistive elements have nonlinear u–y curves lying in the first and third quadrants; examples are shown in Figures 6.2(a) and (b). Notice that the tunnel-diode characteristic of Figure 6.2(b) is still passive even though the curve has negative slope in some region. As an example of an element that is not passive, Figure 6.2(c) shows the u–y characteristic of a negative resistance that was used in Section 1.2.4 to construct the negative resistance oscillator. Such characteristic can be only realized using active devices such as the twin tunnel-diode circuit of Figure 1.7. For a multiport network where u and y are vectors, the power flow into the network is the inner product $u^T y = \Sigma_{i=1}^{p} u_i y_i = \Sigma_{i=1}^{p} u_i h_i(u)$. The network is passive if $u^T y \geq 0$ for all u. This concept of passivity is now abstracted and assigned to any function $y = h(t, u)$ irrespective of its physical origin. We think of $u^T y$ as the power flow into the system and say that the system is passive if $u^T y \geq 0$ for all u. For the scalar case, the graph of the input–output relation must lie in the first and third quadrants. We also say that the graph belongs to the sector $[0, \infty]$, where zero and infinity are the slopes of the boundaries of the first–third quadrant region. The graphical representation is valid even when h is time varying. In this case, the u–y curve will be changing with time, but will always belong to the sector $[0, \infty]$. For a vector function, we can give a graphical representation in the special case when $h(t, u)$ is decoupled in the sense that $h_i(t, u)$ depends only on u_i; that is,

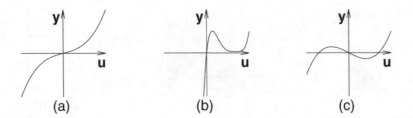

Figure 6.2: (a) and (b) are examples of nonlinear passive resistor characteristics; (c) is an example of a nonpassive resistor.

$$h(t, u) = \begin{bmatrix} h_1(t, u_1) \\ h_2(t, u_2) \\ \vdots \\ h_p(t, u_p) \end{bmatrix} \tag{6.1}$$

In this case, the graph of each component belongs to the sector $[0, \infty]$. In the general case, such graphical representation is not possible, but we will continue to use the sector terminology by saying that h belongs to the sector $[0, \infty]$ if $u^T h(t, u) \geq 0$ for all (t, u).

An extreme case of passivity happens when $u^T y = 0$. In this case, we say that the system is lossless. An example of a lossless system is the ideal transformer shown in Figure 6.3. Here $y = Su$, where

$$u = \begin{bmatrix} v_1 \\ i_2 \end{bmatrix}, \quad y = \begin{bmatrix} i_1 \\ v_2 \end{bmatrix}, \quad S = \begin{bmatrix} 0 & -N \\ N & 0 \end{bmatrix}$$

The matrix S is skew-symmetric; that is, $S + S^T = 0$. Hence, $u^T y = u^T S u = (1/2) u^T (S + S^T) u = 0$.

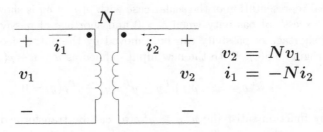

Figure 6.3: Ideal transformer

Consider now a function h satisfying $u^T y \geq u^T \varphi(u)$ for some function $\varphi(u)$. When $u^T \varphi(u) > 0$ for all $u \neq 0$, h is called *input strictly passive* because passivity is strict in the sense that $u^T y = 0$ only if $u = 0$. Equivalently, in the scalar case,

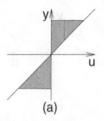 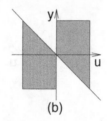 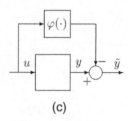

(a)   (b)   (c)

Figure 6.4: A graphical representation of $u^T y \geq \varepsilon u^T u$ for (a) $\varepsilon > 0$ (excess of passivity); (b) $\varepsilon < 0$ (shortage of passivity); (c) removal of excess or shortage of passivity by input-feedforward operation.

the u–y graph does not touch the u-axis, except at the origin. The term $u^T \varphi(u)$ represents the "excess" of passivity. On the other hand, if $u^T \varphi(u)$ is negative for some values of u, then the function h is not necessarily passive. The term $u^T \varphi(u)$ represents the "shortage" of passivity. Excess and shortage of passivity are more transparent when h is scalar and $\varphi(u) = \varepsilon u$. In this case, h belongs to the sector $[\varepsilon, \infty]$, shown in Figure 6.4, with excess of passivity when $\varepsilon > 0$ and shortage of passivity when $\varepsilon < 0$. Excess or shortage of passivity can be removed by the input-feedforward operation shown in Figure 6.4(c). With the new output defined as $\tilde{y} = y - \varphi(u)$, we have

$$u^T \tilde{y} = u^T [y - \varphi(u)] \geq u^T \varphi(u) - u^T \varphi(u) = 0$$

Thus, any function satisfying $u^T y \geq u^T \varphi(u)$ can be transformed into a function that belongs to the sector $[0, \infty]$ via input feedforward. Such a function is called *input-feedforward passive*. On the other hand, suppose $u^T y \geq y^T \rho(y)$ for some function $\rho(y)$. Similar to the foregoing case, there is excess of passivity when $y^T \rho(y) > 0$ for all $y \neq 0$, and shortage of passivity when $y^T \rho(y)$ is negative for some values of y. A graphical representation of the scalar case with $\rho(y) = \delta y$ is shown in Figure 6.5. There is "excess" of passivity when $\delta > 0$ and shortage of passivity when $\delta < 0$. Excess or shortage of passivity can be removed by the output-feedback operation shown in Figure 6.5(c). With the new input defined as $\tilde{u} = u - \rho(y)$, we have

$$\tilde{u}^T y = [u - \rho(y)]^T y \geq y^T \rho(y) - y^T \rho(y) = 0$$

Hence, any function satisfying $u^T y \geq y^T \rho(y)$ can be transformed into a function that belongs to the sector $[0, \infty]$ via output feedback. Such a function is called *output-feedback passive*. When $y^T \rho(y) > 0$ for all $y \neq 0$, the function is called *output strictly passive* because passivity is strict in the sense that $u^T y = 0$ only if $y = 0$. Equivalently, in the scalar case, the u–y graph does not touch the y-axis, except at the origin. For convenience, we summarize the various notions of passivity in the next definition.

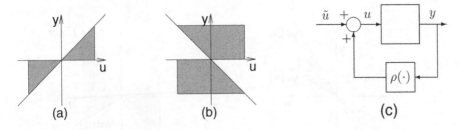

Figure 6.5: A graphical representation of $u^T y \geq \delta y^T y$ for (a) $\delta > 0$ (excess of passivity); (b) $\delta < 0$ (shortage of passivity); (c) removal of excess or shortage of passivity by output-feedback operation.

Definition 6.1 *The system $y = h(t, u)$ is*

- *passive if $u^T y \geq 0$.*

- *lossless if $u^T y = 0$.*

- *input-feedforward passive if $u^T y \geq u^T \varphi(u)$ for some function φ.*

- *input strictly passive if $u^T y \geq u^T \varphi(u)$ and $u^T \varphi(u) > 0$, $\forall\, u \neq 0$.*

- *output-feedback passive if $u^T y \geq y^T \rho(y)$ for some function ρ.*

- *output strictly passive if $u^T y \geq y^T \rho(y)$ and $y^T \rho(y) > 0$, $\forall\, y \neq 0$.*

In all cases, the inequality should hold for all (t, u).

Consider next a scalar function $y = h(t, u)$, which satisfies the inequality

$$\alpha u^2 \leq u h(t, u) \leq \beta u^2 \tag{6.2}$$

for all (t, u), where α and β are real numbers with $\beta \geq \alpha$. The graph of this function belongs to a sector whose boundaries are the lines $y = \alpha u$ and $y = \beta u$. We say that h belongs to the sector $[\alpha, \beta]$. Figure 6.6 shows the sector $[\alpha, \beta]$ for $\beta > 0$ and different signs of α. If strict inequality is satisfied on either side of (6.2), we say that h belongs to a sector $(\alpha, \beta]$, $[\alpha, \beta)$, or (α, β), with obvious implications. Comparing the sectors of Figure 6.6 with those of Figures 6.4 and 6.5 shows that a function in the sector $[\alpha, \beta]$ combines input-feedforward passivity with output strict passivity since the sector $[\alpha, \beta]$ is the intersection of the sectors $[\alpha, \infty]$ and $[0, \beta]$. Indeed, we can show that such a function can be transformed into a function that belongs to the sector $[0, \infty]$ by a sequence of input-feedforward and output-feedback operations. Before we do that, we extend the sector definition to the vector case. Toward that end, note that (6.2) is equivalent to

$$[h(t, u) - \alpha u][h(t, u) - \beta u] \leq 0 \tag{6.3}$$

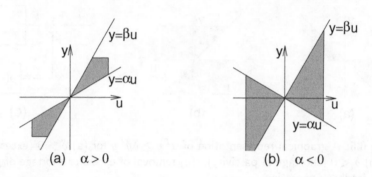

Figure 6.6: The sector $[\alpha, \beta]$ for $\beta > 0$ and (a) $\alpha > 0$; (b) $\alpha < 0$.

for all (t, u). For the vector case, let us consider first a function $h(t, u)$ that is decoupled as in (6.1). Suppose each component h_i satisfies the sector condition (6.2) with constants α_i and $\beta_i > \alpha_i$. Taking

$$K_1 = \mathrm{diag}(\alpha_1, \alpha_2, \ldots, \alpha_p), \quad K_2 = \mathrm{diag}(\beta_1, \beta_2, \ldots, \beta_p)$$

it can be easily seen that

$$[h(t, u) - K_1 u]^T [h(t, u) - K_2 u] \leq 0 \tag{6.4}$$

for all (t, u). Note that $K = K_2 - K_1$ is a positive definite symmetric (diagonal) matrix. Inequality (6.4) may hold for more general vector functions. For example, suppose $h(t, u)$ satisfies the inequality

$$\|h(t, u) - Lu\|_2 \leq \gamma \|u\|_2$$

for all (t, u). Taking $K_1 = L - \gamma I$ and $K_2 = L + \gamma I$, we can write

$$[h(t, u) - K_1 u]^T [h(t, u) - K_2 u] = \|h(t, u) - Ly\|_2^2 - \gamma^2 \|u\|_2^2 \leq 0$$

Once again, $K = K_2 - K_1$ is a positive definite symmetric (diagonal) matrix. We use inequality (6.4) with a positive definite symmetric matrix $K = K_2 - K_1$ as a definition of the sector $[K_1, K_2]$ in the vector case. The next definition summaries the sector terminology.

Definition 6.2 *A memoryless function $h : [0, \infty) \times R^p \to R^p$ is said to belong to the sector*

- $[0, \infty]$ *if* $u^T h(t, u) \geq 0$.

- $[K_1, \infty]$ *if* $u^T [h(t, u) - K_1 u] \geq 0$.

- $[0, K_2]$ *with* $K_2 = K_2^T > 0$ *if* $h^T(t, u)[h(t, u) - K_2 u] \leq 0$.

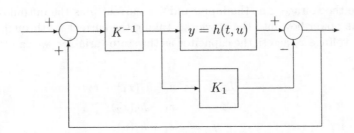

Figure 6.7: A function in the sector $[K_1, K_2]$, where $K = K_2 - K_1 = K^T > 0$, can be transformed into a function in the sector $[0, \infty]$ by input feedforward followed by output feedback.

- $[K_1, K_2]$ *with* $K = K_2 - K_1 = K^T > 0$ *if*

$$[h(t, u) - K_1 u]^T [h(t, u) - K_2 u] \leq 0 \tag{6.5}$$

In all cases, the inequality should hold for all (t, u)*. If in any case the inequality is strict, we write the sector as* $(0, \infty)$*,* (K_1, ∞)*,* $(0, K_2)$*, or* (K_1, K_2)*. In the scalar case, we write* $(\alpha, \beta]$*,* $[\alpha, \beta)$*, or* (α, β) *to indicate that one or both sides of (6.2) is satisfied as a strict inequality.*

The sector $[0, \infty]$ corresponds to passivity. The sector $[K_1, \infty]$ corresponds to input-feedforward passivity with $\varphi(u) = K_1 u$. The sector $[0, K_2]$ with $K_2 = (1/\delta)I > 0$ corresponds to output strict passivity with $\rho(y) = \delta y$. We leave it to the reader (Exercise 6.1) to verify that a function in the sector $[K_1, K_2]$ can be transformed into a function in the sector $[0, \infty]$ by input feedforward followed by output feedback, as shown in Figure 6.7.

6.2 State Models

Let us now define passivity for a dynamical system represented by the state model

$$\dot{x} = f(x, u) \tag{6.6}$$
$$y = h(x, u) \tag{6.7}$$

where $f : R^n \times R^p \to R^n$ is locally Lipschitz, $h : R^n \times R^p \to R^p$ is continuous, $f(0, 0) = 0$, and $h(0, 0) = 0$. The system has the same number of inputs and outputs. The following RLC circuit motivates the definition.

Example 6.1 The RLC circuit of Figure 6.8 features a voltage source connected to an RLC network with linear inductor and capacitor and nonlinear resistors. The nonlinear resistors 1 and 3 are represented by their v–i characteristics $i_1 = h_1(v_1)$ and $i_3 = h_3(v_3)$, while resistor 2 is represented by its i–v characteristic $v_2 = h_2(i_2)$.

We take the voltage u as the input and the current y as the output. The product uy is the power flow into the network. Taking the current x_1 through the inductor and the voltage x_2 across the capacitor as the state variables, we can write the state model as

$$
\begin{aligned}
L\dot{x}_1 &= u - h_2(x_1) - x_2 \\
C\dot{x}_2 &= x_1 - h_3(x_2) \\
y &= x_1 + h_1(u)
\end{aligned}
$$

The new feature of an RLC network over a resistive network is the presence of the energy-storing elements L and C. The system is passive if the energy absorbed by the network over any period of time $[0, t]$ is greater than or equal to the increase in the energy stored in the network over the same period; that is,

$$
\int_0^t u(s)y(s)\ ds \geq V(x(t)) - V(x(0)) \tag{6.8}
$$

where $V(x) = (1/2)Lx_1^2 + (1/2)Cx_2^2$ is the energy stored in network. If (6.8) holds with strict inequality, then the difference between the absorbed energy and the increase in the stored energy must be the energy dissipated in the resistors. Since (6.8) must hold for every $t \geq 0$, the instantaneous power inequality

$$
u(t)y(t) \geq \dot{V}(x(t), u(t)) \tag{6.9}
$$

must hold for all t; that is, the power flow into the network must be greater than or equal to the rate of change of the energy stored in the network. We can investigate inequality (6.9) by calculating the derivative of V along the trajectories of the system. We have

$$
\begin{aligned}
\dot{V} &= Lx_1\dot{x}_1 + Cx_2\dot{x}_2 = x_1[u - h_2(x_1) - x_2] + x_2[x_1 - h_3(x_2)] \\
&= x_1[u - h_2(x_1)] - x_2h_3(x_2) \\
&= [x_1 + h_1(u)]u - uh_1(u) - x_1h_2(x_1) - x_2h_3(x_2) \\
&= uy - uh_1(u) - x_1h_2(x_1) - x_2h_3(x_2)
\end{aligned}
$$

Thus,

$$
uy = \dot{V} + uh_1(u) + x_1h_2(x_1) + x_2h_3(x_2)
$$

If h_1, h_2, and h_3 are passive, $uy \geq \dot{V}$ and the system is passive. Other possibilities are illustrated by four different special cases of the network.

Case 1: If $h_1 = h_2 = h_3 = 0$, $uy = \dot{V}$ and there is no energy dissipation in the network; that is, the system is lossless.

Case 2: If h_2 and h_3 belong to the sector $[0, \infty]$,

$$
uy \geq \dot{V} + uh_1(u)
$$

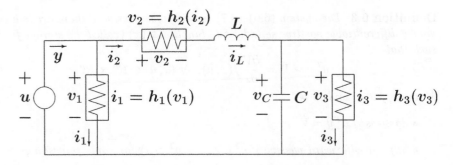

Figure 6.8: RLC circuit of Example 6.1.

The term $uh_1(u)$ could represent excess or shortage of passivity. If $uh_1(u) > 0$ for all $u \neq 0$, there is excess of passivity since the energy absorbed over $[0, t]$ will be greater than the increase in the stored energy, unless the input $u(t)$ is identically zero. This is a case of input strict passivity. On the other hand, if $uh_1(u)$ is negative for some values of u, there is shortage of passivity. As we saw with memoryless functions, this type of excess or shortage of passivity can be removed by input feedforward shown in Figure 6.4(c).

Case 3: If $h_1 = 0$ and $h_3 \in [0, \infty]$,

$$uy \geq \dot{V} + yh_2(y)$$

Excess or shortage of passivity of h_2 results in the same property for the network. Once again, as with memoryless functions, this type of excess or shortage of passivity can be removed by output feedback, as in Figure 6.5(c). When $yh_2(y) > 0$ for all $y \neq 0$, we have output strict passivity because the energy absorbed over $[0, t]$ will be greater than the increase in the stored energy, unless the output $y(t)$ is identically zero.

Case 4: If $h_1 \in [0, \infty]$, $h_2 \in (0, \infty)$, and $h_3 \in (0, \infty)$,

$$uy \geq \dot{V} + x_1 h_2(x_1) + x_2 h_3(x_2)$$

where $x_1 h_2(x_1) + x_2 h_3(x_2)$ is a positive definite function of x. This is a case of state strict passivity because the energy absorbed over $[0, t]$ will be greater than the increase in the stored energy, unless the state $x(t)$ is identically zero. A system having this property is called *state strictly passive* or, simply, *strictly passive*. Clearly, there is no counterpart for state strict passivity in memoryless functions since there is no state.

$\triangle$

Definition 6.3 *The system (6.6)–(6.7) is said to be passive if there exists a continuously differentiable positive semidefinite function $V(x)$ (called the storage function) such that*

$$u^T y \geq \dot{V} = \frac{\partial V}{\partial x} f(x, u), \quad \forall\, (x, u) \in R^n \times R^p \tag{6.10}$$

Moreover, it is said to be

- *lossless if $u^T y = \dot{V}$.*

- *input-feedforward passive if $u^T y \geq \dot{V} + u^T \varphi(u)$ for some function φ.*

- *input strictly passive if $u^T y \geq \dot{V} + u^T \varphi(u)$ and $u^T \varphi(u) > 0$, $\forall\, u \neq 0$.*

- *output-feedback passive if $u^T y \geq \dot{V} + y^T \rho(y)$ for some function ρ.*

- *output strictly passive if $u^T y \geq \dot{V} + y^T \rho(y)$ and $y^T \rho(y) > 0$, $\forall\, y \neq 0$.*

- *strictly passive if $u^T y \geq \dot{V} + \psi(x)$ for some positive definite function ψ.*

In all cases, the inequality should hold for all (x, u).

Definition 6.3 reads almost the same as Definition 6.1 for memoryless functions, except for the presence of a storage function $V(x)$. If we adopt the convention that $V(x) = 0$ for a memoryless function, Definition 6.3 can be used for both state models and memoryless functions.

Example 6.2 The integrator of Figure 6.9(a), represented by

$$\dot{x} = u, \qquad y = x$$

is a lossless system since, with $V(x) = (1/2)x^2$ as the storage function, we have $uy = \dot{V}$. When a memoryless function is connected in parallel with the integrator, as shown in Figure 6.9(b), the system is represented by

$$\dot{x} = u, \qquad y = x + h(u)$$

Clearly, the system is input-feedforward passive since the parallel path $h(u)$ can be cancelled by feedforward from the input. With $V(x) = (1/2)x^2$ as the storage function, we have $uy = \dot{V} + uh(u)$. If $h \in [0, \infty]$, the system is passive. If $uh(u) > 0$ for all $u \neq 0$, the system is input strictly passive. When the loop is closed around an integrator with a memoryless function, as in Figure 6.9(c), the system is represented by

$$\dot{x} = -h(x) + u, \qquad y = x$$

Plainly, the system is output-feedback passive since the feedback path can be cancelled by a feedback from the output. With $V(x) = (1/2)x^2$ as the storage function, we have $uy = \dot{V} + yh(y)$. If $h \in [0, \infty]$, the system is passive. If $yh(y) > 0$ for all $y \neq 0$, the system is output strictly passive. $\triangle$

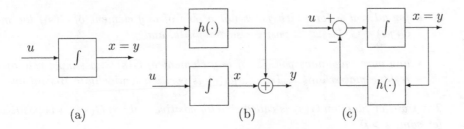

Figure 6.9: Example 6.2

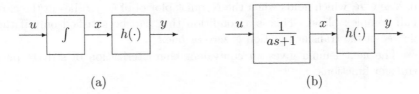

Figure 6.10: Example 6.3

Example 6.3 The cascade connection of an integrator and a passive memoryless function, shown in Figure 6.10(a), is represented by

$$\dot{x} = u, \qquad y = h(x)$$

Passivity of h guarantees that $\int_0^x h(\sigma)\, d\sigma \geq 0$ for all x. With $V(x) = \int_0^x h(\sigma)\, d\sigma$ as the storage function, we have $\dot{V} = h(x)\dot{x} = yu$. Hence, the system is lossless. Suppose now the integrator is replaced by the transfer function $1/(as + 1)$ with $a > 0$, as shown in Figure 6.10(b). The system can be represented by the state model

$$a\dot{x} = -x + u, \qquad y = h(x)$$

With $V(x) = a \int_0^x h(\sigma)\, d\sigma$ as the storage function, we have

$$\dot{V} = h(x)(-x + u) = yu - xh(x) \leq yu$$

Hence, the system is passive. When $xh(x) > 0$ for all $x \neq 0$, the system is strictly passive. $\triangle$

6.3 Positive Real Transfer Functions

Definition 6.4 *A $p \times p$ proper rational transfer function matrix $G(s)$ is called positive real if*

- *poles of all elements of $G(s)$ are in $Re[s] \leq 0$,*

- *for all real ω for which $j\omega$ is not a pole of any element of $G(s)$, the matrix $G(j\omega) + G^T(-j\omega)$ is positive semidefinite, and*

- *any pure imaginary pole $j\omega$ of any element of $G(s)$ is a simple pole and the residue matrix $\lim_{s \to j\omega}(s - j\omega)G(s)$ is positive semidefinite Hermitian.*

The transfer function $G(s)$ is called strictly positive real [1] *if $G(s - \varepsilon)$ is positive real for some $\varepsilon > 0$.*

When $p = 1$, the second condition of Definition 6.4 reduces to $Re[G(j\omega)] \geq 0$, $\forall \, \omega \in R$, which holds when the Nyquist plot of of $G(j\omega)$ lies in the closed right-half complex plane. This is a condition that can be satisfied only if the relative degree of the transfer function is zero or one.[2]

The next lemma gives an equivalent characterization of strictly positive real transfer functions.

Lemma 6.1 *Let $G(s)$ be a $p \times p$ proper rational transfer function matrix, and suppose $\det[G(s) + G^T(-s)]$ is not identically zero.*[3] *Then, $G(s)$ is strictly positive real if and only if*

- *$G(s)$ is Hurwitz; that is, poles of all elements of $G(s)$ have negative real parts,*

- *$G(j\omega) + G^T(-j\omega)$ is positive definite for all $\omega \in R$, and*

- *either $G(\infty) + G^T(\infty)$ is positive definite or it is positive semidefinite and $\lim_{\omega \to \infty} \omega^2 M^T[G(j\omega) + G^T(-j\omega)]M$ is positive definite for any $p \times (p-q)$ full-rank matrix M such that $M^T[G(\infty) + G^T(\infty)]M = 0$, where $q = \text{rank}[G(\infty) + G^T(\infty)]$.*

Proof: See Appendix C.11.

If $G(\infty) + G^T(\infty) = 0$, we can take $M = I$. In the scalar case $(p = 1)$, the frequency-domain condition of the lemma reduces to $Re[G(j\omega)] > 0$ for all $\omega \in R$ and either $G(\infty) > 0$ or $G(\infty) = 0$ and $\lim_{\omega \to \infty} \omega^2 Re[G(j\omega)] > 0$.

Example 6.4 The transfer function $G(s) = 1/s$ is positive real since it has no poles in $Re[s] > 0$, has a simple pole at $s = 0$ whose residue is 1, and

$$Re[G(j\omega)] = Re\left[\frac{1}{j\omega}\right] = 0, \quad \forall \, \omega \neq 0$$

---

[1] The definition of strictly positive real transfer functions is not uniform in the literature. (See [206] for various definitions and the relationship between them.)

[2] The relative degree of a rational transfer function $G(s) = n(s)/d(s)$ is deg d - deg n. For a proper transfer function, the relative degree is a nonnegative integer.

[3] Equivalently, $G(s) + G^T(-s)$ has a normal rank p over the field of rational functions of s.

It is not strictly positive real since $1/(s - \varepsilon)$ has a pole in $Re[s] > 0$ for any $\varepsilon > 0$. The transfer function $G(s) = 1/(s + a)$ with $a > 0$ is positive real, since it has no poles in $Re[s] \geq 0$ and

$$Re[G(j\omega)] = \frac{a}{\omega^2 + a^2} > 0, \quad \forall \, \omega \in R$$

Since this is so for every $a > 0$, we see that for any $\varepsilon \in (0, a)$ the transfer function $G(s - \varepsilon) = 1/(s + a - \varepsilon)$ will be positive real. Hence, $G(s) = 1/(s + a)$ is strictly positive real. The same conclusion can be drawn from Lemma 6.1 by noting that

$$\lim_{\omega \to \infty} \omega^2 Re[G(j\omega)] = \lim_{\omega \to \infty} \frac{\omega^2 a}{\omega^2 + a^2} = a > 0$$

The transfer function

$$G(s) = \frac{1}{s^2 + s + 1}$$

is not positive real because its relative degree is two. We can see it also by calculating

$$Re[G(j\omega)] = \frac{1 - \omega^2}{(1 - \omega^2)^2 + \omega^2} < 0, \quad \forall \, |\omega| > 1$$

Consider the 2×2 transfer function matrix

$$G(s) = \frac{1}{s + 1} \begin{bmatrix} 1 & 1 \\ 1 & 1 \end{bmatrix}$$

We cannot apply Lemma 6.1 because $\det[G(s) + G^T(-s)] \equiv 0 \, \forall \, s$. However, $G(s)$ is strictly positive real, as can be seen by checking the conditions of Definition 6.4. Note that, for $\varepsilon < 1$, the poles of the elements of $G(s - \varepsilon)$ are in $Re[s] < 0$ and

$$G(j\omega - \varepsilon) + G^T(-j\omega - \varepsilon) = \frac{2(1 - \varepsilon)}{\omega^2 + (1 - \varepsilon)^2} \begin{bmatrix} 1 & 1 \\ 1 & 1 \end{bmatrix}$$

is positive semidefinite for all $\omega \in R$. Similarly, it can be seen that the 2×2 transfer function matrix

$$G(s) = \frac{1}{s + 1} \begin{bmatrix} s & 1 \\ -1 & 2s + 1 \end{bmatrix}$$

is strictly positive real. This time, however, $\det[G(s) + G^T(-s)]$ is not identically zero, and we can apply Lemma 6.1 to arrive at the same conclusion by noting that $G(\infty) + G^T(\infty)$ is positive definite and

$$G(j\omega) + G^T(-j\omega) = \frac{2}{\omega^2 + 1} \begin{bmatrix} \omega^2 & -j\omega \\ j\omega & 2\omega^2 + 1 \end{bmatrix}$$

is positive definite for all $\omega \in R$. Finally, the 2×2 transfer function matrix

$$G(s) = \begin{bmatrix} \frac{s}{s+1} & \frac{1}{s+2} \\ \frac{-1}{s+2} & \frac{2}{s+1} \end{bmatrix}$$

has

$$G(\infty) + G^T(\infty) = \begin{bmatrix} 2 & 0 \\ 0 & 0 \end{bmatrix}$$

It can be verified that

$$G(j\omega) + G^T(-j\omega) = \begin{bmatrix} \frac{2\omega^2}{1+\omega^2} & \frac{-2j\omega}{4+\omega^2} \\ \frac{2j\omega}{4+\omega^2} & \frac{4}{1+\omega^2} \end{bmatrix}$$

is positive definite for all $\omega \in R$. Taking $M^T = \begin{bmatrix} 0 & 1 \end{bmatrix}$, it can be verified that

$$\lim_{\omega \to \infty} \omega^2 M^T [G(j\omega) + G^T(-j\omega)] M = 4$$

Consequently, by Lemma 6.1, we conclude that $G(s)$ is strictly positive real. $\triangle$

Passivity properties of positive real transfer functions can be shown by using the next two lemmas, which are known, respectively, as the *positive real lemma* and the *Kalman–Yakubovich–Popov lemma*. The lemmas give algebraic characterization of positive real and strictly positive real transfer functions.

Lemma 6.2 (Positive Real) *Let $G(s) = C(sI - A)^{-1}B + D$ be a $p \times p$ transfer function matrix where (A, B) is controllable and (A, C) is observable. Then, $G(s)$ is positive real if and only if there exist matrices $P = P^T > 0$, L, and W such that*

$$PA + A^T P = -L^T L \tag{6.11}$$
$$PB = C^T - L^T W \tag{6.12}$$
$$W^T W = D + D^T \tag{6.13}$$

$\diamond$

Proof: See Appendix C.12.

Lemma 6.3 (Kalman–Yakubovich–Popov) *Let $G(s) = C(sI - A)^{-1}B + D$ be a $p \times p$ transfer function matrix, where (A, B) is controllable and (A, C) is observable. Then, $G(s)$ is strictly positive real if and only if there exist matrices $P = P^T > 0$, L, and W, and a positive constant ε such that*

$$PA + A^T P = -L^T L - \varepsilon P \tag{6.14}$$
$$PB = C^T - L^T W \tag{6.15}$$
$$W^T W = D + D^T \tag{6.16}$$

$\diamond$

Proof: Suppose there exist $P = P^T > 0$, L, W, and $\varepsilon > 0$ that satisfy (6.14) through (6.16). Set $\mu = \varepsilon/2$ and recall that $G(s - \mu) = C(sI - \mu I - A)^{-1}B + D$. From (6.14), we have

$$P(A + \mu I) + (A + \mu I)^T P = -L^T L \qquad (6.17)$$

It follows from Lemma 6.2 that $G(s - \mu)$ is positive real. Hence, $G(s)$ is strictly positive real. On the other hand, suppose $G(s)$ is strictly positive real. There exists $\mu > 0$ such that $G(s - \mu)$ is positive real. It follows from Lemma 6.2 that there are matrices $P = P^T > 0$, L, and W, which satisfy (6.15) through (6.17). Setting $\varepsilon = 2\mu$ shows that P, L, W, and ε satisfy (6.14) through (6.16). $\qquad \square$

Lemma 6.4 *The linear time-invariant minimal realization*

$$\begin{aligned}\dot{x} &= Ax + Bu \\ y &= Cx + Du\end{aligned}$$

with $G(s) = C(sI - A)^{-1}B + D$ is

- *passive if $G(s)$ is positive real;*

- *strictly passive if $G(s)$ is strictly positive real.*

$\diamond$

Proof: Apply Lemmas 6.2 and 6.3, respectively, and use $V(s) = (1/2)x^T Px$ as the storage function.

$$\begin{aligned}u^T y - \frac{\partial V}{\partial x}(Ax + Bu) &= u^T(Cx + Du) - x^T P(Ax + Bu) \\ &= u^T Cx + \tfrac{1}{2}u^T(D + D^T)u - \tfrac{1}{2}x^T(PA + A^T P)x - x^T PBu \\ &= u^T(B^T P + W^T L)x + \tfrac{1}{2}u^T W^T Wu \\ &\quad + \tfrac{1}{2}x^T L^T Lx + \tfrac{1}{2}\varepsilon x^T Px - x^T PBu \\ &= \tfrac{1}{2}(Lx + Wu)^T(Lx + Wu) + \tfrac{1}{2}\varepsilon x^T Px \ \geq \ \tfrac{1}{2}\varepsilon x^T Px\end{aligned}$$

In the case of Lemma 6.2, $\varepsilon = 0$, and we conclude that the system is passive, while in the case of Lemma 6.3, $\varepsilon > 0$, and we conclude that the system is strictly passive. $\quad \square$

6.4 $\mathcal{L}_2$ and Lyapunov Stability

In this section, we study $\mathcal{L}_2$ and Lyapunov stability of passive systems of the form

$$\begin{aligned}\dot{x} &= f(x, u) &(6.18) \\ y &= h(x, u) &(6.19)\end{aligned}$$

where $f : R^n \times R^p \to R^n$ is locally Lipschitz, $h : R^n \times R^p \to R^p$ is continuous, $f(0, 0) = 0$, and $h(0, 0) = 0$.

Lemma 6.5 *If the system (6.18)–(6.19) is output strictly passive with $u^T y \geq \dot{V} + \delta y^T y$, for some $\delta > 0$, then it is finite-gain $\mathcal{L}_2$ stable and its $\mathcal{L}_2$ gain is less than or equal to $1/\delta$.*

Proof: The derivative of the storage function $V(x)$ satisfies

$$
\begin{aligned}
\dot{V} &\leq u^T y - \delta y^T y = -\frac{1}{2\delta}(u - \delta y)^T(u - \delta y) + \frac{1}{2\delta}u^T u - \frac{\delta}{2}y^T y \\
&\leq \frac{1}{2\delta}u^T u - \frac{\delta}{2}y^T y
\end{aligned}
$$

integrating both sides over $[0, \tau]$ yields

$$
\int_0^\tau y^T(t)y(t)\ dt \leq \frac{1}{\delta^2}\int_0^\tau u^T(t)u(t)\ dt - \frac{2}{\delta}[V(x(\tau)) - V(x(0))]
$$

Thus,

$$
\|y_\tau\|_{\mathcal{L}_2} \leq \frac{1}{\delta}\|u_\tau\|_{\mathcal{L}_2} + \sqrt{\frac{2}{\delta}V(x(0))}
$$

where we used the facts that $V(x) \geq 0$ and $\sqrt{a^2 + b^2} \leq a + b$ for nonnegative numbers a and b. $\qquad\square$

Lemma 6.6 *If the system (6.18)–(6.19) is passive with a positive definite storage function $V(x)$, then the origin of $\dot{x} = f(x, 0)$ is stable.*

Proof: Take V as a Lyapunov function candidate for $\dot{x} = f(x, 0)$. Then $\dot{V} \leq 0$. $\quad\square$

To show asymptotic stability of the origin of $\dot{x} = f(x, 0)$, we need to either show that $\dot{V}$ is negative definite or apply the invariance principle. In the next lemma, we apply the invariance principle by considering a case where $\dot{V} = 0$ when $y = 0$ and then require the additional property that

$$
y(t) \equiv 0 \Rightarrow x(t) \equiv 0 \tag{6.20}
$$

for all solutions of (6.18) when $u = 0$. Equivalently, no solutions of $\dot{x} = f(x, 0)$ can stay identically in $S = \{x \in R^n \mid h(x, 0) = 0\}$, other than the trivial solution $x(t) \equiv 0$. The property (6.20) can be interpreted as an observability condition. Recall that for the linear system

$$
\dot{x} = Ax, \qquad y = Cx
$$

observability is equivalent to

$$
y(t) = Ce^{At}x(0) \equiv 0 \ \Leftrightarrow \ x(0) = 0 \ \Leftrightarrow \ x(t) \equiv 0
$$

For easy reference, we define (6.20) as an observability property of the system.

Definition 6.5 *The system* (6.18)–(6.19) *is said to be zero-state observable if no solution of* $\dot{x} = f(x, 0)$ *can stay identically in* $S = \{x \in R^n \mid h(x, 0) = 0\}$, *other than the trivial solution* $x(t) \equiv 0$.

Lemma 6.7 *Consider the system* (6.18)–(6.19). *The origin of* $\dot{x} = f(x, 0)$ *is asymptotically stable if the system is*

- *strictly passive or*

- *output strictly passive and zero-state observable.*

Furthermore, if the storage function is radially unbounded, the origin will be globally asymptotically stable. $\diamond$

Proof: Suppose the system is strictly passive and let $V(x)$ be its storage function. Then, with $u = 0$, $\dot{V}$ satisfies the inequality $\dot{V} \leq -\psi(x)$, where $\psi(x)$ is positive definite. We can use this inequality to show that $V(x)$ is positive definite. In particular, for any $x \in R^n$, the equation $\dot{x} = f(x, 0)$ has a solution $\phi(t; x)$, starting from x at $t = 0$ and defined on some interval $[0, \delta]$. Integrating the inequality $\dot{V} \leq -\psi(x)$ yields

$$V(\phi(\tau, x)) - V(x) \leq -\int_0^\tau \psi(\phi(t; x)) \, dt, \quad \forall \, \tau \in [0, \delta]$$

Using $V(\phi(\tau, x)) \geq 0$, we obtain

$$V(x) \geq \int_0^\tau \psi(\phi(t; x)) \, dt$$

Suppose now that there is $\bar{x} \neq 0$ such that $V(\bar{x}) = 0$. The foregoing inequality implies

$$\int_0^\tau \psi(\phi(t; \bar{x})) \, dt = 0, \; \forall \, \tau \in [0, \delta] \; \Rightarrow \; \psi(\phi(t; \bar{x})) \equiv 0 \; \Rightarrow \; \phi(t; \bar{x}) \equiv 0 \; \Rightarrow \; \bar{x} = 0$$

which contradicts the claim that $\bar{x} \neq 0$. Thus, $V(x) > 0$ for all $x \neq 0$. This qualifies $V(x)$ as a Lyapunov function candidate, and since $\dot{V}(x) \leq -\psi(x)$, we conclude that the origin is asymptotically stable.

Suppose now the system is output strictly passive and let $V(x)$ be its storage function. Then, with $u = 0$, $\dot{V}$ satisfies the inequality $\dot{V} \leq -y^T \rho(y)$, where $y^T \rho(y) > 0$ for all $y \neq 0$. By repeating the preceding argument, we can use the inequality to show that $V(x)$ is positive definite. In particular, for any $x \in R^n$, we have

$$V(x) \geq \int_0^\tau h^T(\phi(t; x), 0) \rho(h(\phi(t; x), 0)) \, dt$$

Suppose now that there is $\bar{x} \neq 0$ such that $V(\bar{x}) = 0$. The foregoing inequality implies

$$\int_0^\tau h^T(\phi(t;\bar{x}),0)\rho(h(\phi(t;\bar{x}),0))\, dt = 0, \quad \forall\, \tau \in [0,\delta] \quad \Rightarrow \quad h(\phi(t;\bar{x}),0) \equiv 0$$

which, due to zero-state observability, implies

$$\phi(t;\bar{x}) \equiv 0 \quad \Rightarrow \quad \bar{x} = 0$$

Hence, $V(x) > 0$ for all $x \neq 0$. This qualifies $V(x)$ as a Lyapunov function candidate, and since $\dot{V}(x) \leq -y^T\rho(y)$ and $y(t) \equiv 0 \Rightarrow x(t) \equiv 0$, we conclude by the invariance principle that the origin is asymptotically stable. Finally, if $V(x)$ is radially unbounded, we can infer global asymptotic stability from Theorem 4.2 and Corollary 4.2, respectively. $\qquad\qquad\square$

Example 6.5 Consider the p-input–p-output system[4]

$$\begin{aligned} \dot{x} &= f(x) + G(x)u \\ y &= h(x) \end{aligned}$$

where f is locally Lipschitz, G and h are continuous, $f(0) = 0$, and $h(0) = 0$. Suppose there is a continuously differentiable positive semidefinite function $V(x)$ such that

$$\frac{\partial V}{\partial x}f(x) \leq 0, \qquad \frac{\partial V}{\partial x}G(x) = h^T(x)$$

Then,

$$u^T y - \frac{\partial V}{\partial x}[f(x) + G(x)u] = u^T h(x) - \frac{\partial V}{\partial x}f(x) - h^T(x)u = -\frac{\partial V}{\partial x}f(x) \geq 0$$

which shows that the system is passive. If $V(x)$ is positive definite, we can conclude that the origin of $\dot{x} = f(x)$ is stable. If we have the stronger condition

$$\frac{\partial V}{\partial x}f(x) \leq -kh^T(x)h(x), \qquad \frac{\partial V}{\partial x}G(x) = h^T(x)$$

for some $k > 0$, then

$$u^T y - \frac{\partial V}{\partial x}[f(x) + G(x)u] \geq -ky^T y$$

and the system is output strictly passive with $\rho(y) = ky$. It follows from Lemma 6.5 that the system is finite-gain $\mathcal{L}_2$ stable and its $\mathcal{L}_2$ gain is less than or equal to $1/k$. If, in addition, the system is zero-state observable, then the origin of $\dot{x} = f(x)$ is asymptotically stable. Furthermore, if $V(x)$ is radially unbounded, the origin will be globally asymptotically stable. $\qquad\qquad\triangle$

---

[4]$\mathcal{L}_2$ stability of this system was studied in Examples 5.9 and 5.10.

Example 6.6 Consider the single-input–single-output system[5]

$$\dot{x}_1 = x_2$$
$$\dot{x}_2 = -ax_1^3 - kx_2 + u$$
$$y = x_2$$

where a and k are positive constants. Consider also the positive definite, radially unbounded function $V(x) = (1/4)ax_1^4 + (1/2)x_2^2$ as a storage function candidate. The derivative $\dot{V}$ is given by

$$\dot{V} = ax_1^3 x_2 + x_2(-ax_1^3 - kx_2 + u) = -ky^2 + yu$$

Therefore, the system is output strictly passive with $\rho(y) = ky$. It follows from Lemma 6.5 that the system is finite-gain $\mathcal{L}_2$ stable with $\mathcal{L}_2$ gain less than or equal to $1/k$. Moreover, when $u = 0$,

$$y(t) \equiv 0 \;\Rightarrow\; x_2(t) \equiv 0 \;\Rightarrow\; ax_1^3(t) \equiv 0 \;\Rightarrow\; x_1(t) \equiv 0$$

Hence, the system is zero-state observable. It follows from Lemma 6.7 that the origin of the unforced system is globally asymptotically stable. $\triangle$

6.5 Feedback Systems: Passivity Theorems

Consider the feedback connection of Figure 6.11 where each of the feedback components H_1 and H_2 is either a time-invariant dynamical system represented by the state model

$$\dot{x}_i = f_i(x_i, e_i) \tag{6.21}$$
$$y_i = h_i(x_i, e_i) \tag{6.22}$$

or a (possibly time-varying) memoryless function represented by

$$y_i = h_i(t, e_i) \tag{6.23}$$

We are interested in using passivity properties of the feedback components H_1 and H_2 to analyze stability of the feedback connection. We will study both $\mathcal{L}_2$ and Lyapunov stability. We require the feedback connection to have a well-defined state model. When both components H_1 and H_2 are dynamical systems, the closed-loop state model takes the form

$$\dot{x} = f(x, u) \tag{6.24}$$
$$y = h(x, u) \tag{6.25}$$

---

[5]$\mathcal{L}_2$ and Lyapunov stability of this system were studied in Examples 5.8 and 4.9.

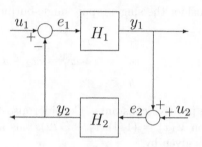

Figure 6.11: Feedback connection.

where

$$x = \left[\begin{array}{c} x_1 \\ x_2 \end{array} \right], \quad u = \left[\begin{array}{c} u_1 \\ u_2 \end{array} \right], \quad \text{and} \quad y = \left[\begin{array}{c} y_1 \\ y_2 \end{array} \right]$$

We assume that f is locally Lipschitz, h is continuous, $f(0,0) = 0$, and $h(0,0) = 0$. It can be easily verified that the feedback connection will have a well-defined state model if the equations

$$e_1 = u_1 - h_2(x_2, e_2) \tag{6.26}$$
$$e_2 = u_2 + h_1(x_1, e_1) \tag{6.27}$$

have a unique solution (e_1, e_2) for every (x_1, x_2, u_1, u_2). The properties $f(0,0) = 0$ and $h(0,0) = 0$ follow from $f_i(0,0) = 0$ and $h_i(0,0) = 0$. It is also easy to see that (6.26) and (6.27) will always have a unique solution if h_1 is independent of e_1 or h_2 is independent of e_2. In this case, the functions f and h of the closed-loop state model inherit smoothness properties of the functions f_i and h_i of the feedback components. In particular, if f_i and h_i are locally Lipschitz, so are f and h. For linear systems, requiring h_i to be independent of e_i is equivalent to requiring the transfer function of H_i to be strictly proper.[6]

When one component, H_1 say, is a dynamical system, while the other one is a memoryless function, the closed-loop state model takes the form

$$\dot{x} = f(t, x, u) \tag{6.28}$$
$$y = h(t, x, u) \tag{6.29}$$

where

$$x = x_1, \quad u = \left[\begin{array}{c} u_1 \\ u_2 \end{array} \right], \quad \text{and} \quad y = \left[\begin{array}{c} y_1 \\ y_2 \end{array} \right]$$

We assume that f is piecewise continuous in t and locally Lipschitz in (x, u), h is piecewise continuous in t and continuous in (x, u), $f(t, 0, 0) = 0$, and $h(t, 0, 0) = 0$.

---

[6]The existence of solutions for (6.26) and (6.27) is pursued further in Exercise 6.12.

The feedback connection will have a well-defined state model if the equations

$$e_1 = u_1 - h_2(t, e_2) \qquad (6.30)$$
$$e_2 = u_2 + h_1(x_1, e_1) \qquad (6.31)$$

have a unique solution (e_1, e_2) for every (x_1, t, u_1, u_2). This will be always the case when h_1 is independent of e_1. The case when both components are memoryless functions is less important and follows trivially as a special case when the state x does not exist. In this case, the feedback connection is represented by $y = h(t, u)$.

The starting point of our analysis is the following fundamental property:

Theorem 6.1 *The feedback connection of two passive systems is passive.*

Proof: Let $V_1(x_1)$ and $V_2(x_2)$ be the storage functions for H_1 and H_2, respectively. If either component is a memoryless function, take $V_i = 0$. Then,

$$e_i^T y_i \geq \dot{V}_i$$

From the feedback connection of Figure 6.11, we see that

$$e_1^T y_1 + e_2^T y_2 = (u_1 - y_2)^T y_1 + (u_2 + y_1)^T y_2 = u_1^T y_1 + u_2^T y_2$$

Hence,

$$u^T y = u_1^T y_1 + u_2^T y_2 \geq \dot{V}_1 + \dot{V}_2$$

Taking $V(x) = V_1(x_1) + V_2(x_2)$ as the storage function for the feedback connection, we obtain

$$u^T y \geq \dot{V}$$

$$\square$$

Using Theorem 6.1 and the results of the previous section on stability properties of passive systems, we can arrive at some straightforward conclusions on stability of the feedback connection. We start with $\mathcal{L}_2$ stability. The next lemma is an immediate consequence of Lemma 6.5.

Lemma 6.8 *The feedback connection of two output strictly passive systems with*

$$e_i^T y_i \geq \dot{V}_i + \delta_i y_i^T y_i, \quad \delta_i > 0$$

is finite-gain $\mathcal{L}_2$ stable and its $\mathcal{L}_2$ gain is less than or equal to $1/\min\{\delta_1, \delta_2\}$.

Proof: With $V = V_1 + V_2$ and $\delta = \min\{\delta_1, \delta_2\}$, we have

$$\begin{aligned} u^T y &= e_1^T y_1 + e_2^T y_2 \geq \dot{V}_1 + \delta_1 y_1^T y_1 + \dot{V}_2 + \delta_2 y_2^T y_2 \\ &\geq \dot{V} + \delta(y_1^T y_1 + y_2^T y_2) = \dot{V} + \delta y^T y \end{aligned}$$

□

Reading the proof of Lemma 6.5 shows that we use the inequality

$$u^T y \geq \dot{V} + \delta y^T y \tag{6.32}$$

to arrive at the inequality

$$\dot{V} \leq \frac{1}{2\delta} u^T u - \frac{\delta}{2} y^T y \tag{6.33}$$

which is then used to show finite-gain $\mathcal{L}_2$ stability. In Lemma 6.8, we establish (6.32) for the feedback connection, which then leads to (6.33). However, even if (6.32) does not hold for the feedback connection, we may still be able to show an inequality of the form (6.33). This idea is used in the next theorem to prove a more general result that includes Lemma 6.8 as a special case.

Theorem 6.2 *Consider the feedback connection of Figure 6.11 and suppose each feedback component satisfies the inequality*

$$e_i^T y_i \geq \dot{V}_i + \varepsilon_i e_i^T e_i + \delta_i y_i^T y_i, \quad \text{for } i = 1, 2 \tag{6.34}$$

for some storage function $V_i(x_i)$. Then, the closed-loop map from u to y is finite gain $\mathcal{L}_2$ stable if

$$\varepsilon_1 + \delta_2 > 0 \quad \text{and} \quad \varepsilon_2 + \delta_1 > 0 \tag{6.35}$$

◇

Proof: Adding inequalities (6.34) for $i = 1, 2$ and using

$$
\begin{aligned}
e_1^T y_1 + e_2^T y_2 &= u_1^T y_1 + u_2^T y_2 \\
e_1^T e_1 &= u_1^T u_1 - 2u_1^T y_2 + y_2^T y_2 \\
e_2^T e_2 &= u_2^T u_2 + 2u_2^T y_1 + y_1^T y_1
\end{aligned}
$$

we obtain

$$\dot{V} \leq -y^T L y - u^T M u + u^T N y$$

where

$$L = \begin{bmatrix} (\varepsilon_2 + \delta_1)I & 0 \\ 0 & (\varepsilon_1 + \delta_2)I \end{bmatrix}, \quad M = \begin{bmatrix} \varepsilon_1 I & 0 \\ 0 & \varepsilon_2 I \end{bmatrix}, \quad N = \begin{bmatrix} I & 2\varepsilon_1 I \\ -2\varepsilon_2 I & I \end{bmatrix}$$

and $V(x) = V_1(x_1) + V_2(x_2)$. Let $a = \min\{\varepsilon_2 + \delta_1, \varepsilon_1 + \delta_2\} > 0$, $b = \|N\|_2 \geq 0$, and $c = \|M\|_2 \geq 0$. Then

$$
\begin{aligned}
\dot{V} &\leq -a\|y\|_2^2 + b\|u\|_2 \|y\|_2 + c\|u\|_2^2 \\
&= -\frac{1}{2a}(b\|u\|_2 - a\|y\|_2)^2 + \frac{b^2}{2a}\|u\|_2^2 - \frac{a}{2}\|y\|_2^2 + c\|u\|_2^2 \\
&\leq \frac{k^2}{2a}\|u\|_2^2 - \frac{a}{2}\|y\|_2^2
\end{aligned}
$$

where $k^2 = b^2 + 2ac$. Integrating over $[0, \tau]$, using $V(x) \geq 0$, and taking the square roots, we arrive at

$$\|y_\tau\|_{\mathcal{L}_2} \leq \frac{k}{a} \|u_\tau\|_{\mathcal{L}_2} + \sqrt{2V(x(0))/a}$$

which completes the proof of the theorem. $\qquad \square$

Theorem 6.2 reduces to Lemma 6.8 when (6.34) is satisfied with $\varepsilon_1 = \varepsilon_2 = 0$, $\delta_1 > 0$, and $\delta_2 > 0$. However, condition (6.35) is satisfied in several other cases. For example, it is satisfied when both H_1 and H_2 are input strictly passive with $e_i^T y_i \geq \dot{V}_i + \varepsilon_i u_i^T u_i$ for some $\varepsilon_i > 0$. It is also satisfied when one component (H_1 say) is passive, while the other component satisfies (6.34) with positive ε_2 and δ_2. What is more interesting is that (6.35) can be satisfied even when some of the constants ε_i and δ_i are negative. For example, a negative ε_1 can be compensated for by a positive δ_2. This is a case where shortage of passivity (at the input side) of H_1 is compensated for by excess of passivity (at the output side) of H_2. Similarly, a negative δ_2 can be compensated for by a positive ε_1. This is a case where shortage of passivity (at the output side) of H_2 is compensated for by excess of passivity (at the input side) of H_1.

Example 6.7 Consider the feedback connection of

$$H_1 : \begin{cases} \dot{x} &= f(x) + G(x)e_1 \\ y_1 &= h(x) \end{cases} \qquad \text{and} \qquad H_2 : \ y_2 = ke_2$$

where $k > 0$ and $e_i, \ y_i \in R^p$. Suppose there is a positive definite function $V_1(x)$ such that

$$\frac{\partial V_1}{\partial x} f(x) \leq 0, \qquad \frac{\partial V_1}{\partial x} G(x) = h^T(x), \quad \forall \ x \in R^n$$

Both components are passive. Moreover, H_2 satisfies

$$e_2^T y_2 = ke_2^T e_2 = \gamma ke_2^T e_2 + \frac{(1-\gamma)}{k} y_2^T y_2, \quad 0 < \gamma < 1$$

Thus, (6.34) is satisfied with $\varepsilon_1 = \delta_1 = 0$, $\varepsilon_2 = \gamma k$, and $\delta_2 = (1-\gamma)/k$. This shows that (6.35) is satisfied, and we conclude that the closed-loop map from u to y is finite-gain $\mathcal{L}_2$ stable. $\qquad \triangle$

Example 6.8 Consider the feedback connection of

$$H_1 : \begin{cases} \dot{x}_1 &= x_2 \\ \dot{x}_2 &= -ax_1^3 - \sigma(x_2) + e_1 \\ y_1 &= x_2 \end{cases} \qquad \text{and} \qquad H_2 : \ y_2 = ke_2$$

where $\sigma \in [-\alpha, \infty]$, $a > 0$, $\alpha > 0$, and $k > 0$. If σ was in the sector $[0, \infty]$, we could have shown that H_1 is passive with the storage function $V_1(x) = (a/4)x_1^4 + (1/2)x_2^2$. For $\sigma \in [-\alpha, \infty]$, we have

$$\dot{V}_1 = ax_1^3 x_2 - ax_1^3 x_2 - x_2\sigma(x_2) + x_2 e_1 \leq \alpha x_2^2 + x_2 e_1 = \alpha y_1^2 + y_1 e_1$$

Hence, (6.34) is satisfied for H_1 with $\varepsilon_1 = 0$ and $\delta_1 = -\alpha$. Since

$$e_2 y_2 = k e_2^2 = \gamma k e_2^2 + \frac{(1 - \gamma)}{k} y_2^2, \quad 0 < \gamma < 1$$

(6.34) is satisfied for H_2 with $\varepsilon_2 = \gamma k$ and $\delta_2 = (1 - \gamma)/k$. If $k > \alpha$, we can choose γ such that $\gamma k > \alpha$. Then, $\varepsilon_1 + \delta_2 > 0$ and $\varepsilon_2 + \delta_1 > 0$. We conclude that the closed-loop map from u to y is finite-gain $\mathcal{L}_2$ stable. $\triangle$

Let us turn now to studying Lyapunov stability of the feedback connection. We are interested in studying stability and asymptotic stability of the origin of the closed-loop system when the input $u = 0$. Stability of the origin follows trivially from Theorem 6.1 and Lemma 6.6. Therefore, we focus our attention on studying asymptotic stability. The next theorem is an immediate consequence of Theorem 6.1 and Lemma 6.7.

Theorem 6.3 *Consider the feedback connection of two time-invariant dynamical systems of the form* (6.21)–(6.22). *The origin of the closed-loop system* (6.24) *(when* $u = 0$*) is asymptotically stable if*

- *both feedback components are strictly passive,*

- *both feedback components are output strictly passive and zero-state observable, or*

- *one component is strictly passive and the other one is output strictly passive and zero-state observable.*

Furthermore, if the storage function for each component is radially unbounded, the origin is globally asymptotically stable. $\diamond$

Proof: Let $V_1(x_1)$ and $V_2(x_2)$ be the storage functions for H_1 and H_2, respectively. As in the proof of Lemma 6.7, we can show that $V_1(x_1)$ and $V_2(x_2)$ are positive definite functions. Take $V(x) = V_1(x_1) + V_2(x_2)$ as a Lyapunov function candidate for the closed-loop system. In the first case, the derivative $\dot{V}$ satisfies

$$\dot{V} \leq u^T y - \psi_1(x_1) - \psi_2(x_2) = -\psi_1(x_1) - \psi_2(x_2)$$

since $u = 0$. Hence, the origin is asymptotically stable. In the second case,

$$\dot{V} \leq -y_1^T \rho_1(y_1) - y_2^T \rho_2(y_2)$$

where $y_i^T \rho_i(y_i) > 0$ for all $y_i \neq 0$. Here $\dot{V}$ is only negative semidefinite and $\dot{V} = 0 \Rightarrow y = 0$. To apply the invariance principle, we need to show that $y(t) \equiv 0 \Rightarrow x(t) \equiv 0$. Note that $y_2(t) \equiv 0 \Rightarrow e_1(t) \equiv 0$. Then, zero-state observability of H_1 shows that $y_1(t) \equiv 0 \Rightarrow x_1(t) \equiv 0$. Similarly, $y_1(t) \equiv 0 \Rightarrow e_2(t) \equiv 0$ and zero-state observability of H_2 shows that $y_2(t) \equiv 0 \Rightarrow x_2(t) \equiv 0$. Thus, the origin is asymptotically stable. In the third case (with H_1 as the strictly passive component),

$$\dot{V} \leq -\psi_1(x_1) - y_2^T \rho_2(y_2)$$

and $\dot{V} = 0$ implies $x_1 = 0$ and $y_2 = 0$. Note that $y_2(t) \equiv 0 \Rightarrow e_1(t) \equiv 0$, which together with $x_1(t) \equiv 0$ imply that $y_1(t) \equiv 0$. Hence, $e_2(t) \equiv 0$ and zero-state observability of H_2 shows that $y_2(t) \equiv 0 \Rightarrow x_2(t) \equiv 0$. Thus, the origin is asymptotically stable. Finally, if $V_1(x_1)$ and $V_2(x_2)$ are radially unbounded, so is $V(x)$, and we can conclude global asymptotic stability. $\qquad\square$

The proof uses a simple idea, namely, that the sum of the storage functions for the feedback components is used as a Lyapunov function candidate for the feedback connection. Beyond this simple idea, the rest of the proof is straightforward Lyapunov analysis. In fact, the analysis is restrictive because to show that $\dot{V} = \dot{V}_1 + \dot{V}_2 \leq 0$, we insist that both $\dot{V}_1 \leq 0$ and $\dot{V}_2 \leq 0$. Clearly, this is not necessary. One term, $\dot{V}_1$ say, could be positive over some region as long as the sum $\dot{V} \leq 0$ over the same region. This is again a manifestation of the idea that shortage of passivity of one component can be compensated for by excess of passivity of the other component. This idea is exploited in Examples 6.10 and 6.11, while Example 6.9 is a straightforward application of Theorem 6.3.

Example 6.9 Consider the feedback connection of

$$H_1: \begin{cases} \dot{x}_1 &= x_2 \\ \dot{x}_2 &= -ax_1^3 - kx_2 + e_1 \\ y_1 &= x_2 \end{cases} \quad \text{and} \quad H_2: \begin{cases} \dot{x}_3 &= x_4 \\ \dot{x}_4 &= -bx_3 - x_4^3 + e_2 \\ y_2 &= x_4 \end{cases}$$

where a, b, and k are positive constants. Using $V_1 = (a/4)x_1^4 + (1/2)x_2^2$ as the storage function for H_1, we obtain

$$\dot{V}_1 = ax_1^3 x_2 - ax_1^3 x_2 - kx_2^2 + x_2 e_1 = -ky_1^2 + y_1 e_1$$

Hence, H_1 is output strictly passive. Besides, with $e_1 = 0$, we have

$$y_1(t) \equiv 0 \Leftrightarrow x_2(t) \equiv 0 \Rightarrow x_1(t) \equiv 0$$

which shows that H_1 is zero-state observable. Using $V_2 = (b/2)x_3^2 + (1/2)x_4^2$ as the storage function for H_2, we obtain

$$\dot{V}_2 = bx_3 x_4 - bx_3 x_4 - x_4^4 + x_4 e_2 = -y_2^4 + y_2 e_2$$

Therefore, H_2 is output strictly passive. Moreover, with $e_2 = 0$, we have

$$y_2(t) \equiv 0 \Leftrightarrow x_4(t) \equiv 0 \Rightarrow x_3(t) \equiv 0$$

which shows that H_2 is zero-state observable. Thus, by the second case of Theorem 6.3 and the fact that V_1 and V_2 are radially unbounded, we conclude that the origin is globally asymptotically stable. $\qquad\triangle$

Example 6.10 Reconsider the feedback connection of the previous example, but change the output of H_1 to $y_1 = x_2 + e_1$. From the expression

$$\dot{V}_1 = -kx_2^2 + x_2 e_1 = -k(y_1 - e_1)^2 - e_1^2 + y_1 e_1$$

we can conclude that H_1 is passive, but we cannot conclude strict passivity or output strict passivity. Therefore, we cannot apply Theorem 6.3. Using

$$V = V_1 + V_2 = \tfrac{1}{4}ax_1^4 + \tfrac{1}{2}x_2^2 + \tfrac{1}{2}bx_3^2 + \tfrac{1}{2}x_4^2$$

as a Lyapunov function candidate for the closed-loop system, we obtain

$$
\begin{aligned}
\dot{V} &= -kx_2^2 + x_2 e_1 - x_4^4 + x_4 e_2 \\
&= -kx_2^2 - x_2 x_4 - x_4^4 + x_4(x_2 - x_4) \\
&= -kx_2^2 - x_4^4 - x_4^2 \le 0
\end{aligned}
$$

Moreover, $\dot{V} = 0$ implies that $x_2 = x_4 = 0$ and

$$x_2(t) \equiv 0 \;\Rightarrow\; ax_1^3(t) - x_4(t) \equiv 0 \;\Rightarrow\; x_1(t) \equiv 0$$

$$x_4(t) \equiv 0 \;\Rightarrow\; -bx_3(t) + x_2(t) \equiv 0 \;\Rightarrow\; x_3(t) \equiv 0$$

Thus, by the invariance principle and the fact that V is radially unbounded, we conclude that the origin is globally asymptotically stable. $\triangle$

Example 6.11 Reconsider the system

$$
\begin{aligned}
\dot{x}_1 &= x_2 \\
\dot{x}_2 &= -h_1(x_1) - h_2(x_2)
\end{aligned}
$$

from Examples 4.8 and 4.9, where h_1 and h_2 are locally Lipschitz and belong to the sector $(0, \infty)$. The system can be viewed as the state model of the feedback connection of Figure 6.12, where H_1 consists of a negative feedback loop around the integrator x_2 with h_2 in the feedback path, and H_2 consists of a cascade connection of the integrator x_1 with h_1. We saw in Example 6.2 that H_1 is output strictly passive with the storage function $V_1 = (1/2)x_2^2$ and, in Example 6.3, that H_2 is lossless with the storage function $V_2 = \int_0^{x_1} h_1(\sigma)\, d\sigma$. We cannot apply Theorem 6.3 because H_2 is neither strictly passive nor output strictly passive. However, using $V = V_1 + V_2 = \int_0^{x_1} h_1(\sigma)\, d\sigma + (1/2)x_2^2$ as a Lyapunov function candidate, we can proceed to investigate asymptotic stability of the origin. This is already done in Examples 4.8 and 4.9, where it is shown that the origin is asymptotically stable and will be globally asymptotically stable if $\int_0^y h_1(z)\, dz \to \infty$ as $|y| \to \infty$. We will not repeat the analysis of these two examples here, but let us note that if $h_1(y)$ and $h_2(y)$ belong to the sector $(0, \infty)$ only for $y \in (-a, a)$, then the Lyapunov analysis can be limited to some region around the origin, leading to a local asymptotic stability conclusion, as in Example 4.8. This shows that passivity remains useful as a tool for Lyapunov analysis even when it holds only on a finite region, rather than the whole space. $\triangle$

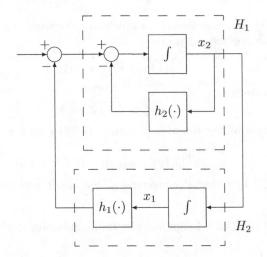

Figure 6.12: Example 6.11.

When the feedback connection has a dynamical system as one component and a memoryless function as the other component, we can perform Lyapunov analysis by using the storage function of the dynamical system as a Lyapunov function candidate. It is important, however, to distinguish between time-invariant and time-varying memoryless functions, for in the latter case the closed-loop system will be nonautonomous and we cannot apply the invariance principle as we did in the proof of Theorem 6.3. We treat these two cases separately in the next two theorems.

Theorem 6.4 *Consider the feedback connection of a strictly passive, time-invariant, dynamical system of the form (6.21)–(6.22) with a passive (possibly time-varying) memoryless function of the form (6.23). Then, the origin of the closed-loop system (6.28) (when $u = 0$) is uniformly asymptotically stable. Furthermore, if the storage function for the dynamical system is radially unbounded, the origin will be globally uniformly asymptotically stable.* ◇

Proof: As in the proof of Lemma 6.7, it can be shown that $V_1(x_1)$ is positive definite. Its derivative is given by

$$\dot{V}_1 = \frac{\partial V_1}{\partial x_1} f_1(x_1, e_1) \leq e_1^T y_1 - \psi_1(x_1) = -e_2^T y_2 - \psi_1(x_1) \leq -\psi_1(x_1)$$

The conclusion follows from Theorem 4.9. □

Theorem 6.5 *Consider the feedback connection of a time-invariant dynamical system H_1 of the form (6.21)–(6.22) with a time-invariant memoryless function H_2 of* *the form (6.23). Suppose that H_1 is zero-state observable and has a positive definite storage function, which satisfies*

$$e_1^T y_1 \geq \dot{V}_1 + y_1^T \rho_1(y_1) \tag{6.36}$$

and that H_2 satisfies

$$e_2^T y_2 \geq e_2^T \varphi_2(e_2) \tag{6.37}$$

Then, the origin of the closed-loop system (6.28) (when $u = 0$) is asymptotically stable if

$$v^T[\rho_1(v) + \varphi_2(v)] > 0, \quad \forall \, v \neq 0 \tag{6.38}$$

Furthermore, if V_1 is radially unbounded, the origin will be globally asymptotically stable. $\diamond$

Proof: Use $V_1(x_1)$ as a Lyapunov function candidate, to obtain

$$\begin{aligned}
\dot{V}_1 &= \frac{\partial V_1}{\partial x_1} f_1(x_1, e_1) \ \leq \ e_1^T y_1 - y_1^T \rho_1(y_1) \\
&= -e_2^T y_2 - y_1^T \rho_1(y_1) \ \leq \ -[y_1^T \varphi_2(y_1) + y_1^T \rho_1(y_1)]
\end{aligned}$$

Inequality (6.38) shows that $\dot{V}_1 \leq 0$ and $\dot{V}_1 = 0 \Rightarrow y_1 = 0$. Noting that $y_1(t) \equiv 0 \Rightarrow e_2(t) \equiv 0 \Rightarrow e_1(t) \equiv 0$, we see that zero-state observability of H_1 implies that $x_1(t) \equiv 0$. The conclusion follows from the invariance principle. $\square$

Example 6.12 Consider the feedback connection of a strictly positive real transfer function and a passive time-varying memoryless function. From Lemma 6.4, we know that the dynamical system is strictly passive with a positive definite storage function of the form $V(x) = (1/2)x^T P x$. From Theorem 6.4, we conclude that the origin of the closed-loop system is globally uniformly asymptotically stable. This is a version of the circle criterion of Section 7.1. $\triangle$

Example 6.13 Consider the feedback connection of

$$H_1 : \begin{cases} \dot{x} &= f(x) + G(x)e_1 \\ y_1 &= h(x) \end{cases} \quad \text{and} \quad H_2 : \ y_2 = \sigma(e_2)$$

where $\sigma \in (0, \infty)$ and $e_i, \, y_i \in R^p$. Suppose there is a radially unbounded positive definite function $V_1(x)$ such that

$$\frac{\partial V_1}{\partial x} f(x) \leq 0, \quad \frac{\partial V_1}{\partial x} G(x) = h^T(x), \quad \forall \, x \in R^n$$

and H_1 is zero-state observable. Both components are passive. Moreover, H_2 satisfies

$$e_2^T y_2 = e_2^T \sigma(e_2)$$

Thus, (6.36) is satisfied with $\rho_1 = 0$, and (6.37) is satisfied with $\varphi_2 = \sigma$. Since $\sigma \in (0, \infty)$, (6.38) is satisfied. It follows from Theorem 6.5 that the origin of the closed-loop system is globally asymptotically stable. $\triangle$

We conclude this section by presenting *loop transformations*, which extend the utility of passivity theorems. Starting with a feedback connection in which one of the two feedback components is not passive or does not satisfy a condition that is needed in one of the theorems, we may be able to reconfigure the feedback connection into an equivalent connection that has the desired properties. We illustrate the process first for loop transformations that use constant gains. Suppose H_1 is a time-invariant dynamical system, while H_2 is a (possibly time-varying) memoryless function that belongs to the sector $[K_1, K_2]$, where $K = K_2 - K_1$ is a positive definite symmetric matrix. We saw in Section 6.1 that a function in the sector $[K_1, K_2]$ can be transformed into a function in the sector $[0, \infty]$ by input feedforward followed by output feedback, as shown in Figure 6.7. Input feedforward on H_2 can be nullified by output feedback on H_1, as shown in Figure 6.13(b), resulting in an equivalent feedback connection, as far as asymptotic stability of the origin is concerned. Similarly, premultiplying the modified H_2 by K^{-1} can be nullified by postmultiplying the modified H_1 by K, as shown in Figure 6.13(c). Finally, output feedback on the component in the feedback path can be nullified by input feedforward on the component in the forward path, as shown in Figure 6.13(d). The reconfigured feedback connection has two components $\tilde{H}_1$ and $\tilde{H}_2$, where $\tilde{H}_2$ is a memoryless function that belongs to the sector $[0, \infty]$. We can now apply Theorem 6.4 or 6.5 if $\tilde{H}_1$ satisfies the conditions of the respective theorem.

Example 6.14 Consider the feedback connection of

$$H_1: \begin{cases} \dot{x}_1 &= x_2 \\ \dot{x}_2 &= -h(x_1) + bx_2 + e_1 \\ y_1 &= x_2 \end{cases} \qquad \text{and} \qquad H_2: \ y_2 = \sigma(e_2)$$

where $\sigma \in [\alpha, \beta]$, $h \in [\alpha_1, \infty]$, $b > 0$, $\alpha_1 > 0$, and $k = \beta - \alpha > 0$. Applying the loop transformation of Figure 6.13(d) (with $K_1 = \alpha$ and $K_2 = \beta$) results in the feedback connection of

$$\tilde{H}_1: \begin{cases} \dot{x}_1 &= x_2 \\ \dot{x}_2 &= -h(x_1) - ax_2 + \tilde{e}_1 \\ \tilde{y}_1 &= kx_2 + \tilde{e}_1 \end{cases} \qquad \text{and} \qquad \tilde{H}_2: \ \tilde{y}_2 = \tilde{\sigma}(\tilde{e}_2)$$

where $\tilde{\sigma} \in [0, \infty]$ and $a = \alpha - b$. If $\alpha > b$, it can be shown (Exercise 6.4) that $\tilde{H}_1$ is strictly passive with a storage function of the form $V_1 = k \int_0^{x_1} h(s) \, ds + x^T P x$, where $P = P^T > 0$. Thus, we conclude from Theorem 6.4 that the origin of the feedback connection is globally asymptotically stable. $\triangle$

Next, we consider loop transformations with dynamic multipliers, as shown in Figure 6.14. Premultiplying H_2 by a transfer function $W(s)$ can by nullified by postmultiplying H_1 by $W^{-1}(s)$, provided the inverse exists. For example, when H_2 is a passive, time-invariant, memoryless function h, we saw in Example 6.3 that premultiplying h by the transfer function $1/(as + 1)$ results in a strictly passive

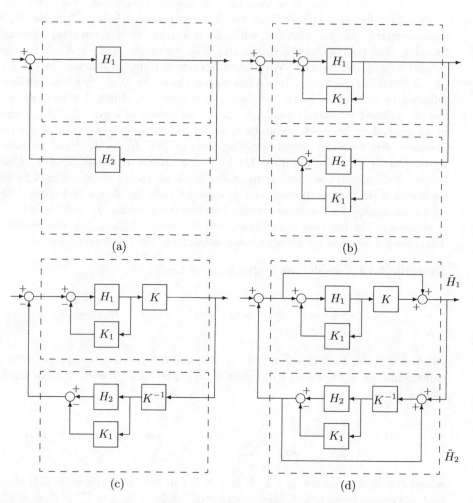

(a)

(b)

(c)

(d)

Figure 6.13: Loop transformation with constant gains. A memoryless function H_2 in the sector $[K_1, K_2]$ is transformed into a memoryless function $\tilde{H}_2$ in the sector $[0, \infty]$.

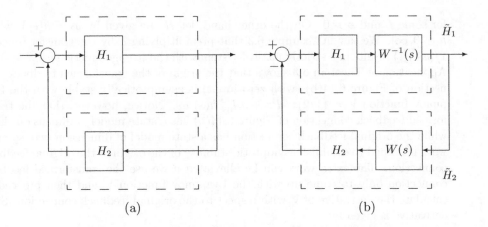

Figure 6.14: Loop transformation with dynamic multipliers.

dynamical system. If postmultiplying H_1 by $(as + 1)$ results in a strictly passive system or an output strictly passive system that is zero-state observable, we can employ Theorem 6.3 to conclude asymptotic stability of the origin. This idea is illustrated in the next two examples for cases where H_1 is linear and nonlinear, respectively.

Example 6.15 Let H_1 be a linear time-invariant system represented by the state model

$$\dot{x} = Ax + Be_1, \quad y_1 = Cx$$

where

$$A = \begin{bmatrix} 0 & 1 \\ -1 & -1 \end{bmatrix}, \quad B = \begin{bmatrix} 0 \\ 1 \end{bmatrix}, \quad \text{and} \quad C = \begin{bmatrix} 1 & 0 \end{bmatrix}$$

Its transfer function $1/(s^2 + s + 1)$ has relative degree two; hence, it is not positive real. Postmultiplying H_1 by $(as+1)$ results in $\tilde{H}_1$, which can be represented by the state model

$$\dot{x} = Ax + Be_1, \quad \tilde{y}_1 = \tilde{C}x$$

where $\tilde{C} = C + aCA = \begin{bmatrix} 1 & a \end{bmatrix}$. Its transfer function $(as + 1)/(s^2 + s + 1)$ satisfies the condition

$$Re \left[\frac{1 + j\omega a}{1 - \omega^2 + j\omega} \right] = \frac{1 + (a - 1)\omega^2}{(1 - \omega^2)^2 + \omega^2} > 0, \quad \forall\, \omega \in R$$

if $a \geq 1$. Thus, choosing $a \geq 1$, we can apply Lemmas 6.3 and 6.4 to conclude that $\tilde{H}_1$ is strictly passive with the storage function $(1/2)x^T Px$ where P satisfies the equations

$$PA + A^T P = -L^T L - \varepsilon P, \quad PB = \tilde{C}^T$$

for some L and $\varepsilon > 0$. On the other hand, let H_2 be given by $y_2 = h(e_2)$, where $h \in [0, \infty]$. We saw in Example 6.3 that premultiplying h by the transfer function $1/(as+1)$ results in a strictly passive system with the storage function $a \int_0^{e_2} h(s) \, ds$. Application of Theorem 6.3 shows that the origin of the transformed feedback connection of Figure 6.14(b) (with zero input) is asymptotically stable with the Lyapunov function $V = (1/2)x^T P x + a \int_0^{e_2} h(s) \, ds$. Notice, however, that the transformed feedback connection of Figure 6.14(b) has a state model of dimension three, while the original feedback connection has a state model of dimension two; so more work is needed to establish asymptotic stability of the origin of the original feedback connection. The extra work can be alleviated if we use the transformed feedback connection only to come up with the Lyapunov function V and then proceed to calculate the derivative of V with respect to the original feedback connection. Such derivative is given by

$$
\begin{aligned}
\dot{V} &= \tfrac{1}{2}x^T P \dot{x} + \tfrac{1}{2}\dot{x}^T P x + a h(e_2) \dot{e}_2 \\
&= \tfrac{1}{2}x^T P [Ax - Bh(e_2)] + \tfrac{1}{2}[Ax - Bh(e_2)]^T P x + a h(e_2) C [Ax - Bh(e_2)] \\
&= -\tfrac{1}{2}x^T L^T L x - (\varepsilon/2)x^T P x - x^T \tilde{C}^T h(e_2) + a h(e_2) C A x \\
&= -\tfrac{1}{2}x^T L^T L x - (\varepsilon/2)x^T P x - x^T [C + aCA]^T h(e_2) + a h(e_2) C A x \\
&= -\tfrac{1}{2}x^T L^T L x - (\varepsilon/2)x^T P x - e_2^T h(e_2) \;\le\; -(\varepsilon/2)x^T P x
\end{aligned}
$$

which shows that the origin is asymptotically stable. In fact, since V is radially unbounded, we conclude that the origin is globally asymptotically stable. $\triangle$

Example 6.16 Consider the feedback connection of

$$
H_1 : \begin{cases} \dot{x}_1 &= x_2 \\ \dot{x}_2 &= -bx_1^3 - kx_2 + e_1 \\ y_1 &= x_1 \end{cases} \quad \text{and} \quad H_2 : \; y_2 = h(e_2)
$$

where $b > 0$, $k > 0$, and $h \in [0, \infty]$. Postmultiplying H_1 by $(as + 1)$ results in a system $\tilde{H}_1$ represented by the same state equation but with a new output $\tilde{y}_1 = x_1 + ax_2$. Using $V_1 = (1/4)bx_1^4 + (1/2)x^T P x$ as a storage function candidate for $\tilde{H}_1$, we obtain

$$
\begin{aligned}
\dot{V}_1 &= b(1 - p_{22})x_1^3 x_2 - p_{12} b x_1^4 + (p_{11}x_1 + p_{12}x_2)x_2 \\
&\quad - (p_{12}x_1 + p_{22}x_2)kx_2 + (p_{12}x_1 + p_{22}x_2)e_1
\end{aligned}
$$

Taking $p_{11} = k$, $p_{12} = p_{22} = 1$, $a = 1$, and assuming that $k > 1$, we obtain

$$
\dot{V}_1 = -bx_1^4 - (k-1)x_2^2 + \tilde{y}_1 e_1
$$

which shows that $\tilde{H}_1$ is strictly passive. On the other hand, premultiplying h by the transfer function $1/(s + 1)$ results in a strictly passive system with the storage function $\int_0^{e_2} h(s) \, ds$. Using the storage function (of the transformed feedback connection)

$$V = (1/4)bx_1^4 + (1/2)x^T P x + \int_0^{e_2} h(s) \, ds$$

as a Lyapunov function candidate for the original feedback connection (when $u = 0$) yields

$$\begin{aligned} \dot{V} &= bx_1^3 x_2 + (kx_1 + x_2)x_2 + (x_1 + x_2)[-bx_1^3 - kx_2 - h(e_2)] + h(e_2)x_2 \\ &= -(k-1)x_2^2 - bx_1^4 - x_1 h(x_1) \end{aligned}$$

which is negative definite. Since V is positive definite and radially unbounded, we conclude that the origin is globally asymptotically stable. $\triangle$

6.6 Exercises

6.1 Verify that a function in the sector $[K_1, K_2]$ can be transformed into a function in the sector $[0, \infty]$ by input feedforward followed by output feedback, as shown in Figure 6.7.

6.2 Consider the system

$$a\dot{x} = -x + \frac{1}{k}h(x) + u, \qquad y = h(x)$$

where a and k are positive constants and $h \in [0, k]$. Show that the system is passive with $V(x) = a \int_0^x h(\sigma) \, d\sigma$ as the storage function.

6.3 Consider the system

$$\dot{x}_1 = x_2, \quad \dot{x}_2 = -h(x_1) - ax_2 + u, \quad y = \alpha x_1 + x_2$$

where $0 < \alpha < a$ and $h \in (0, \infty]$. Show that the system is strictly passive. Hint: Use $V(x)$ of Example 4.5 as the storage function.

6.4 Consider the system

$$\dot{x}_1 = x_2, \quad \dot{x}_2 = -h(x_1) - ax_2 + u, \quad y = kx_2 + u$$

where $a > 0$, $k > 0$, $h \in [\alpha_1, \infty]$, and $\alpha_1 > 0$. Let $V(x) = k \int_0^{x_1} h(s) \, ds + x^T P x$, where $p_{11} = ap_{12}$, $p_{22} = k/2$, and $0 < p_{12} < \min\{2\alpha_1, \, ak/2\}$. Using $V(x)$ as a storage function, show that the system is strictly passive.

6.5 Consider the system represented by the block diagram of Figure 6.15, where $u, y \in R^p$, M and K are positive definite symmetric matrices, $h \in [0, K]$, and $\int_0^x h^T(\sigma)M \, d\sigma \geq 0$ for all x. Show that the system is output strictly passive.

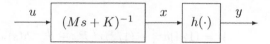

u $(Ms + K)^{-1}$ x $h(\cdot)$ y

Figure 6.15: Exercise 6.5

6.6 Show that the parallel connection of two passive (respectively, input strictly passive, output strictly passive, strictly passive) dynamical systems is passive (respectively, input strictly passive, output strictly passive, strictly passive).

6.7 Show that the transfer function $(b_0 s + b_1)/(s^2 + a_1 s + a_2)$ is strictly positive real if and only if all coefficients are positive and $b_1 < a_1 b_0$.

6.8 Consider equations (6.14) through (6.16) and suppose that $(D + D^T)$ is non-singular. Show that P satisfies the Riccati equation

$$PA_0 + A_0^T P - PB_0 P + C_0 = 0$$

where $A_0 = -(\epsilon/2)I - A + B(D + D^T)^{-1}C$, $B_0 = B(D + D^T)^{-1}B^T$, and $C_0 = -C^T(D + D^T)^{-1}C$.

6.9 Show that if a system is input strictly passive, with $\varphi(u) = \epsilon u$, and finite-gain $\mathcal{L}_2$ stable, then there is a storage function V and positive constants ϵ_1 and δ_1 such that

$$u^T y \geq V + \epsilon_1 u^T u + \delta_1 y^T y$$

6.10 Consider the equations of motion of an m-link robot, described in Exercise 1.4. Assume that $P(q)$ is a positive definite function of q and $g(q) = 0$ has an isolated root at $q = 0$.

(a) Using the total energy $V = \frac{1}{2}\dot{q}^T M(q)\dot{q} + P(q)$ as a storage function, show that the map from u to $\dot{q}$ is passive.

(b) With $u = -K_d \dot{q} + v$, where K_d is a positive diagonal constant matrix, show that the map from v to $\dot{q}$ is output strictly passive.

(c) Show that $u = -K_d \dot{q}$, where K_d is a positive diagonal constant matrix, makes the origin ($q = 0$, $\dot{q} = 0$) asymptotically stable. Under what additional conditions will it be globally asymptotically stable?

6.11 ([151]) Euler equations for a rotating rigid spacecraft are given by

$$
\begin{aligned}
J_1 \dot{\omega}_1 &= (J_2 - J_3)\omega_2 \omega_3 + u_1 \\
J_2 \dot{\omega}_2 &= (J_3 - J_1)\omega_3 \omega_1 + u_2 \\
J_3 \dot{\omega}_3 &= (J_1 - J_2)\omega_1 \omega_2 + u_3
\end{aligned}
$$

where ω_1 to ω_3 are the components of the angular velocity vector along the principal axes, u_1 to u_3 are the torque inputs applied about the principal axes, and J_1 to J_3 are the principal moments of inertia.

(a) Show that the map from $u = [u_1, u_2, u_3]^T$ to $\omega = [\omega_1, \omega_2, \omega_3]^T$ is lossless.

(b) Let $u = -K\omega + v$, where K is a positive definite symmetric matrix. Show that the map from v to ω is finite-gain $\mathcal{L}_2$ stable.

(c) Show that, when $v = 0$, the origin $\omega = 0$ is globally asymptotically stable.

6.12 Consider the feedback system of Figure 6.11 where H_1 and H_2 have the state models

$$\dot{x}_i = f_i(x_i) + G_i(x_i)e_i, \qquad y_i = h_i(x_i) + J_i(x_i)e_i$$

for $i = 1, 2$. Show that the feedback system has a well-defined state model if the matrix $I + J_2(x_2)J_1(x_1)$ is nonsingular for all x_1 and x_2.

6.13 Consider equations (6.26)–(6.27) and (6.30)–(6.31), and suppose $h_1 = h_1(x_1)$, independent of e_1. Show, in each case, that the equations have a unique solution (e_1, e_2).

6.14 Consider the feedback connection of Figure 6.11 with

$$H_1 : \begin{cases} \dot{x}_1 &= x_2 \\ \dot{x}_2 &= -x_1 - h_1(x_2) + e_1 \\ y_1 &= x_2 \end{cases} \quad \text{and} \quad H_2 : \begin{cases} \dot{x}_3 &= -x_3 + e_2 \\ y_2 &= h_2(x_3) \end{cases}$$

where h_1 and h_2 are locally Lipschitz functions, which satisfy $h_1 \in (0, \infty]$, $h_2 \in (0, \infty]$, and $|h_2(z)| \geq |z|/(1 + z^2)$ for all z.

(a) Show that the feedback connection is passive.

(b) Show that the origin of the unforced system is globally asymptotically stable.

6.15 Repeat the previous exercise for

$$H_1 : \begin{cases} \dot{x}_1 &= -x_1 + x_2 \\ \dot{x}_2 &= -x_1^3 - x_2 + e_1 \\ y_1 &= x_2 \end{cases} \quad \text{and} \quad H_2 : \begin{cases} \dot{x}_3 &= -x_3 + e_2 \\ y_2 &= x_3^3 \end{cases}$$

6.16 (**[78]**) Consider the feedback system of Figure 6.11, where H_1 and H_2 are passive dynamical systems of the form (6.21)–(6.22). Suppose the feedback connection has a well-defined state model and the series connection $H_1(-H_2)$, with input e_2 and output y_1, is zero-state observable. Show that the origin is asymptotically stable if H_2 is input strictly passive or H_1 is output strictly passive.

6.17 (**[78]**) Consider the feedback system of Figure 6.11, where H_1 and H_2 are passive dynamical systems of the form (6.21)–(6.22). Suppose the feedback connection has a well-defined state model and the series connection H_2H_1, with input e_1 and output y_2, is zero-state observable. Show that the origin is asymptotically stable if H_1 is input strictly passive or H_2 is output strictly passive.

6.18 ([78]) As a generalization of the concept of passivity, a dynamical system of the form (6.6)–(6.7) is said to be dissipative with respect to a supply rate $w(u, y)$ if there is a positive definite storage function $V(x)$ such that $\dot{V} \leq w$. Consider the feedback system of Figure 6.11 where H_1 and H_2 are zero-state observable, dynamical systems of the form (6.21)–(6.22). Suppose each of H_1 and H_2 is dissipative with storage function $V_i(x_i)$ and supply rate $w_i(u_i, y_i) = y_i^T Q_i y_i + 2 y_i^T S_i u_i + u_i^T R_i u_i$, where Q_i and R_i are real symmetric matrices and S_i is a real matrix. Show that the origin is stable (respectively, asymptotically stable) if the matrix

$$\hat{Q} = \begin{bmatrix} Q_1 + \alpha R_2 & -S_1 + \alpha S_2^T \\ -S_1^T + \alpha S_2 & R_1 + \alpha Q_2 \end{bmatrix}$$

is negative semidefinite (respectively, negative definite) for some $\alpha > 0$.

6.19 Consider the feedback connection of two time-invariant dynamical systems of the form (6.21)–(6.22). Suppose both feedback components are zero-state observable and there exist positive definite storage functions which satisfy

$$e_i^T y_i \geq \dot{V}_i + e_i^T \varphi_i(e_i) + y_i^T \rho_i(y_i), \quad \text{for } i = 1, 2$$

Show that the origin of the closed-loop system (6.24) when $u = 0$ is asymptotically stable if

$$v^T [\rho_1(v) + \varphi_2(v)] > 0 \quad \text{and} \quad v^T [\rho_2(v) - \varphi_1(-v)] > 0, \quad \forall\, v \neq 0$$

Under what additional conditions will the origin be globally asymptotically stable?

Chapter 7

Frequency Domain Analysis of Feedback Systems

Many nonlinear physical systems can be represented as a feedback connection of a linear dynamical system and a nonlinear element, as shown in Figure 7.1. The process of representing a system in this form depends on the particular system involved. For instance, in the case in which a control system's only nonlinearity is in the form of a relay or actuator/sensor nonlinearity, there is no difficulty in representing the system in the feedback form of Figure 7.1. In other cases, the representation may be less obvious. We assume that the external input $r = 0$ and study the behavior of the unforced system. What is unique about this chapter is the use of the frequency response of the linear system, which builds on classical control tools like the Nyquist plot and the Nyquist criterion. In Section 7.1, we study absolute stability. The system is said to absolutely stable if it has a globally uniformly asymptotically stable equilibrium point at the origin for all nonlinearities in a given sector. The circle and Popov criteria give frequency-domain sufficient conditions for absolute stability in

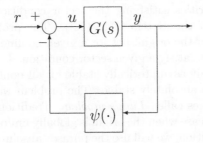

Figure 7.1: Feedback connection.

the form of strict positive realness of certain transfer functions. In the single-input–single-output case, both criteria can be applied graphically. In Section 7.2, we use the describing function method to study the existence of periodic solutions for a single-input–single-output system. We derive frequency-domain conditions, which can be applied graphically, to predict the existence or absence of oscillations and estimate the frequency and amplitude of oscillation when there is one.

7.1   Absolute Stability

Consider the feedback connection of Figure 7.1. We assume that the external input $r = 0$ and study the behavior of the unforced system, represented by

$$\dot{x} = Ax + Bu \tag{7.1}$$

$$y = Cx + Du \tag{7.2}$$

$$u = -\psi(t, y) \tag{7.3}$$

where $x \in R^n$, $u, y \in R^p$, (A, B) is controllable, (A, C) is observable, and $\psi : [0, \infty) \times R^p \to R^p$ is a memoryless, possibly time-varying, nonlinearity, which is piecewise continuous in t and locally Lipschitz in y. We assume that the feedback connection has a well-defined state model, which is the case when

$$u = -\psi(t, Cx + Du) \tag{7.4}$$

has a unique solution u for every (t, x) in the domain of interest. This is always the case when $D = 0$. The transfer function matrix of the linear system

$$G(s) = C(sI - A)^{-1}B + D \tag{7.5}$$

is square and proper. The controllability and observability assumptions ensure that $\{A, B, C, D\}$ is a minimal realization of $G(s)$. From linear system theory, we know that for any rational proper $G(s)$, a minimal realization always exists. The nonlinearity ψ is required to satisfy a sector condition per Definition 6.2. The sector condition may be satisfied globally, that is, for all $y \in R^p$, or satisfied only for $y \in Y$, a subset of R^p, whose interior is connected and contains the origin.

For all nonlinearities satisfying the sector condition, the origin $x = 0$ is an equilibrium point of the system (7.1)–(7.3). The problem of interest here is to study the stability of the origin, not for a given nonlinearity, but rather for a class of nonlinearities that satisfy a given sector condition. If we succeed in showing that the origin is uniformly asymptotically stable for all nonlinearities in the sector, the system is said to be absolutely stable. The problem was originally formulated by Lure and is sometimes called *Lure's problem*. Traditionally, absolute stability has been defined for the case when the origin is globally uniformly asymptotically stable. To keep up this tradition, we will use the phrase "absolute stability" when the sector condition is satisfied globally and the origin is globally uniformly asymptotically stable. Otherwise, we will use the phrase "absolute stability with a finite domain."

Definition 7.1 *Consider the system (7.1)–(7.3), where ψ satisfies a sector condition per Definition 6.2. The system is absolutely stable if the origin is globally uniformly asymptotically stable for any nonlinearity in the given sector. It is absolutely stable with a finite domain if the origin is uniformly asymptotically stable.*

We will investigate asymptotic stability of the origin by using Lyapunov analysis. A Lyapunov function candidate can be chosen by using the passivity tools of the previous chapter. In particular, if the closed-loop system can be represented as a feedback connection of two passive systems, then the sum of the two storage functions can be used as a Lyapunov function candidate for the closed-loop system. The use of loop transformations allows us to cover various sectors and Lyapunov function candidates, leading to the circle and Popov criteria.

7.1.1 Circle Criterion

Theorem 7.1 *The system (7.1)–(7.3) is absolutely stable if*

- $\psi \in [K_1, \infty]$ *and* $G(s)[I + K_1 G(s)]^{-1}$ *is strictly positive real, or*

- $\psi \in [K_1, K_2]$, *with* $K = K_2 - K_1 = K^T > 0$, *and* $[I + K_2 G(s)][I + K_1 G(s)]^{-1}$ *is strictly positive real.*

If the sector condition is satisfied only on a set $Y \subset R^p$, then the foregoing conditions ensure that the system is absolutely stable with a finite domain. $\diamond$

We refer to this theorem as the *multivariable circle criterion*, although the reason for using this name will not be clear until we specialize it to the scalar case. A necessary condition for equation (7.4) to have a unique solution u for every $\psi \in [K_1, \infty]$ or $\psi \in [K_1, K_2]$ is the nonsingularity of the matrix $(I + K_1 D)$. This can be seen by taking $\psi = K_1 y$ in (7.4). Therefore, the transfer function $[I + K_1 G(s)]^{-1}$ is proper.

Proof of Theorem 7.1: We prove the theorem first for the sector $[0, \infty]$ and recover the other cases by loop transformations. If $\psi \in [0, \infty]$ and $G(s)$ is strictly positive real, we have a feedback connection of two passive systems. From Lemma 6.4, we know that the storage function for the linear dynamical system is $V(x) = (1/2)x^T P x$, where $P = P^T > 0$ satisfies the Kalman–Yakubovich–Popov equations

$$PA + A^T P = -L^T L - \varepsilon P \tag{7.6}$$

$$PB = C^T - L^T W \tag{7.7}$$

$$W^T W = D + D^T \tag{7.8}$$

and $\varepsilon > 0$. Using $V(x)$ as a Lyapunov function candidate, we obtain

$$\dot{V} = \tfrac{1}{2}x^T P \dot{x} + \tfrac{1}{2}\dot{x}^T P x = \tfrac{1}{2}x^T (PA + A^T P)x + x^T P B u$$

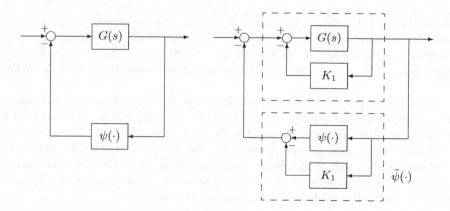

Figure 7.2: $\psi \in [K_1, \infty]$ is transformed to $\tilde{\psi} \in [0, \infty]$ via a loop transformation.

Using (7.6) and (7.7) yields

$$\begin{aligned}
\dot{V} &= -\tfrac{1}{2}x^T L^T L x - \tfrac{1}{2}\varepsilon x^T P x + x^T (C^T - L^T W)u \\
&= -\tfrac{1}{2}x^T L^T L x - \tfrac{1}{2}\varepsilon x^T P x + (Cx + Du)^T u - u^T D u - x^T L^T W u
\end{aligned}$$

Using (7.8) and the fact that $u^T D u = \tfrac{1}{2}u^T(D + D^T)u$, we obtain

$$\dot{V} = -\tfrac{1}{2}\varepsilon x^T P x - \tfrac{1}{2}(Lx + Wu)^T(Lx + Wu) - y^T \psi(t, y)$$

Since $y^T \psi(t, y) \geq 0$, we have

$$\dot{V} \leq -\tfrac{1}{2}\varepsilon x^T P x$$

which shows that the origin is globally exponentially stable. If ψ satisfies the sector condition only for $y \in Y$, the foregoing analysis will be valid in some neighborhood of the origin, showing that the origin is exponentially stable. The case $\psi \in [K_1, \infty]$ can be transformed to a case where the nonlinearity belongs to $[0, \infty]$ via the loop transformation of Figure 7.2. Hence, the system is absolutely stable if $G(s)[I + K_1 G(s)]^{-1}$ is strictly positive real. The case $\psi \in [K_1, K_2]$ can be transformed to a case where the nonlinearity belongs to $[0, \infty]$ via the loop transformation of Figure 7.3. Hence, the system is absolutely stable if

$$I + KG(s)[I + K_1 G(s)]^{-1} = [I + K_2 G(s)][I + K_1 G(s)]^{-1}$$

is strictly positive real.   □

Example 7.1 Consider the system (7.1)–(7.3) and suppose $G(s)$ is Hurwitz and strictly proper. Let

$$\gamma_1 = \sup_{\omega \in R} \sigma_{\max}[G(j\omega)] = \sup_{\omega \in R} \|G(j\omega)\|_2$$

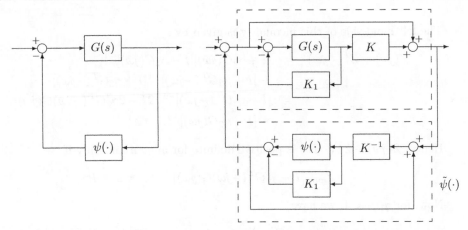

Figure 7.3: $\psi \in [K_1, K_2]$ is transformed to $\tilde\psi \in [0, \infty]$ via a loop transformation.

where $\sigma_{\max}[\cdot]$ denotes the maximum singular value of a complex matrix. The constant γ_1 is finite, since $G(s)$ is Hurwitz. Suppose ψ satisfies the inequality

$$\|\psi(t, y)\|_2 \leq \gamma_2 \|y\|_2, \quad \forall\, t \geq 0, \ \forall\, y \in R^p \tag{7.9}$$

then it belongs to the sector $[K_1, K_2]$ with $K_1 = -\gamma_2 I$ and $K_2 = \gamma_2 I$. To apply Theorem 7.1, we need to show that

$$Z(s) = [I + \gamma_2 G(s)][I - \gamma_2 G(s)]^{-1}$$

is strictly positive real. We note that $\det[Z(s) + Z^T(-s)]$ is not identically zero because $Z(\infty) = I$. We apply Lemma 6.1. Since $G(s)$ is Hurwitz, $Z(s)$ will be Hurwitz if $[I - \gamma_2 G(s)]^{-1}$ is Hurwitz. Noting that[1]

$$\sigma_{\min}[I - \gamma_2 G(j\omega)] \geq 1 - \gamma_1 \gamma_2$$

we see that if $\gamma_1 \gamma_2 < 1$, the plot of $\det[I - \gamma_2 G(j\omega)]$ will not go through nor encircle the origin. Hence, by the multivariable Nyquist criterion,[2] $[I - \gamma_2 G(s)]^{-1}$ is Hurwitz; consequently, $Z(s)$ is Hurwitz. Next, we show that

$$Z(j\omega) + Z^T(-j\omega) > 0, \quad \forall\, \omega \in R$$

---

[1] The following properties of singular values of a complex matrix are used:

$$\det G \neq 0 \Leftrightarrow \sigma_{\min}[G] > 0$$
$$\sigma_{\max}[G^{-1}] = 1/\sigma_{\min}[G], \ \text{if } \sigma_{\min}[G] > 0$$
$$\sigma_{\min}[I + G] \geq 1 - \sigma_{\max}[G]$$
$$\sigma_{\max}[G_1 G_2] \leq \sigma_{\max}[G_1]\sigma_{\max}[G_2]$$

[2] See [33, pp. 160–161] for a statement of the multivariable Nyquist criterion.

The left-hand side of this inequality is given by

$$
\begin{aligned}
Z(j\omega) + Z^T(-j\omega) &= [I + \gamma_2 G(j\omega)][I - \gamma_2 G(j\omega)]^{-1} \\
&\quad + [I - \gamma_2 G^T(-j\omega)]^{-1}[I + \gamma_2 G^T(-j\omega)] \\
&= [I - \gamma_2 G^T(-j\omega)]^{-1}\left[2I - 2\gamma_2^2 G^T(-j\omega)G(j\omega)\right] \\
&\quad \times [I - \gamma_2 G(j\omega)]^{-1}
\end{aligned}
$$

Hence, $Z(j\omega) + Z^T(-j\omega)$ is positive definite for all ω if and only if

$$
\sigma_{\min}\left[I - \gamma_2^2 G^T(-j\omega)G(j\omega)\right] > 0, \quad \forall\, \omega \in R
$$

Now, for $\gamma_1 \gamma_2 < 1$, we have

$$
\begin{aligned}
\sigma_{\min}[I - \gamma_2^2 G^T(-j\omega)G(j\omega)] &\geq 1 - \gamma_2^2 \sigma_{\max}[G^T(-j\omega)]\sigma_{\max}[G(j\omega)] \\
&\geq 1 - \gamma_1^2 \gamma_2^2 > 0
\end{aligned}
$$

Finally, $Z(\infty) + Z^T(\infty) = 2I$. Thus, all the conditions of Lemma 6.1 are satisfied and we conclude that $Z(s)$ is strictly positive real and the system is absolutely stable if $\gamma_1 \gamma_2 < 1$. This is a robustness result, which shows that closing the loop around a Hurwitz transfer function with a nonlinearity satisfying (7.9), with a sufficiently small γ_2, does not destroy the stability of the system.[3]   △

In the scalar case $p = 1$, the conditions of Theorem 7.1 can be verified graphically by examining the Nyquist plot of $G(j\omega)$. For $\psi \in [\alpha, \beta]$, with $\beta > \alpha$, the system is absolutely stable if the scalar transfer function

$$
Z(s) = \frac{1 + \beta G(s)}{1 + \alpha G(s)}
$$

is strictly positive real. To verify that $Z(s)$ is strictly positive real, we can use Lemma 6.1 which states that $Z(s)$ is strictly positive real if it is Hurwitz and

$$
\mathrm{Re}\left[\frac{1 + \beta G(j\omega)}{1 + \alpha G(j\omega)}\right] > 0, \quad \forall\, \omega \in [-\infty, \infty] \tag{7.10}
$$

To relate condition (7.10) to the Nyquist plot of $G(j\omega)$, we have to distinguish between three different cases, depending on the sign of α. Consider first the case when $\beta > \alpha > 0$. In this case, condition (7.10) can be rewritten as

$$
\mathrm{Re}\left[\frac{\frac{1}{\beta} + G(j\omega)}{\frac{1}{\alpha} + G(j\omega)}\right] > 0, \quad \forall\, \omega \in [-\infty, \infty] \tag{7.11}
$$

For a point q on the Nyquist plot of $G(j\omega)$, the two complex numbers $(1/\beta) + G(j\omega)$ and $(1/\alpha) + G(j\omega)$ can be represented by the lines connecting q to $-(1/\beta) + j0$ and

---

[3]The inequality $\gamma_1 \gamma_2 < 1$ can be derived also from the small-gain theorem. (See Example 5.13.)

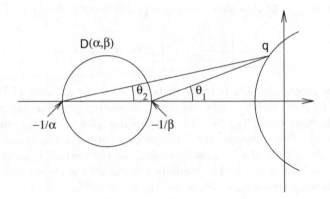

Figure 7.4: Graphical representation of the circle criterion.

$-(1/\alpha) + j0$, respectively, as shown in Figure 7.4. The real part of the ratio of two complex numbers is positive when the angle difference between the two numbers is less than $\pi/2$; that is, the angle $(\theta_1 - \theta_2)$ in Figure 7.4 is less than $\pi/2$. If we define $D(\alpha, \beta)$ to be the closed disk in the complex plane whose diameter is the line segment connecting the points $-(1/\alpha) + j0$ and $-(1/\beta) + j0$, then it is simple to see that the angle $(\theta_1 - \theta_2)$ is less than $\pi/2$ when q is outside the disk $D(\alpha, \beta)$. Since (7.11) is required to hold for all ω, all points on the Nyquist plot of $G(j\omega)$ must be strictly outside the disk $D(\alpha, \beta)$. On the other hand, $Z(s)$ is Hurwitz if $G(s)/[1 + \alpha G(s)]$ is Hurwitz. The Nyquist criterion states that $G(s)/[1 + \alpha G(s)]$ is Hurwitz if and only if the Nyquist plot of $G(j\omega)$ does not intersect the point $-(1/\alpha) + j0$ and encircles it exactly m times in the counterclockwise direction, where m is the number of poles of $G(s)$ in the open right-half complex plane.[4] Therefore, the conditions of Theorem 7.1 are satisfied if the Nyquist plot of $G(j\omega)$ does not enter the disk $D(\alpha, \beta)$ and encircles it m times in the counterclockwise direction. Consider, next, the case when $\beta > 0$ and $\alpha = 0$. For this case, Theorem 7.1 requires $1 + \beta G(s)$ to be strictly positive real. This is the case if $G(s)$ is Hurwitz and

$$\text{Re}[1 + \beta G(j\omega)] > 0, \quad \forall \, \omega \in [-\infty, \infty]$$

The latter condition can be rewritten as

$$\text{Re}[G(j\omega)] > -\frac{1}{\beta}, \quad \forall \, \omega \in [-\infty, \infty]$$

which is equivalent to the graphical condition that the Nyquist plot of $G(j\omega)$ lies to the right of the vertical line defined by $\text{Re}[s] = -1/\beta$. Finally, consider the case

---

[4]When $G(s)$ has poles on the imaginary axis, the Nyquist path is indented in the right-half plane, as usual.

when $\alpha < 0 < \beta$. In this case, condition (7.10) is equivalent to

$$\text{Re}\left[\frac{\frac{1}{\beta} + G(j\omega)}{\frac{1}{\alpha} + G(j\omega)}\right] < 0, \quad \forall\, \omega \in [-\infty, \infty] \tag{7.12}$$

where the inequality sign is reversed because, as we go from (7.10) to (7.12), we multiply by α/β, which is now negative. Repeating previous arguments, it can be easily seen that for (7.12) to hold, the Nyquist plot of $G(j\omega)$ must lie inside the disk $D(\alpha, \beta)$. Consequently, the Nyquist plot cannot encircle the point $-(1/\alpha) + j0$. Therefore, from the Nyquist criterion, we see that $G(s)$ must be Hurwitz for $G(s)/[1 + \alpha G(s)]$ to be so. The stability criteria for the three cases are summarized in the following theorem, which is known as the *circle criterion*.

Theorem 7.2 *Consider a scalar system of the form (7.1)–(7.3), where $\{A, B, C, D\}$ is a minimal realization of $G(s)$ and $\psi \in [\alpha, \beta]$. Then, the system is absolutely stable if one of the following conditions is satisfied, as appropriate:*

1. *If $0 < \alpha < \beta$, the Nyquist plot of $G(j\omega)$ does not enter the disk $D(\alpha, \beta)$ and encircles it m times in the counterclockwise direction, where m is the number of poles of $G(s)$ with positive real parts.*

2. *If $0 = \alpha < \beta$, $G(s)$ is Hurwitz and the Nyquist plot of $G(j\omega)$ lies to the right of the vertical line defined by $\text{Re}[s] = -1/\beta$.*

3. *If $\alpha < 0 < \beta$, $G(s)$ is Hurwitz and the Nyquist plot of $G(j\omega)$ lies in the interior of the disk $D(\alpha, \beta)$.*

If the sector condition is satisfied only on an interval $[a, b]$, then the foregoing conditions ensure that the system is absolutely stable with a finite domain. ◇

The circle criterion allows us to investigate absolute stability by using only the Nyquist plot of $G(j\omega)$. This is important because the Nyquist plot can be determined directly from experimental data. Given the Nyquist plot of $G(j\omega)$, we can determine permissible sectors for which the system is absolutely stable. The next two examples illustrate the use of the circle criterion.

Example 7.2 Let

$$G(s) = \frac{4}{(s+1)(\frac{1}{2}s+1)(\frac{1}{3}s+1)}$$

The Nyquist plot of $G(j\omega)$ is shown in Figure 7.5. Since $G(s)$ is Hurwitz, we can allow α to be negative and apply the third case of the circle criterion. So, we need to determine a disk $D(\alpha, \beta)$ that encloses the Nyquist plot. Clearly, the choice of the disk is not unique. Suppose we decide to locate the center of the disk at the origin of the complex plane. This means that we will work with a disk $D(-\gamma_2, \gamma_2)$, where the radius $(1/\gamma_2) > 0$ is to be chosen. The Nyquist plot will be inside this

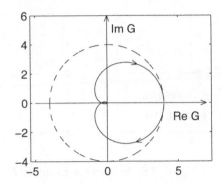

Figure 7.5: Nyquist plot for Example 7.2.

disk if $|G(j\omega)| < 1/\gamma_2$. In particular, if we set $\gamma_1 = \sup_{\omega \in R} |G(j\omega)|$, then γ_2 must be chosen to satisfy $\gamma_1 \gamma_2 < 1$. This is the same condition we found in Example 7.1. It is not hard to see that $|G(j\omega)|$ is maximum at $\omega = 0$ and $\gamma_1 = 4$. Thus, γ_2 must be less than 0.25. Hence, we can conclude that the system is absolutely stable for all nonlinearities in the sector $[-0.25 + \varepsilon, 0.25 - \varepsilon]$, where $\varepsilon > 0$ can be arbitrarily small. Inspection of the Nyquist plot and the disk $D(-0.25, 0.25)$ in Figure 7.5 suggests that the choice to locate the center at the origin may not be the best one. By locating the center at another point, we might be able to obtain a disk that encloses the Nyquist plot more tightly. For example, let us locate the center at the point $1.5 + j0$. The maximum distance from this point to the Nyquist plot is 2.834. Hence, choosing the radius of the disk to be 2.9 ensures that the Nyquist plot is inside the disk $D(-1/4.4, 1/1.4)$, and we can conclude that the system is absolutely stable for all nonlinearities in the sector $[-0.227, 0.714]$. Comparing this sector with the previous one (see Figure 7.6) shows that by giving in a little bit on the lower bound of the sector, we achieve a significant improvement in the upper bound. Clearly, there is still room for optimizing the choice of the center of the disk, but we will not pursue it. The point we wanted to show is that the graphical representation used in the circle criterion gives us a closer look at the problem, compared with the use of norm inequalities as in Example 7.1, which allows us to obtain less conservative estimates of the sector. Another direction we can pursue in applying the circle criterion is to restrict α to zero and apply the second case of the circle criterion. The Nyquist plot lies to the right of the vertical line $\text{Re}[s] = -0.857$. Hence, we can conclude that the system is absolutely stable for all nonlinearities in the sector $[0, 1.166]$. This sector is sketched in Figure 7.6, together with the previous two sectors. It gives the best estimate of β, which is achieved at the expense of limiting the nonlinearity to be a first-quadrant–third-quadrant nonlinearity. To appreciate how this flexibility in using the circle criterion could be useful in applications, let us suppose that we are interested in studying the stability of the system of Figure 7.7, which includes a limiter or saturation nonlinearity (a typical nonlinearity in feedback control systems

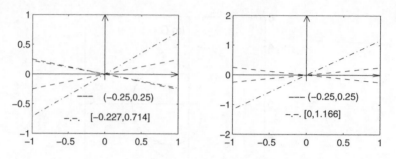

Figure 7.6: Sectors for Example 7.2.

due to constraints on physical variables). The saturation nonlinearity belongs to a sector $[0, 1]$. Therefore, it is included in the sector $[0, 1.166]$, but not in the sector $(-0.25, 0.25)$ or $[-0.227, 0.714]$. Thus, based on the application of the second case of the circle criterion, we can conclude that the feedback system of Figure 7.7 has a globally asymptotically stable equilibrium point at the origin.   △

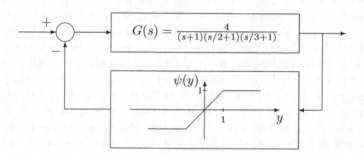

Figure 7.7: Feedback connection with saturation nonlinearity.

Example 7.3 Let
$$G(s) = \frac{4}{(s-1)(\frac{1}{2}s+1)(\frac{1}{3}s+1)}$$

This transfer function is not Hurwitz, since it has a pole in the open right-half plane. So, we must restrict α to be positive and apply the first case of the circle criterion. The Nyquist plot of $G(j\omega)$ is shown in Figure 7.8. From the circle criterion, we know that the Nyquist plot must encircle the disk $D(\alpha, \beta)$ once in the counterclockwise direction. Inspection of the Nyquist plot shows that a disk can be encircled by the Nyquist plot only if it is totally inside one of the two lobes formed by the Nyquist plot in the left-half plane. A disk inside the right lobe is encircled once in the clockwise direction. Hence, it does not satisfy the circle criterion. A disk inside the left lobe is encircled once in the counterclockwise direction. Thus, we need to

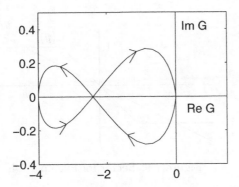

Figure 7.8: Nyquist plot for Example 7.3.

choose α and β to locate the disk $D(\alpha, \beta)$ inside the left lobe. Let us locate the center of the disk at the point $-3.2 + j0$, about halfway between the two ends of the lobe on the real axis. The minimum distance from this center to the Nyquist plot is 0.1688. Hence, choosing the radius to be 0.168, we conclude that the system is absolutely stable for all nonlinearities in the sector $[0.2969, 0.3298]$. $\triangle$

In Examples 7.1 through 7.3, we have considered cases where the sector condition is satisfied globally. In the next example, the sector condition is satisfied only on a finite interval.

Example 7.4 Consider the feedback connection of Figure 7.1, where the linear system is represented by the transfer function

$$G(s) = \frac{s + 2}{(s + 1)(s - 1)}$$

and the nonlinear element is $\psi(y) = \text{sat}(y)$. The nonlinearity belongs globally to the sector $[0, 1]$. However, since $G(s)$ is not Hurwitz, we must apply the first case of the circle criterion, which requires the sector condition to hold with a positive α. Thus, we cannot conclude absolute stability by using the circle criterion.[5] The best we can hope for is to show absolute stability with a finite domain. Figure 7.9 shows that on the interval $[-a, a]$, the nonlinearity ψ belongs to the sector $[\alpha, \beta]$ with $\alpha = 1/a$ and $\beta = 1$. Since $G(s)$ has a pole with positive real part, the Nyquist plot of $G(j\omega)$, shown in Figure 7.10, must encircle the disk $D(\alpha, 1)$ once in the counterclockwise direction. It can be verified, analytically, that condition (7.10) is satisfied for $\alpha > 0.5359$. Thus, choosing $\alpha = 0.55$, the sector condition is satisfied on the interval $[-1.818, 1.818]$ and the disk $D(0.55, 1)$ is encircled once by the Nyquist plot in the counterclockwise direction. From the first case of the circle criterion, we

---

[5]In fact, the origin is not globally asymptotically stable because the system has three equilibrium points.

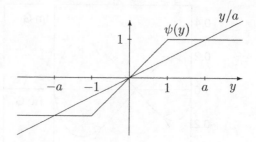

Figure 7.9: Sector for Example 7.4.

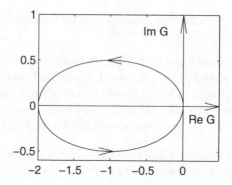

Figure 7.10: Nyquist plot for Example 7.4.

conclude that the system is absolutely stable with a finite domain. We can also use a quadratic Lyapunov function $V(x) = x^T P x$ to estimate the region of attraction. Consider the state model

$$\begin{aligned}
\dot{x}_1 &= x_2 \\
\dot{x}_2 &= x_1 + u \\
y &= 2x_1 + x_2 \\
u &= -\psi(y)
\end{aligned}$$

The loop transformation of Figure 7.3 is given by

$$\begin{aligned}
u &= -\alpha y + \tilde{u} = -0.55y + \tilde{u} \\
\tilde{y} &= (\beta - \alpha)y + \tilde{u} = 0.45y + \tilde{u}
\end{aligned}$$

Thus, the transformed linear system is given by

$$\dot{x} = Ax + B\tilde{u}, \quad \tilde{y} = Cx + D\tilde{u}$$

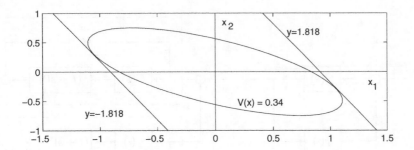

Figure 7.11: Region of attraction for Example 7.4.

where

$$A = \begin{bmatrix} 0 & 1 \\ -0.1 & -0.55 \end{bmatrix}, \quad B = \begin{bmatrix} 0 \\ 1 \end{bmatrix}, \quad C = \begin{bmatrix} 0.9 & 0.45 \end{bmatrix}, \quad \text{and} \quad D = 1$$

The matrix P is the solution of equations (7.6) through (7.8). It can be verified that[6]

$$\varepsilon = 0.02, \quad P = \begin{bmatrix} 0.4946 & 0.4834 \\ 0.4834 & 1.0774 \end{bmatrix}, \quad L = \begin{bmatrix} 0.2946 & -0.4436 \end{bmatrix}, \quad \text{and} \quad W = \sqrt{2}$$

satisfy (7.6) through (7.8). Thus, $V(x) = x^T P x$ is a Lyapunov function for the system. We estimate the region of attraction by

$$\Omega_c = \{x \in R^2 \mid V(x) \le c\}$$

where $c \le \min_{\{|y|=1.818\}} V(x) = 0.3445$ to ensure that Ω_c is contained in the set $\{|y| \le 1.818\}$. Taking $c = 0.34$ gives the estimate shown in Figure 7.11. $\triangle$

7.1.2 Popov Criterion

Consider a special case of the system (7.1)–(7.3), given by

$$\dot{x} = Ax + Bu \tag{7.13}$$
$$y = Cx \tag{7.14}$$
$$u_i = -\psi_i(y_i), \quad 1 \le i \le p \tag{7.15}$$

where $x \in R^n$, $u, y \in R^p$, (A, B) is controllable, (A, C) is observable, and $\psi_i : R \to R$ is a locally Lipschitz memoryless nonlinearity that belongs to the sector $[0, k_i]$. In this special case, the transfer function $G(s) = C(sI - A)^{-1}B$ is strictly proper

---

[6]The value of ε is chosen such that $G(s - \varepsilon/2)$ is positive real and $[(\varepsilon/2)I + A]$ is Hurwitz, where $G(s) = C(sI - A)^{-1}B + D$. Then, P is calculated by solving a Riccati equation, as described in Exercise 6.8.

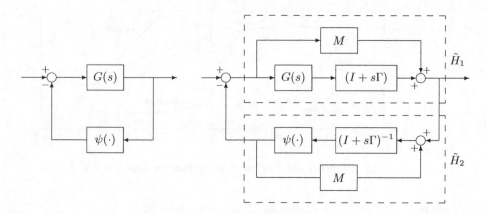

Figure 7.12: Loop transformation.

and ψ is time invariant and decoupled; that is, $\psi_i(y) = \psi_i(y_i)$. Since $D = 0$, the feedback connection has a well-defined state model. The following theorem, known as the multivariable Popov criterion, is proved by using a (Lure-type) Lyapunov function of the form $V = (1/2)x^T P x + \sum \gamma_i \int_0^{y_i} \psi_i(\sigma)\, d\sigma$, which is motivated by the application of a loop transformation that transforms the system (7.13)–(7.15) into the feedback connection of two passive dynamical systems.

Theorem 7.3 *The system (7.13)–(7.15) is absolutely stable if, for $1 \leq i \leq p$, $\psi_i \in [0, k_i]$, $0 < k_i \leq \infty$, and there exists a constant $\gamma_i \geq 0$, with $(1 + \lambda_k \gamma_i) \neq 0$ for every eigenvalue λ_k of A, such that $M + (I + s\Gamma)G(s)$ is strictly positive real, where $\Gamma = \text{diag}(\gamma_1, \cdots, \gamma_p)$ and $M = \text{diag}(1/k_1, \cdots, 1/k_p)$. If the sector condition $\psi_i \in [0, k_i]$ is satisfied only on a set $Y \subset R^p$, then the foregoing conditions ensure that the system is absolutely stable with a finite domain.* $\diamond$

Proof: The loop transformation of Figure 7.12 results in a feedback connection of $\tilde{H}_1$ and $\tilde{H}_2$, where $\tilde{H}_1$ is a linear system whose transfer function is

$$
\begin{aligned}
M + (I + s\Gamma)G(s) &= M + (I + s\Gamma)C(sI - A)^{-1}B \\
&= M + C(sI - A)^{-1}B + \Gamma C s(sI - A)^{-1}B \\
&= M + C(sI - A)^{-1}B + \Gamma C(sI - A + A)(sI - A)^{-1}B \\
&= M + (C + \Gamma CA)(sI - A)^{-1}B + \Gamma CB
\end{aligned}
$$

Thus, $M + (I + s\Gamma)G(s)$ can be realized by the state model $\{\mathcal{A}, \mathcal{B}, \mathcal{C}, \mathcal{D}\}$, where $\mathcal{A} = A$, $\mathcal{B} = B$, $\mathcal{C} = C + \Gamma CA$, and $\mathcal{D} = M + \Gamma CB$. Let λ_k be an eigenvalue of A and v_k be the associated eigenvector. Then

$$
(C + \Gamma CA)v_k = (C + \Gamma C\lambda_k)v_k = (I + \lambda_k \Gamma)Cv_k
$$

The condition $(1 + \lambda_k \gamma_i) \neq 0$ implies that $(\mathcal{A}, \mathcal{C})$ is observable; hence, the realization $\{\mathcal{A}, \mathcal{B}, \mathcal{C}, \mathcal{D}\}$ is minimal. If $M + (I + s\Gamma)G(s)$ is strictly positive real, we can apply the Kalman–Yakubovich–Popov lemma to conclude that there are matrices $P = P^T > 0$, L, and W, and a positive constant ε that satisfy

$$PA + A^T P = -L^T L - \varepsilon P \tag{7.16}$$

$$PB = (C + \Gamma CA)^T - L^T W \tag{7.17}$$

$$W^T W = 2M + \Gamma CB + B^T C^T \Gamma \tag{7.18}$$

and $V = (1/2)x^T P x$ is a storage function for $\tilde{H}_1$. One the other hand, it can be verified (Exercise 6.2) that $\tilde{H}_2$ is passive with the storage function $\sum_{i=1}^{p} \gamma_i \int_0^{y_i} \psi_i(\sigma)\, d\sigma$. Thus, the storage function for the transformed feedback connection of Figure 7.12 is

$$V = \tfrac{1}{2}x^T P x + \sum_{i=1}^{p} \gamma_i \int_0^{y_i} \psi_i(\sigma)\, d\sigma$$

We use V as a Lyapunov function candidate for the original feedback connection (7.13)–(7.15). The derivative $\dot{V}$ is given by

$$
\begin{aligned}
\dot{V} &= \tfrac{1}{2}x^T P \dot{x} + \tfrac{1}{2}\dot{x}^T P x + \psi^T(y)\Gamma \dot{y} \\
&= \tfrac{1}{2}x^T (PA + A^T P)x + x^T PBu + \psi^T(y)\Gamma C(Ax + Bu)
\end{aligned}
$$

Using (7.16) and (7.17) yields

$$
\begin{aligned}
\dot{V} &= -\tfrac{1}{2}x^T L^T L x - \tfrac{1}{2}\varepsilon x^T P x + x^T (C^T + A^T C^T \Gamma - L^T W)u \\
&\quad + \psi^T(y)\Gamma CAx + \psi^T(y)\Gamma CBu
\end{aligned}
$$

Substituting $u = -\psi(y)$ and using (7.18), we obtain

$$\dot{V} = -\tfrac{1}{2}\varepsilon x^T P x - \tfrac{1}{2}(Lx + Wu)^T(Lx + Wu) - \psi(y)^T[y - M\psi(y)] \leq -\tfrac{1}{2}\varepsilon x^T P x$$

which shows that the origin is globally asymptotically stable. If ψ satisfies the sector condition only for $y \in Y$, the foregoing analysis will be valid in some neighborhood of the origin, showing that the origin is asymptotically stable. $\square$

For $M + (I + s\Gamma)G(s)$ to be strictly positive real, $G(s)$ must be Hurwitz. As we have done in the circle criterion, this restriction on $G(s)$ may be removed by performing a loop transformation that replaces $G(s)$ by $G(s)[I + K_1 G(s)]^{-1}$. We will not repeat this idea in general, but will illustrate it by an example. In the scalar case $p = 1$, we can test the strict positive realness of $Z(s) = (1/k) + (1 + s\gamma)G(s)$ graphically. By Lemma 6.1, $Z(s)$ is strictly positive real if $G(s)$ is Hurwitz and

$$\frac{1}{k} + \mathrm{Re}[G(j\omega)] - \gamma\omega\,\mathrm{Im}[G(j\omega)] > 0, \quad \forall\, \omega \in [-\infty, \infty] \tag{7.19}$$

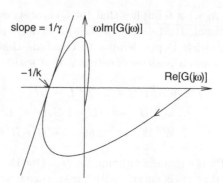

Figure 7.13: Popov plot.

where $G(j\omega) = \text{Re}[G(j\omega)] + j\text{Im}[G(j\omega)]$. If we plot $\text{Re}[G(j\omega)]$ versus $\omega\text{Im}[G(j\omega)]$ with ω as a parameter, then condition (7.19) is satisfied if the plot lies to the right of the line that intercepts the point $-(1/k) + j0$ with a slope $1/\gamma$. (See Figure 7.13.) Such a plot is known as a Popov plot, in contrast to a Nyquist plot, which is a plot of $\text{Re}[G(j\omega)]$ versus $\text{Im}[G(j\omega)]$. If condition (7.19) is satisfied only for $\omega \in (-\infty, \infty)$, while the left-hand side approaches zero as ω tends to ∞, then we need to analytically verify that

$$\lim_{\omega \to \infty} \omega^2 \left\{ \frac{1}{k} + \text{Re}[G(j\omega)] - \gamma\omega\text{Im}[G(j\omega)] \right\} > 0$$

This case arises when $k = \infty$ and $G(s)$ has relative degree two.

With $\gamma = 0$, condition (7.19) reduces to the circle criterion condition $\text{Re}[G(j\omega)] > -1/k$, which shows that, for the system (7.13)–(7.15), the conditions of the Popov criterion are weaker than those of the circle criterion. In other words, with $\gamma > 0$, absolute stability can be established under less stringent conditions.

Example 7.5 Consider the second-order system

$$\begin{aligned} \dot{x}_1 &= x_2 \\ \dot{x}_2 &= -x_2 - h(y) \\ y &= x_1 \end{aligned}$$

This system would fit the form (7.13)–(7.15) if we took $\psi = h$, but the matrix A would not be Hurwitz. Adding and subtracting the term αy to the right-hand side of the second state equation, where $\alpha > 0$, and defining $\psi(y) = h(y) - \alpha y$, the system takes the form (7.13)–(7.15), with

$$A = \begin{bmatrix} 0 & 1 \\ -\alpha & -1 \end{bmatrix}, \quad B = \begin{bmatrix} 0 \\ 1 \end{bmatrix}, \quad \text{and} \quad C = \begin{bmatrix} 1 & 0 \end{bmatrix}$$

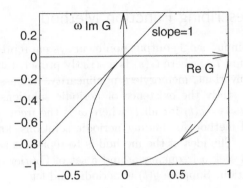

Figure 7.14: Popov plot for Example 7.5.

Assume that h belongs to a sector $[\alpha, \beta]$, where $\beta > \alpha$. Then, ψ belongs to the sector $[0, k]$, where $k = \beta - \alpha$. Condition (7.19) takes the form

$$\frac{1}{k} + \frac{\alpha - \omega^2 + \gamma \omega^2}{(\alpha - \omega^2)^2 + \omega^2} > 0, \quad \forall \, \omega \in [-\infty, \infty]$$

For all finite positive values of α and k, this inequality is satisfied by choosing $\gamma > 1$. Even at $k = \infty$, the foregoing inequality is satisfied for all $\omega \in (-\infty, \infty)$ and

$$\lim_{\omega \to \infty} \frac{\omega^2(\alpha - \omega^2 + \gamma \omega^2)}{(\alpha - \omega^2)^2 + \omega^2} = \gamma - 1 > 0$$

Hence, the system is absolutely stable for all nonlinearities h in the sector $[\alpha, \infty]$, where α can be arbitrarily small. Figure 7.14 shows the Popov plot of $G(j\omega)$ for $\alpha = 1$. The plot is drawn only for $\omega \geq 0$, since $\text{Re}[G(j\omega)]$ and $\omega\text{Im}[G(j\omega)]$ are even functions of ω. The Popov plot asymptotically approaches the line through the origin of unity slope from the right side. Therefore, it lies to the right of any line of slope less than one that intersects the real axis at the origin and approaches it asymptotically as ω tends to ∞. To see the advantage of having $\gamma > 0$, let us take $\gamma = 0$ and apply the circle criterion. From the second case of Theorem 7.2, the system is absolutely stable if the Nyquist plot of $G(j\omega)$ lies to the right of the vertical line defined by $\text{Re}[s] = -1/k$. Since a portion of the Nyquist plot lies in the left-half plane, k cannot be arbitrarily large. The maximum permissible value of k can be determined analytically from the condition

$$\frac{1}{k} + \frac{\alpha - \omega^2}{(\alpha - \omega^2)^2 + \omega^2} > 0, \quad \forall \, \omega \in [-\infty, \infty]$$

which yields $k < 1 + 2\sqrt{\alpha}$. Thus, using the circle criterion, we can only conclude that the system is absolutely stable for all nonlinearities h in the sector $[\alpha, 1 + \alpha + 2\sqrt{\alpha} - \varepsilon]$, where $\alpha > 0$ and $\varepsilon > 0$ can be arbitrarily small. $\triangle$

7.2   The Describing Function Method

Consider a single-input–single-output nonlinear system represented by the feedback connection of Figure 7.1, where $G(s)$ is a strictly proper, rational transfer function and ψ is a time-invariant, memoryless nonlinearity. We assume that the external input $r = 0$ and study the existence of periodic solutions. A periodic solution satisfies $y(t + 2\pi/\omega) = y(t)$ for all t, where ω is the frequency of oscillation. We will use a general method for finding periodic solutions, known as *the method of harmonic balance*. The idea of the method is to represent a periodic solution by a Fourier series and seek a frequency ω and a set of Fourier coefficients that satisfy the system's equation. Suppose $y(t)$ is periodic and let

$$y(t) = \sum_{k=-\infty}^{\infty} a_k \exp(jk\omega t)$$

be its Fourier series, where a_k are complex coefficients,[7] $a_k = \bar{a}_{-k}$ and $j = \sqrt{-1}$. Since $\psi(\cdot)$ is a time-invariant nonlinearity, $\psi(y(t))$ is periodic with the same frequency ω and can be written as

$$\psi(y(t)) = \sum_{k=-\infty}^{\infty} c_k \exp(jk\omega t)$$

where each complex coefficient c_k is a function of all a_i's. For $y(t)$ to be a solution of the feedback system, it must satisfy the differential equation

$$d(p)y(t) + n(p)\psi(y(t)) = 0$$

where p is the differential operator $p(\cdot) = d(\cdot)/dt$ and $n(s)$ and $d(s)$ are the numerator and denominator polynomials of $G(s)$. Because

$$p\exp(jk\omega t) = \frac{d}{dt}\exp(jk\omega t) = jk\omega \exp(jk\omega t)$$

we have

$$d(p) \sum_{k=-\infty}^{\infty} a_k \exp(jk\omega t) = \sum_{k=-\infty}^{\infty} d(jk\omega)a_k \exp(jk\omega t)$$

and

$$n(p) \sum_{k=-\infty}^{\infty} c_k \exp(jk\omega t) = \sum_{k=-\infty}^{\infty} n(jk\omega)c_k \exp(jk\omega t)$$

Substituting these expressions back into the differential equation yields

$$\sum_{k=-\infty}^{\infty} [d(jk\omega)a_k + n(jk\omega)c_k] \exp(jk\omega t) = 0$$

---

[7]A bar over a complex variable denotes its complex conjugate.

Using the orthogonality of the functions $\exp(jk\omega t)$ for different values of k, we find that the Fourier coefficients must satisfy

$$G(jk\omega)c_k + a_k = 0 \tag{7.20}$$

for all integers k. Because $G(jk\omega) = \bar{G}(-jk\omega)$, $a_k = \bar{a}_{-k}$, and $c_k = \bar{c}_{-k}$, we need only look at (7.20) for $k \geq 0$. Equation (7.20) is an infinite-dimensional equation, which we can hardly solve. We need to find a finite-dimensional approximation of (7.20). Noting that the transfer function $G(s)$ is strictly proper, that is, $G(j\omega) \to 0$ as $\omega \to \infty$, it is reasonable to assume that there is an integer $q > 0$ such that for all $k > q$, $|G(jk\omega)|$ is small enough to replace $G(jk\omega)$ (and consequently a_k) by 0. This approximation reduces (7.20) to a finite-dimensional problem

$$G(jk\omega)\hat{c}_k + \hat{a}_k = 0, \quad k = 0, 1, 2, \ldots, q \tag{7.21}$$

where the Fourier coefficients are written with a hat accent to emphasize that a solution of (7.21) is only an approximation to the solution of (7.20). In essence, we can proceed to solve (7.21). However, the complexity of the problem will grow with q and, for a large q, the finite-dimensional problem (7.21) might still be difficult to solve. The simplest problem results if we can choose $q = 1$. This, of course, requires the transfer function $G(s)$ to have sharp "low-pass filtering" characteristics to allow us to approximate $G(jk\omega)$ by 0 for all $k > 1$. Even though we know $G(s)$, we cannot judge whether this is a good approximation, since we do not know the frequency of oscillation ω. Nevertheless, the classical describing function method makes this approximation and sets $\hat{a}_k = 0$ for $k > 1$ to reduce the problem to one of solving the two equations

$$G(0)\hat{c}_0(\hat{a}_0, \hat{a}_1) + \hat{a}_0 = 0 \tag{7.22}$$
$$G(j\omega)\hat{c}_1(\hat{a}_0, \hat{a}_1) + \hat{a}_1 = 0 \tag{7.23}$$

Notice that (7.22) and (7.23) define one real equation (7.22) and one complex equation (7.23) in two real unknowns, ω and $\hat{a}_0$, and a complex unknown $\hat{a}_1$. When expressed as real quantities, they define three equations in four unknowns. This is expected because the time origin is arbitrary for an autonomous system, so if $(\hat{a}_0, \hat{a}_1)$ satisfies the equation, then $(\hat{a}_0, \hat{a}_1 e^{j\theta})$ will give another solution for arbitrary real θ. To take care of this nonuniqueness, we take the first harmonic of $y(t)$ to be $a \sin \omega t$, with $a \geq 0$; that is, we choose the time origin such that the phase of the first harmonic is zero. Using

$$a \sin \omega t = \frac{a}{2j}[\exp(j\omega t) - \exp(-j\omega t)] \;\Rightarrow\; \hat{a}_1 = \frac{a}{2j}$$

we rewrite (7.22) and (7.23) as

$$G(0)\hat{c}_0\left(\hat{a}_0, \frac{a}{2j}\right) + \hat{a}_0 = 0 \tag{7.24}$$

$$G(j\omega)\hat{c}_1\left(\hat{a}_0, \frac{a}{2j}\right) + \frac{a}{2j} = 0 \tag{7.25}$$

Since (7.24) does not depend on ω, it may be solved for $\hat{a}_0$ as a function of a. Note that if $\psi(\cdot)$ is an odd function, that is,

$$\psi(-y) = -\psi(y)$$

then $\hat{a}_0 = \hat{c}_0 = 0$ is a solution of (7.24) because

$$\hat{c}_0 = \frac{\omega}{2\pi} \int_0^{2\pi/\omega} \psi(\hat{a}_0 + a \sin \omega t)\, dt$$

For convenience, let us restrict our attention to nonlinearities with odd symmetry and take $\hat{a}_0 = \hat{c}_0 = 0$. Then, we can rewrite (7.25) as

$$G(j\omega)\hat{c}_1\left(0, \frac{a}{2j}\right) + \frac{a}{2j} = 0 \tag{7.26}$$

The coefficient $\hat{c}_1(0, a/2j)$ is the complex Fourier coefficient of the first harmonic at the output of the nonlinearity when its input is the sinusoidal signal $a \sin \omega t$. It is given by

$$
\begin{aligned}
\hat{c}_1(0, a/2j) &= \frac{\omega}{2\pi} \int_0^{2\pi/\omega} \psi(a \sin \omega t) \exp(-j\omega t)\, dt \\
&= \frac{\omega}{2\pi} \int_0^{2\pi/\omega} [\psi(a \sin \omega t) \cos \omega t - j\psi(a \sin \omega t) \sin \omega t]\, dt
\end{aligned}
$$

The first term under the integral sign is an odd function, while the second term is an even function. Therefore, the integration of the first term over one complete cycle is zero, and the integral simplifies to

$$\hat{c}_1(0, a/2j) = -j\frac{\omega}{\pi} \int_0^{\pi/\omega} \psi(a \sin \omega t) \sin \omega t\, dt$$

Define a function $\Psi(a)$ by

$$\Psi(a) = \frac{\hat{c}_1(0, a/2j)}{a/2j} = \frac{2\omega}{\pi a} \int_0^{\pi/\omega} \psi(a \sin \omega t) \sin \omega t\, dt \tag{7.27}$$

so that (7.26) can be rewritten as

$$[G(j\omega)\Psi(a) + 1]a = 0 \tag{7.28}$$

Since we are not interested in a solution with $a = 0$, we can solve (7.28) completely by finding all solutions of

$$G(j\omega)\Psi(a) + 1 = 0 \tag{7.29}$$

Equation (7.29) is known as the *first-order harmonic balance equation*, or simply the *harmonic balance equation*. The function $\Psi(a)$ defined by (7.27) is called *the describing function* of the nonlinearity ψ. It is obtained by applying a sinusoidal signal $a \sin \omega t$ at the input of the nonlinearity and by calculating the ratio of the Fourier coefficient of the first harmonic at the output to a. It can be thought of as an "equivalent gain" of a linear time-invariant element whose response to $a \sin \omega t$ is $\Psi(a) a \sin \omega t$. This equivalent gain concept (sometimes called *equivalent linearization*) can be applied to more general time-varying nonlinearities or nonlinearities with memory, like hysteresis and backlash.[8] In that general context, the describing function might be complex and dependent on both a and ω. We will only deal with describing functions of odd, time-invariant, memoryless nonlinearities for which $\Psi(a)$ is real, dependent only on a, and given by the expression

$$\Psi(a) = \frac{2}{\pi a} \int_0^\pi \psi(a \sin \theta) \sin \theta \; d\theta \tag{7.30}$$

which is obtained from (7.27) by changing the integration variable from t to $\theta = \omega t$.

The describing function method states that if (7.29) has a solution (a_s, ω_s), then there is "probably" a periodic solution of the system with frequency and amplitude (at the input of the nonlinearity) close to ω_s and a_s. Conversely, if (7.29) has no solutions, then the system "probably" does not have a periodic solution. More analysis is needed to replace the word "probably" with "certainly" and to quantify the phrase "close to ω_s and a_s" when there is a periodic solution. We will postpone these investigations until a later point in the section. For now, we would like to look more closely at the calculation of the describing function and the question of solving the harmonic balance equation (7.29). The next three examples illustrate the calculation of the describing function for odd nonlinearities.

Example 7.6 Consider the signum nonlinearity $\psi(y) = \text{sgn}(y)$. The describing function is given by

$$\Psi(a) = \frac{2}{\pi a} \int_0^\pi \psi(a \sin \theta) \sin \theta \; d\theta = \frac{2}{\pi a} \int_0^\pi \sin \theta \; d\theta = \frac{4}{\pi a}$$

$$\triangle$$

Example 7.7 Consider the *piecewise-linear* function of Figure 7.15. If a sinusoidal input to this nonlinearity has amplitude $a \le \delta$, the nonlinearity will act as a linear gain. The output will be a sinusoid with amplitude $s_1 a$. Hence, the describing function is $\Psi(a) = s_1$, independent of a. When $a > \delta$, we divide the integral on the right-hand side of (7.30) into pieces, with each piece corresponding to a linear portion of $\psi(\cdot)$. Furthermore, using the odd symmetry of the output waveform, we simplify the integration to

$$\Psi(a) \quad = \quad \frac{2}{\pi a} \int_0^\pi \psi(a \sin \theta) \sin \theta \; d\theta \quad = \quad \frac{4}{\pi a} \int_0^{\pi/2} \psi(a \sin \theta) \sin \theta \; d\theta$$

---

[8]See [18] or [85].

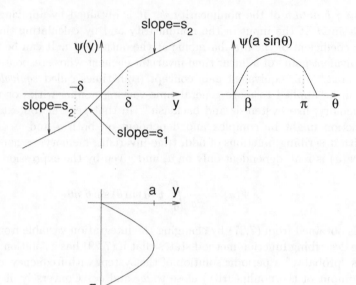

Figure 7.15: Piecewise-linear function.

$$= \frac{4}{\pi a} \int_0^{\beta} a s_1 \sin^2 \theta \, d\theta$$

$$+ \frac{4}{\pi a} \int_{\beta}^{\pi/2} [\delta s_1 + s_2(a \sin \theta - \delta)] \sin \theta \, d\theta, \quad \beta = \sin^{-1}\left(\frac{\delta}{a}\right)$$

$$= \frac{2s_1}{\pi}\left(\beta - \frac{1}{2}\sin 2\beta\right) + \frac{4\delta(s_1 - s_2)}{\pi a}\left(\cos \beta - \cos \frac{\pi}{2}\right)$$

$$+ \frac{2s_2}{\pi}\left(\frac{\pi}{2} - \frac{1}{2}\sin \pi - \beta + \frac{1}{2}\sin 2\beta\right)$$

$$= \frac{2(s_1 - s_2)}{\pi}\left(\beta + \frac{\delta}{a}\cos \beta\right) + s_2$$

Thus,

$$\Psi(a) = \frac{2(s_1 - s_2)}{\pi}\left[\sin^{-1}\left(\frac{\delta}{a}\right) + \frac{\delta}{a}\sqrt{1 - \left(\frac{\delta}{a}\right)^2}\right] + s_2$$

A sketch of the describing function is shown in Figure 7.16. By selecting specific values for δ and the slopes s_1 and s_2, we can obtain the describing function of several common nonlinearities. For example, the saturation nonlinearity is a special case of the piecewise-linear function of Figure 7.15 with $\delta = 1$, $s_1 = 1$, and $s_2 = 0$. Hence,

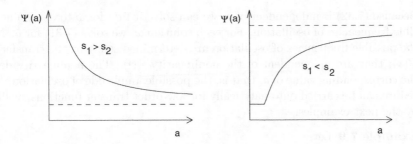

Figure 7.16: Describing function for the piecewise-linear function of Figure 7.15.

its describing function is given by

$$\Psi(a) = \begin{cases} 1, & \text{if } 0 \leq a \leq 1 \\ \frac{2}{\pi}\left[\sin^{-1}\left(\frac{1}{a}\right) + \frac{1}{a}\sqrt{1 - \left(\frac{1}{a}\right)^2}\right], & \text{if } a > 1 \end{cases}$$

$\triangle$

Example 7.8 Consider an odd nonlinearity that satisfies the sector condition

$$\alpha y^2 \leq y\psi(y) \leq \beta y^2$$

for all $y \in R$. The describing function $\Psi(a)$ satisfies the lower bound

$$\Psi(a) = \frac{2}{\pi a}\int_0^\pi \psi(a\sin\theta)\sin\theta \, d\theta \geq \frac{2\alpha}{\pi}\int_0^\pi \sin^2\theta \, d\theta = \alpha$$

and the upper bound

$$\Psi(a) = \frac{2}{\pi a}\int_0^\pi \psi(a\sin\theta)\sin\theta \, d\theta \leq \frac{2\beta}{\pi}\int_0^\pi \sin^2\theta \, d\theta = \beta$$

Therefore,

$$\alpha \leq \Psi(a) \leq \beta, \quad \forall \, a \geq 0$$

$\triangle$

Since the describing function $\Psi(a)$ is real, (7.29) can be rewritten as

$$\{\text{Re}[G(j\omega)] + j\text{Im}[G(j\omega)]\}\Psi(a) + 1 = 0$$

This equation is equivalent to the two real equations

$$1 + \Psi(a)\text{Re}[G(j\omega)] = 0 \tag{7.31}$$
$$\text{Im}[G(j\omega)] = 0 \tag{7.32}$$

Because (7.32) is independent of a, we can solve it first for ω to determine the possible frequencies of oscillation. For each solution ω, we solve (7.31) for a. Note that the possible frequencies of oscillation are determined solely by the transfer function $G(s)$; they are independent of the nonlinearity $\psi(\cdot)$. The nonlinearity determines the corresponding value of a, that is, the possible amplitude of oscillation. This procedure can be carried out analytically for low-order transfer functions, as illustrated by the next examples.

Example 7.9 Let

$$G(s) = \frac{1}{s(s+1)(s+2)}$$

and consider two nonlinearities: the signum nonlinearity and the saturation nonlinearity. By simple manipulation, we can write $G(j\omega)$ as

$$G(j\omega) = \frac{-3\omega - j\left(2 - \omega^2\right)}{9\omega^3 + \omega\left(2 - \omega^2\right)^2}$$

Equation (7.32) takes the form

$$\frac{\left(2 - \omega^2\right)}{9\omega^3 + \omega\left(2 - \omega^2\right)^2} = 0$$

which has one positive root $\omega = \sqrt{2}$. Note that for each positive root of (7.32), there is a negative root of equal magnitude. We only consider the positive roots. Note also that a root at $\omega = 0$ would be of no interest because it would not give rise to a nontrivial periodic solution. Evaluating $\text{Re}[G(j\omega)]$ at $\omega = \sqrt{2}$ and substituting it in (7.31), we obtain $\Psi(a) = 6$. All this information has been gathered without specifying the nonlinearity $\psi(\cdot)$. Consider now the signum nonlinearity. We found in Example 7.6 that $\Psi(a) = 4/\pi a$. Therefore, $\Psi(a) = 6$ has a unique solution $a = 2/3\pi$. Now we can say that the nonlinear system formed of $G(s)$ and the signum nonlinearity will "probably" oscillate with frequency close to $\sqrt{2}$ and amplitude (at the input of the nonlinearity) close to $2/3\pi$. Consider next the saturation nonlinearity. We found in Example 7.7 that $\Psi(a) \leq 1$ for all a. Therefore, $\Psi(a) = 6$ has no solutions. Therefore, we expect that the nonlinear system formed of $G(s)$ and the saturation nonlinearity will not have a sustained oscillation. $\triangle$

Example 7.10 Let

$$G(s) = \frac{-s}{s^2 + 0.8s + 8}$$

and consider two nonlinearities: the saturation nonlinearity and a dead-zone nonlinearity that is a special case of the piecewise-linear function of Example 7.7 with $s_1 = 0$, $s_2 = 0.5$, and $\delta = 1$. We can write $G(j\omega)$ as

$$G(j\omega) = \frac{-0.8\omega^2 - j\omega\left(8 - \omega^2\right)}{0.64\omega^2 + \left(8 - \omega^2\right)^2}$$

Equation (7.32) has a unique positive root $\omega = 2\sqrt{2}$. Evaluating $\text{Re}[G(j\omega)]$ at $\omega = 2\sqrt{2}$ and substituting it in (7.31), we obtain $\Psi(a) = 0.8$. For the saturation nonlinearity, the describing function is given in Example 7.7, and $\Psi(a) = 0.8$ has the unique solution $a = 1.455$. Therefore, we expect that the nonlinear system formed of $G(s)$ and the saturation nonlinearity will oscillate with frequency close to $2\sqrt{2}$ and amplitude (at the input of the nonlinearity) close to 1.455. For the dead-zone nonlinearity, the describing function $\Psi(a)$ is less than 0.8 for all a. Thus, $\Psi(a) = 0.8$ has no solutions, and we expect that the nonlinear system formed of $G(s)$ and the dead-zone nonlinearity will not have sustained oscillations. In this particular example, we can confirm the no oscillation conjecture by showing that the system is absolutely stable for a class of sector nonlinearities, which includes the given dead-zone nonlinearity. It can be easily checked that

$$\text{Re}[G(j\omega)] \geq -1.25, \quad \forall\, \omega \in R$$

Therefore, from the circle criterion (Theorem 7.2), we know that the system is absolutely stable for a sector $[0, \beta]$ with $\beta < 0.8$. The given dead-zone nonlinearity belongs to this sector. Consequently, the origin of the state space is globally asymptotically stable and the system cannot have a sustained oscillation. $\triangle$

Example 7.11 Consider Raleigh's equation

$$\ddot{z} + z = \varepsilon \left(\dot{z} - \tfrac{1}{3}\dot{z}^3 \right)$$

where ε is a positive constant. To study existence of periodic solutions, we represent the equation in the feedback form of Figure 7.1. Let $u = -\dot{z}^3/3$ and rewrite the system's equation as

$$\begin{aligned} \ddot{z} - \varepsilon\dot{z} + z &= \varepsilon u \\ u &= -\tfrac{1}{3}\dot{z}^3 \end{aligned}$$

The first equation defines a linear system. Taking $y = \dot{z}$ to be its output, its transfer function is

$$G(s) = \frac{\varepsilon s}{s^2 - \varepsilon s + 1}$$

The second equation defines a nonlinearity $\psi(y) = y^3/3$. The two equations together represent the system in the feedback form of Figure 7.1. The describing function of $\psi(y) = y^3/3$ is given by

$$\Psi(a) = \frac{2}{3\pi a} \int_0^\pi (a\sin\theta)^3 \sin\theta\, d\theta = \tfrac{1}{4}a^2$$

The function $G(j\omega)$ can be written as

$$G(j\omega) = \frac{j\varepsilon\omega[(1 - \omega^2) + j\varepsilon\omega]}{(1 - \omega^2)^2 + \varepsilon^2\omega^2}$$

The equation $\text{Im}[G(j\omega)] = 0$ yields $\omega(1 - \omega^2) = 0$; hence, there is a unique positive solution $\omega = 1$. Then,

$$1 + \Psi(a)\text{Re}[G(j)] = 0 \;\Rightarrow\; a = 2$$

Therefore, we expect that Raleigh's equation has a periodic solution of frequency near 1 rad/sec and that the amplitude of oscillation in $\dot{z}$ is near 2. $\triangle$

For higher-order transfer functions, solving the harmonic balance equation (7.29) analytically might be very complicated. Of course, we can always resort to numerical methods for solving (7.29). However, the power of the describing function method is not in solving (7.29) analytically or numerically; rather, it is the graphical solution of (7.29) that made the method popular. Equation (7.29) can be rewritten as

$$G(j\omega) = -\,\frac{1}{\Psi(a)} \tag{7.33}$$

or

$$\frac{1}{G(j\omega)} = -\Psi(a) \tag{7.34}$$

Equation (7.33) suggests that we can solve (7.29) by plotting the Nyquist plot of $G(j\omega)$ for $\omega > 0$ and the locus of $-1/\Psi(a)$ for $a \geq 0$. Intersections of these loci give the solutions of (7.29). Since $\Psi(a)$ is real for odd nonlinearities, the locus of $-1/\Psi(a)$ in the complex plane will be confined to the real axis. Equation (7.34) suggests a similar procedure by plotting the inverse Nyquist plot of $G(j\omega)$ (that is, the locus in the complex plane of $1/G(j\omega)$ as ω varies) and the locus of $-\Psi(a)$. The important role of Nyquist plots in classical control theory made this graphical implementation of the describing function method a popular tool with control engineers as they faced nonlinearities.

Example 7.12 Consider again the transfer function $G(s)$ of Example 7.9. The Nyquist plot of $G(j\omega)$ is shown in Figure 7.17. It intersects the real axis at $(-1/6, 0)$. For odd nonlinearities, (7.29) will have a solution if the locus of $-1/\Psi(a)$ on the real axis includes this point of intersection. $\triangle$

Let us turn now to the question of justifying the describing function method. Being an approximate method for solving the infinite-dimensional equation (7.20), the describing function method can be justified by providing estimates of the error caused by the approximation. In the interest of simplicity, we will pursue this analysis only for nonlinearities with the following two features:[9]

- Odd nonlinearity, that is, $\psi(y) = -\psi(-y)$, $\forall\, y \neq 0$.

- Single-valued nonlinearity with a slope between α and β; that is,

$$\alpha(y_2 - y_1) \leq [\psi(y_2) - \psi(y_1)] \leq \beta(y_2 - y_1)$$

   for all real numbers y_1 and $y_2 > y_1$.

---

[9]See [24], [129], and [189] for describing function theory for more general nonlinearities.

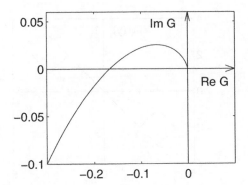

Figure 7.17: Nyquist plot for Example 7.12.

A nonlinearity $\psi(\cdot)$ with these features belongs to a sector $[\alpha, \beta]$. Hence, from Example 7.8, its describing function satisfies $\alpha \leq \Psi(a) \leq \beta$ for all $a \geq 0$. It should be noted, however, that the slope restriction is not the same as the sector condition. A nonlinearity may satisfy the foregoing slope restriction with bounds α and β, and could belong to a sector $[\bar{\alpha}, \bar{\beta}]$ with different bounds $\bar{\alpha}$ and $\bar{\beta}$.[10] We emphasize that in the forthcoming analysis, we should use the slope bounds α and β, not the sector boundaries $\bar{\alpha}$ and $\bar{\beta}$.

Example 7.13 Consider the piecewise-linear odd nonlinearity

$$\psi(y) = \begin{cases} y, & \text{for } 0 \leq y \leq 2 \\ 4 - y, & \text{for } 2 \leq y \leq 3 \\ y - 2, & \text{for } y \geq 3 \end{cases}$$

shown in Figure 7.18. The nonlinearity satisfies the slope restriction

$$-1 \leq \frac{\psi(y_2) - \psi(y_1)}{y_2 - y_1} \leq 1$$

as well as the sector condition

$$\frac{1}{3} \leq \frac{\psi(y)}{y} \leq 1$$

In the forthcoming analysis, we should take $\alpha = -1$ and $\beta = 1$. $\triangle$

We will restrict our attention to the question of the existence of half-wave symmetric periodic solutions;[11] that is, periodic solutions that only have odd harmonics. This is a reasonable restriction in view of the odd symmetry of ψ. The Fourier coefficients

---

[10]Verify that $[\bar{\alpha}, \bar{\beta}] \subset [\alpha, \beta]$.

[11]This restriction is made only for convenience. See [128] for a more general analysis that does not make this assumption.

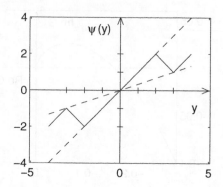

Figure 7.18: Nonlinearity of Example 7.13.

of the odd harmonics of a periodic solution $y(t)$ satisfy (7.20) for $k = 1, 3, 5, \ldots$. The basic idea of the error analysis is to split the periodic solution $y(t)$ into a first harmonic $y_1(t)$ and higher harmonics $y_h(t)$. We choose the time origin such that the phase of the first harmonic is zero; that is, $y_1(t) = a \sin \omega t$. Thus,

$$y(t) = a \sin \omega t + y_h(t)$$

Using this representation, the Fourier coefficients of the first harmonic of $y(t)$ and $\psi(y(t))$ are

$$a_1 = \frac{a}{2j}$$

$$c_1 = \frac{\omega}{\pi} \int_0^{\pi/\omega} \psi(a \sin \omega t + y_h(t)) \exp(-j\omega t) \, dt$$

From (7.20), with $k = 1$, we have

$$G(j\omega)c_1 + a_1 = 0$$

Introducing the function

$$\Psi^*(a, y_h) = \frac{c_1}{a_1} = j\frac{2\omega}{\pi a} \int_0^{\pi/\omega} \psi(a \sin \omega t + y_h(t)) \exp(-j\omega t) \, dt$$

we can rewrite the equation as

$$\frac{1}{G(j\omega)} + \Psi^*(a, y_h) = 0 \tag{7.35}$$

Adding $\Psi(a)$ to both sides of (7.35), we can rewrite it as

$$\frac{1}{G(j\omega)} + \Psi(a) = \delta\Psi \tag{7.36}$$

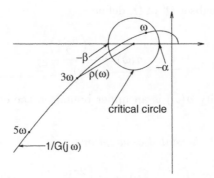

Figure 7.19: Finding $\rho(\omega)$.

where

$$\delta\Psi = \Psi(a) - \Psi^*(a, y_h)$$

When $y_h = 0$, $\Psi^*(a, 0) = \Psi(a)$. Thus, $\delta\Psi = 0$ and (7.36) reduces to the harmonic balance equation

$$\frac{1}{G(j\omega)} + \Psi(a) = 0 \tag{7.37}$$

Therefore, the harmonic balance equation (7.37) is an approximate version of the exact equation (7.36). The error term $\delta\Psi$ cannot be found exactly, but its size can often be estimated. Our next step is to find an upper bound on $\delta\Psi$. To that end, let us define two functions $\rho(\omega)$ and $\sigma(\omega)$. Start by drawing the locus of $1/G(j\omega)$ in the complex plane. On the same graph paper, draw a (critical) circle with the interval $[-\beta, -\alpha]$ on the real axis as a diameter. Notice that the locus of $-\Psi(a)$ lies inside this circle on the real axis, since $\alpha \leq \Psi(a) \leq \beta$. Now consider an ω such that the points on the locus $1/G$ corresponding to $k\omega$ ($k > 1$ and odd) lie outside the critical circle, as shown in Figure 7.19. The distance from any one of these points to the center of the critical circle is

$$\left| \frac{\alpha + \beta}{2} + \frac{1}{G(jk\omega)} \right|$$

Define

$$\rho(\omega) = \inf_{k>1; k \text{ odd}} \left| \frac{\alpha + \beta}{2} + \frac{1}{G(jk\omega)} \right| \tag{7.38}$$

Note that we have defined $\rho(\omega)$ only for ω at which $1/G(jk\omega)$ lies outside the critical circle for all $k = 3, 5, \ldots$; that is, for ω in the set

$$\Omega = \{\omega \mid \rho(\omega) > \tfrac{1}{2}(\beta - \alpha)\}$$

On any connected subset Ω' of Ω, define

$$\sigma(\omega) = \frac{\left(\frac{\beta-\alpha}{2}\right)^2}{\rho(\omega) - \frac{\beta-\alpha}{2}} \tag{7.39}$$

The positive quantity $\sigma(\omega)$ is an upper bound on the error term $\delta\Psi$, as stated in the next lemma.

Lemma 7.1 *Under the stated assumptions,*

$$\frac{\omega}{\pi} \int_0^{2\pi/\omega} y_h^2(t) \, dt \leq \left[\frac{2\sigma(\omega)a}{\beta-\alpha}\right]^2, \quad \forall \, \omega \in \Omega' \tag{7.40}$$

$$|\delta\Psi| \leq \sigma(\omega), \quad \forall \, \omega \in \Omega' \tag{7.41}$$

$\diamond$

Proof: See Appendix C.13.

The proof of Lemma 7.1 is based on writing an equation for $y_h(t)$ in the form $y_h = T(y_h)$ and showing that $T(\cdot)$ is a contraction mapping. This allows us to calculate the upper bound of (7.40), which is then used to calculate the upper bound of (7.41) on the error term. The slope restrictions on the nonlinearity ψ are used in showing that $T(\cdot)$ is a contraction mapping.

Using the bound of (7.41) in (7.36), we see that a necessary condition for the existence of a half-wave symmetric periodic solution with $\omega \in \Omega'$ is

$$\left|\frac{1}{G(j\omega)} + \Psi(a)\right| \leq \sigma(\omega)$$

Geometrically, this condition states that the point $-\Psi(a)$ must be contained in a circle with a center at $1/G(j\omega)$ and radius $\sigma(\omega)$. For each $\omega \in \Omega' \subset \Omega$, we can draw such an error circle. The envelope of all error circles over the connected set Ω' forms an uncertainty band. The reason for choosing a subset of Ω is that, as ω approaches the boundary of Ω, the error circles become arbitrarily large and cease to give any useful information. The subset Ω' should be chosen with the objective of drawing a narrow band. If $G(j\omega)$ has sharp low-pass filtering characteristics, the uncertainty band can be quite narrow over Ω'. Note that $\rho(\omega)$ is a measure of the low-pass filtering characteristics of $G(j\omega)$; for the smaller $|G(jk\omega)|$ for $k > 1$, the larger $\rho(\omega)$, as seen from (7.38). A large $\rho(\omega)$ results in a small radius $\sigma(\omega)$ for the error circle, as seen from (7.39).

We are going to look at intersections of the uncertainty band with the locus of $-\Psi(a)$. If no part of the band intersects the $-\Psi(a)$ locus, then clearly (7.36) has no solution with $\omega \in \Omega'$. If the band intersects the locus completely, as in Figure 7.20, then we expect that there is a solution. This is indeed true, provided

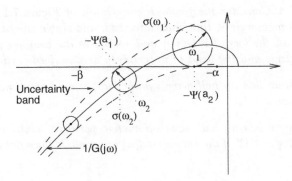

Figure 7.20: A complete intersection.

we exclude some degenerate cases. Actually, we can find error bounds by examining the intersection. Let a_1 and a_2 be the amplitudes corresponding to the intersections of the boundary of the uncertainty band with the $-\Psi(a)$ locus. Let ω_1 and ω_2 be the frequencies corresponding to the error circles of radii $\sigma(\omega_1)$ and $\sigma(\omega_2)$, which are tangent to the $-\Psi(a)$ locus on either side of it. Define a rectangle Γ in the (ω, a) plane by

$$\Gamma = \{(\omega, a) \mid \omega_1 < \omega < \omega_2, \ a_1 < a < a_2\}$$

The rectangle Γ contains the point (ω_s, a_s) for which the loci of $1/G$ and $-\Psi$ intersect, that is, the solution of the harmonic balance equation (7.37). It turns out that if certain regularity conditions hold, then it is possible to show that (7.36) has a solution in the closure of Γ. These regularity conditions are

$$\left. \frac{d}{da}\Psi(a) \right|_{a=a_s} \neq 0; \quad \left. \frac{d}{d\omega}\mathrm{Im}[G(j\omega)] \right|_{\omega=\omega_s} \neq 0$$

A complete intersection between the uncertainty band and the $-\Psi(a)$ locus can now be precisely defined as taking place when the $1/G(j\omega)$ locus intersects the $-\Psi(a)$ locus and a finite set Γ can be defined, as shown, such that (ω_s, a_s) is the unique intersection point in Γ and the regularity conditions hold.

Finally, notice that at high frequencies for which all harmonics (including the first) have the corresponding $1/G(j\omega)$ points outside the critical circle, we do not need to draw the uncertainty band. Therefore, we define a set

$$\tilde{\Omega} = \left\{ \omega \ \middle| \ \left| \frac{\alpha + \beta}{2} + \frac{1}{G(jk\omega)} \right| > \frac{\beta - \alpha}{2}, \ k = 1, 3, 5, \dots \right\}$$

and take the smallest frequency in $\tilde{\Omega}$ as the largest frequency in Ω', then decrease ω until the error circles become uncomfortably large.

The next theorem on the justification of the describing function method is the main result of this section.

Theorem 7.4 *Consider the feedback connection of Figure 7.1, where the nonlinearity $\psi(\cdot)$ is memoryless, time invariant, odd, and single valued with slopes between α and β. Draw the loci of $1/G(j\omega)$ and $-\Psi(a)$ in the complex plane and construct the critical circle and the band of uncertainty as described earlier. Then,*

- *the system has no half-wave symmetric periodic solutions with fundamental frequency $\omega \in \tilde{\Omega}$.*

- *the system has no half-wave symmetric periodic solutions with fundamental frequency $\omega \in \Omega'$ if the corresponding error circle does not intersect the $-\Psi(a)$ locus.*

- *for each complete intersection defining a set Γ in the (ω, a) plane, there is at least one half-wave symmetric periodic solution*

$$y(t) = a \sin \omega t + y_h(t)$$

with (ω, a) in $\bar{\Gamma}$ and $y_h(t)$ satisfies the bound of (7.40). ◇

Proof: See Appendix C.14.

Note that the theorem gives a sufficient condition for oscillation and a sufficient condition for nonoscillation. Between the two conditions, there is an area of ambiguity where we cannot reach conclusions of oscillation or nonoscillation.

Example 7.14 Consider again

$$G(s) = \frac{-s}{s^2 + 0.8s + 8}$$

together with the saturation nonlinearity. We have seen in Example 7.10 that the harmonic balance equation has a unique solution $\omega_s = 2\sqrt{2} \approx 2.83$ and $a_s = 1.455$. The saturation nonlinearity satisfies the slope restrictions with $\alpha = 0$ and $\beta = 1$. Therefore, the critical circle is centered at -0.5 and its radius is 0.5. The function $1/G(j\omega)$ is given by

$$\frac{1}{G(j\omega)} = -0.8 + j\frac{8 - \omega^2}{\omega}$$

Hence, the locus of $1/G(j\omega)$ lies on the line $\mathrm{Re}[s] = -0.8$, as shown in Figure 7.21. The radius of the error circle $\sigma(\omega)$ has been calculated for eight frequencies starting with $\omega = 2.65$ and ending with $\omega = 3.0$, with uniform increments of 0.05. The centers of the error circles are spread on the line $\mathrm{Re}[s] = -0.8$ inside the critical circle. The value of $\sigma(\omega)$ at $\omega = 2.65$ is 0.0388 and at $\omega = 3.0$ is 0.0321, with monotonic change between the two extremes. In all cases, the closest harmonic to the critical circle is the third harmonic, so that the infimum in (7.38) is achieved at $k = 3$. The boundaries of the uncertainty band are almost vertical. The intersection of the uncertainty band with the $-\Psi(a)$ locus correspond to the points $a_1 = 1.377$

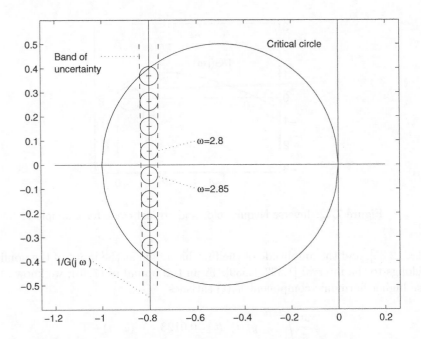

Figure 7.21: Uncertainty band for Example 7.14.

and $a_2 = 1.539$. The error circle corresponding to $\omega = 2.85$ is almost tangent to the real axis from the lower side, so we take $\omega_2 = 2.85$. The error circle corresponding to $\omega = 2.8$ is the closest circle to be tangent to the real axis from the upper side. This means that $\omega_1 > 2.8$. Trying $\omega = 2.81$, we have obtained a circle that is almost tangent to the real axis. Therefore, we define the set Γ as

$$\Gamma = \{(\omega, a) \mid 2.81 < \omega < 2.85, \ 1.377 < a < 1.539\}$$

There is only one intersection point in Γ. We need to check the regularity conditions. The derivative

$$\frac{d}{da}\Psi(a) = \frac{2}{\pi}\frac{d}{da}\left[\sin^{-1}\left(\frac{1}{a}\right) + \frac{1}{a}\sqrt{1 - \left(\frac{1}{a}\right)^2}\right] = -\frac{4}{\pi a^3}\sqrt{a^2 - 1}$$

is different from zero at $a = 1.455$, and

$$\frac{d}{d\omega}\mathrm{Im}[G(j\omega)]\bigg|_{\omega=\sqrt{8}} = \frac{2}{(0.8)^2} \neq 0$$

Thus, by Theorem 7.4, we conclude that the system indeed has a periodic solution. Moreover, we conclude that the frequency of oscillation ω belongs to the interval

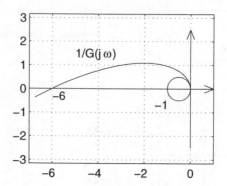

Figure 7.22: Inverse Nyquist plot and critical circle for Example 7.15.

$[2.81, 2.85]$, and the amplitude of the first harmonic at the input of the nonlinearity belongs to the interval $[1.377, 1.539]$. From the bound of (7.40), we know also that the higher harmonic component $y_h(t)$ satisfies

$$\frac{\omega}{\pi} \int_0^{2\pi/\omega} y_h^2(t) \, dt \leq 0.0123, \quad \forall \, (\omega, a) \in \Gamma$$

which shows that the waveform of the oscillating signal at the nonlinearity input is fairly close to its first harmonic $a \sin \omega t$. △

Example 7.15 Reconsider Example 7.9 with

$$G(s) = \frac{1}{s(s+1)(s+2)}$$

and the saturation nonlinearity. The nonlinearity satisfies the slope restriction with $\alpha = 0$ and $\beta = 1$. The inverse Nyquist plot of $G(j\omega)$, shown in Figure 7.22, lies outside the critical circle for all $\omega > 0$. Hence, $\tilde{\Omega} = (0, \infty)$, and we conclude that there is no oscillation. △

7.3   Exercises

7.1 Using the circle criterion, study absolute stability for each of the scalar transfer functions given next. In each case, find a sector $[\alpha, \beta]$ for which the system is absolutely stable.

$$(1) \qquad G(s) = \frac{s}{s^2 - s + 1}$$

$$(2) \qquad G(s) = \frac{1}{(s+2)(s+3)}$$

$$(3) \qquad G(s) = \frac{1}{s^2 + s + 1}$$

$$(4) \qquad G(s) = \frac{s^2 - 1}{(s+1)(s^2+1)}$$

$$(5) \qquad G(s) = \frac{1 - s}{(s+1)^2}$$

$$(6) \qquad G(s) = \frac{s+1}{(s+2)^2(s-1)}$$

$$(7) \qquad G(s) = \frac{1}{(s+1)^4}$$

$$(8) \qquad G(s) = \frac{1}{(s+1)^2(s+2)^2}$$

7.2 Consider the feedback connection of Figure 7.1 with $G(s) = 2s/(s^2 + s + 1)$.

(a) Show that the system is absolutely stable for nonlinearities in the sector $[0, 1]$.

(b) Show that the system has no limit cycles when $\psi(y) = \text{sat}(y)$.

7.3 Consider the system

$$\dot{x}_1 = -x_1 - h(x_1 + x_2), \qquad \dot{x}_2 = x_1 - x_2 - 2h(x_1 + x_2)$$

where h is a smooth function satisfying

$$yh(y) \geq 0, \ \forall \ y \in R, \quad h(y) = \begin{cases} c, & y \geq a_2 \\ 0, & |y| \leq a_1 \\ -c & y \leq -a_2 \end{cases}$$

$$|h(y)| \leq c, \quad \text{for } a_1 < y < a_2 \text{ and } -a_2 < y < -a_1$$

(a) Show that the origin is the unique equilibrium point.

(b) Show, using the circle criterion, that the origin is globally asymptotically stable.

7.4 ([201]) Consider the system

$$\dot{x}_1 = x_2, \qquad \dot{x}_2 = -(\mu^2 + a^2 - q\cos\omega t)x_1 - 2\mu x_2$$

where μ, a, q, and ω are positive constants. Represent the system in the form of Figure 7.1 with $\psi(t, y) = qy\cos\omega t$ and use the circle criterion to derive conditions on μ, a, q, and ω, which ensure that the origin is exponentially stable.

7.5 Consider the linear time-varying system $\dot{x} = [A + BE(t)C]x$, where A is Hurwitz, $\|E(t)\|_2 \leq 1$, $\forall \ t \geq 0$, and $\sup_{\omega \in R} \sigma_{\max}[C(j\omega I - A)^{-1}B] < 1$. Show that the origin is uniformly asymptotically stable.

7.6 Consider the system $\dot{x} = Ax + Bu$ and let $u = -Fx$ be a stabilizing state feedback control; that is, the matrix $(A - BF)$ is Hurwitz. Suppose that, due to physical limitations, we have to use a limiter to limit the value of u_i to $|u_i(t)| \leq L$. The closed-loop system can be represented by $\dot{x} = Ax - BL \, \mathrm{sat}(Fx/L)$, where $\mathrm{sat}(v)$ is a vector whose ith component is the saturation function.

(a) Show that the system can be represented in the form of Figure 7.1 with $G(s) = F(sI - A + BF)^{-1}B$ and $\psi(y) = L \, \mathrm{sat}(y/L) - y$.

(b) Derive a condition for asymptotic stability of the origin using the multivariable circle criterion.

(c) Apply the result to the case

$$A = \begin{bmatrix} 0 & 1 \\ 0.5 & 1 \end{bmatrix}, \quad B = \begin{bmatrix} 0 \\ 1 \end{bmatrix}, \quad F = \begin{bmatrix} 1 & 2 \end{bmatrix}, \quad \text{and} \quad L = 1$$

and estimate the region of attraction.

7.7 Repeat Exercise 7.1 using the Popov criterion.

7.8 In this exercise, we derive a version of the Popov criterion for a scalar transfer function $G(s)$ with all poles in the open left-half plane, except for a simple pole on the imaginary axis having a positive residue. The system is represented by

$$\dot{z} = Az - B\psi(y), \quad \dot{v} = -\psi(y), \quad \text{and} \quad y = Cz + dv$$

where $d > 0$, A is Hurwitz, (A, B) is controllable, (A, C) is observable, and ψ belongs to a sector $(0, k]$. Let $V(z, v) = z^T P z + a(y - Cz)^2 + b \int_0^y \psi(\sigma) \, d\sigma$, where $P = P^T > 0$, $a > 0$, and $b \geq 0$.

(a) Show that V is positive definite and radially unbounded.

(b) Show that $\dot{V}$ satisfies the inequality

$$\dot{V} \leq z^T (PA + A^T P)z - 2z^T (PB - w)\psi(y) - \gamma\psi^2(y)$$

where $w = adC^T + (1/2)bA^T C^T$ and $\gamma = (2ad/k) + b(d + CB)$. Assume b is chosen such that $\gamma \geq 0$.

(c) Show that the system is absolutely stable if

$$\frac{1}{k} + \mathrm{Re}[(1 + j\omega\eta)G(j\omega)] > 0, \quad \forall \, \omega \in R, \text{ where } \eta = \frac{b}{2ad}$$

7.9 ([85]) The feedback system of Figure 7.23 represents a control system where $H(s)$ is the (scalar) transfer function of the plant and the inner loop models the actuator. Let $H(s) = (s + 6)/(s + 2)(s + 3)$ and suppose $k \geq 0$ and ψ belongs to a sector $(0, \beta]$, where β could be arbitrarily large, but finite.

(a) Show that the system can be represented as the feedback connection of Figure 7.1 with $G(s) = [H(s) + k]/s$.

(b) Using the version of the Popov criterion in Exercise 7.8, find a lower bound k_c such that the system is absolutely stable for all $k > k_c$.

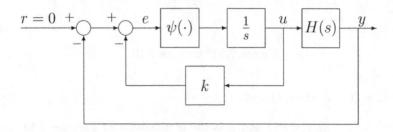

Figure 7.23: Exercise 7.9.

7.10 For each odd nonlinearity $\psi(y)$ on the following list, verify the given expression of the describing function $\Psi(a)$:

(1)　$\psi(y) = y^5; \quad \Psi(a) = 5a^4/8$

(2)　$\psi(y) = y^3|y|; \quad \Psi(a) = 32a^3/15\pi$

(3)　$\psi(y) \quad : \quad$ Figure 7.24(a); $\quad \Psi(a) = k + \dfrac{4A}{\pi a}$

(4)　$\psi(y) \quad : \quad$ Figure 7.24(b)

$$\Psi(a) = \begin{cases} 0, & \text{for } a \leq A \\ (4B/\pi a)[1 - (A/a)^2]^{1/2}, & \text{for } a \geq A \end{cases}$$

(5)　$\psi(y) \quad : \quad$ Figure 7.24(c)

$$\Psi(a) = \begin{cases} 0, & \text{for } a \leq A \\ k[1 - N(a/A)], & \text{for } A \leq a \leq B \\ k[N(a/B) - N(a/A)], & \text{for } a \geq B \end{cases}$$

where

$$N(x) = \frac{2}{\pi}\left[\sin^{-1}\left(\frac{1}{x}\right) + \frac{1}{x}\sqrt{1 - \left(\frac{1}{x}\right)^2} \right]$$

7.11 Using the describing function method, investigate the existence of periodic solutions and the possible frequency and amplitude of oscillation in the feedback connection of Figure 7.1 for each of the following cases:

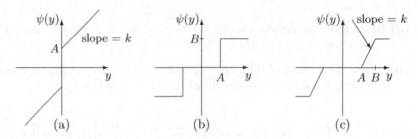

Figure 7.24: Exercise 7.10.

(1) $G(s) = (1 - s)/s(s + 1)$ and $\psi(y) = y^5$.

(2) $G(s) = (1 - s)/s(s + 1)$ and ψ is the nonlinearity of Exercise 7.10, part (5), with $A = 1$, $B = 3/2$, and $k = 2$.

(3) $G(s) = 1/(s + 1)^6$ and $\psi(y) = \text{sgn}(y)$.

(4) $G(s) = (s + 6)/s(s + 2)(s + 3)$ and $\psi(y) = \text{sgn}(y)$.

(5) $G(s) = s/(s^2 - s + 1)$ and $\psi(y) = y^5$.

(6) $G(s) = 5(s + 0.25)/s^2(s + 2)^2$ and ψ is the nonlinearity of Exercise 7.10, part (3), with $A = 1$ and $k = 2$.

(7) $G(s) = 5(s + 0.25)/s^2(s + 2)^2$ and ψ is the nonlinearity of Exercise 7.10, part (4), with $A = 1$ and $B = 1$.

(8) $G(s) = 5(s + 0.25)/s^2(s + 2)^2$ and ψ is the nonlinearity of Exercise 7.10, part (5), with $A = 1$, $B = 3/2$, and $k = 2$.

(9) $G(s) = 1/(s + 1)^3$ and $\psi(y) = \text{sgn}(y)$.

(10) $G(s) = 1/(s + 1)^3$ and $\psi(y) = \text{sat}(y)$.

7.12 Apply the describing function method to study the existence of periodic solutions in the negative resistance oscillator of Section 1.2.4 with $h(v) = -v + v^3 - v^5/5$ and $\varepsilon = 1$. For each possible periodic solution, estimate the frequency and amplitude of oscillation. Using computer simulation, determine how accurate the describing function results are.

7.13 Consider the feedback connection of Figure 7.1 with $G(s) = 2bs/(s^2 - bs + 1)$ and $\psi(y) = \text{sat}(y)$. Using the describing function method, show that for sufficiently small $b > 0$ the system has a periodic solution. Confirm your conclusion by applying Theorem 7.4 and estimate the frequency and amplitude of oscillation.

7.14 Consider the feedback connection of Figure 7.1 with

$$G(s) = \frac{1}{(s+1)^2(s+2)^2}, \qquad \psi(y) = \begin{cases} by & -1 \leq by \leq 1 \\ \\ \text{sgn}(y) & b|y| > 1 \end{cases}$$

where $b > 0$.

(a) Using the circle criterion, find the largest b for which we can confirm that the origin of the closed-loop system is globally asymptotically stable.

(b) Using the Popov criterion, find the largest b for which we can confirm that the origin of the closed-loop system is globally asymptotically stable.

(c) Using the describing function method, find the smallest b for which the system will oscillate and estimate the frequency of oscillation.

(d) For $b = 10$, study the existence of periodic solutions by using Theorem 7.4. For each oscillation, if any,

    i. find the frequency interval $[\omega_1, \omega_2]$ and the amplitude interval $[a_1, a_2]$;

    ii. use Lemma 7.1 to find an upper bound on the energy content of the higher-order harmonics and express it as a percentage of the energy content of the first harmonic; and

    iii. simulate the system and compare the simulation results with the foregoing analytical results.

(e) Repeat part (d) for $b = 30$.

7.15 Repeat parts (a) to (c) of the previous exercise for $G(s) = 10/(s+1)^2(s+2)$.

7.16 Consider the feedback connection of Figure 7.1, where $G(s) = 1/(s+1)^3$ and $\psi(y)$ is the piecewise-linear function of Figure 7.15 with $\delta = 1/k$, $s_1 = k$, and $s_2 = 0$.

(a) Using the describing function method, investigate the existence of periodic solutions and the possible frequency and amplitude of oscillation when $k = 10$.

(b) Continuing with $k = 10$, apply Theorem 7.4. For each oscillation, if any, find the frequency interval $[\omega_1, \omega_2]$ and the amplitude interval $[a_1, a_2]$.

(c) What is the largest slope $k > 0$ for which Theorem 7.4 ensures that there is no oscillation?

7.17 For each of the following cases, apply Theorem 7.4 to study the existence of periodic solutions in the feedback connection of Figure 7.1. For each oscillation, if any, find the frequency interval $[\omega_1, \omega_2]$ and the amplitude interval $[a_1, a_2]$.

(1) $G(s) = 2(s-1)/s^3(s+1)$ and $\psi(y) = \text{sat}(y)$.

(2) $G(s) = -s/(s^2 + 0.8s + 8)$ and $\psi(y) = (1/2)\sin y$.

(3) $G(s) = -s/(s^2 + 0.8s + 8)$ and $\psi(y)$ is the nonlinearity of Example 7.13.

(4) $G(s) = -24/s^2(s+1)^3$ and $\psi(y)$ is an odd nonlinearity defined by

$$\psi(y) = \begin{cases} y^3 + y/2, & \text{for } 0 \le y \le 1 \\ 2y - 1/2, & \text{for } y \ge 1 \end{cases}$$

Chapter 8

Advanced Stability Analysis

In Chapter 4, we gave the basic concepts and tools of Lyapunov stability. In this chapter, we examine some of these concepts more closely and present a number of extensions and refinements.

We saw in Chapter 4 how to use linearization to study stability of equilibrium points of autonomous systems. We saw also that linearization fails when the Jacobian matrix, evaluated at the equilibrium point, has some eigenvalues with zero real parts and no eigenvalues with positive real parts. In Section 8.1, we introduce the center manifold theorem and use it to study stability of equilibrium points of autonomous systems in the critical case when linearization fails.

The concept of the region of attraction of an asymptotically stable equilibrium point was introduced in Section 4.1. In Section 8.2, we elaborate further on that concept and present some ideas for providing estimates of this region.

LaSalle's invariance principle for autonomous systems is very useful in applications. For a general nonautonomous system, there is no invariance principle in the same form that was presented in Theorem 4.4. There are, however, theorems which capture some features of the invariance principle. Two such theorems are given in Section 8.3. The first theorem shows convergence of the trajectory to a set, while the second one shows uniform asymptotic stability of the origin.

Finally, in Section 8.4, we introduce notions of stability of periodic solutions and invariant sets.

8.1 The Center Manifold Theorem

Consider the autonomous system

$$\dot{x} = f(x) \tag{8.1}$$

where $f : D \to R^n$ is continuously differentiable and $D \subset R^n$ is a domain that contains the origin $x = 0$. Suppose that the origin is an equilibrium point of (8.1).

Theorem 4.7 states that if the linearization of f at the origin, that is, the matrix

$$A = \left.\frac{\partial f}{\partial x}(x)\right|_{x=0}$$

has all eigenvalues with negative real parts, then the origin is asymptotically stable; if it has some eigenvalues with positive real parts, then the origin is unstable. If A has some eigenvalues with zero real parts with the rest of the eigenvalues having negative real parts, then linearization fails to determine the stability properties of the origin. In this section, we take a closer look into the case when linearization fails. Failure of linearization leaves us with the task of analyzing the nth-order nonlinear system (8.1) in order to determine stability of the origin. The interesting finding that we are going to present in the next few pages is that stability properties of the origin can be determined by analyzing a lower order nonlinear system — a system whose order is exactly equal to the number of eigenvalues of A with zero real parts. This will follow as an application of the *center manifold theory*.[1]

A k-dimensional manifold in R^n $(1 \leq k < n)$ has a rigorous mathematical definition.[2] For our purpose here, it is sufficient to think of a k-dimensional manifold as the solution of the equation

$$\eta(x) = 0$$

where $\eta : R^n \to R^{n-k}$ is sufficiently smooth (that is, sufficiently many times continuously differentiable). For example, the unit circle

$$\{x \in R^2 \mid x_1^2 + x_2^2 = 1\}$$

is a one-dimensional manifold in R^2. Similarly, the unit sphere

$$\{x \in R^n \mid \sum_{i=1}^{n} x_i^2 = 1\}$$

is an $(n-1)$-dimensional manifold in R^n. A manifold $\{\eta(x) = 0\}$ is said to be an invariant manifold for (8.1) if

$$\eta(x(0)) = 0 \Rightarrow \eta(x(t)) \equiv 0, \quad \forall\, t \in [0, t_1) \subset R$$

where $[0, t_1)$ is any time interval over which the solution $x(t)$ is defined.

Suppose now that $f(x)$ is twice continuously differentiable. Equation (8.1) can be represented as

$$\dot{x} = Ax + \left[f(x) - \frac{\partial f}{\partial x}(0)\, x \right] = Ax + \tilde{f}(x)$$

---

[1]The center manifold theory has several applications to dynamical systems. It is presented here only insofar as it relates to determining the stability of the origin. For a broader viewpoint of the theory, the reader may consult [34].

[2]See, for example, [71].

where

$$\tilde{f}(x) = f(x) - \frac{\partial f}{\partial x}(0)\, x$$

is twice continuously differentiable and

$$\tilde{f}(0) = 0; \quad \frac{\partial \tilde{f}}{\partial x}(0) = 0$$

Since our interest is in the case when linearization fails, assume that A has k eigenvalues with zero real parts and $m = n - k$ eigenvalues with negative real parts. We can always find a similarity transformation T that transforms A into a block diagonal matrix, that is,

$$TAT^{-1} = \left[\begin{array}{cc} A_1 & 0 \\ 0 & A_2 \end{array} \right]$$

where all eigenvalues of A_1 have zero real parts and all eigenvalues of A_2 have negative real parts. Clearly, A_1 is $k \times k$ and A_2 is $m \times m$. The change of variables

$$\left[\begin{array}{c} y \\ z \end{array} \right] = Tx; \quad y \in R^k; \; z \in R^m$$

transforms (8.1) into the form

$$\dot{y} = A_1 y + g_1(y, z) \tag{8.2}$$
$$\dot{z} = A_2 z + g_2(y, z) \tag{8.3}$$

where g_1 and g_2 inherit properties of $\tilde{f}$. In particular, they are twice continuously differentiable and

$$g_i(0,0) = 0; \quad \frac{\partial g_i}{\partial y}(0,0) = 0; \quad \frac{\partial g_i}{\partial z}(0,0) = 0 \tag{8.4}$$

for $i = 1, 2$. If $z = h(y)$ is an invariant manifold for (8.2)–(8.3) and h is smooth, then it is called a *center manifold* if

$$h(0) = 0; \quad \frac{\partial h}{\partial y}(0) = 0$$

Theorem 8.1 *If g_1 and g_2 are twice continuously differentiable and satisfy (8.4), all eigenvalues of A_1 have zero real parts, and all eigenvalues of A_2 have negative real parts, then there exist a constant $\delta > 0$ and a continuously differentiable function $h(y)$, defined for all $\|y\| < \delta$, such that $z = h(y)$ is a center manifold for (8.2)–(8.3).*
$\diamond$

Proof: See Appendix C.15.

If the initial state of the system (8.2)–(8.3) lies in the center manifold; that is, $z(0) = h(y(0))$, then the solution $(y(t), z(t))$ will lie in the manifold for all $t \geq 0$;

that is, $z(t) \equiv h(y(t))$. In this case, the motion of the system in the center manifold is described by the kth-order differential equation

$$\dot{y} = A_1 y + g_1(y, h(y)) \tag{8.5}$$

which we refer to as the *reduced system*. If $z(0) \neq h(y(0))$, then the difference $z(t) - h(y(t))$ represents the deviation of the trajectory from the center manifold at any time t. The change of variables

$$\begin{bmatrix} y \\ w \end{bmatrix} = \begin{bmatrix} y \\ z - h(y) \end{bmatrix}$$

transforms (8.2)–(8.3) into

$$\dot{y} = A_1 y + g_1(y, w + h(y)) \tag{8.6}$$

$$\dot{w} = A_2[w + h(y)] + g_2(y, w + h(y)) - \frac{\partial h}{\partial y}(y) \left[A_1 y + g_1(y, w + h(y))\right] \tag{8.7}$$

In the new coordinates, the center manifold is $w = 0$. The motion in the manifold is characterized by

$$w(t) \equiv 0 \; \Rightarrow \; \dot{w}(t) \equiv 0$$

Substituting these identities into (8.7) results in

$$0 = A_2 h(y) + g_2(y, h(y)) - \frac{\partial h}{\partial y}(y) \left[A_1 y + g_1(y, h(y))\right] \tag{8.8}$$

Since the equation must be satisfied by any solution that lies in the center manifold, we conclude that the function $h(y)$ must satisfy the partial differential equation (8.8). Adding and subtracting $g_1(y, h(y))$ to the right-hand side of (8.6), and subtracting (8.8) from (8.7), we can rewrite the equation in the transformed coordinates as

$$\dot{y} = A_1 y + g_1(y, h(y)) + N_1(y, w) \tag{8.9}$$

$$\dot{w} = A_2 w + N_2(y, w) \tag{8.10}$$

where

$$N_1(y, w) = g_1(y, w + h(y)) - g_1(y, h(y))$$

and

$$N_2(y, w) = g_2(y, w + h(y)) - g_2(y, h(y)) - \frac{\partial h}{\partial y}(y) \, N_1(y, w)$$

It is not difficult to verify that N_1 and N_2 are twice continuously differentiable, and

$$N_i(y, 0) = 0; \quad \frac{\partial N_i}{\partial w}(0, 0) = 0$$

for $i = 1, 2$. Consequently, in the domain

$$\left\| \begin{array}{c} y \\ w \end{array} \right\|_2 < \rho$$

N_1 and N_2 satisfy

$$\|N_i(y, w)\|_2 \leq k_i \|w\|, \quad i = 1, 2$$

where the positive constants k_1 and k_2 can be made arbitrarily small by choosing ρ small enough. These inequalities, together with the fact that A_2 is Hurwitz, suggest that the stability properties of the origin are determined by the reduced system (8.5). The next theorem, known as the *reduction principle*, confirms this conjecture.

Theorem 8.2 *Under the assumptions of Theorem 8.1, if the origin $y = 0$ of the reduced system (8.5) is asymptotically stable (respectively, unstable) then the origin of the full system (8.2) and (8.3) is also asymptotically stable (respectively, unstable).*
                                                                                        $\diamond$

Proof: The change of coordinates from (y, z) to (y, w) does not change the stability properties of the origin (Exercise 4.26); therefore, we can work with the system (8.9) and (8.10). If the origin of the reduced system (8.5) is unstable, then, by invariance, the origin of (8.9) and (8.10) is unstable. This is so because for any solution $y(t)$ of (8.5), there is a corresponding solution $(y(t), 0)$ of (8.9) and (8.10). Suppose now that the origin of the reduced system (8.5) is asymptotically stable. By (the converse Lyapunov) Theorem 4.16, there is a continuously differentiable function $V(y)$ that is positive definite and satisfies the inequalities

$$\frac{\partial V}{\partial y}[A_1 y + g_1(y, h(y))] \leq -\alpha_3(\|y\|_2)$$

$$\left\| \frac{\partial V}{\partial y} \right\|_2 \leq \alpha_4(\|y\|_2) \leq k$$

in a neighborhood of the origin, where α_3 and α_4 are class $\mathcal{K}$ functions. On the other hand, since A_2 is Hurwitz, the Lyapunov equation

$$PA_2 + A_2^T P = -I$$

has a unique positive definite solution P. Consider

$$\nu(y, w) = V(y) + \sqrt{w^T P w}$$

as a Lyapunov function candidate[3] for the full system (8.9) and (8.10). The derivative of ν along the trajectories of the system is given by

$$\dot{\nu}(y, w) = \frac{\partial V}{\partial y}[A_1 y + g_1(y, h(y)) + N_1(y, w)]$$

---

[3]The function $\nu(y, w)$ is continuously differentiable everywhere around the origin, except on the manifold $w = 0$. Both $\nu(y, w)$ and $\dot{\nu}(y, w)$ are defined and continuous around the origin. It can be easily seen that the statement of Theorem 4.1 is still valid.

$$+ \frac{1}{2\sqrt{w^T P w}} \left[w^T (P A_2 + A_2^T P) w + 2 w^T P N_2(y,w) \right]$$

$$\leq \quad -\alpha_3(\|y\|_2) + k k_1 \|w\|_2 - \frac{\|w\|_2}{2\sqrt{\lambda_{\max}(P)}} + \frac{k_2 \lambda_{\max}(P)}{\sqrt{\lambda_{\min}(P)}} \|w\|_2$$

$$= \quad -\alpha_3(\|y\|_2) - \frac{1}{4\sqrt{\lambda_{\max}(P)}} \|w\|_2$$

$$- \left[\frac{1}{4\sqrt{\lambda_{\max}(P)}} - k k_1 - k_2 \frac{\lambda_{\max}(P)}{\sqrt{\lambda_{\min}(P)}} \right] \|w\|_2$$

Since k_1 and k_2 can be made arbitrarily small by restricting the domain around the origin to be sufficiently small, we can choose them small enough to ensure that

$$\frac{1}{4\sqrt{\lambda_{\max}(P)}} - k k_1 - k_2 \frac{\lambda_{\max}(P)}{\sqrt{\lambda_{\min}(P)}} > 0$$

Hence,

$$\dot{\nu}(y,w) \leq -\alpha_3(\|y\|_2) - \frac{1}{4\sqrt{\lambda_{\max}(P)}} \|w\|_2$$

which shows that $\dot{\nu}(y,w)$ is negative definite. Consequently, the origin of the full system (8.9)–(8.10) is asymptotically stable.   □

We leave it to the reader (Exercises 8.1 and 8.2) to extend the proof of Theorem 8.2 to prove the next two corollaries.

Corollary 8.1 *Under the assumptions of Theorem 8.1, if the origin $y = 0$ of the reduced system (8.5) is stable and there is a continuously differentiable Lyapunov function $V(y)$ such that* [4]

$$\frac{\partial V}{\partial y} \left[A_1 y + g_1(y, h(y)) \right] \leq 0$$

in some neighborhood of $y = 0$, then the origin of the full system (8.2)–(8.3) is stable.   ◇

Corollary 8.2 *Under the assumptions of Theorem 8.1, the origin of the reduced system (8.5) is asymptotically stable if and only if the origin of the full system (8.2)–(8.3) is asymptotically stable.*   ◇

---

[4]The existence of the Lyapunov function $V(y)$ cannot be inferred from a converse Lyapunov theorem. The converse Lyapunov theorem for stability [72, 107] guarantees the existence of a Lyapunov function $V(t,y)$ whose derivative satisfies $\dot{V}(t,y) \leq 0$. In general, this function cannot be made independent of t. (See [72, page 228].) Even though we can choose $V(t,y)$ to be continuously differentiable in its arguments, it cannot be guaranteed that the partial derivatives $\partial V / \partial y_i$, $\partial V / \partial t$ will be uniformly bounded in a neighborhood of the origin for all $t \geq 0$. (See [107, page 53].)

To use Theorem 8.2, we need to find the center manifold $z = h(y)$. The function h is a solution of the partial differential equation

$$\mathcal{N}(h(y)) \stackrel{\text{def}}{=} \frac{\partial h}{\partial y}(y) \left[A_1 y + g_1(y, h(y)) \right] - A_2 h(y) - g_2(y, h(y)) = 0 \qquad (8.11)$$

with boundary conditions

$$h(0) = 0; \quad \frac{\partial h}{\partial y}(0) = 0 \qquad (8.12)$$

This equation for h cannot be solved exactly in most cases (to do so would imply that a solution of the full system (8.2)–(8.3) has been found), but its solution can be approximated arbitrarily closely as a Taylor series in y.

Theorem 8.3 *If a continuously differentiable function $\phi(y)$ with $\phi(0) = 0$ and $[\partial \phi / \partial y](0) = 0$ can be found such that $\mathcal{N}(\phi(y)) = O(\|y\|^p)$ for some $p > 1$, then for sufficiently small $\|y\|$*

$$h(y) - \phi(y) = O(\|y\|^p)$$

and the reduced system can be represented as

$$\dot{y} = A_1 y + g_1(y, \phi(y)) + O(\|y\|^{p+1})$$

$\diamond$

Proof: See Appendix C.15.

The order of magnitude notation $O(\cdot)$ will be formally introduced in Chapter 10 (Definition 10.1). For our purpose here, it is enough to think of $f(y) = O(\|y\|^p)$ as a shorthand notation for $\|f(y)\| \leq k\|y\|^p$ for sufficiently small $\|y\|$. Let us now illustrate the application of the center manifold theorem by examples. In the first two examples, we will make use of the observation that for a scalar state equation of the form

$$\dot{y} = ay^p + O\left(|y|^{p+1}\right)$$

where p is a positive integer, the origin is asymptotically stable if p is odd and $a < 0$. It is unstable if p is odd and $a > 0$, or p is even and $a \neq 0$.[5]

Example 8.1 Consider the system

$$\begin{aligned} \dot{x}_1 &= x_2 \\ \dot{x}_2 &= -x_2 + ax_1^2 + bx_1 x_2 \end{aligned}$$

where $a \neq 0$. The system has a unique equilibrium point at the origin. The linearization at the origin results in the matrix

$$A = \begin{bmatrix} 0 & 1 \\ 0 & -1 \end{bmatrix}$$

---

[5]See Exercise 4.2.

which has eigenvalues at 0 and -1. Let M be a matrix whose columns are the eigenvectors of A; that is,

$$M = \begin{bmatrix} 1 & 1 \\ 0 & -1 \end{bmatrix}$$

and take $T = M^{-1}$. Then,

$$TAT^{-1} = \begin{bmatrix} 0 & 0 \\ 0 & -1 \end{bmatrix}$$

The change of variables

$$\begin{bmatrix} y \\ z \end{bmatrix} = T \begin{bmatrix} x_1 \\ x_2 \end{bmatrix} = \begin{bmatrix} x_1 + x_2 \\ -x_2 \end{bmatrix}$$

puts the system into the form

$$\begin{aligned} \dot{y} &= a(y+z)^2 - b(yz + z^2) \\ \dot{z} &= -z - a(y+z)^2 + b(yz + z^2) \end{aligned}$$

The center manifold equation (8.11) with the boundary condition (8.12) becomes

$$\begin{aligned} \mathcal{N}(h(y)) = \ & h'(y)[a(y + h(y))^2 - b(yh(y) + h^2(y))] + h(y) \\ & + a(y + h(y))^2 - b(yh(y) + h^2(y)) = 0, \quad h(0) = h'(0) = 0 \end{aligned}$$

We set $h(y) = h_2 y^2 + h_3 y^3 + \cdots$ and substitute this series in the center manifold equation to find the unknown coefficients $h_2, h_3, \ldots$ by matching coefficients of like powers in y (since the equation holds as an identity in y). We do not know in advance how many terms of the series we need. We start with the simplest approximation $h(y) \approx 0$. We substitute $h(y) = O(|y|^2)$ into the reduced system and study stability of its origin. If the stability properties of the origin can be determined, we are done. Otherwise, we calculate the coefficient h_2, substitute $h(y) = h_2 y^2 + O(|y|^3)$, and study stability of the origin. If it cannot be resolved, we proceed to the approximation $h(y) \approx h_2 y^2 + h_3 y^3$, and so on. Let us start with the approximation $h(y) \approx 0$. The reduced system is

$$\dot{y} = ay^2 + O(|y|^3)$$

Notice that an $O(|y|^2)$ error in $h(y)$ results in an $O(|y|^3)$ error in the right-hand side of the reduced system. This is a consequence of the fact that the function $g_1(y, z)$, which appears on the right-hand side of the reduced system (8.5) as $g_1(y, h(y))$, has a partial derivative with respect to z that vanishes at the origin. Clearly, this observation is also valid for higher order approximations; that is, an error of order $O(|y|^k)$ in $h(y)$ results in an error of order $O(|y|^{k+1})$ in $g_1(y, h(y))$, for $k \geq 2$. The term ay^2 is the dominant term on the right-hand side of the reduced system. For $a \neq 0$, the origin of the reduced system is unstable. Consequently, by Theorem 8.2, the origin of the full system is unstable. $\triangle$

Example 8.2 Consider the system

$$\dot{y} = yz$$
$$\dot{z} = -z + ay^2$$

which is already represented in the (y, z) coordinates. The center manifold equation (8.11) with the boundary condition (8.12) is

$$h'(y)[yh(y)] + h(y) - ay^2 = 0, \quad h(0) = h'(0) = 0$$

We start by trying $\phi(y) = 0$. The reduced system is

$$\dot{y} = O(|y|^3)$$

Clearly, we cannot reach any conclusion about the stability of the origin. Therefore, we substitute $h(y) = h_2 y^2 + O(|y|^3)$ into the center manifold equation and calculate h_2, by matching coefficients of y^2, to obtain $h_2 = a$. The reduced system is[6]

$$\dot{y} = ay^3 + O(|y|^4)$$

Therefore, the origin is asymptotically stable if $a < 0$ and unstable if $a > 0$. Consequently, by Theorem 8.2, we conclude that the origin of the full system is asymptotically stable if $a < 0$ and unstable if $a > 0$. If $a = 0$, the center manifold equation (8.11) with the boundary condition (8.12) reduces to

$$h'(y)[yh(y)] + h(y) = 0, \quad h(0) = h'(0) = 0$$

which has the exact solution $h(y) = 0$. The reduced system $\dot{y} = 0$ has a stable origin with $V(y) = y^2$ as a Lyapunov function. Therefore, by Corollary 8.1, we conclude that the origin of the full system is stable if $a = 0$ △

Example 8.3 Consider the system (8.2)–(8.3) with

$$A_1 = \begin{bmatrix} 0 & 1 \\ -1 & 0 \end{bmatrix}, \ g_1 = \begin{bmatrix} -y_1^3 \\ -y_2^3 + z^2 \end{bmatrix}, \ A_2 = -1, \ \text{and} \ g_2 = y_1^3 - 3y_1^5 + 3y_1^2 y_2$$

It can be verified that $\phi(y) = 0$ results in $\mathcal{N}(\phi(y)) = O\left(\|y\|_2^3\right)$ and

$$\dot{y} = \begin{bmatrix} -y_1^3 + y_2 \\ -y_1 - y_2^3 \end{bmatrix} + O\left(\|y\|_2^4\right)$$

Using $V(y) = (y_1^2 + y_2^2)/2$ as a Lyapunov function candidate, we obtain

$$\dot{V} = -y_1^4 - y_2^4 + y^T O\left(\|y\|_2^4\right) \le -\|y\|_2^4 + k\|y\|_2^5$$

---

[6]The error on the right-hand side of the reduced system is actually $O(|y|^5)$ since, if we write $h(y) = h_2 y^2 + h_3 y^3 + \cdots$, we will find that $h_3 = 0$.

in some neighborhood of the origin where $k > 0$. Hence,

$$\dot{V} \leq -\tfrac{1}{2}\|y\|_2^4, \quad \text{for } \|y\|_2 < \frac{1}{2k}$$

which shows that the origin of the reduced system is asymptotically stable. Consequently, the origin of the full system is asymptotically stable. $\triangle$

Notice that in the preceding example it is not enough to study the system

$$\dot{y} = \left[\begin{array}{c} -y_1^3 + y_2 \\ -y_1 - y_2^3 \end{array} \right]$$

We have to find a Lyapunov function that confirms asymptotic stability of the origin for all perturbations of the order $O\left(\|y\|_2^4\right)$. The importance of this observation is illustrated by the next example.

Example 8.4 Consider the previous example, but change A_1 to

$$A_1 = \left[\begin{array}{cc} 0 & 1 \\ 0 & 0 \end{array} \right]$$

With $\phi(y) = 0$, the reduced system can be represented as

$$\dot{y} = \left[\begin{array}{c} -y_1^3 + y_2 \\ -y_2^3 \end{array} \right] + O\left(\|y\|_2^4\right)$$

Without the perturbation term $O\left(\|y\|_2^4\right)$, the origin of this system is asymptotically stable.[7] If you try to find a Lyapunov function $V(y)$ to show asymptotic stability in the presence of the perturbation term, you will not succeed. In fact, it can be verified that the center manifold equation (8.11) with the boundary condition (8.12) has the exact solution $h(y) = y_1^3$, so that the reduced system is given by the equation

$$\dot{y} = \left[\begin{array}{c} -y_1^3 + y_2 \\ y_1^6 - y_2^3 \end{array} \right]$$

whose origin is unstable.[8] $\triangle$

8.2   Region of Attraction

Quite often, it is not sufficient to determine that a given system has an asymptotically stable equilibrium point. Rather, it is important to find the region of attraction of that point, or at least an estimate of it. To appreciate the importance of determining the region of attraction, let us run a scenario of events that could

---

[7]See Exercise 4.56.
[8]See Exercise 4.13.

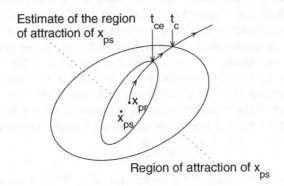

Figure 8.1: Critical clearance time.

happen in the operation of a nonlinear system. Suppose that a nonlinear system has an asymptotically stable equilibrium point, which is denoted by x_{pr} in Suppose the system is operating at steady state at x_{pr}. Then, at time t_0 a fault that changes the structure of the system takes place, for example, a short circuit in an electrical network. Suppose the faulted system does not have equilibrium points at x_{pr} or in its neighborhood. The trajectory of the system will be driven away from x_{pr}. Suppose further that the fault is cleared at time t_1 and the postfault system has an asymptotically stable equilibrium point at x_{ps}, where either $x_{ps} = x_{pr}$ or x_{ps} is sufficiently close to x_{pr} so that steady-state operation at x_{ps} is still acceptable. At time t_1 the state of the system, say, $x(t_1)$, could be far from the postfault equilibrium x_{ps}. Whether or not the system will return to steady-state operation at x_{ps} depends on whether $x(t_1)$ belongs to the region of attraction of x_{ps}, as determined by the postfault system equation. A crucial factor in determining how far $x(t_1)$ could be from x_{ps} is the time it takes the operators of the system to remove the fault, that is, the time difference $(t_1 - t_0)$. If $(t_1 - t_0)$ is very short, then, by continuity of the solution with respect to t, it is very likely that $x(t_1)$ will be in the region of attraction of x_{ps}. However, operators need time to detect the fault and fix it. How much time they have is a critical question. In planning such a system, it is valuable to give operators a "critical clearance time," say t_c, such that they have to clear the fault within this time; that is, $(t_1 - t_0)$ must be less than t_c. If we know the region of attraction of x_{ps}, we can find t_c by Figure 8.1. integrating the faulted system equation starting from the prefault equilibrium x_{pr} until the trajectory hits the boundary of the region of attraction. The time it takes the trajectory to reach the boundary can be taken as the critical clearance time because if the fault is cleared before that time the state $x(t_1)$ will be within the region of attraction. Of course, we are assuming that x_{pr} belongs to the region of attraction of x_{ps}, which is reasonable. If the actual region of attraction is not known, and an estimate t_{ce} of t_c is obtained by using an estimate of the region of attraction, then $t_{ce} < t_c$, since the boundary of the estimate of the region of attraction will be inside the actual boundary of the region. (See Figure 8.1.) This scenario shows an example where finding the region of attraction is needed in planning the operation of a nonlinear system. It also shows the importance of finding estimates of the region of attraction that are not too conservative. A very conservative estimate of the region of attraction would result in t_{ce} that is too small to be useful. Let us conclude this motivating discussion by saying that the scenario of events described here is not hypothetical. It is the essence of the transient stability problem in power systems.[9]

Let the origin $x = 0$ be an asymptotically stable equilibrium point for the nonlinear system

$$\dot{x} = f(x) \tag{8.13}$$

where $f : D \to R^n$ is locally Lipschitz and $D \subset R^n$ is a domain containing the origin. Let $\phi(t; x)$ be the solution of (8.13) that starts at initial state x at time $t = 0$. The region of attraction of the origin, denoted by R_A, is defined by

$$R_A = \{x \in D \mid \phi(t; x) \text{ is defined } \forall \, t \geq 0 \text{ and } \phi(t; x) \to 0 \text{ as } t \to \infty\}$$

Some properties of the region of attraction are stated in the next lemma, whose proof is given in Appendix C.16.

Lemma 8.1 *If $x = 0$ is an asymptotically stable equilibrium point for (8.13), then its region of attraction R_A is an open, connected, invariant set. Moreover, the boundary of R_A is formed by trajectories.* $\diamond$

Lemma 8.1 suggests that one way to determine the region of attraction is to characterize those trajectories that lie on the boundary of R_A. There are some methods that approach the problem from this viewpoint, but they use geometric notions from the theory of dynamical systems that are not introduced in this book. Therefore, we will not describe this class of methods.[10] We may, however, get a flavor of these geometric methods in the case of second-order systems ($n = 2$) by employing phase portraits. Examples 8.5 and 8.6 show typical cases in the state plane. In the first example, the boundary of the region of attraction is a limit cycle, while in the second one the boundary is formed of stable trajectories of saddle points. Example 8.7 shows a rather pathological case where the boundary is a closed curve of equilibrium points.

Example 8.5 The second-order system

$$\begin{aligned} \dot{x}_1 &= -x_2 \\ \dot{x}_2 &= x_1 + (x_1^2 - 1)x_2 \end{aligned}$$

is a Van der Pol equation in reverse time, that is, with t replaced by $-t$. The system has one equilibrium point at the origin and one unstable limit cycle, as determined from the phase portrait shown in Figure 8.2. The phase portrait shows that the

---

[9]See [170] for an introduction to the transient stability problem in power systems.
[10]Examples of these methods can be found in [36] and [216].

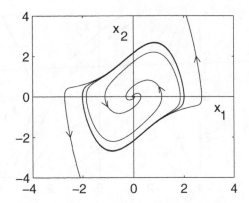

Figure 8.2: Phase portrait for Example 8.5.

origin is a stable focus; hence, it is asymptotically stable. This can be confirmed by linearization, since

$$A = \left.\frac{\partial f}{\partial x}\right|_{x=0} = \begin{bmatrix} 0 & -1 \\ 1 & -1 \end{bmatrix}$$

has eigenvalues at $-1/2 \pm j\sqrt{3}/2$. Clearly, the region of attraction is bounded because trajectories starting outside the limit cycle cannot cross it to reach the origin. Because there are no other equilibrium points, the boundary of R_A must be the limit cycle. Inspection of the phase portrait shows that indeed all trajectories starting inside the limit cycle spiral toward the origin.   △

Example 8.6 Consider the second-order system

$$\begin{aligned} \dot{x}_1 &= x_2 \\ \dot{x}_2 &= -x_1 + \tfrac{1}{3}x_1^3 - x_2 \end{aligned}$$

This system has three isolated equilibrium points at $(0,0)$, $(\sqrt{3},0)$, and $(-\sqrt{3},0)$. The phase portrait of the system is shown in Figure 8.3. The phase portrait shows that the origin is a stable focus, and the other two equilibria are saddle points. Thus, the origin is asymptotically stable and the other equilibria are unstable; a fact that can be confirmed by linearization. From the phase portrait, we can also see that the stable trajectories of the saddle points form two separatrices that are the boundaries of the region of attraction. The region is unbounded.   △

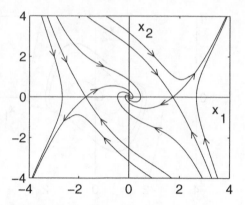

Figure 8.3: Phase portrait for Example 8.6.

Example 8.7 The system

$$
\begin{aligned}
\dot{x}_1 &= -x_1(1 - x_1^2 - x_2^2) \\
\dot{x}_2 &= -x_2(1 - x_1^2 - x_2^2)
\end{aligned}
$$

has an isolated equilibrium point at the origin and a continuum of equilibrium points on the unit circle; that is, every point on the unit circle is an equilibrium point. Clearly, R_A must be confined to the interior of the unit circle. The trajectories of the system are the radii of the unit circle. This can be seen by transforming the system into polar coordinates. The change of variables

$$
x_1 = \rho \cos \theta, \quad x_2 = \rho \sin \theta
$$

yields

$$
\dot{\rho} = -\rho(1 - \rho^2), \quad \dot{\theta} = 0
$$

All trajectories starting with $\rho < 1$ approach the origin as $t \to \infty$. Therefore, R_A is the interior of the unit circle. $\triangle$

Lyapunov's method can be used to find the region of attraction R_A or an estimate of it. The basic tool for finding the boundary of R_A is Zubov's theorem, which is given in Exercise 8.10. The theorem, however, has the character of an existence theorem and requires the solution of a partial differential equation. Via much simpler procedures, we can find estimates of R_A by using Lyapunov's method. By an estimate of R_A, we mean a set $\Omega \subset R_A$ such that every trajectory starting in Ω approaches the origin as $t \to \infty$. For the rest of this section, we will discuss some aspects of estimating R_A. Let us start by showing that the domain D of Theorem 4.1 (or Corollary 4.1) is not an estimate of R_A. We have seen in Theorem 4.1 and Corollary 4.1 that if D is a domain that contains the origin, and if we can find a Lyapunov function $V(x)$ that is positive definite in D and $\dot{V}(x)$ is negative definite in D or negative semidefinite, but no solution can stay identically in the set $\{\dot{V}(x) = 0\}$ except for the zero solution $x = 0$, then the origin is asymptotically stable. One may jump to the conclusion that D is an estimate of R_A. This conjecture is not true, as illustrated by the next example.

Example 8.8 Consider again the system of Example 8.6:

$$
\begin{aligned}
\dot{x}_1 &= x_2 \\
\dot{x}_2 &= -x_1 + \tfrac{1}{3}x_1^3 - x_2
\end{aligned}
$$

This system is a special case of that of Example 4.5 with

$$
h(x_1) = x_1 - \tfrac{1}{3}x_1^3 \quad \text{and} \quad a = 1
$$

Therefore, a Lyapunov function is given by

$$
\begin{aligned}
V(x) &= \tfrac{1}{2}x^T \begin{bmatrix} \tfrac{1}{2} & \tfrac{1}{2} \\ \tfrac{1}{2} & 1 \end{bmatrix} x + \int_0^{x_1} (y - \tfrac{1}{3}y^3)\, dy \\
&= \tfrac{3}{4}x_1^2 - \tfrac{1}{12}x_1^4 + \tfrac{1}{2}x_1 x_2 + \tfrac{1}{2}x_2^2
\end{aligned}
$$

and

$$
\dot{V}(x) = -\tfrac{1}{2}x_1^2(1 - \tfrac{1}{3}x_1^2) - \tfrac{1}{2}x_2^2
$$

Defining a domain D by

$$
D = \{x \in R^2 \mid -\sqrt{3} < x_1 < \sqrt{3}\}
$$

it can be easily seen that $V(x) > 0$ and $\dot{V}(x) < 0$ in $D - \{0\}$. Inspecting the phase portrait in Figure 8.3 shows that D is not a subset of R_A. $\triangle$

In view of this example, it is not difficult to see why D of Theorem 4.1 or Corollary 4.1 is not an estimate of R_A. Even though a trajectory starting in D will move from one Lyapunov surface $V(x) = c_1$ to an inner Lyapunov surface $V(x) = c_2$, with $c_2 < c_1$, there is no guarantee that the trajectory will remain forever in D. Once the trajectory leaves D, there is no guarantee that $\dot{V}(x)$ will be negative. Consequently, the whole argument about $V(x)$ decreasing to zero falls apart. This problem does not arise when R_A is estimated by a compact positively invariant subset of D; that is, a compact set $\Omega \subset D$ such that every trajectory starting in Ω stays in Ω for all future time. Theorem 4.4 shows that Ω is a subset of R_A. The simplest such estimate is the set[11]

$$
\Omega_c = \{x \in R^n \mid V(x) \leq c\}
$$

---

[11]The set $\{V(x) \leq c\}$ may have more than one component, but there can be only one bounded component in D, and that is the component we work with. For example, if $V(x) = x^2/(1 + x^4)$ and $D = \{|x| < 1\}$, the set $\{V(x) \leq 1/4\}$ has two components: $\left\{|x| \leq \sqrt{2 - \sqrt{3}}\right\}$ and $\left\{|x| \geq \sqrt{2 + \sqrt{3}}\right\}$. We work with $\left\{|x| \leq \sqrt{2 - \sqrt{3}}\right\}$.

when Ω_c is bounded and contained in D. For a quadratic Lyapunov function $V(x) = x^T P x$ and $D = \{\|x\|_2 < r\}$, we can ensure that $\Omega_c \subset D$ by choosing

$$c < \min_{\|x\|_2 = r} x^T P x = \lambda_{\min}(P) r^2$$

For $D = \{|b^T x| < r\}$, where $b \in R^n$,[12]

$$\min_{|b^T x| = r} x^T P x = \frac{r^2}{b^T P^{-1} b}$$

Therefore, $\{x^T P x \leq c\}$ will be a subset of $D = \{|b_i^T x| < r_i, \ i = 1, \ldots p\}$, if we choose

$$c < \min_{1 \leq i \leq p} \frac{r_i^2}{b_i^T P^{-1} b_i}$$

The simplicity of estimating the region of attraction by $\Omega_c = \{x^T P x \leq c\}$ has increased significance in view of the linearization results of Section 4.3. There, we saw that if the Jacobian matrix

$$A = \frac{\partial f}{\partial x}\bigg|_{x=0}$$

is Hurwitz, then we can always find a quadratic Lyapunov function $V(x) = x^T P x$ by solving the Lyapunov equation $PA + A^T P = -Q$ for any positive definite matrix Q. Putting the pieces together, we see that *whenever A is Hurwitz, we can estimate the region of attraction of the origin.* This is illustrated by the next example.

Example 8.9 The second-order system

$$\begin{aligned}
\dot{x}_1 &= -x_2 \\
\dot{x}_2 &= x_1 + (x_1^2 - 1)x_2
\end{aligned}$$

was treated in Example 8.5. There, we saw that the origin is asymptotically stable since

$$A = \frac{\partial f}{\partial x}\bigg|_{x=0} = \begin{bmatrix} 0 & -1 \\ 1 & -1 \end{bmatrix}$$

is Hurwitz. A Lyapunov function for the system can be found by taking $Q = I$ and solving the Lyapunov equation

$$PA + A^T P = -I$$

---

[12]Following [122, Section 10.3], the Lagrangian associated with the constrained optimization problem is $\mathcal{L}(x, \lambda) = x^T P x + \lambda[(b^T x)^2 - r^2]$. The first-order necessary conditions are $2Px + 2\lambda(b^T x)b = 0$ and $(b^T x)^2 - r^2 = 0$. It can be verified that the solutions $\lambda = -1/(b^T P^{-1} b)$ and $x = \pm r P^{-1} b/(b^T P^{-1} b)$ yield the minimal value $r^2/(b^T P^{-1} b)$.

for P. The unique solution is the positive definite matrix

$$P = \begin{bmatrix} 1.5 & -0.5 \\ -0.5 & 1 \end{bmatrix}$$

The quadratic function $V(x) = x^T P x$ is a Lyapunov function for the system in a certain neighborhood of the origin. Because our interest here is in estimating the region of attraction, we need to determine a domain D about the origin where $\dot{V}(x)$ is negative definite and a constant $c > 0$ such that $\Omega_c = \{V(x) \leq c\}$ is a subset of D. We are interested in the largest set Ω_c that we can determine, that is, the largest value for the constant c. Notice that we do not have to worry about checking positive definiteness of $V(x)$ in D because $V(x)$ is positive definite for all x. Moreover, $V(x)$ is radially unbounded; hence Ω_c is bounded for any $c > 0$. The derivative of $V(x)$ along the trajectories of the system is given by

$$\dot{V}(x) = -(x_1^2 + x_2^2) - (x_1^3 x_2 - 2x_1^2 x_2^2)$$

The right-hand side of $\dot{V}(x)$ is written as the sum of two terms. The first term, $-\|x\|_2^2$, is the contribution of the linear part Ax, while the second term is the contribution of the nonlinear term $g(x) = f(x) - Ax$. Since

$$\frac{\|g(x)\|_2}{\|x\|_2} \to 0 \quad \text{as} \quad \|x\|_2 \to 0$$

we know that there is an open ball $D = \{x \in R^2 \mid \|x\|_2 < r\}$ such that $\dot{V}(x)$ is negative definite in D. Once we find such a ball, we can find $\Omega_c \subset D$ by choosing

$$c < \min_{\|x\|_2 = r} V(x) = \lambda_{\min}(P) r^2$$

Thus, to enlarge the estimate of the region of attraction, we need to find the largest ball on which $\dot{V}(x)$ is negative definite. We have

$$\dot{V}(x) \leq -\|x\|_2^2 + |x_1|\,|x_1 x_2|\,|x_1 - 2x_2| \leq -\|x\|_2^2 + \frac{\sqrt{5}}{2}\|x\|_2^4$$

where we used $|x_1| \leq \|x\|_2$, $|x_1 x_2| \leq \|x\|_2^2/2$, and $|x_1 - 2x_2| \leq \sqrt{5}\|x\|_2$. Thus, $\dot{V}(x)$ is negative definite on a ball D of radius given by $r^2 = 2/\sqrt{5} = 0.8944$. In this second-order example, a less conservative estimate of Ω_c can be found by searching for the ball D in polar coordinates. Taking

$$x_1 = \rho \cos \theta, \quad x_2 = \rho \sin \theta$$

we get

$$\begin{aligned}
\dot{V} &= -\rho^2 + \rho^4 \cos^2 \theta \sin \theta (2 \sin \theta - \cos \theta) \\
&\leq -\rho^2 + \rho^4 |\cos^2 \theta \sin \theta| \cdot |2 \sin \theta - \cos \theta| \\
&\leq -\rho^2 + \rho^4 \times 0.3849 \times 2.2361 \\
&\leq -\rho^2 + 0.861 \rho^4 < 0, \quad \text{for} \quad \rho^2 < \frac{1}{0.861}
\end{aligned}$$

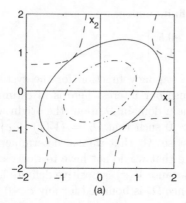
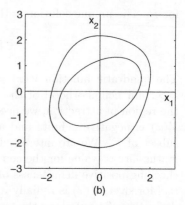

Figure 8.4: (a) Contours of $\dot{V}(x) = 0$ (dashed), $V(x) = 0.8$ (dash-dot), and $V(x) = 2.25$ (solid) for Example 8.9; (b) comparison of the region of attraction with its estimate.

Using this last equation, together with $\lambda_{\min}(P) \geq 0.69$, we choose

$$c = 0.8 < \frac{0.69}{0.861} = 0.801$$

The set Ω_c with $c = 0.8$ is an estimate of the region of attraction. A less conservative (that is, larger) estimate can be obtained by plotting contours of $\dot{V}(x) = 0$ and $V(x) = c$ for increasing values of c until we determine the largest c for which $V(x) = c$ will be in $\{\dot{V}(x) < 0\}$. This is shown in Figure 8.4(a) where c is determined to be $c = 2.25$. Figure 8.4(b) compares this estimate with the region of attraction whose boundary is a limit cycle. $\triangle$

Estimating the region of attraction by $\Omega_c = \{V(x) \leq c\}$ is simple, but usually conservative. According to LaSalle's theorem (Theorem 4.4), we can work with any compact set $\Omega \subset D$ provided we can show that Ω is positively invariant. It typically requires investigating the vector field at the boundary of Ω to ensure that trajectories starting in Ω cannot leave it. The next example illustrates this idea.

Example 8.10 Consider the system

$$
\begin{aligned}
\dot{x}_1 &= x_2 \\
\dot{x}_2 &= -4(x_1 + x_2) - h(x_1 + x_2)
\end{aligned}
$$

where $h : R \to R$ is a locally Lipschitz function that satisfies

$$h(0) = 0; \quad uh(u) \geq 0, \; \forall \, |u| \leq 1$$

Consider the quadratic function

$$V(x) = x^T \begin{bmatrix} 2 & 1 \\ 1 & 1 \end{bmatrix} x = 2x_1^2 + 2x_1 x_2 + x_2^2$$

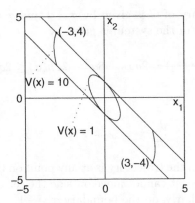

Figure 8.5: Estimates of the region of attraction for Example 8.10.

as a Lyapunov function candidate.[13] The derivative $\dot{V}(x)$ is given by

$$
\begin{aligned}
\dot{V}(x) &= (4x_1 + 2x_2)\dot{x}_1 + 2(x_1 + x_2)\dot{x}_2 \\
&= -2x_1^2 - 6(x_1 + x_2)^2 - 2(x_1 + x_2)h(x_1 + x_2) \\
&\leq -2x_1^2 - 6(x_1 + x_2)^2, \quad \forall \, |x_1 + x_2| \leq 1 \\
&= -x^T \begin{bmatrix} 8 & 6 \\ 6 & 6 \end{bmatrix} x
\end{aligned}
$$

Therefore, $\dot{V}(x)$ is negative definite in the set

$$
G = \{x \in R^2 \mid |x_1 + x_2| \leq 1\}
$$

and we can conclude that the origin is asymptotically stable. To estimate R_A, let us start by an estimate of the form $\Omega_c = \{V(x) \leq c\}$. The largest $c > 0$ for which $\Omega_c \subset G$ is given by

$$
c = \min_{|x_1 + x_2| = 1} x^T P x = \frac{1}{b^T P^{-1} b} = 1
$$

where $b^T = [1 \ \ 1]$. Hence, Ω_c with $c = 1$ is an estimate of R_A. (See Figure 8.5.) In this example, we can obtain a better estimate of R_A by not restricting ourselves to estimates of the form Ω_c. A key point in the development is to observe that trajectories inside G cannot leave through certain segments of the boundary $|x_1 + x_2| = 1$. This can be seen by examining the vector field at the boundary or by the following analysis: Let

$$
\sigma = x_1 + x_2
$$

---

[13]This Lyapunov function candidate can be derived by using the variable gradient method or by applying the circle criterion and the Kalman–Yakubovich–Popov lemma.

such that the boundary of G is given by $\sigma = 1$ and $\sigma = -1$. The derivative of σ^2 along the trajectories of the system is given by

$$\frac{d}{dt}\sigma^2 = 2\sigma(\dot{x}_1 + \dot{x}_2) = 2\sigma x_2 - 8\sigma^2 - 2\sigma h(\sigma) \leq 2\sigma x_2 - 8\sigma^2, \quad \forall \, |\sigma| \leq 1$$

On the boundary $\sigma = 1$,

$$\frac{d}{dt}\sigma^2 \leq 2x_2 - 8 \leq 0, \quad \forall \, x_2 \leq 4$$

This implies that when the trajectory is at any point on the segment of the boundary $\sigma = 1$ for which $x_2 \leq 4$, it cannot move outside the set G, because at such point σ^2 is nonincreasing. Similarly, on the boundary $\sigma = -1$,

$$\frac{d}{dt}\sigma^2 \leq -2x_2 - 8 \leq 0, \quad \forall \, x_2 \geq -4$$

Hence, the trajectory cannot leave the set G through the segment of the boundary $\sigma = -1$ for which $x_2 \geq -4$. This information can be used to form a closed, bounded, positively invariant set Ω that satisfies the conditions of Theorem 4.4. Using the two segments of the boundary of G just identified to define the boundary of Ω, we now need two other segments to close the set. These segments should have the property that trajectories cannot leave the set through them. We can take them as segments of a Lyapunov surface. Let c_1 be such that the Lyapunov surface $V(x) = c_1$ intersects the boundary $x_1 + x_2 = 1$ at $x_2 = 4$, that is, at the point $(-3, 4)$. (See Figure 8.5.) Let c_2 be such that the Lyapunov surface $V(x) = c_2$ intersects the boundary $x_1 + x_2 = -1$ at $x_2 = -4$, that is, at the point $(3, -4)$. The required Lyapunov surface is defined by $V(x) = \min\{c_1, c_2\}$. The constants c_1 and c_2 are given by

$$c_1 = V(x)|_{x_1=-3, x_2=4} = 10, \qquad c_2 = V(x)|_{x_1=3, x_2=-4} = 10$$

Therefore, we take $c = 10$ and define the set Ω by

$$\Omega = \{x \in R^2 \mid V(x) \leq 10 \text{ and } |x_1 + x_2| \leq 1\}$$

This set is closed, bounded, and positively invariant. Moreover, $\dot{V}(x)$ is negative definite in Ω, since $\Omega \subset G$. Thus, all the conditions of Theorem 4.4 are satisfied and we can conclude that all trajectories starting in Ω approach the origin as $t \to \infty$; that is, $\Omega \subset R_A$. $\triangle$

8.3   Invariance-like Theorems

In the case of autonomous systems, LaSalle's invariance theorem (Theorem 4.4) shows that the trajectory of the system approaches the largest invariant set in E, where E is the set of all points in Ω where $\dot{V}(x) = 0$. In the case of nonautonomous systems, it may not even be clear how to define a set E, since $\dot{V}(t, x)$ is a function of both t and x. The situation will be simpler if it can be shown that

$$\dot{V}(t, x) \leq -W(x) \leq 0$$

for, then, a set E may be defined as the set of points where $W(x) = 0$. We may expect that the trajectory of the system approaches E as t tends to ∞. This is, basically, the statement of the next theorem. Before we state the theorem, we state a lemma that will be used in the proof of the theorem. The lemma is interesting in its own sake and is known as *Barbalat's lemma*.

Lemma 8.2 *Let $\phi : R \to R$ be a uniformly continuous function on $[0, \infty)$. Suppose that $\lim_{t \to \infty} \int_0^t \phi(\tau) \, d\tau$ exists and is finite. Then,*

$$\phi(t) \to 0 \quad \text{as} \quad t \to \infty$$

$\diamond$

Proof: If it is not true, then there is a positive constant k_1 such that for every $T > 0$, we can find $T_1 \geq T$ with $|\phi(T_1)| \geq k_1$. Since $\phi(t)$ is uniformly continuous, there is a positive constant k_2 such that $|\phi(t + \tau) - \phi(t)| < k_1/2$ for all $t \geq 0$ and all $0 \leq \tau \leq k_2$. Hence,

$$
\begin{aligned}
|\phi(t)| &= |\phi(t) - \phi(T_1) + \phi(T_1)| \\
&\geq |\phi(T_1)| - |\phi(t) - \phi(T_1)| \\
&> k_1 - \tfrac{1}{2}k_1 = \tfrac{1}{2}k_1, \quad \forall \, t \in [T_1, T_1 + k_2]
\end{aligned}
$$

Therefore,

$$\left| \int_{T_1}^{T_1+k_2} \phi(t) \, dt \right| = \int_{T_1}^{T_1+k_2} |\phi(t)| \, dt > \tfrac{1}{2}k_1 k_2$$

where the equality holds, since $\phi(t)$ retains the same sign for $T_1 \leq t \leq T_1 + k_2$. Thus, $\int_0^t \phi(\tau) \, d\tau$ cannot converge to a finite limit as $t \to \infty$, a contradiction. $\square$

Theorem 8.4 *Let $D \subset R^n$ be a domain containing $x = 0$ and suppose $f(t, x)$ is piecewise continuous in t and locally Lipschitz in x, uniformly in t, on $[0, \infty) \times D$. Furthermore, suppose $f(t, 0)$ is uniformly bounded for all $t \geq 0$. Let $V : [0, \infty) \times D \to R$ be a continuously differentiable function such that*

$$W_1(x) \leq V(t, x) \leq W_2(x)$$

$$\dot{V}(t, x) = \frac{\partial V}{\partial t} + \frac{\partial V}{\partial x} f(t, x) \leq -W(x)$$

$\forall\, t \geq 0$, $\forall\, x \in D$, where $W_1(x)$ and $W_2(x)$ are continuous positive definite functions and $W(x)$ is a continuous positive semidefinite function on D. Choose $r > 0$ such that $B_r \subset D$ and let $\rho < \min_{\|x\|=r} W_1(x)$. Then, all solutions of $\dot{x} = f(t,x)$ with $x(t_0) \in \{x \in B_r \mid W_2(x) \leq \rho\}$ are bounded and satisfy

$$W(x(t)) \to 0 \quad \text{as}\ \ t \to \infty$$

Moreover, if all the assumptions hold globally and $W_1(x)$ is radially unbounded, the statement is true for all $x(t_0) \in R^n$. $\diamond$

Proof: Similar to the proof of Theorem 4.8, it can be shown that

$$x(t_0) \in \{x \in B_r \mid W_2(x) \leq \rho\} \Rightarrow x(t) \in \Omega_{t,\rho} \subset \{x \in B_r \mid W_1(x) \leq \rho\}, \quad \forall\, t \geq t_0$$

since $\dot{V}(t,x) \leq 0$. Hence, $\|x(t)\| < r$ for all $t \geq t_0$. Because $V(t,x(t))$ is monotonically nonincreasing and bounded from below by zero, it converges as $t \to \infty$. Now,

$$\int_{t_0}^{t} W(x(\tau))\, d\tau \leq -\int_{t_0}^{t} \dot{V}(\tau,x(\tau))\, d\tau = V(t_0, x(t_0)) - V(t, x(t))$$

Therefore, $\lim_{t\to\infty} \int_{t_0}^{t} W(x(\tau))\, d\tau$ exists and is finite. Since $x(t)$ is bounded, $\dot{x}(t) = f(t, x(t))$ is bounded, uniformly in t, for all $t \geq t_0$. Hence, $x(t)$ is uniformly continuous in t on $[t_0, \infty)$. Consequently, $W(x(t))$ is uniformly continuous in t on $[t_0, \infty)$ because $W(x)$ is uniformly continuous in x on the compact set B_r. Therefore, by Lemma 8.2, we conclude that $W(x(t)) \to 0$ as $t \to \infty$. If all the assumptions hold globally and $W_1(x)$ is radially unbounded, then for any $x(t_0)$, we can choose ρ so large that $x(t_0) \in \{x \in R^n \mid W_2(x) \leq \rho\}$. $\square$

The limit $W(x(t)) \to 0$ implies that $x(t)$ approaches E as $t \to \infty$, where

$$E = \{x \in D \mid W(x) = 0\}$$

Therefore, the positive limit set of $x(t)$ is a subset of E. The mere knowledge that $x(t)$ approaches E is much weaker than the invariance principle for autonomous systems, which states that $x(t)$ approaches the largest invariant set in E. The stronger conclusion in the case of autonomous systems is a consequence of the property of autonomous systems stated in Lemma 4.1, namely the positive limit set is an invariant set. There are some special classes of nonautonomous systems where positive limit sets have some sort of an invariance property.[14] However, for a general nonautonomous system, the positive limit sets are not invariant. The fact that, in the case of autonomous systems, $x(t)$ approaches the largest invariant set

---

[14]Examples are periodic systems, almost-periodic systems, and asymptotically autonomous systems. See [154, Chapter 8] for invariance theorems for these classes of systems. See, also, [136] for a different generalization of the invariance principle.

in E allowed us to arrive at Corollary 4.1, where asymptotic stability of the origin is established by showing that the set E does not contain an entire trajectory of the system, other than the trivial solution. For a general nonautonomous system, there is no extension of Corollary 4.1 that would show uniform asymptotic stability. However, the next theorem shows that it is possible to conclude uniform asymptotic stability if, in addition to $\dot{V}(t,x) \leq 0$, we can show that V decreases over the interval $[t, t+\delta]$.[15]

Theorem 8.5 *Let $D \subset R^n$ be a domain containing $x = 0$ and suppose $f(t,x)$ is piecewise continuous in t and locally Lipschitz in x for all $t \geq 0$ and $x \in D$. Let $x = 0$ be an equilibrium point for $\dot{x} = f(t,x)$ at $t = 0$. Let $V : [0, \infty) \times D \to R$ be a continuously differentiable function such that*

$$W_1(x) \leq V(t,x) \leq W_2(x)$$

$$\dot{V}(t,x) = \frac{\partial V}{\partial t} + \frac{\partial V}{\partial x} f(t,x) \leq 0$$

$$V(t+\delta, \phi(t+\delta; t, x)) - V(t,x) \leq -\lambda V(t,x), \quad 0 < \lambda < 1 \text{[16]}$$

$\forall\, t \geq 0$, $\forall\, x \in D$, for some $\delta > 0$, where $W_1(x)$ and $W_2(x)$ are continuous positive definite functions on D and $\phi(\tau; t, x)$ is the solution of the system that starts at (t,x). Then, the origin is uniformly asymptotically stable. If all the assumptions hold globally and $W_1(x)$ is radially unbounded, then the origin is globally uniformly asymptotically stable. If

$$W_1(x) \geq k_1 \|x\|^c, \ W_2(x) \leq k_2 \|x\|^c, \ k_1 > 0, \ k_2 > 0, \ c > 0$$

then the origin is exponentially stable. $\diamond$

Proof: Choose $r > 0$ such that $B_r \in D$. Similar to the proof of Theorem 4.8, it can be shown that

$$x(t_0) \in \{x \in B_r \mid W_2(x) \leq \rho\} \Rightarrow x(t) \in \Omega_{t,\rho}, \ \ \forall\, t \geq t_0$$

where $\rho < \min_{\|x\|=r} W_1(x)$, because $\dot{V}(t,x) \leq 0$. Now, for all $t \geq t_0$, we have

$$V(t+\delta, x(t+\delta)) \leq V(t, x(t)) - \lambda V(t, x(t)) = (1-\lambda)V(t, x(t))$$

Moreover, since $\dot{V}(t,x) \leq 0$,

$$V(\tau, x(\tau)) \leq V(t, x(t)), \ \ \forall\, \tau \in [t, t+\delta]$$

---

[15]It is shown in [1] that the condition $\dot{V} \leq 0$ can be dropped and uniform asymptotic stability can be shown if

$$V(t+\delta, \phi(t+\delta; t, x)) - V(t,x) \leq -\gamma(\|x\|)$$

for some class $\mathcal{K}$ function γ.

[16]There is no loss of generality in assuming that $\lambda < 1$, for if the inequality is satisfied with $\lambda_1 \geq 1$, then it is satisfied for any positive $\lambda < 1$, since $-\lambda_1 V \leq -\lambda V$. Notice, however, that this inequality could not be satisfied with $\lambda > 1$, since $V(t,x) > 0$, $\forall\, x \neq 0$.

For any $t \geq t_0$, let N be the smallest positive integer such that $t \leq t_0 + N\delta$. Divide the interval $[t_0, t_0 + (N-1)\delta]$ into $(N-1)$ equal subintervals of length δ each. Then,

$$
\begin{aligned}
V(t, x(t)) &\leq V(t_0 + (N-1)\delta, x(t_0 + (N-1)\delta)) \\
&\leq (1 - \lambda)V(t_0 + (N-2)\delta, x(t_0 + (N-2)\delta)) \\
&\ \ \vdots \\
&\leq (1 - \lambda)^{(N-1)}V(t_0, x(t_0)) \\
&\leq \frac{1}{(1 - \lambda)}(1 - \lambda)^{(t-t_0)/\delta}V(t_0, x(t_0)) \\
&= \frac{1}{(1 - \lambda)}e^{-b(t-t_0)}V(t_0, x(t_0))
\end{aligned}
$$

where

$$
b = \frac{1}{\delta} \ln \frac{1}{(1 - \lambda)}
$$

Taking

$$
\sigma(r, s) = \frac{r}{(1 - \lambda)}e^{-bs}
$$

it can be easily seen that $\sigma(r, s)$ is a class $\mathcal{KL}$ function and $V(t, x(t))$ satisfies

$$
V(t, x(t)) \leq \sigma(V(t_0, x(t_0)), t - t_0), \quad \forall\, V(t_0, x(t_0)) \in [0, \rho]
$$

From this point on, the rest of the proof is identical to that of Theorem 4.9. The proof of the statements on global uniform asymptotic stability and exponential stability are the same as the proofs of Theorems 4.9 and 4.10. $\square$

Example 8.11 Consider the linear time-varying system

$$
\dot{x} = A(t)x
$$

where $A(t)$ is continuous for all $t \geq 0$. Suppose there is a continuously differentiable, symmetric matrix $P(t)$ that satisfies

$$
0 < c_1 I \leq P(t) \leq c_2 I, \quad \forall\, t \geq 0
$$

as well as the matrix differential equation

$$
-\dot{P}(t) = P(t)A(t) + A^T(t)P(t) + C^T(t)C(t)
$$

where $C(t)$ is continuous in t. The derivative of the quadratic function

$$
V(t, x) = x^T P(t)x
$$

along the trajectories of the system is

$$
\dot{V}(t, x) = -x^T C^T(t)C(t)x \leq 0
$$

The solution of the linear system is given by $\phi(\tau; t, x) = \Phi(\tau, t)x$, where $\Phi(\tau, t)$ is the state transition matrix. Therefore,

$$
\begin{aligned}
V(t + \delta, \phi(t + \delta; t, x)) - V(t, x) &= \int_t^{t+\delta} \dot{V}(\tau, \phi(\tau; t, x)) \, d\tau \\
&= -x^T \int_t^{t+\delta} \Phi^T(\tau, t) C^T(\tau) C(\tau) \Phi(\tau, t) \, d\tau \; x \\
&= -x^T W(t, t + \delta) x
\end{aligned}
$$

where

$$
W(t, t + \delta) = \int_t^{t+\delta} \Phi^T(\tau, t) C^T(\tau) C(\tau) \Phi(\tau, t) \, d\tau
$$

Suppose there is a positive constant $k < c_2$ such that

$$
W(t, t + \delta) \geq kI, \quad \forall \, t \geq 0
$$

then

$$
V(t + \delta, \phi(t + \delta; t, x)) - V(t, x) \leq -k \|x\|_2^2 \leq -\frac{k}{c_2} V(t, x)
$$

Thus, all the assumptions of Theorem 8.5 are satisfied globally with

$$
W_i(x) = c_i \|x\|_2^2, \; i = 1, 2, \quad \lambda = \frac{k}{c_2} < 1
$$

and we conclude that the origin is globally exponentially stable. Readers familiar with linear system theory will recognize that the matrix $W(t, t + \delta)$ is the observability Gramian of the pair $(A(t), C(t))$ and that the inequality $W(t, t + \delta) \geq kI$ is implied by uniform observability of $(A(t), C(t))$. Comparing this example with Example 4.21 shows that Theorem 8.5 allows us to replace the positive definiteness requirement on the matrix $Q(t)$ of (4.28) by the weaker requirement $Q(t) = C^T(t)C(t)$, where the pair $(A(t), C(t))$ is uniformly observable. $\triangle$

Theorems 8.4 and 8.5 and their application to linear systems, as in Example 8.11, are extensively used in the analysis of adaptive control systems.[17] As an example, we analyze the adaptive control system of Section 1.2.6.

Example 8.12 In Section 1.2.6, we saw that the closed-loop equation of a model reference adaptive control system, with plant $\dot{y}_p = a_p y_p + k_p u$ and reference model $\dot{y}_m = a_m y_m + k_m r$, is given by

$$
\begin{aligned}
\dot{e}_o &= a_m e_o + k_p \phi_1 r(t) + k_p \phi_2 [e_o + y_m(t)] \\
\dot{\phi}_1 &= -\gamma e_o r(t) \\
\dot{\phi}_2 &= -\gamma e_o [e_o + y_m(t)]
\end{aligned}
$$

---

[17]See, for example, [87] and [168].

where $\gamma > 0$ is the adaptation gain, $e_o = y_p - y_m$ is the output error, and ϕ_1 and ϕ_2 are the parameter errors. It was assumed that $k_p > 0$ and, of course, the reference model must have $a_m < 0$. Furthermore, we assume that $r(t)$ is piecewise continuous and bounded. Using

$$V = \tfrac{1}{2}\left[\frac{e_o^2}{k_p} + \frac{1}{\gamma}(\phi_1^2 + \phi_2^2)\right]$$

as a Lyapunov function candidate, we obtain

$$\dot{V} = \frac{a_m}{k_p}e_o^2 + e_o(\phi_1 r + \phi_2 e_o + \phi_2 y_m) - \phi_1 e_o r - \phi_2 e_o(e_o + y_m) = \frac{a_m}{k_p}\,e_o^2 \le 0$$

By applying Theorem 8.4, we conclude that for any $c > 0$ and for all initial states in the set $\{V \le c\}$, all state variables are bounded for all $t \ge t_0$ and $\lim_{t\to\infty} e_o(t) = 0$. This shows that the output of the plant y_p tracks the desired output y_m, but says nothing about the convergence of the parameter errors ϕ_1 and ϕ_2 to zero. In fact, they may not converge to zero. For example, if r and y_m are nonzero constant signals, the closed-loop system will have an equilibrium subspace $\{e_o = 0,\ \phi_2 = (a_m/k_m)\phi_1\}$, which shows clearly that, in general, ϕ_1 and ϕ_2 do not converge to zero. To derive conditions under which ϕ_1 and ϕ_2 will converge to zero, we apply Theorem 8.5. This will yield conditions under which the origin $(e_o = 0,\ \phi_1 = 0,\ \phi_2 = 0)$ is uniformly asymptotically stable. Since we have already shown that all state variables are bounded, we can represent the closed-loop system as the linear time-varying system

$$\dot{x} = \begin{bmatrix} a_m & k_p r(t) & k_p y_p(t) \\ -\gamma r(t) & 0 & 0 \\ -\gamma y_p(t) & 0 & 0 \end{bmatrix} x, \quad \text{where} \quad x = \begin{bmatrix} e_o \\ \phi_1 \\ \phi_2 \end{bmatrix}$$

Suppose the reference signal $r(t)$ has a steady-state value $r_{\mathrm{ss}}(t)$; that is, $\lim_{t\to\infty}[r(t) - r_{\mathrm{ss}}(t)] = 0$. Then, $\lim_{t\to\infty}[y_m(t) - y_{\mathrm{ss}}(t)] = 0$, where $y_{\mathrm{ss}}(t)$ is the steady-state response of the reference model. These limits, together with $\lim_{t\to\infty} e_o(t) = 0$, show that the linear system can be represented by

$$\dot{x} = [A(t) + B(t)]x$$

where

$$A(t) = \begin{bmatrix} a_m & k_p r_{\mathrm{ss}}(t) & k_p y_{\mathrm{ss}}(t) \\ -\gamma r_{\mathrm{ss}}(t) & 0 & 0 \\ -\gamma y_{\mathrm{ss}}(t) & 0 & 0 \end{bmatrix}, \quad \text{and} \quad \lim_{t\to\infty} B(t) = 0$$

If we can show that the origin of $\dot{x} = A(t)x$ is uniformly asymptotically stable, we can use the property $\lim_{t\to\infty} B(t) = 0$ to show that the origin of $\dot{x} = [A(t) + B(t)]x$ is uniformly asymptotically stable.[18] Therefore, we concentrate our attention on

---

[18]See Example 9.6.

the system $\dot{x} = A(t)x$. Once again, using V as a Lyapunov function candidate, we obtain

$$\dot{V} = \frac{a_m}{k_p}\, e_o^2 = -x^T C^T C x, \quad \text{where} \quad C = \sqrt{\frac{-a_m}{k_p}} \begin{bmatrix} 1 & 0 & 0 \end{bmatrix}$$

From Example 8.12, we see that the origin will be uniformly asymptotically stable if the pair $(A(t), C)$ is uniformly observable. Since uniform observability of $(A(t), C)$ is equivalent to uniform observability of $(A(t) - K(t)C, C)$ for any piecewise continuous, bounded matrix $K(t)$,[19] we take

$$K(t) = \sqrt{\frac{k_p}{-a_m}} \begin{bmatrix} a_m & -\gamma r_{\mathrm{ss}}(t) & -\gamma y_{\mathrm{ss}}(t) \end{bmatrix}^T$$

to simplify the pair to

$$A(t) - K(t)C = \begin{bmatrix} 0 & k_p r_{\mathrm{ss}}(t) & k_p y_{\mathrm{ss}}(t) \\ 0 & 0 & 0 \\ 0 & 0 & 0 \end{bmatrix}, \quad C = \sqrt{\frac{-a_m}{k_p}} \begin{bmatrix} 1 & 0 & 0 \end{bmatrix}$$

By investigating observability of this pair for a given reference signal, we can determine whether the conditions of Theorem 8.5 are satisfied. For example, if r is a nonzero constant signal, it can be easily seen that the pair is not observable. This is not surprising, since we have already seen that in this case the origin is not uniformly asymptotically stable. On the other hand, if $r(t) = a \sin \omega t$ with positive a and ω, we have $r_{\mathrm{ss}}(t) = r(t)$ and $y_{\mathrm{ss}}(t) = aM \sin(\omega t + \delta)$, where M and δ are determined by the transfer function of the reference model. It can be verified that the pair is uniformly observable; hence the origin ($e_o = 0$, $\phi_1 = 0$, $\phi_2 = 0$) is uniformly asymptotically stable and the parameter errors $\phi_1(t)$ and $\phi_2(t)$ converge to zero as t tends to infinity.[20] $\triangle$

8.4   Stability of Periodic Solutions

In Chapter 4, we developed an extensive theory for the stability of equilibrium points. In this section, we consider the corresponding problem for periodic solutions. If $u(t)$ is a periodic solution of the system

$$\dot{x} = f(t, x) \tag{8.14}$$

what can we say about other solutions that start arbitrarily close to $u(t)$? Will they remain in some neighborhood of $u(t)$ for all t? Will they eventually approach

---

[19]See [87, Lemma 4.8.1].

[20]For this example, the reference $r(t) = a \sin \omega t$ is said to be persistently exciting, while a constant reference is not persistently exciting. To read more about persistence of excitation, see [5], [15], [87], [139], [168], or Section 13.4 of the second edition of this book.

$u(t)$? Such stability properties of the periodic solution $u(t)$ can be characterized and investigated in the sense of Lyapunov. Let

$$y = x - u(t)$$

so that the origin $y = 0$ becomes an equilibrium point for the nonautonomous system

$$\dot{y} = f(t, y + u(t)) - f(t, u(t)) \tag{8.15}$$

The behavior of solutions of (8.14) near $u(t)$ is equivalent to the behavior of solutions of (8.15) near $y = 0$. Therefore, we can characterize stability properties of $u(t)$ from those of the equilibrium $y = 0$. In particular, we say that the periodic solution $u(t)$ is uniformly asymptotically stable if $y = 0$ is a uniformly asymptotically stable equilibrium point for the system (8.15). Similar statements can be made for other stability properties, like uniform stability. Thus, investigating the stability of $u(t)$ has been reduced to studying the stability of an equilibrium point of a nonautonomous system, which we studied in Chapter 4. We shall find this notion of uniform asymptotic stability of periodic solutions in the sense of Lyapunov to be useful when we study nonautonomous systems dependent on small parameters in Chapter 10. The notion, however, is too restrictive when we analyze periodic solutions of autonomous systems. The next example illustrates the restrictive nature of this notion.

Example 8.13 Consider the second-order system

$$
\begin{aligned}
\dot{x}_1 &= x_1 \left[\frac{\left(1 - x_1^2 - x_2^2\right)^3}{x_1^2 + x_2^2} \right] - x_2 \left[1 + \left(1 - x_1^2 - x_2^2\right)^2 \right] \\
\dot{x}_2 &= x_2 \left[\frac{\left(1 - x_1^2 - x_2^2\right)^3}{x_1^2 + x_2^2} \right] + x_1 \left[1 + \left(1 - x_1^2 - x_2^2\right)^2 \right]
\end{aligned}
$$

which is represented in the polar coordinates

$$x_1 = r \cos \theta, \qquad x_2 = r \sin \theta$$

by

$$\dot{r} = \frac{(1 - r^2)^3}{r}, \qquad \dot{\theta} = 1 + (1 - r^2)^2$$

The solution starting at (r_0, θ_0) is given by

$$
\begin{aligned}
r(t) &= \left[1 - \frac{1 - r_0^2}{\sqrt{1 + 4t \left(1 - r_0^2\right)^2}} \right]^{1/2} \\
\theta(t) &= \theta_0 + t + \tfrac{1}{4} \ln \left[1 + 4t(1 - r_0^2)^2 \right]
\end{aligned}
$$

From these expressions, we see that the system has a periodic solution

$$\bar{x}_1(t) = \cos t, \qquad \bar{x}_2(t) = \sin t$$

The corresponding periodic orbit is the unit circle $r = 1$. All nearby solutions spiral toward this periodic orbit as $t \to \infty$. This spiralling is clearly the kind of "asymptotically stable" behavior we expect to see with a periodic orbit. In fact, the periodic orbit has been known classically as a stable limit cycle. However, the periodic solution $\bar{x}(t)$ is not uniformly asymptotically stable in the sense of Lyapunov. Recall that for the solution to be uniformly asymptotically stable, we must have

$$[r(t) \cos \theta(t) - \cos t]^2 + [r(t) \sin \theta(t) - \sin t]^2 \to 0 \quad \text{as} \quad t \to \infty$$

for sufficiently small $[r_0 \cos \theta_0 - 1]^2 + [r_0 \sin \theta_0]^2$. Because $r(t) \to 1$ as $t \to \infty$, we must have

$$|1 - \cos(\theta(t) - t)| \to 0 \quad \text{as} \quad t \to \infty$$

which clearly is not satisfied when $r_0 \neq 1$, since $(\theta(t) - t)$ is an ever-growing monotonically increasing function of t. $\triangle$

The point illustrated by this example is true in general. In particular, a nontrivial periodic solution of an autonomous system can never be asymptotically stable in the sense of Lyapunov.[21]

The stability-like properties of the periodic orbit of Example 8.13 can be captured by extending the notion of stability in the sense of Lyapunov from stability of an equilibrium point to stability of an invariant set. Consider the autonomous system

$$\dot{x} = f(x) \tag{8.16}$$

where $f : D \to R^n$ is a continuously differentiable map from a domain $D \subset R^n$ into R^n. Let $M \subset D$ be a closed invariant set of (8.16). Define an ε-neighborhood of M by

$$U_\varepsilon = \{x \in R^n \mid \text{dist}(x, M) < \varepsilon\}$$

where $\text{dist}(x, M)$ is the minimum distance from x to a point in M; that is,

$$\text{dist}(x, M) = \inf_{y \in M} \|x - y\|$$

Definition 8.1 *The closed invariant set M of (8.16) is*

- *stable if, for each $\varepsilon > 0$, there is $\delta > 0$ such that*

$$x(0) \in U_\delta \Rightarrow x(t) \in U_\varepsilon, \quad \forall\, t \geq 0$$

---

[21]See [72, Theorem 81.1] for a proof of this statement.

- *asymptotically stable if it is stable and δ can be chosen such that*

$$x(0) \in U_\delta \Rightarrow \lim_{t \to \infty} \text{dist}(x(t), M) = 0$$

This definition reduces to Definition 4.1 when M is an equilibrium point. Lyapunov stability theory for equilibrium points, as presented in Chapter 4, can be extended to invariant sets.[22] For example, by repeating the proof of Theorem 4.1, it is not hard to see that if there is a function $V(x)$, which is zero on M and positive in some neighborhood D of M, excluding M itself, and if the derivative $\dot{V}(x) = [\partial V/\partial x]f(x) \leq 0$ in D, then M is stable. Furthermore, if $\dot{V}(x)$ is negative in D, excluding M, then M is asymptotically stable.

Stability and asymptotic stability of invariant sets are interesting concepts in their own sake. We will apply them here to the specific case when the invariant set M is the closed orbit associated with a periodic solution. Let $u(t)$ be a nontrivial periodic solution of the autonomous system (8.16) with period T, and let γ be the closed orbit defined by

$$\gamma = \{x \in R^n \mid x = u(t),\ 0 \leq t \leq T\}$$

The periodic orbit γ is the image of $u(t)$ in the state space. It is an invariant set whose stability properties are characterized by Definition 8.1. It is common, especially for second-order systems, to refer to asymptotically stable periodic orbits as stable limit cycles

Example 8.14 The harmonic oscillator

$$\dot{x}_1 = x_2$$
$$\dot{x}_2 = -x_1$$

has a continuum of periodic orbits, which are concentric circles with a center at the origin. Any one of these periodic orbits is stable. Consider, for example, the periodic orbit γ_c defined by

$$\gamma_c = \{x \in R^2 \mid r = c > 0\},\quad \text{where } r = \sqrt{x_1^2 + x_2^2}$$

The U_ε neighborhood of γ_c is defined by the annular region

$$U_\varepsilon = \{x \in R^2 \mid c - \varepsilon < r < c + \varepsilon\}$$

This annular region itself is an invariant set. Thus, given $\varepsilon > 0$, we can take $\delta = \varepsilon$ and see that any solution starting in the U_δ neighborhood at $t = 0$ will remain in the U_ε neighborhood for all $t \geq 0$. Hence, the periodic orbit γ_c is stable. However, it is not asymptotically stable, because a solution starting in a U_δ neighborhood

---

[22]See, for example, [213] and [221] for comprehensive coverage and [118] for some interesting results on converse Lyapunov theorems.

of γ_c does not approach γ_c as $t \to \infty$, no matter how small δ is. Stability of the periodic orbit $\{r = c\}$ can be also shown by the Lyapunov function

$$V(x) = (r^2 - c^2)^2 = (x_1^2 + x_2^2 - c^2)^2$$

whose derivative along the trajectories of the system is

$$\dot{V}(x) = 4(r^2 - c^2)r\dot{r} = 0$$

$\triangle$

Example 8.15 Consider the system of Example 8.13. It has an isolated periodic orbit

$$\gamma = \{x \in R^2 \mid r = 1\}, \quad \text{where } r = \sqrt{x_1^2 + x_2^2}$$

For $x \notin \gamma$, we have

$$\text{dist}(x, \gamma) = \inf_{y \in \gamma} \|x - y\|_2 = \inf_{y \in \gamma} \sqrt{(x_1 - y_1)^2 + (x_2 - y_2)^2} = |r - 1|$$

Recalling that

$$r(t) = \left[1 - \frac{1 - r_0^2}{\sqrt{1 + 4t\left(1 - r_0^2\right)^2}} \right]^{1/2}$$

it can be easily seen that the ε–δ requirement for stability is satisfied and

$$\text{dist}(x(t), \gamma) \to 0, \quad \text{as } t \to \infty$$

Hence, the periodic orbit is asymptotically stable. The same conclusion can be arrived at using the Lyapunov function

$$V(x) = (r^2 - 1)^2 = (x_1^2 + x_2^2 - 1)^2$$

whose derivative along the trajectories of the system is

$$\dot{V}(x) = 4(r^2 - 1)r\dot{r} = -4(r^2 - 1)^4 < 0, \quad \text{for } r \neq 1$$

$\triangle$

Having defined the stability properties of periodic orbits, we can now define the stability properties of periodic solutions.

Definition 8.2 *A nontrivial periodic solution $u(t)$ of (8.16) is*

- *orbitally stable if the closed orbit γ generated by $u(t)$ is stable.*

- *asymptotically orbitally stable if the closed orbit γ generated by $u(t)$ is asymptotically stable.*

Notice that different terminology is used depending on whether we are talking about the periodic solution or the corresponding periodic orbit. In Example 8.15, we say that the unit circle is an asymptotically stable periodic orbit, but we say that the periodic solution $(\cos t, \sin t)$ is orbitally asymptotically stable.

8.5   Exercises

8.1 Prove Corollary 8.1.

8.2 Prove Corollary 8.2.

8.3 Suppose the conditions of Theorem 8.1 are satisfied in a case where $g_1(y, 0) = 0$, $g_2(y, 0) = 0$, and $A_1 = 0$. Show that the origin of the full system is stable.

8.4 Reconsider Example 8.1 with $a = 0$. Show that the origin is stable.

8.5 ([88]) Consider the system

$$
\begin{aligned}
\dot{x}_a &= f_a(x_a, x_b) \\
\dot{x}_b &= A_b x_b + f_b(x_a, x_b)
\end{aligned}
$$

where $\dim(x_a) = n_1$, $\dim(x_b) = n_2$, A_b is Hurwitz, f_a and f_b are continuously differentiable, $[\partial f_b / \partial x_b](0, 0) = 0$, and $f_b(x_a, 0) = 0$ in a neighborhood of $x_a = 0$.

(a) Show that if $x_a = 0$ is an exponentially stable equilibrium point of $\dot{x}_a = f_a(x_a, 0)$, then $(x_a, x_b) = (0, 0)$ is an exponentially stable equilibrium point of the full system.

(b) Show that if $x_a = 0$ is an asymptotically (but not exponentially) stable equilibrium point of $\dot{x}_a = f_a(x_a, 0)$, then $(x_a, x_b) = (0, 0)$ is an asymptotically stable equilibrium point of the full system.

8.6 ([70]) For each of the following systems, investigate stability of the origin by using the center manifold theorem:

(1) $\quad \begin{aligned} \dot{x}_1 &= -x_2^2 \\ \dot{x}_2 &= -x_2 + x_1^2 + x_1 x_2 \end{aligned}$
$\qquad$
(2) $\quad \begin{aligned} \dot{x}_1 &= ax_1^2 - x_2^2, \quad a \neq 0 \\ \dot{x}_2 &= -x_2 + x_1^2 + x_1 x_2 \end{aligned}$

(3) $\quad \begin{aligned} \dot{x}_1 &= -x_2 + x_1 x_3 \\ \dot{x}_2 &= x_1 + x_2 x_3 \\ \dot{x}_3 &= -x_3 - (x_1^2 + x_2^2) + x_3^2 \end{aligned}$
$\qquad$
(4) $\quad \begin{aligned} \dot{x}_1 &= x_1^2 x_2 \\ \dot{x}_2 &= -x_1^3 - x_2 \end{aligned}$

(5) $\quad \begin{aligned} \dot{x}_1 &= x_1 x_2^3 \\ \dot{x}_2 &= -x_2 - x_1^2 + 2x_1^8 \end{aligned}$
$\qquad$
(6) $\quad \begin{aligned} \dot{x}_1 &= -x_1 + x_2^3(x_1 + x_2 - 1) \\ \dot{x}_2 &= x_2^3(x_1 + x_2 - 1) \end{aligned}$

(7) $\quad \begin{aligned} \dot{x}_1 &= x_2 \\ \dot{x}_2 &= -x_2 + ax_1^3/(1 + x_1^2) \\ & \qquad a \neq 0 \end{aligned}$
$\qquad$
(8) $\quad \begin{aligned} \dot{x}_1 &= -2x_1 - 3x_2 + x_3 + x_3^2 \\ \dot{x}_2 &= x_1 + x_1^2 + x_2 \\ \dot{x}_3 &= x_1^2 \end{aligned}$

8.7 ([34]) Consider the system

$$
\dot{x}_1 = x_1 x_2 + ax_1^3 + bx_1 x_2^2, \qquad \dot{x}_2 = -x_2 + cx_1^2 + dx_1^2 x_2
$$

Investigate stability of the origin by using the center manifold theorem for each of the following cases:

(1) $a + c > 0$.   (2) $a + c < 0$.
(3) $a + c = 0$ and $cd + bc^2 < 0$.   (4) $a + c = 0$ and $cd + bc^2 > 0$.
(5) $a + c = cd + bc^2 = 0$.

8.8 ([34]) Consider the system

$$\dot{x}_1 = ax_1^3 + x_1^2 x_2, \qquad \dot{x}_2 = -x_2 + x_2^2 + x_1 x_2 - x_1^3$$

Investigate stability of the origin by using the center manifold theorem for all possible values of the real parameter a.

8.9 ([88]) Consider the system

$$\dot{x}_1 = ax_1 x_2 - x_1^3, \qquad \dot{x}_2 = -x_2 + bx_1 x_2 + cx_1^2$$

Investigate stability of the origin by using the center manifold theorem for all possible values of the real constants a, b, and c.

8.10 (Zubov's Theorem) Consider the system (8.13) and let $G \subset R^n$ be a domain containing the origin. Suppose there exist two functions $V : G \to R$ and $h : R^n \to R$ with the following properties:

- V is continuously differentiable and positive definite in G and satisfies

$$0 < V(x) < 1, \quad \forall\, x \in G - \{0\}$$

- As x approaches the boundary of G, or in case of unbounded G as $\|x\| \to \infty$, $\lim V(x) = 1$.

- h is continuous and positive definite on R^n.

- For $x \in G$, $V(x)$ satisfies the partial differential equation

$$\frac{\partial V}{\partial x} f(x) = -h(x)[1 - V(x)] \qquad (8.17)$$

Show that $x = 0$ is asymptotically stable and G is the region of attraction.

8.11 ([72]) Consider the second-order system

$$\dot{x}_1 = -h_1(x_1) + g_2(x_2), \qquad \dot{x}_2 = -g_1(x_1)$$

where

$$h_1(0) = 0, \quad z h_1(z) > 0 \;\; \forall \, -a_1 < z < b_1$$

$$g_i(0) = 0, \quad zg_i(z) > 0 \ \forall \ - a_i < z < b_i$$

$$\int_0^z g_i(\sigma) \, d\sigma \to \infty \text{ as } z \to -a_i \text{ or } z \to b_i$$

for some positive constants a_i, b_i ($a_i = \infty$ or $b_i = \infty$ is allowed). Apply Zubov's theorem to show that the region of attraction is $\{x \in R^2 \mid -a_i < x_i < b_i\}$.
Hint: Take $h(x) = g_1(x_1)h_1(x_1)$ and seek a solution of the partial differential equation (8.17) in the form $V(x) = 1 - W_1(x_1)W_2(x_2)$. Note that, with this choice of h, $\dot{V}(x)$ is only negative semidefinite; apply LaSalle's invariance principle.

8.12 Find the region of attraction of the system

$$\dot{x}_1 = -x_1 + x_2, \qquad \dot{x}_2 = -\tan(x_1)$$

Hint: Use the previous exercise.

8.13 Let Ω be an open, positively invariant set containing the origin. Suppose every trajectory in Ω approaches the origin as $t \to \infty$. Show that Ω is connected.

8.14 Consider a second-order system $\dot{x} = f(x)$ with asymptotically stable origin. Let $V(x) = x_1^2 + x_2^2$, and $D = \{x \in R^2 \mid |x_2| < 1, \ |x_1 - x_2| < 1\}$. Suppose $[\partial V/\partial x] \, f(x)$ is negative definite in D. Estimate the region of attraction.

8.15 Consider the system

$$\dot{x}_1 = x_2, \qquad \dot{x}_2 = -x_1 - x_2 - (2x_2 + x_1)(1 - x_2^2)$$

(a) Using $V(x) = 5x_1^2 + 2x_1x_2 + 2x_2^2$, show that the origin is asymptotically stable.

(b) Let

$$S = \{x \in R^2 \mid V(x) \le 5\} \cap \{x \in R^2 \mid |x_2| \le 1\}$$

Show that S is an estimate of the region of attraction.

8.16 Show that the origin of

$$\dot{x}_1 = x_2, \qquad \dot{x}_2 = -x_2 - x_1 + x_1^3$$

is asymptotically stable and estimate the region of attraction.

8.17 Consider a second-order system $\dot{x} = f(x)$, together with a Lyapunov function $V(x)$. Suppose that $\dot{V}(x) < 0$ for all $x_1^2 + x_2^2 \ge a^2$. The sketch, given in Figure 8.6, shows four different directions of the vector field at a point on the circle $x_1^2 + x_2^2 = a^2$. Which of these directions are possible and which are not? Justify your answer.

8.18 Consider the system

$$\dot{x}_1 = x_2, \qquad \dot{x}_2 = -x_2 - \sin x_1 - 2 \, \text{sat}(x_1 + x_2)$$

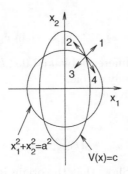

Figure 8.6: Exercise 8.17.

(a) Show that the origin is the unique equilibrium point.

(b) Show, using linearization, that the origin is asymptotically stable.

(c) Let $\sigma = x_1 + x_2$. Show that $\sigma\,\dot\sigma \le -|\sigma|$ for $|\sigma| \ge 1$.

(d) Let $V(x) = x_1^2 + 0.5x_2^2 + 1 - \cos x_1$. Show that

$$M_c = \{x \in R^2 \mid V(x) \le c\} \cap \{x \in R^2 \mid |\sigma| \le 1\}, \quad c > 0$$

is positively invariant and trajectories in M_c approach the origin as $t \to \infty$.

(e) Show that the origin is globally asymptotically stable.

8.19 Consider the synchronous generator model described in Exercise 1.8. Take the state variables and parameters as in parts (a) and (b) of the exercise. Moreover, take $\tau = 6.6$ sec, $M = 0.0147$ (per unit power) $\times$ sec^2/rad, and $D/M = 4$ sec^{-1}.

(a) Find all equilibrium points in the region $-\pi \le x_1 \le \pi$, and determine the stability properties of each equilibrium by using linearization.

(b) Estimate the region of attraction of each asymptotically stable equilibrium.

8.20 ([113]) Consider the system

$$\dot{x}_1 = x_2, \qquad \dot{x}_2 = -x_1 - g(t)x_2$$

where $g(t)$ is continuously differentiable and $0 < k_1 \le g(t) \le k_2$ for all $t \ge 0$.

(a) Show that the origin is exponentially stable.

(b) Would (a) be true if $g(t)$ were not bounded? Consider $g(t) = 2 + \exp(t)$.

8.21 Consider the system

$$\dot{x}_1 = x_2, \qquad \dot{x}_2 = -\sin x_1 - g(t)x_2$$

where $g(t)$ is continuously differentiable and $0 < k_1 \leq g(t) \leq k_2$ for all $t \geq 0$. Show that the origin is exponentially stable.
Hint: Use the previous exercise.

8.22 Consider the system

$$\dot{x}_1 = -x_1 - x_2 - \alpha(t)x_3, \quad \dot{x}_2 = x_1, \quad \dot{x}_3 = \alpha(t)x_1$$

where $\alpha(t) = \sin t + \sin 2t$. Show that the origin is exponentially stable.

8.23 Consider the single-input–single-output nonlinear system

$$
\begin{aligned}
\dot{x}_i &= x_{i+1}, \quad 1 \leq i \leq n-1 \\
\dot{x}_n &= f_0(x) + (\theta^*)^T f_1(x) + g_0(x)u
\end{aligned}
$$

where f_0, f_1, and g_0 are known smooth functions of x, defined for all $x \in R^n$, while $\theta^* \in R^p$ is a vector of unknown constant parameters. The function $g_0(x)$ is bounded away from zero; that is, $|g_0(x)| \geq k_0 > 0$, for all $x \in R^n$. We assume that all state variables can be measured. It is desired to design a state feedback adaptive controller such that x_1 asymptotically tracks a desired reference signal $r(t)$, where r and its derivatives up to $r^{(n)}$ are continuous and bounded for all $t \geq 0$.

(a) Taking $e_i = x_i - r^{(i-1)}$ and $e = [e_1, \ldots, e_n]^T$, show that e satisfies the equation

$$\dot{e} = Ae + B[f_0(x) + (\theta^*)^T f_1(x) + g_0(x)u - r^{(n)}]$$

where (A, B) is a controllable pair.

(b) Design K such that $A - BK$ is Hurwitz and let P be the positive definite solution of the Lyapunov equation $P(A - BK) + (A - BK)^T P = -I$. Using the Lyapunov function candidate $V = e^T Pe + \phi^T \Gamma^{-1} \phi$, where $\phi = \theta - \theta^*$ and Γ is a symmetric positive definite matrix, show that the adaptive controller

$$
\begin{aligned}
u &= \frac{1}{g_0(x)} \left[-f_0(x) - \theta^T f_1(x) + r^{(n)} - Ke \right] \\
\dot{\theta} &= \Gamma f_1(x) e^T PB
\end{aligned}
$$

ensures that all state variables are bounded and $\lim_{t\to\infty} e(t) = 0$.

(c) Let

$$\bar{A}(t) = \begin{bmatrix} 0_{n\times n} & -Bf_1^T(\mathcal{R}) \\ 0_{p\times n} & 0_{p\times p} \end{bmatrix}, \qquad C = \begin{bmatrix} I_n & 0_{n\times p} \end{bmatrix}$$

where $\mathcal{R} = [r, \ldots, r^{(n-1)}]^T$. Show that if $(\bar{A}(t), C)$ is uniformly observable, then the parameter error ϕ converges to zero as $t \to \infty$.

Chapter 9

Stability of Perturbed Systems

Consider the system

$$\dot{x} = f(t, x) + g(t, x) \tag{9.1}$$

where $f : [0, \infty) \times D \to R^n$ and $g : [0, \infty) \times D \to R^n$ are piecewise continuous in t and locally Lipschitz in x on $[0, \infty) \times D$, and $D \subset R^n$ is a domain that contains the origin $x = 0$. We think of this system as a perturbation of the nominal system

$$\dot{x} = f(t, x) \tag{9.2}$$

The perturbation term $g(t, x)$ could result from modeling errors, aging, or uncertainties and disturbances, which exist in any realistic problem. In a typical situation, we do not know $g(t, x)$, but we know some information about it, like knowing an upper bound on $\|g(t, x)\|$. Here, we represent the perturbation as an additive term on the right-hand side of the state equation. Uncertainties that do not change the system's order can always be represented in this form. For if the perturbed right-hand side is some function $\tilde{f}(t, x)$, then by adding and subtracting $f(t, x)$, we can rewrite the right-hand side as

$$\tilde{f}(t, x) = f(t, x) + [\tilde{f}(t, x) - f(t, x)]$$

and define

$$g(t, x) = \tilde{f}(t, x) - f(t, x)$$

Suppose the nominal system (9.2) has a uniformly asymptotically stable equilibrium point at the origin, what can we say about the stability behavior of the perturbed system (9.1)? A natural approach to address this question is to use a Lyapunov function for the nominal system as a Lyapunov function candidate for the perturbed system. This is what we have done in the analysis of the linearization approach in Sections 4.3 and 4.6. The new element here is that the perturbation term could be more general than the perturbation term in the case of linearization. The conclusions we can arrive at depend critically on whether the perturbation term vanishes at the origin. If $g(t, 0) = 0$, the perturbed system (9.2) has an equilibrium point at the origin. In this case, we analyze the stability behavior of the origin as an equilibrium point of the perturbed system. If $g(t, 0) \neq 0$, the origin will not be an equilibrium point of the perturbed system. In this case, we study ultimate boundedness of the solutions of the perturbed system.

The cases of vanishing and nonvanishing perturbations are treated in Sections 9.1 and 9.2, respectively. In Section 9.3, we restrict our attention to the case when the nominal system has an exponentially stable equilibrium point at the origin and use the comparison lemma to derive some sharper results on the asymptotic behavior of the solution of the perturbed system. In Section 9.4, we give a result that establishes continuity of the solution of the state equation on the infinite-time interval.

The last two sections deal with interconnected systems and slowly varying systems, respectively. In both cases, stability analysis is simplified by viewing the system as a perturbation of a simpler system. In the case of interconnected systems, the analysis is simplified by decomposing the system into smaller isolated subsystems, while in the case of slowly varying systems, a nonautonomous system with slowly varying inputs is approximated by an autonomous system where the slowly varying inputs are treated as constant parameters.

9.1   Vanishing Perturbation

Let us start with the case $g(t, 0) = 0$. Suppose $x = 0$ is an exponentially stable equilibrium point of the nominal system (9.2), and let $V(t, x)$ be a Lyapunov function that satisfies

$$c_1 \|x\|^2 \leq V(t, x) \leq c_2 \|x\|^2 \tag{9.3}$$

$$\frac{\partial V}{\partial t} + \frac{\partial V}{\partial x} f(t, x) \leq -c_3 \|x\|^2 \tag{9.4}$$

$$\left\| \frac{\partial V}{\partial x} \right\| \leq c_4 \|x\| \tag{9.5}$$

for all $(t, x) \in [0, \infty) \times D$ for some positive constants c_1, c_2, c_3, and c_4. The existence of a Lyapunov function satisfying (9.3) through (9.5) is guaranteed by Theorem 4.14, under some additional assumptions. Suppose the perturbation term $g(t, x)$ satisfies the linear growth bound

$$\|g(t, x)\| \leq \gamma \|x\|, \quad \forall \, t \geq 0, \, \forall \, x \in D \tag{9.6}$$

where γ is a nonnegative constant. This bound is natural in view of the assumptions on $g(t, x)$. In fact, any function $g(t, x)$ that vanishes at the origin and is locally Lipschitz in x, uniformly in t for all $t \geq 0$, in a bounded neighborhood of the origin satisfies (9.6) over that neighborhood.[1] We use V as a Lyapunov function candidate

---

[1] Note, however, that the linear growth bound (9.6) becomes restrictive when required to hold globally, because that would require g to be globally Lipschitz in x.

to investigate the stability of the origin as an equilibrium point for the perturbed system (9.1). The derivative of V along the trajectories of (9.1) is given by

$$\dot{V}(t,x) = \frac{\partial V}{\partial t} + \frac{\partial V}{\partial x}f(t,x) + \frac{\partial V}{\partial x}g(t,x)$$

The first two terms on the right-hand side constitute the derivative of $V(t,x)$ along the trajectories of the nominal system, which is negative definite and satisfies (9.4). The third term, $[\partial V/\partial x]g$, is the effect of the perturbation. Since we do not have complete knowledge of g, we cannot judge whether this term helps or hurts the cause of making $\dot{V}(t,x)$ negative definite. With the growth bound (9.6) as our only information on g, the best we can do is worst case analysis where $[\partial V/\partial x]g$ is bounded by a nonnegative term. Using (9.4) through (9.6), we obtain

$$\dot{V}(t,x) \leq -c_3\|x\|^2 + \left\|\frac{\partial V}{\partial x}\right\| \ \|g(t,x)\| \leq -c_3\|x\|^2 + c_4\gamma\|x\|^2$$

If γ is small enough to satisfy the bound

$$\gamma < \frac{c_3}{c_4} \tag{9.7}$$

then

$$\dot{V}(t,x) \leq -(c_3 - \gamma c_4)\|x\|^2, \quad (c_3 - \gamma c_4) > 0$$

Therefore, by Theorem 4.10, we conclude the next lemma.

Lemma 9.1 *Let $x = 0$ be an exponentially stable equilibrium point of the nominal system (9.2). Let $V(t,x)$ be a Lyapunov function of the nominal system that satisfies (9.3) through (9.5) in $[0,\infty) \times D$. Suppose the perturbation term $g(t,x)$ satisfies (9.6) and (9.7). Then, the origin is an exponentially stable equilibrium point of the perturbed system (9.1). Moreover, if all the assumptions hold globally, then the origin is globally exponentially stable.* $\diamond$

This lemma is conceptually important because it shows that exponential stability of the origin is robust with respect to a class of perturbations that satisfy (9.6) and (9.7). To assert this robustness property, we do not have to know $V(t,x)$ explicitly. It is just enough to know that the origin is an exponentially stable equilibrium of the nominal system. Sometimes, we may be able to show that the origin is exponentially stable without actually finding a Lyapunov function that satisfies (9.3) through (9.5).[2] Irrespective of the method we use to show exponential stability of the origin, we can assert the existence of $V(t,x)$ satisfying (9.3) through (9.5) by application of Theorem 4.14 (provided the Jacobian matrix $[\partial f/\partial x]$ is bounded). However, if we do not know the Lyapunov function $V(t,x)$ we cannot calculate the

---

[2]This is the case, for example, when exponential stability of the origin is shown using Theorem 8.5.

bound of (9.7). Consequently, our robustness conclusion becomes a qualitative one where we say that the origin is exponentially stable for all perturbations satisfying

$$\|g(t,x)\| \le \gamma \|x\|$$

with sufficiently small γ. On the other hand, if we know $V(t,x)$, we can calculate the bound of (9.7), which is an additional piece of information. We should be careful not to overemphasize the usefulness of such bounds because they could be conservative for a given perturbation $g(t,x)$. The conservatism is a consequence of the worst case analysis we have adopted from the beginning.

Example 9.1 Consider the system

$$\dot{x} = Ax + g(t,x)$$

where A is Hurwitz and $\|g(t,x)\|_2 \le \gamma \|x\|_2$ for all $t \ge 0$ and all $x \in R^n$. Let $Q = Q^T > 0$ and solve the Lyapunov equation

$$PA + A^T P = -Q$$

for P. From Theorem 4.6, we know that there is a unique solution $P = P^T > 0$. The quadratic Lyapunov function $V(x) = x^T P x$ satisfies (9.3) through (9.5). In particular,

$$\lambda_{\min}(P)\|x\|_2^2 \le V(x) \le \lambda_{\max}(P)\|x\|_2^2$$

$$\frac{\partial V}{\partial x} Ax = -x^T Q x \le -\lambda_{\min}(Q)\|x\|_2^2$$

$$\left\| \frac{\partial V}{\partial x} \right\|_2 = \|2x^T P\|_2 \le 2\|P\|_2 \|x\|_2 = 2\lambda_{\max}(P)\|x\|_2$$

The derivative of $V(x)$ along the trajectories of the perturbed system satisfies

$$\dot{V}(x) \le -\lambda_{\min}(Q)\|x\|_2^2 + 2\lambda_{\max}(P)\gamma\|x\|_2^2$$

Hence, the origin is globally exponentially stable if $\gamma < \lambda_{\min}(Q)/2\lambda_{\max}(P)$. Since this bound depends on the choice of Q, one may wonder how to choose Q to maximize the ratio $\lambda_{\min}(Q)/\lambda_{\max}(P)$. It turns out that this ratio is maximized with the choice $Q = I$ (Exercise 9.1).   △

Example 9.2 Consider the second-order system

$$\dot{x}_1 = x_2$$
$$\dot{x}_2 = -4x_1 - 2x_2 + \beta x_2^3$$

where the constant $\beta \ge 0$ is unknown. We view the system as a perturbed system of the form (9.1) with

$$f(x) = Ax = \begin{bmatrix} 0 & 1 \\ -4 & -2 \end{bmatrix} \begin{bmatrix} x_1 \\ x_2 \end{bmatrix} \quad \text{and} \quad g(x) = \begin{bmatrix} 0 \\ \beta x_2^3 \end{bmatrix}$$

The eigenvalues of A are $-1 \pm j\sqrt{3}$. Hence, A is Hurwitz. The solution of the Lyapunov equation

$$PA + A^T P = -I$$

is given by

$$P = \begin{bmatrix} \frac{3}{2} & \frac{1}{8} \\ \frac{1}{8} & \frac{5}{16} \end{bmatrix}$$

As we saw in Example 9.1, the Lyapunov function $V(x) = x^T P x$ satisfies inequalities (9.3) through (9.5) with $c_3 = 1$ and

$$c_4 = 2\lambda_{\max}(P) = 2 \times 1.513 = 3.026$$

The perturbation term $g(x)$ satisfies

$$\|g(x)\|_2 = \beta|x_2|^3 \le \beta k_2^2 |x_2| \le \beta k_2^2 \|x\|_2$$

for all $|x_2| \le k_2$. At this point in the analysis, we do not know a bound on $x_2(t)$, although we know that $x_2(t)$ will be bounded whenever the trajectory $x(t)$ is confined to a compact set. We keep k_2 undetermined and proceed with the analysis. Using $V(x)$ as a Lyapunov function candidate for the perturbed system, we obtain

$$\dot{V}(x) \le -\|x\|_2^2 + 3.026\beta k_2^2 \|x\|_2^2$$

Hence, $\dot{V}(x)$ will be negative definite if

$$\beta < \frac{1}{3.026 k_2^2}$$

To estimate the bound k_2, let $\Omega_c = \{x \in R^2 \mid V(x) \le c\}$. For any positive constant c, the set Ω_c is closed and bounded. The boundary of Ω_c is the Lyapunov surface

$$V(x) = \tfrac{3}{2}x_1^2 + \tfrac{1}{4}x_1 x_2 + \tfrac{5}{16}x_2^2 = c$$

The largest value of $|x_2|$ on the surface $V(x) = c$ can be determined by differentiating the surface equation partially with respect to x_1. This results in

$$3x_1 + \tfrac{1}{4}x_2 = 0$$

Therefore, the extreme values of x_2 are obtained at the intersection of the line $x_1 = -x_2/12$ with the Lyapunov surface. Simple calculations show that the largest value of x_2^2 on the Lyapunov surface is $96c/29$. Thus, all points inside Ω_c satisfy the bound

$$|x_2| \le k_2, \quad \text{where} \quad k_2^2 = \frac{96c}{29}$$

Therefore, if

$$\beta < \frac{29}{3.026 \times 96c} \approx \frac{0.1}{c}$$

$\dot{V}(x)$ will be negative definite in Ω_c and we can conclude that the origin $x = 0$ is exponentially stable with Ω_c as an estimate of the region of attraction. The inequality $\beta < 0.1/c$ shows a tradeoff between the estimate of the region of attraction and the estimate of the upper bound on β. The smaller the upper bound on β, the larger the estimate of the region of attraction. This tradeoff is not artificial; it does exist in this example. The change of variables

$$
\begin{aligned}
z_1 &= \sqrt{\frac{3\beta}{2}} x_2 \\
z_2 &= \sqrt{\frac{3\beta}{8}} (4x_1 + 2x_2 - \beta x_2^3) = -\sqrt{\frac{3\beta}{8}} \dot{x}_2 \\
\tau &= 2t
\end{aligned}
$$

transforms the state equation into

$$
\begin{aligned}
\frac{dz_1}{d\tau} &= -z_2 \\
\frac{dz_2}{d\tau} &= z_1 + (z_1^2 - 1)z_2
\end{aligned}
$$

which was shown in Example 8.5 to have a bounded region of attraction surrounded by an unstable limit cycle. When transformed into the x-coordinates, the region of attraction will expand with decreasing β and shrink with increasing β. Finally, let us use this example to illustrate our remarks on the conservative nature of the bound of (9.7). Using this bound, we came up with the inequality $\beta < 1/3.026k_2^2$, which allows the perturbation term $g(t, x)$ to be any second-order vector that satisfies $\|g(t,x)\|_2 \le \beta k_2^2 \|x\|_2$. This class of perturbations is more general than the perturbation we have in this specific problem. We have a *structured perturbation* in the sense that the first component of g is always zero, while our analysis allowed for an *unstructured perturbation* where the vector g could change in all directions. Such disregard of the structure of the perturbation will, in general, lead to conservative bounds. Suppose we repeat the analysis, this time taking into consideration the structure of the perturbation. Instead of using the general bound of (9.7), we calculate the derivative of $V(t, x)$ along the trajectories of the perturbed system to obtain

$$
\begin{aligned}
\dot{V}(x) &= -\|x\|_2^2 + 2x^T P g(x) \\
&= -\|x\|_2^2 + 2\beta x_2^2 \left(\tfrac{1}{8} x_1 x_2 + \tfrac{5}{16} x_2^2 \right) \\
&\le -\|x\|_2^2 + 2\beta x_2^2 \left(\tfrac{1}{16} \|x\|_2^2 + \tfrac{5}{16} \|x\|_2^2 \right) \\
&\le -\|x\|_2^2 + \tfrac{3}{4} \beta k_2^2 \|x\|_2^2
\end{aligned}
$$

Hence, $\dot{V}(x)$ is negative definite for $\beta < 4/3k_2^2$. Using, again, the fact that for all $x \in \Omega_c$, $|x_2|^2 \le k_2^2 = 96c/29$, we arrive at the bound $\beta < 0.4/c$, which is four times the bound we obtained by using (9.7). $\triangle$

When the origin of the nominal system (9.2) is uniformly asymptotically stable, but not exponentially stable, the stability analysis of the perturbed system is more involved. Suppose the nominal system has a positive definite, decrescent Lyapunov function $V(t, x)$ that satisfies

$$\frac{\partial V}{\partial t} + \frac{\partial V}{\partial x} f(t, x) \leq -W_3(x)$$

for all $(t, x) \in [0, \infty) \times D$, where $W_3(x)$ is positive definite and continuous. The derivative of V along the trajectories of (9.1) is given by

$$
\begin{aligned}
\dot{V}(t, x) &= \frac{\partial V}{\partial t} + \frac{\partial V}{\partial x} f(t, x) + \frac{\partial V}{\partial x} g(t, x) \\
&\leq -W_3(x) + \left\| \frac{\partial V}{\partial x} g(t, x) \right\|
\end{aligned}
$$

Our task now is to show that

$$\left\| \frac{\partial V}{\partial x} g(t, x) \right\| < W_3(x)$$

for all $(t, x) \in [0, \infty) \times D$, a task that cannot be done by putting a simple order of magnitude bound on $\|g(t, x)\|$, as we have done in the exponential stability case. The growth bound on $\|g(t, x)\|$ will depend on the nature of the Lyapunov function of the nominal system. One class of Lyapunov functions for which the analysis is almost as simple as in exponential stability is the case when $V(t, x)$ is positive definite, decrescent, and satisfies

$$\frac{\partial V}{\partial t} + \frac{\partial V}{\partial x} f(t, x) \leq -c_3 \phi^2(x) \tag{9.8}$$

$$\left\| \frac{\partial V}{\partial x} \right\| \leq c_4 \phi(x) \tag{9.9}$$

for all $(t, x) \in [0, \infty) \times D$ for some positive constants c_3 and c_4, where $\phi : R^n \to R$ is positive definite and continuous. A Lyapunov function satisfying (9.8) and (9.9) is usually called a *quadratic-type* Lyapunov function. It is clear that a Lyapunov function satisfying (9.3) through (9.5) is quadratic type, but a quadratic-type Lyapunov function may exist even when the origin is not exponentially stable. We will illustrate this point shortly by an example. If the nominal system (9.2) has a quadratic-type Lyapunov function $V(t, x)$, then its derivative along the trajectories of (9.1) satisfies

$$\dot{V}(t, x) \leq -c_3 \phi^2(x) + c_4 \phi(x) \|g(t, x)\|$$

Suppose now that the perturbation term satisfies the bound

$$\|g(t, x)\| \leq \gamma \phi(x), \quad \gamma < \frac{c_3}{c_4}$$

Then,

$$\dot{V}(t,x) \leq -(c_3 - c_4\gamma)\phi^2(x)$$

which shows that $\dot{V}(t,x)$ is negative definite.

Example 9.3 Consider the scalar system

$$\dot{x} = -x^3 + g(t,x)$$

The nominal system

$$\dot{x} = -x^3$$

has a globally asymptotically stable equilibrium point at the origin, but, as we saw in Example 4.23, the origin is not exponentially stable. Thus, there is no Lyapunov function that satisfies (9.3) through (9.5). The Lyapunov function $V(x) = x^4$ satisfies (9.8) and (9.9), with $\phi(x) = |x|^3$, $c_3 = 4$, and $c_4 = 4$. Suppose the perturbation term $g(t,x)$ satisfies the bound $|g(t,x)| \leq \gamma|x|^3$ for all x, with $\gamma < 1$. Then, the derivative of V along the trajectories of the perturbed system satisfies

$$\dot{V}(t,x) \leq -4(1-\gamma)\phi^2(x)$$

Hence, the origin is a globally uniformly asymptotically stable equilibrium point of the perturbed system. $\triangle$

In contrast to the case of exponential stability, it is important to notice that a nominal system with uniformly asymptotically stable, but not exponentially stable, origin is not robust to smooth perturbations with arbitrarily small linear growth bounds of the form of (9.6). This point is illustrated by the next example.[3]

Example 9.4 Consider the scalar system of the previous example with perturbation $g = \gamma x$ where $\gamma > 0$; that is,

$$\dot{x} = -x^3 + \gamma x$$

It can be easily seen, via linearization, that for any $\gamma > 0$ the origin is unstable, no matter how small γ is. $\triangle$

9.2   Nonvanishing Perturbation

Let us turn now to the more general case when we do not know that $g(t,0) = 0$. The origin $x = 0$ may not be an equilibrium point of the perturbed system (9.1). We can no longer study stability of the origin as an equilibrium point, nor should we expect the solution of the perturbed system to approach the origin as $t \to \infty$. The best we can hope for is that $x(t)$ will be ultimately bounded by a small bound, if the perturbation term $g(t,x)$ is small in some sense. We start with the case when the origin of the nominal system (9.2) is exponentially stable.

---

[3]See, also, Exercise 9.7.

Lemma 9.2 *Let $x = 0$ be an exponentially stable equilibrium point of the nominal system (9.2). Let $V(t, x)$ be a Lyapunov function of the nominal system that satisfies (9.3) through (9.5) in $[0, \infty) \times D$, where $D = \{x \in R^n \mid \|x\| < r\}$. Suppose the perturbation term $g(t, x)$ satisfies*

$$\|g(t,x)\| \le \delta < \frac{c_3}{c_4}\sqrt{\frac{c_1}{c_2}}\theta r \tag{9.10}$$

for all $t \ge 0$, all $x \in D$, and some positive constant $\theta < 1$. Then, for all $\|x(t_0)\| < \sqrt{c_1/c_2}\,r$, the solution $x(t)$ of the perturbed system (9.1) satisfies

$$\|x(t)\| \le k \exp[-\gamma(t - t_0)]\|x(t_0)\|, \quad \forall\, t_0 \le t < t_0 + T$$

and

$$\|x(t)\| \le b, \quad \forall\, t \ge t_0 + T$$

for some finite T, where

$$k = \sqrt{\frac{c_2}{c_1}}, \quad \gamma = \frac{(1-\theta)c_3}{2c_2}, \quad b = \frac{c_4}{c_3}\sqrt{\frac{c_2}{c_1}}\frac{\delta}{\theta}$$

$\diamond$

Proof: We use $V(t, x)$ as a Lyapunov function candidate for the perturbed system (9.1). The derivative of $V(t, x)$ along the trajectories of (9.1) satisfies

$$
\begin{aligned}
\dot{V}(t,x) &\le -c_3\|x\|^2 + \left\|\frac{\partial V}{\partial x}\right\|\|g(t,x)\| \\
&\le -c_3\|x\|^2 + c_4\delta\|x\| \\
&= -(1-\theta)c_3\|x\|^2 - \theta c_3\|x\|^2 + c_4\delta\|x\|, \quad 0 < \theta < 1 \\
&\le -(1-\theta)c_3\|x\|^2, \quad \forall\, \|x\| \ge \delta c_4/\theta c_3
\end{aligned}
$$

Applying Theorem 4.18 and Exercise 4.51 completes the proof. $\square$

Note that the ultimate bound b in Lemma 9.2 is proportional to the upper bound on the perturbation δ. Once again, this result can be viewed as a robustness property of nominal systems having exponentially stable equilibria at the origin, because it shows that arbitrarily small (uniformly bounded) perturbations will not result in large steady-state deviations from the origin.

Example 9.5 Consider the second-order system

$$
\begin{aligned}
\dot{x}_1 &= x_2 \\
\dot{x}_2 &= -4x_1 - 2x_2 + \beta x_2^3 + d(t)
\end{aligned}
$$

where $\beta \ge 0$ is unknown and $d(t)$ is a uniformly bounded disturbance that satisfies $|d(t)| \le \delta$ for all $t \ge 0$. This is the same system we studied in Example 9.2, except for the additional perturbation term $d(t)$. Again, the system can be viewed as a perturbation of a nominal linear system that has a Lyapunov function $V(x) = x^T P x$, where

$$
P = \begin{bmatrix} \frac{3}{2} & \frac{1}{8} \\[2mm] \frac{1}{8} & \frac{5}{16} \end{bmatrix}
$$

We use $V(x)$ as a Lyapunov function candidate for the perturbed system, but we treat the two perturbation terms βx_2^3 and $d(t)$ differently, since the first term vanishes at the origin while the second one does not. Calculating the derivative of $V(x)$ along the trajectories of the perturbed system, we obtain

$$
\begin{aligned}
\dot{V}(t,x) &= -\|x\|_2^2 + 2\beta x_2^2 \left(\tfrac{1}{8} x_1 x_2 + \tfrac{5}{16} x_2^2 \right) + 2d(t) \left(\tfrac{1}{8} x_1 + \tfrac{5}{16} x_2 \right) \\
&\leq -\|x\|_2^2 + \tfrac{3}{4}\beta k_2^2 \|x\|_2^2 + \frac{\sqrt{29}\delta}{8} \|x\|_2
\end{aligned}
$$

where we have used the inequality

$$
|2x_1 + 5x_2| \leq \|x\|_2 \sqrt{4 + 25}
$$

and k_2 is an upper bound on $|x_2|$. Suppose $\beta \leq 4(1 - \zeta)/3k_2^2$, where $0 < \zeta < 1$. Then,

$$
\dot{V}(t,x) \leq -\zeta\|x\|_2^2 + \frac{\sqrt{29}\delta}{8} \|x\|_2 \leq -(1 - \theta)\zeta\|x\|_2^2, \quad \forall\ \|x\|_2 \geq \mu = \frac{\sqrt{29}\delta}{8\zeta\theta}
$$

where $0 < \theta < 1$. As we saw in Example 9.2, $|x_2|^2$ is bounded on Ω_c by $96c/29$. Thus, if $\beta \leq 0.4(1 - \zeta)/c$ and δ is so small that $\mu^2 \lambda_{\max}(P) < c$, then $B_\mu \subset \Omega_c$ and all trajectories starting inside Ω_c remain for all future time in Ω_c. Furthermore, the conditions of Theorem 4.18 are satisfied in Ω_c. Therefore, the solutions of the perturbed system are uniformly ultimately bounded by

$$
b = \frac{\sqrt{29}\delta}{8\zeta\theta} \sqrt{\frac{\lambda_{\max}(P)}{\lambda_{\min}(P)}}
$$

$\triangle$

In the more general case when the origin $x = 0$ is a uniformly asymptotically stable equilibrium point of the nominal system (9.2), rather than exponentially stable, the analysis of the perturbed system proceeds in a similar manner.

Lemma 9.3 *Let $x = 0$ be a uniformly asymptotically stable equilibrium point of the nominal system (9.2). Let $V(t,x)$ be a Lyapunov function of the nominal system that satisfies the inequalities*[4]

$$
\alpha_1(\|x\|) \leq V(t,x) \leq \alpha_2(\|x\|) \tag{9.11}
$$

---

[4]The existence of a Lyapunov function satisfying these inequalities (on a bounded domain) is guaranteed by Theorem 4.16 under some additional assumptions.

$$\frac{\partial V}{\partial t} + \frac{\partial V}{\partial x} f(t,x) \leq -\alpha_3(\|x\|) \tag{9.12}$$

$$\left\|\frac{\partial V}{\partial x}\right\| \leq \alpha_4(\|x\|) \tag{9.13}$$

in $[0,\infty) \times D$, *where* $D = \{x \in R^n \mid \|x\| < r\}$ *and* $\alpha_i(\cdot)$, $i = 1,2,3,4$, *are class* $\mathcal{K}$ *functions. Suppose the perturbation term* $g(t,x)$ *satisfies the uniform bound*

$$\|g(t,x)\| \leq \delta < \frac{\theta\alpha_3(\alpha_2^{-1}(\alpha_1(r)))}{\alpha_4(r)} \tag{9.14}$$

for all $t \geq 0$, *all* $x \in D$, *and some positive constant* $\theta < 1$. *Then, for all* $\|x(t_0)\| < \alpha_2^{-1}(\alpha_1(r))$, *the solution* $x(t)$ *of the perturbed system* (9.1) *satisfies*

$$\|x(t)\| \leq \beta(\|x(t_0)\|, t - t_0), \quad \forall\, t_0 \leq t < t_0 + T$$

and

$$\|x(t)\| \leq \rho(\delta), \quad \forall\, t \geq t_0 + T$$

for some class $\mathcal{KL}$ *function* β *and some finite* T, *where* ρ *is a class* $\mathcal{K}$ *function of* δ *defined by*

$$\rho(\delta) = \alpha_1^{-1}\left(\alpha_2\left(\alpha_3^{-1}\left(\frac{\delta\alpha_4(r)}{\theta}\right)\right)\right)$$

$\diamond$

Proof: We use $V(t,x)$ as a Lyapunov function candidate for the perturbed system (9.1). The derivative of $V(t,x)$ along the trajectories of (9.1) satisfies

$$\begin{aligned}
\dot{V}(t,x) &\leq -\alpha_3(\|x\|) + \left\|\frac{\partial V}{\partial x}\right\| \|g(t,x)\| \\
&\leq -\alpha_3(\|x\|) + \delta\alpha_4(\|x\|) \\
&\leq -(1-\theta)\alpha_3(\|x\|) - \theta\alpha_3(\|x\|) + \delta\alpha_4(r), \quad 0 < \theta < 1 \\
&\leq -(1-\theta)\alpha_3(\|x\|), \quad \forall\, \|x\| \geq \alpha_3^{-1}\left(\frac{\delta\alpha_4(r)}{\theta}\right)
\end{aligned}$$

Applying Theorem 4.18 completes the proof. $\square$

This lemma is similar to the one we arrived at in the special case of exponential stability. However, there is an important feature of our analysis in the case of exponential stability, which has no counterpart in the more general case of uniform asymptotic stability. In the case of exponential stability, δ is required to satisfy (9.10). The right-hand side of (9.10) approaches ∞ as $r \to \infty$. Therefore, if the assumptions hold globally, we can conclude that *for all uniformly bounded disturbances, the solution of the perturbed system will be uniformly bounded.* This is the case because, for any δ, we can choose r large enough to satisfy (9.10). In the case of uniform asymptotic stability, δ is required to satisfy (9.14). Inspection of (9.14) shows that, without further information about the class $\mathcal{K}$ functions, we cannot say anything about the limit of the right-hand side as $r \to \infty$. Thus, we cannot conclude that uniformly bounded perturbations of a nominal system with a uniformly asymptotically stable equilibrium at the origin will have bounded solutions irrespective of the size of the perturbation. Of course the fact that we cannot show it, does not mean it is not true. It turns out, however, that such a statement is not true. It is possible to construct examples (Exercise 9.13) where the origin is globally uniformly asymptotically stable, but a bounded perturbation could drive the solution of the perturbed system to infinity.

9.3   Comparison Method

Consider the perturbed system (9.1). Let $V(t, x)$ be a Lyapunov function for the nominal system (9.2) and suppose the derivative of V along the trajectories of (9.1) satisfies the differential inequality

$$\dot{V} \leq h(t, V)$$

By (the comparison) Lemma 3.4,

$$V(t, x(t)) \leq y(t)$$

where $y(t)$ is the solution of the differential equation

$$\dot{y} = h(t, y), \quad y(t_0) = V(t_0, x(t_0))$$

This approach is particularly useful when the differential inequality is linear, that is, when $h(t, V) = a(t)V + b(t)$, for then we can write down a closed-form expression for the solution of the first-order linear differential equation of y. Arriving at a linear differential inequality is possible when the origin of the nominal system (9.2) is exponentially stable.

Let $V(t, x)$ be a Lyapunov function of the nominal system (9.2) that satisfies (9.3) through (9.5) for all $(t, x) \in [0, \infty) \times D$, where $D = \{x \in R^n \mid \|x\| < r\}$. Suppose the perturbation term $g(t, x)$ satisfies the bound

$$\|g(t, x)\| \leq \gamma(t)\|x\| + \delta(t), \quad \forall\, t \geq 0,\ \forall\, x \in D \tag{9.15}$$

where $\gamma : R \to R$ is nonnegative and continuous for all $t \geq 0$, and $\delta : R \to R$ is nonnegative, continuous, and bounded for all $t \geq 0$. The derivative of V along the trajectories of (9.1) satisfies

$$
\begin{aligned}
\dot{V}(t, x) &= \frac{\partial V}{\partial t} + \frac{\partial V}{\partial x} f(t, x) + \frac{\partial V}{\partial x} g(t, x) \\
&\leq -c_3 \|x\|^2 + \left\| \frac{\partial V}{\partial x} \right\| \, \|g(t, x)\| \\
&\leq -c_3 \|x\|^2 + c_4 \gamma(t) \|x\|^2 + c_4 \delta(t) \|x\|
\end{aligned}
\tag{9.16}
$$

Using (9.3), we can find an upper bound on $\dot{V}$ as

$$\dot{V} \leq -\left[\frac{c_3}{c_2} - \frac{c_4}{c_1}\gamma(t)\right]V + c_4\delta(t)\sqrt{\frac{V}{c_1}}$$

To obtain a linear differential inequality, we take $W(t) = \sqrt{V(t, x(t))}$ and use the fact $\dot{W} = \dot{V}/2\sqrt{V}$, when $V \neq 0$, to obtain

$$\dot{W} \leq -\frac{1}{2}\left[\frac{c_3}{c_2} - \frac{c_4}{c_1}\gamma(t)\right]W + \frac{c_4}{2\sqrt{c_1}}\delta(t) \tag{9.17}$$

When $V = 0$, it can be shown[5] that $D^+W(t) \leq c_4\delta(t)/2\sqrt{c_1}$. Hence, $D^+W(t)$ satisfies (9.17) for all values of V. By the comparison lemma, $W(t)$ satisfies the inequality

$$W(t) \leq \phi(t, t_0)W(t_0) + \frac{c_4}{2\sqrt{c_1}}\int_{t_0}^{t}\phi(t, \tau)\delta(\tau)\,d\tau \tag{9.18}$$

where the transition function $\phi(t, t_0)$ is given by

$$\phi(t, t_0) = \exp\left[-\frac{c_3}{2c_2}(t - t_0) + \frac{c_4}{2c_1}\int_{t_0}^{t}\gamma(\tau)\,d\tau\right]$$

Using (9.3) in (9.18), we obtain

$$\|x(t)\| \leq \sqrt{\frac{c_2}{c_1}}\phi(t, t_0)\|x(t_0)\| + \frac{c_4}{2c_1}\int_{t_0}^{t}\phi(t, \tau)\delta(\tau)\,d\tau \tag{9.19}$$

Suppose now that $\gamma(t)$ satisfies the condition

$$\int_{t_0}^{t}\gamma(\tau)\,d\tau \leq \varepsilon(t - t_0) + \eta \tag{9.20}$$

for some nonnegative constants ε and η, where

$$\varepsilon < \frac{c_1 c_3}{c_2 c_4} \tag{9.21}$$

Defining the constants α and ρ by

$$\alpha = \frac{1}{2}\left[\frac{c_3}{c_2} - \varepsilon\frac{c_4}{c_1}\right] > 0, \quad \rho = \exp\left(\frac{c_4\eta}{2c_1}\right) \geq 1 \tag{9.22}$$

and using (9.20) and (9.21) in (9.19), we obtain

$$\|x(t)\| \leq \sqrt{\frac{c_2}{c_1}}\rho\|x(t_0)\|e^{-\alpha(t - t_0)} + \frac{c_4\rho}{2c_1}\int_{t_0}^{t}e^{-\alpha(t - \tau)}\delta(\tau)\,d\tau \tag{9.23}$$

---

[5]See Exercise 9.14.

For this bound to be valid, we must ensure that $\|x(t)\| < r$ for all $t \geq t_0$. Noting that[6]

$$
\begin{aligned}
\|x(t)\| &\leq \sqrt{\frac{c_2}{c_1}} \rho \|x(t_0)\| e^{-\alpha(t-t_0)} + \frac{c_4 \rho}{2\alpha c_1} \left[1 - e^{-\alpha(t-t_0)} \right] \sup_{t \geq t_0} \delta(t) \\
&\leq \max \left\{ \sqrt{\frac{c_2}{c_1}} \rho \|x(t_0)\|, \ \frac{c_4 \rho}{2\alpha c_1} \sup_{t \geq t_0} \delta(t) \right\}
\end{aligned}
$$

we see that the condition $\|x(t)\| < r$ will be satisfied if

$$
\|x(t_0)\| < \frac{r}{\rho} \sqrt{\frac{c_1}{c_2}} \tag{9.24}
$$

and

$$
\sup_{t \geq t_0} \delta(t) < \frac{2c_1 \alpha r}{c_4 \rho} \tag{9.25}
$$

For easy reference, we summarize our findings in the next lemma.

Lemma 9.4 *Let $x = 0$ be an exponentially stable equilibrium point of the nominal system (9.2). Let $V(t, x)$ be a Lyapunov function of the nominal system that satisfies (9.3) through (9.5) in $[0, \infty) \times D$, where $D = \{ x \in R^n \mid \|x\|_2 < r \}$. Suppose the perturbation term $g(t, x)$ satisfies (9.15), where $\gamma(t)$ satisfies (9.20) and (9.21). Then, provided $x(t_0)$ satisfies (9.24) and $\sup_{t \geq t_0} \delta(t)$ satisfies (9.25), the solution of the perturbed system (9.1) satisfies (9.23). Furthermore, if all the assumptions hold globally, then (9.23) is satisfied for any $x(t_0)$ and any bounded $\delta(t)$.*   ◇

Specializing the foregoing lemma to the case of vanishing perturbations; that is, when $\delta(t) \equiv 0$, we obtain the following result:

Corollary 9.1 *Let $x = 0$ be an exponentially stable equilibrium point of the nominal system (9.2). Let $V(t, x)$ be a Lyapunov function of the nominal system that satisfies (9.3) through (9.5) in $[0, \infty) \times D$. Suppose the perturbation term $g(t, x)$ satisfies*

$$
\|g(t, x)\| \leq \gamma(t) \|x\|
$$

where $\gamma(t)$ satisfies (9.20) and (9.21). Then, the origin is an exponentially stable equilibrium point of the perturbed system (9.1). Moreover, if all the assumptions hold globally, then the origin is globally exponentially stable.   ◇

If $\gamma(t) \equiv \gamma = \text{constant}$, then Corollary 9.1 requires γ to satisfy the bound $\gamma < c_1 c_3 / c_2 c_4$, which has no advantage over the bound $\gamma < c_3 / c_4$ required by Lemma 9.1, since $(c_1/c_2) \leq 1$. In fact, whenever $(c_1/c_2) < 1$, the current bound will be more conservative (that is, smaller) than the bound required by Lemma 9.1. The advantage of Corollary 9.1 is seen in the case when the integral of $\gamma(t)$ satisfies conditions (9.20) and (9.21), even when $\sup_{t \geq t_0} \gamma(t)$ is not small enough to satisfy $\sup_{t \geq t_0} \gamma(t) < c_3 / c_4$. Three such cases are given in the next lemma.

---

[6]We use the fact that the function $ae^{-\alpha t} + b(1 - e^{-\alpha t})$, with positive a, b, and α, relaxes monotonically from its initial value a to its final value b. Hence, it is bounded by the maximum of the two numbers.

Lemma 9.5

    1. If

$$\int_0^\infty \gamma(\tau) \, d\tau \leq k$$

    then (9.20) is satisfied with $\varepsilon = 0$ and $\eta = k$.

    2. If

$$\gamma(t) \to 0 \quad \text{as} \quad t \to \infty$$

    then for any $\varepsilon > 0$, there is $\eta = \eta(\varepsilon) > 0$ such that (9.20) is satisfied.

    3. If there are constants $\Delta > 0$, $T \geq 0$, and $\varepsilon_1 > 0$ such that

$$\frac{1}{\Delta} \int_t^{t+\Delta} \gamma(\tau) \, d\tau \leq \varepsilon_1, \quad \forall \, t \geq T$$

    then (9.20) is satisfied with $\varepsilon = \varepsilon_1$ and $\eta = \varepsilon_1 \Delta + \int_0^T \gamma(t) \, dt$. $\diamond$

Proof: The first case is obvious. To prove the second case, note that, because $\lim_{t\to\infty} \gamma(t) = 0$, for any $\varepsilon > 0$, there is $T_1 = T_1(\varepsilon) > 0$ such that $\gamma(t) < \varepsilon$ for all $t \geq T_1$. Let $\eta = \int_0^{T_1} \gamma(t) \, dt$. If $t_0 \geq T_1$, then

$$\int_{t_0}^t \gamma(\tau) \, d\tau \leq \int_{t_0}^t \varepsilon \, d\tau = \varepsilon(t - t_0)$$

If $t \leq T_1$, then

$$\int_{t_0}^t \gamma(\tau) \, d\tau \leq \int_0^{T_1} \gamma(\tau) \, d\tau = \eta$$

If $t_0 \leq T_1 \leq t$, then

$$\int_{t_0}^t \gamma(\tau) \, d\tau = \int_{t_0}^{T_1} \gamma(\tau) \, d\tau + \int_{T_1}^t \gamma(\tau) \, d\tau$$

$$\leq \int_0^{T_1} \gamma(\tau) \, d\tau + \varepsilon(t - T_1) \leq \eta + \varepsilon(t - t_0)$$

In the last case, if $t \leq T$, then

$$\int_{t_0}^t \gamma(\tau) \, d\tau \leq \int_0^T \gamma(\tau) \, d\tau < \eta$$

For $t \geq t_1 \geq T$, let N be the integer for which $(N-1)\Delta \leq t - t_1 \leq N\Delta$. Then,

$$\int_{t_1}^t \gamma(\tau) \, d\tau = \sum_{i=0}^{i=N-2} \int_{t_1+i\Delta}^{t_1+(i+1)\Delta} \gamma(\tau) \, d\tau + \int_{t_1+(N-1)\Delta}^t \gamma(\tau) \, d\tau$$

$$\leq \sum_{i=0}^{i=N-2} \varepsilon_1 \Delta + \varepsilon_1 \Delta \leq \varepsilon_1(t - t_1) + \varepsilon_1 \Delta$$

This inequality is used next with $t_1 = t_0$ when $t \geq t_0 \geq T$, and with $t_1 = T$ when $t_0 \leq T \leq t$. If $t \geq t_0 \geq T$, then

$$\int_{t_0}^{t} \gamma(\tau) \, d\tau \leq \varepsilon_1(t - t_0) + \varepsilon_1 \Delta \;\; < \;\; \varepsilon_1(t - t_0) + \eta$$

while if $t_0 \leq T \leq t$, then

$$\int_{t_0}^{t} \gamma(\tau) \, d\tau \;\; = \;\; \int_{t_0}^{T} \gamma(\tau) \, d\tau + \int_{T}^{t} \gamma(\tau) \, d\tau$$

$$\leq \;\; \int_{0}^{T} \gamma(\tau) \, d\tau + \varepsilon_1(t - T) + \varepsilon_1 \Delta \leq \varepsilon_1(t - t_0) + \eta$$

$\Box$

In the first case of the foregoing lemma, condition (9.20) is satisfied with $\varepsilon = 0$, while in the second case, it is satisfied with arbitrarily small ε. Therefore, in both cases, condition (9.21) is always satisfied and the origin of the perturbed system (9.2) is exponentially stable. The third case of the lemma sets a bound on a *moving average* of $\gamma(t)$ as t becomes sufficiently large. The origin of the perturbed system (9.2) will be exponentially stable if this bound is sufficiently small.

Example 9.6 Consider the linear system

$$\dot{x} = [A(t) + B(t)]x$$

where $A(t)$ and $B(t)$ are continuous and $A(t)$ is bounded on $[0, \infty)$. Suppose the origin is an exponentially stable equilibrium point of the nominal system

$$\dot{x} = A(t)x$$

and

$$B(t) \to 0 \text{ as } t \to \infty$$

From Theorem 4.12, we know that there is a quadratic Lyapunov function $V(t, x) = x^T P(t)x$ that satisfies (9.3) through (9.5) globally. The perturbation term $B(t)x$ satisfies the inequality

$$\|B(t)x\| \leq \|B(t)\| \, \|x\|$$

Since $\|B(t)\| \to 0$ as $t \to \infty$, we conclude from Corollary 9.1 and the second case of Lemma 9.5 that the origin is a globally exponentially stable equilibrium point of the perturbed system. $\triangle$

Similar conclusions can be drawn when $\int_0^\infty \|B(t)\| \, dt < \infty$ (Exercise 9.15) and $\int_0^\infty \|B(t)\|^2 \, dt < \infty$ (Exercise 9.16).

In the case of nonvanishing perturbations, that is, when $\delta(t) \not\equiv 0$, the next lemma states a number of conclusions concerning the asymptotic behavior of $x(t)$ as $t \to \infty$.

Lemma 9.6 *Suppose the conditions of Lemma 9.4 are satisfied, and let $x(t)$ denote the solution of the perturbed system (9.1).*

1. *If*

$$\int_{t_0}^{t} e^{-\alpha(t-\tau)} \delta(\tau) \, d\tau \leq \beta, \quad \forall \ t \geq t_0$$

for some positive constant β, then $x(t)$ is uniformly ultimately bounded with the ultimate bound

$$b = \frac{c_4 \rho \beta}{2 c_1 \theta}$$

where $\theta \in (0, 1)$ is an arbitrary constant.

2. *If*

$$\lim_{t \to \infty} \delta(t) = \delta_\infty > 0$$

then $x(t)$ is uniformly ultimately bounded with the ultimate bound

$$b = \frac{c_4 \rho \delta_\infty}{2 \alpha c_1 \theta}$$

where $\theta \in (0, 1)$ is an arbitrary constant.

3. *If*

$$\lim_{t \to \infty} \delta(t) = 0, \quad \text{then} \quad \lim_{t \to \infty} x(t) = 0$$

If the conditions of Lemma 9.4 are satisfied globally, then the foregoing statements hold for any initial state $x(t_0)$. $\diamond$

Proof: All three cases follow easily from inequality (9.23). In the first two cases, we use the property that if $u(t) = w(t) + a$ with $a > 0$ and $\lim_{t \to \infty} w(t) = 0$, then $u(t)$ is ultimately bounded by a/θ for any positive $\theta < 1$. This is so because there is a finite time T such that $|w(t)| \leq a(1 - \theta)/\theta$ for all $t \geq T$. In the last two cases, we use the property that if $u(t) = \int_{t_0}^{t} \exp(-\alpha(t - \tau)) w(\tau) \, d\tau$ where $w(t)$ is bounded and $\lim_{t \to \infty} w(t) = w_\infty$, then $\lim_{t \to \infty} u(t) = w_\infty/\alpha$.[7] $\square$

9.4   Continuity of Solutions on the Infinite Interval

In Section 3.2, we studied continuous dependence of the solution of the state equation on initial states and parameters. In particular, in Theorem 3.4, we examined the nominal system

$$\dot{x} = f(t, x) \tag{9.26}$$

---

[7] See [33, Theorem 3.3.2.33].

and the perturbed system

$$\dot{x} = f(t, x) + g(t, x) \tag{9.27}$$

under the assumption that $\|g(t, x)\| \leq \delta$ in the domain of interest. Using the Gronwall–Bellman inequality, we found that if $y(t)$ and $z(t)$ are well-defined solutions of the nominal and perturbed systems, respectively, then

$$\|y(t) - z(t)\| \leq \|y(t_0) - z(t_0)\| \exp[L(t - t_0)] + \frac{\delta}{L}\{\exp[L(t - t_0)] - 1\} \tag{9.28}$$

where L is a Lipschitz constant for f. This bound is valid only on compact time intervals, since the exponential term $\exp[L(t - t_0)]$ grows unbounded as $t \to \infty$. In fact, the bound is useful only on an interval $[t_0, t_1]$ where t_1 is reasonably small, for if t_1 is large, the bound will be too large to be of any use. This is not surprising, because in Section 3.2, we did not impose any stability conditions on the system. In this section, we use Lemma 9.4 to calculate a bound on the error between the solutions of (9.26) and (9.27) that is valid uniformly in t for all $t \geq t_0$.

Theorem 9.1 *Let $D \subset R^n$ be domain that contains the origin and suppose*

- *$f(t, x)$ and its first partial derivatives with respect to x are continuous, bounded, and Lipschitz in x, uniformly in t, for all $(t, x) \in [0, \infty) \times D_0$, for every compact set $D_0 \subset D$;*

- *$g(t, x)$ is piecewise continuous in t, locally Lipschitz in x, and*

$$\|g(t, x)\| \leq \delta, \quad \forall \ (t, x) \in [0, \infty) \times D \tag{9.29}$$

- *the origin $x = 0$ is an exponentially stable equilibrium point of the nominal system (9.26);*

- *there is a Lyapunov function $V(t, x)$ that satisfies the conditions of Theorem 4.9 for the nominal system (9.26) for $(t, x) \in [0, \infty) \times D$ and $\{W_1(x) \leq c\}$ is a compact subset of D.*

Let $y(t)$ and $z(t)$ denote solutions of the nominal system (9.26) and the perturbed system (9.27), respectively. Then, for each compact set $\Omega \subset \{W_2(x) \leq \rho c, \ 0 < \rho < 1\}$, there exist positive constants β, γ, η, μ, and k, independent of δ, such that if $y(t_0) \in \Omega$, $\delta < \eta$, and $\|z(t_0) - y(t_0)\| < \mu$, the solutions $y(t)$ and $z(t)$ will be uniformly bounded for all $t \geq t_0 \geq 0$ and

$$\|z(t) - y(t)\| \leq ke^{-\gamma(t - t_0)}\|z(t_0) - y(t_0)\| + \beta\delta \tag{9.30}$$

$\diamond$

While the origin is exponentially stable, the Lyapunov function V is required to satisfy the conditions of uniform asymptotic stability, rather than (the more stringent) conditions of exponential stability. This provides less conservative estimates of the set Ω. When the nominal system (9.26) is autonomous, the function V is provided by (the converse Lyapunov) Theorem 4.17 and the set Ω can be any compact subset of the region of attraction. Exponential stability is used only locally when the error $z(t) - y(t)$ is sufficiently small.

Proof of Theorem 9.1: The derivative of V along the trajectories of the perturbed system (9.27) satisfies

$$\dot{V} = \frac{\partial V}{\partial t} + \frac{\partial V}{\partial x} f(t, x) + \frac{\partial V}{\partial x} g(t, x) \leq -W_3(x) + k_1 \delta$$

for all $x \in \{W_1(x) \leq c\}$, where k_1 is an upper bound on $\partial V / \partial x$ over $\{W_1(x) \leq c\}$. Let $k_2 > 0$ be the minimum of $W_3(x)$ over the compact set $\Lambda = \{W_1(x) \leq c \text{ and } W_2(x) \geq c\}$. Then

$$\dot{V} \leq -\tfrac{1}{2} W_3(x) - \tfrac{1}{2} k_2 + k_1 \delta \leq -\tfrac{1}{2} W_3(x), \quad \forall\, x \in \Lambda, \ \forall\, \delta \leq \frac{k_2}{2k_1}$$

This shows that $\dot{V}$ is negative on $V(t, x) = c$; hence the set $\{V(t, x) \leq c\}$ is positively invariant. Therefore, for all $z(t_0) \in \{W_2(x) \leq c\}$, the solution $z(t)$ of (9.27) is uniformly bounded. Since Ω is in the interior of $\{W_2(x) \leq c\}$, there is $\mu_1 > 0$ such that $z(t_0) \in \{W_2(x) \leq c\}$ whenever $y(t_0) \in \Omega$ and $\|z(t_0) - y(t_0)\| \leq \mu_1$. It is also clear that for $y(t_0) \in \Omega$, $y(t)$ is uniformly bounded and $y(t) \to 0$ as $t \to \infty$, uniformly in t_0. The error $e(t) = z(t) - y(t)$ satisfies the equation

$$\dot{e} = \dot{z} - \dot{y} = f(t, z) + g(t, z) - f(t, y) = f(t, e) + \Delta(t, e) + g(t, z) \qquad (9.31)$$

where

$$\Delta(t, e) = f(t, y(t) + e) - f(t, y(t)) - f(t, e)$$

We analyze the error equation (9.31) over the ball $\{\|e\| \leq r\} \subset D$. Equation (9.31) can be viewed as a perturbation of the system

$$\dot{e} = f(t, e)$$

whose origin is exponentially stable. By Theorem 4.14, there exists a Lyapunov function $V(t, e)$ that satisfies (9.3) through (9.5) for $\|e\| < r_0 < r$. By the mean value theorem, the error term Δ_i can be written as

$$\Delta_i(t, e) = \left[\frac{\partial f_i}{\partial x}(t, \lambda_1 e + y) - \frac{\partial f_i}{\partial x}(t, \lambda_2 e) \right] e$$

where $0 < \lambda_i < 1$. Since the Jacobian matrix $[\partial f / \partial x]$ is Lipschitz in x, uniformly in t, the perturbation term $(\Delta + g)$ satisfies

$$\|\Delta(t, e) + g(t, z)\| \leq L_1 \|e\|^2 + L_2 \|e\| \, \|y(t)\| + \delta$$

where $y(t) \to 0$ as $t \to \infty$, uniformly in t_0. Consequently,

$$\|\Delta(t,e) + g(t,z)\| \leq \{L_1 r_1 + L_2 \|y(t)\|\} \|e\| + \delta$$

for all $\|e\| \leq r_1 < r_0$. This inequality takes the form (9.15) with

$$\gamma(t) = \{L_1 r_1 + L_2 \|y(t)\|\} \quad \text{and} \quad \delta(t) \equiv \delta$$

Given any $\varepsilon_1 > 0$, there is $T_1 > 0$ such that $\|y(t)\| \leq \varepsilon_1$ for all $t \geq t_0 + T_1$. Therefore, (9.20) is satisfied with

$$\int_{t_0}^{t} \gamma(\tau)\, d\tau \leq (\varepsilon_1 + L_1 r_1)(t - t_0) + T_1 \max_{t \geq t_0} L_2 \|y(t)\|$$

By taking ε_1 and r_1 small enough, we can satisfy (9.21). Thus, all the assumptions of Lemma 9.4 are satisfied and (9.30) follows from (9.23).   □

9.5   Interconnected Systems

When we analyze the stability of a nonlinear dynamical system, the complexity of the analysis grows rapidly as the order of the system increases. This situation motivates us to look for ways to simplify the analysis. If the system can be modeled as an interconnection of lower order subsystems, then we may pursue the stability analysis in two steps. In the first step, we decompose the system into smaller isolated subsystems by ignoring interconnections, and analyze the stability of each subsystem. In the second step, we combine our conclusions from the first step with information about the interconnections to draw conclusions about the stability of the interconnected system. In this section, we illustrate how this idea can be utilized in searching for Lyapunov functions for interconnected systems.

Consider the interconnected system

$$\dot{x}_i = f_i(t, x_i) + g_i(t, x), \quad i = 1, 2, \ldots, m \tag{9.32}$$

where $x_i \in R^{n_i}$, $n_1 + \cdots + n_m = n$, and $x = \left[x_1^T, \ldots, x_m^T\right]^T$. Suppose f_i and g_i are smooth enough to ensure local existence and uniqueness of the solution for all initial conditions in a domain of interest, and that

$$f_i(t, 0) = 0, \quad g_i(t, 0) = 0, \quad \forall\, i$$

so that the origin $x = 0$ is an equilibrium point of the system. Ignoring the interconnection terms g_i, the system decomposes into m isolated subsystems:

$$\dot{x}_i = f_i(t, x_i) \tag{9.33}$$

with each one having an equilibrium point at its origin $x_i = 0$. We start by searching for Lyapunov functions that establish uniform asymptotic stability of the origin for each isolated subsystem. Suppose this search has been successful and that, for each subsystem, we have a positive definite decrescent Lyapunov function $V_i(t, x_i)$ whose derivative along the trajectories of the isolated subsystem (9.33) is negative definite. The function

$$V(t, x) = \sum_{i=1}^{m} d_i V_i(t, x_i), \quad d_i > 0$$

is a *composite Lyapunov function* for the collection of the m isolated subsystems for all values of the positive constants d_i. Viewing the interconnected system (9.32) as a perturbation of the isolated subsystems (9.33), it is reasonable to try $V(t, x)$ as a Lyapunov function candidate for (9.32). The derivative of $V(t, x)$ along the trajectories of (9.32) is given by

$$\dot{V}(t, x) = \sum_{i=1}^{m} d_i \left[\frac{\partial V_i}{\partial t} + \frac{\partial V_i}{\partial x_i} f_i(t, x_i) \right] + \sum_{i=1}^{m} d_i \frac{\partial V_i}{\partial x_i} g_i(t, x)$$

The first term on the right-hand side is negative definite by virtue of the fact that V_i is a Lyapunov function for the ith isolated subsystem, but the second term is, in general, indefinite. The situation is similar to our earlier investigation of perturbed systems in Section 9.1. Therefore, we may approach the problem by performing worst case analysis where the term $[\partial V_i / \partial x_i] g_i$ is bounded by a nonnegative upper bound. Let us illustrate the idea by using quadratic-type Lyapunov functions, introduced in Section 9.1. Suppose that, for $i = 1, 2, \ldots, m$, $V_i(t, x_i)$ satisfies

$$\frac{\partial V_i}{\partial t} + \frac{\partial V_i}{\partial x_i} f_i(t, x_i) \leq -\alpha_i \phi_i^2(x_i) \tag{9.34}$$

$$\left\| \frac{\partial V_i}{\partial x_i} \right\| \leq \beta_i \phi_i(x_i) \tag{9.35}$$

for all $t \geq 0$ and $\|x\| < r$ for some positive constants α_i and β_i, where $\phi_i : R^{n_i} \to R$ are positive definite and continuous. Furthermore, suppose that the interconnection terms $g_i(t, x)$ satisfy the bound

$$\|g_i(t, x)\| \leq \sum_{j=1}^{m} \gamma_{ij} \phi_j(x_j) \tag{9.36}$$

for all $t \geq 0$ and $\|x\| < r$ for some nonnegative constants γ_{ij}. Then, the derivative of $V(t, x) = \sum_{i=1}^{m} d_i V_i(t, x_i)$ along the trajectories of the interconnected system (9.32) satisfies the inequality

$$\dot{V}(t, x) \leq \sum_{i=1}^{m} d_i \left[-\alpha_i \phi_i^2(x_i) + \sum_{j=1}^{m} \beta_i \gamma_{ij} \phi_i(x_i) \phi_j(x_j) \right]$$

The right-hand side is a quadratic form in $\phi_1, \ldots, \phi_m$, which we rewrite as

$$\dot{V}(t,x) \leq -\tfrac{1}{2}\phi^T(DS + S^T D)\phi$$

where

$$\phi = [\phi_1, \ldots, \phi_m]^T, \qquad D = \text{diag}\,(d_1, \ldots, d_m)$$

and S is an $m \times m$ matrix whose elements are defined by

$$s_{ij} = \begin{cases} \alpha_i - \beta_i \gamma_{ii}, & i = j \\[2mm] -\beta_i \gamma_{ij}, & i \neq j \end{cases} \tag{9.37}$$

If there is a positive diagonal matrix D such that

$$DS + S^T D > 0$$

then $\dot{V}(t,x)$ is negative definite, since $\phi(x) = 0$ if and only if $x = 0$; recall that $\phi_i(x_i)$ is a positive definite function of x_i. Thus, a sufficient condition for uniform asymptotic stability of the origin as an equilibrium point of the interconnected system is the existence of a positive diagonal matrix D such that $DS + S^T D$ is positive definite. The matrix S is special in that its off-diagonal elements are nonpositive. The next lemma applies to this class of matrices.

Lemma 9.7 *There exists a positive diagonal matrix D such that $DS + S^T D$ is positive definite if and only if S is an M-matrix; that is, the leading principal minors of S are positive:*

$$\det \begin{bmatrix} s_{11} & s_{12} & \cdots & s_{1k} \\ s_{21} & & & \\ \vdots & & & \\ s_{k1} & \cdots & \cdots & s_{kk} \end{bmatrix} > 0, \quad k = 1, 2, \ldots, m$$

$\diamond$

Proof: See [57].

The M-matrix condition can be interpreted as a requirement that the diagonal elements of S be "larger as a whole" than the off-diagonal elements. It can be seen (Exercise 9.22) that diagonally dominant matrices with nonpositive off-diagonal elements are M-matrices. The diagonal elements of S are measures of the "degree of stability" for the isolated subsystems in the sense that the constant α_i gives a lower bound on the rate of decrease of the Lyapunov function V_i with respect to $\phi_i^2(x_i)$. The off-diagonal elements of S represent the "strength of the interconnections" in the sense that they give an upper bound on $g_i(t,x)$ with respect to $\phi_j(x_j)$ for $j = 1, \ldots, m$. Thus, the M-matrix condition says that *if the degrees of stability for the isolated subsystems are larger as a whole than the strength of the interconnections, then the interconnected system has a uniformly asymptotically stable equilibrium at the origin.* We summarize our conclusion in the next theorem.

Theorem 9.2 *Consider the system (9.32) and suppose there are positive definite decrescent Lyapunov functions $V_i(t, x_i)$ that satisfy (9.34) and (9.35) and that $g_i(t, x)$ satisfies (9.36) for all $t \geq 0$ and $\|x\| < r$. Suppose the matrix S defined by (9.37) is an M-matrix. Then, the origin is uniformly asymptotically stable. Moreover, if all the assumptions hold globally and $V_i(t, x_i)$ are radially unbounded, it will be globally uniformly asymptotically stable.* $\diamond$

Example 9.7 Consider the second-order system

$$
\begin{aligned}
\dot{x}_1 &= -x_1 - 1.5x_1^2 x_2^3 \\
\dot{x}_2 &= -x_2^3 + 0.5x_1^2 x_2^2
\end{aligned}
$$

The system can be represented in the form (9.32) with

$$f_1(x_1) = -x_1, \quad g_1(x) = -1.5x_1^2 x_2^3, \quad f_2(x_2) = -x_2^3, \quad \text{and} \quad g_2(x) = 0.5x_1^2 x_2^2$$

The first isolated subsystem $\dot{x}_1 = -x_1$ has a Lyapunov function $V_1(x_1) = x_1^2/2$, which satisfies

$$\frac{\partial V_1}{\partial x_1} f_1(x_1) = -x_1^2 = -\alpha_1 \phi_1^2(x_1)$$

where $\alpha_1 = 1$ and $\phi_1(x_1) = |x_1|$. The second isolated subsystem $\dot{x}_2 = -x_2^3$ has a Lyapunov function $V_2(x_2) = x_2^4/4$, which satisfies

$$\frac{\partial V_2}{\partial x_2} f_2(x_2) = -x_2^6 = -\alpha_2 \phi_2^2(x_2)$$

where $\alpha_2 = 1$ and $\phi_2(x_2) = |x_2|^3$. The Lyapunov functions satisfy (9.35) with $\beta_1 = \beta_2 = 1$. The interconnection term $g_1(x)$ satisfies the inequality

$$|g_1(x)| = 1.5x_1^2 |x_2|^3 \leq 1.5c_1^2 \phi_2(x_2)$$

for all $|x_1| \leq c_1$. The interconnection term $g_2(x)$ satisfies the inequality

$$|g_2(x)| = 0.5x_1^2 x_2^2 \leq 0.5c_1 c_2^2 \phi_1(x_1)$$

for all $|x_1| \leq c_1$ and $|x_2| \leq c_2$. Thus, if we restrict our attention to the set

$$G = \{x \in R^2 \mid |x_1| \leq c_1, \ |x_2| \leq c_2\}$$

we can conclude that the interconnection terms satisfy (9.36) with

$$\gamma_{11} = 0, \quad \gamma_{12} = 1.5c_1^2, \quad \gamma_{21} = 0.5c_1 c_2^2, \quad \text{and} \quad \gamma_{22} = 0$$

The matrix

$$S = \begin{bmatrix} 1 & -1.5c_1^2 \\ -0.5c_1 c_2^2 & 1 \end{bmatrix}$$

is an M-matrix if $0.75c_1^3c_2^2 < 1$. This will be the case, for example, when $c_1 = c_2 = 1$. Thus, the origin is asymptotically stable. If we are interested in estimating the region of attraction, we need to know the composite Lyapunov function $V = d_1V_1 + d_2V_2$; that is, we need to know a positive diagonal matrix D such that $DS + S^TD > 0$. Taking $c_1 = c_2 = 1$, we have

$$DS + S^TD = \begin{bmatrix} 2d_1 & -1.5d_1 - 0.5d_2 \\ -1.5d_1 - 0.5d_2 & 2d_2 \end{bmatrix}$$

which is positive definite for $1 < d_2/d_1 < 9$. Since there is no loss of generality in multiplying a Lyapunov function by a positive constant, we take $d_1 = 1$ and write the composite Lyapunov function as

$$V(x) = \tfrac{1}{2}x_1^2 + \tfrac{1}{4}d_2x_2^4, \quad 1 < d_2 < 9$$

An estimate of the region of attraction is given by

$$\Omega_c = \{x \in R^2 \mid V(x) \le c\}$$

where $c \le \min\{1/2, d_2/4\}$ to ensure that Ω_c is inside the rectangle $|x_i| \le 1$. Noting that the surface $V(x) = c$ intersects the x_1-axis and the x_2-axis at $\sqrt{2c}$ and $(4c/d_2)^{1/4}$, respectively, we maximize these distances by choosing $d_2 = 2$ and $c = 0.5$. $\triangle$

Example 9.8 The mathematical model of an artificial neural network was presented in Section 1.2.5, and its stability properties were analyzed in Example 4.11 by using LaSalle's invariance principle. A key assumption in Example 4.11 is the symmetry requirement $T_{ij} = T_{ji}$, which allows us to represent the right-hand side of the state equation as the gradient of a scalar function. Let us relax this requirement and allow $T_{ij} \ne T_{ji}$. We will analyze the stability properties of the network by viewing it as an interconnection of subsystems; each subsystem corresponds to one neuron. We find it convenient here to work with the voltages at the amplifier inputs u_i. The equations of motion are

$$C_i\dot{u}_i = \sum_j T_{ij}g_j(u_j) - \frac{1}{R_i}u_i + I_i$$

for $i = 1, 2, \ldots, n$, where $g_i(\cdot)$ are sigmoid functions, I_i are constant current inputs, $R_i > 0$, and $C_i > 0$. We assume that the system has a finite number of isolated equilibrium points. Each equilibrium point u^* satisfies the equation

$$0 = \sum_j T_{ij}g_j(u_j^*) - \frac{1}{R_i}u_i^* + I_i$$

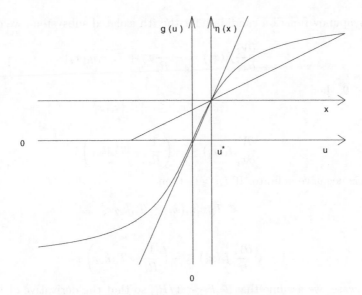

Figure 9.1: The sector nonlinearity $\eta_i(x_i)$ of Example 9.8.

To analyze the stability properties of a given equilibrium point u^*, we shift it to the origin. Let $x_i = u_i - u_i^*$. Then,

$$\dot{x}_i = \frac{1}{C_i}\dot{u}_i = \frac{1}{C_i}\left[\sum_j T_{ij}g_j(x_j + u_j^*) - \frac{1}{R_i}(x_i + u_i^*) + I_i\right]$$

$$= \frac{1}{C_i}\left[\sum_j T_{ij}\eta_j(x_j) - \frac{1}{R_i}x_i\right]$$

where

$$\eta_i(x_i) = g_i(x_i + u_i^*) - g_i(u_i^*)$$

Assume that $\eta_i(\cdot)$ satisfies the sector condition

$$\sigma^2 k_{i1} \le \sigma\eta_i(\sigma) \le \sigma^2 k_{i2}, \quad \text{for } \sigma \in [-r_i, r_i]$$

where k_{i1} and k_{i2} are positive constants. Figure 9.1 shows that such condition is indeed satisfied when $g_i(u_i) = (2V_M/\pi)\tan^{-1}(\lambda\pi u_i/2V_M)$, $\lambda > 0$. We can recast this system in the form (9.32) with

$$f_i(x_i) = -\frac{1}{C_i R_i}x_i + \frac{1}{C_i}T_{ii}\eta_i(x_i), \qquad g_i(x) = \frac{1}{C_i}\sum_{j\neq i}T_{ij}\eta_j(x_j)$$

Using

$$V_i(x_i) = \tfrac{1}{2}C_i x_i^2$$

as a Lyapunov function candidate for the ith isolated subsystem, we obtain

$$\frac{\partial V_i}{\partial x_i} f_i(x_i) = -\frac{1}{R_i} x_i^2 + T_{ii} x_i \eta_i(x_i)$$

If $T_{ii} \leq 0$, then

$$T_{ii} x_i \eta_i(x_i) \leq -|T_{ii}| k_{i1} x_i^2$$

and

$$\frac{\partial V_i}{\partial x_i} f_i(x_i) \leq -\left(\frac{1}{R_i} + |T_{ii}| k_{i1}\right) x_i^2$$

which is negative definite. If $T_{ii} > 0$, then

$$T_{ii} x_i \eta_i(x_i) \leq T_{ii} k_{i2} x_i^2$$

and

$$\frac{\partial V_i}{\partial x_i} f_i(x_i) \leq -\left(\frac{1}{R_i} - T_{ii} k_{i2}\right) x_i^2$$

In this case, we assume that $T_{ii} k_{i2} < 1/R_i$, so that the derivative of V_i is negative definite. To simplify the notation, let

$$\delta_i = \begin{cases} |T_{ii}| k_{i1}, & \text{if } T_{ii} \leq 0 \\ \\ -T_{ii} k_{i2}, & \text{if } T_{ii} > 0 \end{cases}$$

Then, $V_i(x_i)$ satisfies (9.34) and (9.35) on the interval $[-r_i, r_i]$ with

$$\alpha_i = \left(\frac{1}{R_i} + \delta_i\right), \quad \beta_i = C_i, \quad \phi_i(x_i) = |x_i|$$

where α_i is positive by assumption. The interconnection term $g_i(x)$ satisfies the inequality

$$|g_i(x)| \leq \frac{1}{C_i} \sum_{j \neq i} |T_{ij}| |\eta_j(x_j)| \leq \frac{1}{C_i} \sum_{j \neq i} |T_{ij}| k_{j2} |x_j|$$

Thus, $g_i(x)$ satisfies (9.36) with $\gamma_{ii} = 0$ and $\gamma_{ij} = k_{j2} |T_{ij}|/C_i$ for $i \neq j$. Now we can form the matrix S as

$$s_{ij} = \begin{cases} \delta_i + 1/R_i, & \text{for } i = j \\ \\ -|T_{ij}| k_{j2} & \text{for } i \neq j \end{cases}$$

The equilibrium point u^* is asymptotically stable if S is an M-matrix. We may estimate the region of attraction by the set

$$\Omega_c = \left\{ x \in R^n \ \middle| \ \sum_{i=1}^n d_i V_i(x_i) \leq c \right\}$$

where $c \leq 0.5 \min_i \{d_i C_i r_i^2\}$ to ensure that Ω_c is inside the set $|x_i| \leq r_i$. This analysis is repeated for each asymptotically stable equilibrium point. The conclusions we could arrive at in this example are more conservative compared with the conclusions we arrived at using LaSalle's invariance principle. First, the interconnection coefficients T_{ij} must be restricted to satisfy the M-matrix condition. Second, we obtain only local estimates of the regions of attractions for the isolated equilibrium points. The union of these estimates does not cover the whole domain of interest. On the other hand, we do not have to assume that $T_{ij} = T_{ji}$. $\triangle$

9.6   Slowly Varying Systems

The system

$$\dot{x} = f(x, u(t)) \tag{9.38}$$

where $x \in R^n$ and $u(t) \in \Gamma \subset R^m$ for all $t \geq 0$ is considered to be slowly varying if $u(t)$ is continuously differentiable and $\|\dot{u}(t)\|$ is "sufficiently" small. The components of $u(t)$ could be input variables or time-varying parameters. In the analysis of (9.38), one usually treats u as a "frozen" parameter and assumes that for each fixed $u = \alpha \in \Gamma$, the frozen system has an isolated equilibrium point defined by $x = h(\alpha)$. If a property of $x = h(\alpha)$ is uniform in α, then it is reasonable to expect that the slowly varying system (9.38) will possess a similar property. The underlying characteristic of such systems is that the motion caused by changes of initial conditions is much faster than that caused by inputs or time-varying parameters. In this section, we will see how Lyapunov stability can be used to analyze slowly varying systems.

Suppose $f(x, u)$ is locally Lipschitz on $R^n \times \Gamma$, and for every $u \in \Gamma$ the equation

$$0 = f(x, u)$$

has a continuously differentiable isolated root $x = h(u)$; that is,

$$0 = f(h(u), u)$$

Furthermore, suppose

$$\left\| \frac{\partial h}{\partial u} \right\| \leq L, \quad \forall \, u \in \Gamma \tag{9.39}$$

To analyze the stability properties of the frozen equilibrium point $x = h(\alpha)$, we shift it to the origin via the change of variables $z = x - h(\alpha)$ to obtain the equation

$$\dot{z} = f(z + h(\alpha), \alpha) \stackrel{\text{def}}{=} g(z, \alpha) \tag{9.40}$$

Now we search for a Lyapunov function to show that $z = 0$ is asymptotically stable. Since $g(z, \alpha)$ depends on the parameter α, a Lyapunov function for the system may depend, in general, on α. Suppose we can find a Lyapunov function $V(z, \alpha)$ that satisfies the conditions

$$c_1 \|z\|^2 \leq V(z, \alpha) \leq c_2 \|z\|^2 \tag{9.41}$$

$$\frac{\partial V}{\partial z} g(z, \alpha) \leq -c_3 \|z\|^2 \tag{9.42}$$

$$\left\| \frac{\partial V}{\partial z} \right\| \leq c_4 \|z\| \tag{9.43}$$

$$\left\| \frac{\partial V}{\partial \alpha} \right\| \leq c_5 \|z\|^2 \tag{9.44}$$

for all $z \in D = \{z \in R^n \mid \|z\| < r\}$ and $\alpha \in \Gamma$, where c_i, $i = 1, 2, \ldots, 5$ are positive constants independent of α. Inequalities (9.41) and (9.42) state the usual requirements that V be positive definite and decrescent and has a negative definite derivative along the trajectories of the system (9.40). Furthermore, they show that the origin $z = 0$ is exponentially stable. The special requirement here is that these inequalities hold uniformly in α. Inequalities (9.43) and (9.44) are needed to handle the perturbations of (9.40), which will result from the fact that $u(t)$ is not constant, but a time-varying function. With $V(z, u)$ as a Lyapunov function candidate, the analysis of (9.38) proceeds as follows: The change of variables $z = x - h(u)$ transforms (9.38) into the form

$$\dot{z} = g(z, u) - \frac{\partial h}{\partial u} \dot{u} \tag{9.45}$$

where the effect of the time variation of u appears as a perturbation of the frozen system (9.40). The derivative of $V(z, u)$ along the trajectories (9.45) is given by

$$
\begin{aligned}
\dot{V} &= \frac{\partial V}{\partial z} \dot{z} + \frac{\partial V}{\partial u} \dot{u}(t) \\
&= \frac{\partial V}{\partial z} g(z, u) + \left[\frac{\partial V}{\partial u} - \frac{\partial V}{\partial z} \frac{\partial h}{\partial u} \right] \dot{u}(t) \\
&\leq -c_3 \|z\|^2 + c_5 \|z\|^2 \|\dot{u}(t)\| + c_4 L \|z\| \ \|\dot{u}(t)\|
\end{aligned}
$$

Setting

$$\gamma(t) = \frac{c_5}{c_4} \|\dot{u}(t)\| \ \text{ and } \ \delta(t) = L \|\dot{u}(t)\|$$

we can rewrite the last inequality as

$$\dot{V} \leq -c_3 \|z\|^2 + c_4 \gamma(t) \|z\|^2 + c_4 \delta(t) \|z\|$$

which takes the form of inequality (9.16) of Section 9.3. Therefore, by applying the comparison lemma, as in Section 9.3, it can be shown that, if $\dot{u}(t)$ satisfies

$$\int_{t_0}^{t} \|\dot{u}(\tau)\| \ d\tau \leq \varepsilon_1 (t - t_0) + \eta_1, \ \text{ where } \ \varepsilon_1 < \frac{c_1 c_3}{c_2 c_5} \tag{9.46}$$

and

$$\|z(0)\| < \frac{r}{\rho_1}\sqrt{\frac{c_1}{c_2}}; \quad \sup_{t \geq 0}\|\dot{u}(t)\| \leq \frac{2c_1\alpha_1 r}{c_4\rho_1 L}$$

in which α_1 and ρ_1 are defined by

$$\alpha_1 = \frac{1}{2}\left[\frac{c_3}{c_2} - \varepsilon_1\frac{c_5}{c_1}\right] > 0, \quad \rho_1 = \exp\left(\frac{c_5\eta_1}{2c_1}\right) \geq 1$$

then $z(t)$ satisfies the inequality

$$\|z(t)\| \leq \sqrt{\frac{c_2}{c_1}}\rho_1\|z(0)\|e^{-\alpha_1 t} + \frac{c_4\rho_1 L}{2c_1}\int_0^t e^{-\alpha_1(t-\tau)}\|\dot{u}(\tau)\|\,d\tau \qquad (9.47)$$

Depending upon the assumptions for $\|\dot{u}\|$, several conclusions can be drawn from the foregoing inequality. Some of these conclusions are stated in the next theorem.

Theorem 9.3 *Consider the system* (9.45). *Suppose that* $[\partial h/\partial u]$ *satisfies* (9.39), $\|\dot{u}(t)\| \leq \varepsilon$ *for all* $t \geq 0$, *and there is a Lyapunov function* $V(z, u)$ *that satisfies* (9.41) *through* (9.44). *If*

$$\varepsilon < \frac{c_1 c_3}{c_2 c_5} \times \frac{r}{r + c_4 L/c_5}$$

then for all $\|z(0)\| < r\sqrt{c_1/c_2}$, *the solutions of* (9.45) *are uniformly bounded for all* $t \geq 0$ *and uniformly ultimately bounded by*

$$b = \frac{c_2 c_4 L\varepsilon}{\theta(c_1 c_3 - \varepsilon c_2 c_5)}$$

where $\theta \in (0, 1)$ *is an arbitrary constant. If, in addition,* $\dot{u}(t) \to 0$ *as* $t \to \infty$, *then* $z(t) \to 0$ *as* $t \to \infty$. *Finally, if* $h(u) = 0$ *for all* $u \in \Gamma$ *and* $\varepsilon < c_3/c_5$, *then* $z = 0$ *is an exponentially stable equilibrium point of* (9.45). *Equivalently,* $x = 0$ *is an exponentially stable equilibrium point of* (9.38). $\diamond$

Proof: Since $\|\dot{u}(t)\| \leq \varepsilon < c_1 c_3/c_2 c_5$, inequality (9.46) is satisfied with $\varepsilon_1 = \varepsilon$ and $\eta_1 = 0$. Hence,

$$\alpha_1 = \frac{1}{2}\left[\frac{c_3}{c_2} - \varepsilon\frac{c_5}{c_1}\right], \quad \rho_1 = 1$$

Using the given upper bound on ε, we have

$$\begin{aligned}
\frac{2c_1\alpha_1 r}{c_4 L} &= \frac{c_1 r}{c_4 L}\left[\frac{c_3}{c_2} - \varepsilon\frac{c_5}{c_1}\right] \\
&> \frac{c_1 r}{c_4 L}\left[\frac{c_3}{c_2} - \frac{c_3}{c_2} \times \frac{r}{r + c_4 L/c_5}\right] \\
&= \frac{c_1 c_3}{c_2 c_5} \times \frac{r}{r + c_4 L/c_5} > \varepsilon
\end{aligned}$$

Hence, the inequality $\sup_{t \geq 0} \|\dot{u}(t)\| < 2c_1\alpha_1 r/c_4 L$ is satisfied and from (9.47), we obtain

$$
\begin{aligned}
\|z(t)\| &\leq \sqrt{\frac{c_2}{c_1}}\|z(0)\|e^{-\alpha_1 t} + \frac{c_4 L}{2c_1}\int_0^t e^{-\alpha_1(t-\tau)}\varepsilon \, d\tau \\
&\leq \sqrt{\frac{c_2}{c_1}}\|z(0)\|e^{-\alpha_1 t} + \frac{c_4 L\varepsilon}{2c_1\alpha_1} = \sqrt{\frac{c_2}{c_1}}\|z(0)\|e^{-\alpha_1 t} + b\theta
\end{aligned}
$$

After a finite time, the exponentially decaying term will be less than $(1-\theta)b$, which shows that $z(t)$ will be ultimately bounded by b. If, in addition, $\dot{u}(t) \to 0$ as $t \to \infty$, then it is clear from (9.47) that $z(t) \to 0$ as $t \to \infty$. If $h(u) = 0$ for all $u \in \Gamma$, we can take $L = 0$. Consequently, the upper bound on $\dot{V}$ simplifies to

$$
\dot{V} \leq -(c_3 - c_5\varepsilon)\|z\|^2
$$

which shows that $z = 0$ will be exponentially stable if $\varepsilon < c_3/c_5$. $\square$

Theorem 9.3 requires the existence of a Lyapunov function $V(z, \alpha)$ for the frozen system (9.40), which satisfies inequalities (9.41) through (9.44). Lemma 9.8 shows that such Lyapunov function will exist, under some mild smoothness requirements, if the equilibrium point $z = 0$ of the frozen system is exponentially stable uniformly in α. This is done by deriving a converse Lyapunov function for the system, as in the converse Lyapunov theorems of Section 4.7.

Lemma 9.8 *Consider the system (9.40) and suppose $g(z, \alpha)$ is continuously differentiable and the Jacobian matrices $[\partial g/\partial z]$ and $[\partial g/\partial \alpha]$ satisfy*

$$
\left\|\frac{\partial g}{\partial z}(z, \alpha)\right\| \leq L_1, \quad \left\|\frac{\partial g}{\partial \alpha}(z, \alpha)\right\| \leq L_2\|z\|
$$

for all $(z, \alpha) \in D \times \Gamma$, where $D = \{z \in R^n \mid \|z\| < r\}$. Let k, γ, and r_0 be positive constants with $r_0 < r/k$, and define $D_0 = \{z \in R^n \mid \|z\| < r_0\}$. Assume that the trajectories of the system satisfy

$$
\|z(t)\| \leq k\|z(0)\|e^{-\gamma t}, \quad \forall \, z(0) \in D_0, \, \alpha \in \Gamma, \, t \geq 0
$$

Then, there is a function $V : D_0 \times \Gamma \to R$ that satisfies (9.41) through (9.44). Moreover, if all the assumptions hold globally (in z), then $V(z, \alpha)$ is defined and satisfies (9.41) through (9.44) on $R^n \times \Gamma$. $\diamond$

Proof: Owing to the equivalence of norms, it is sufficient to prove the lemma for the 2-norm. Let $\phi(t; z, \alpha)$ be the solution of (9.40) that starts at $(0, z)$; that is, $\phi(0; z, \alpha) = z$. The notation emphasizes the dependence of the solution on the parameter α. Let

$$
V(z, \alpha) = \int_0^T \phi^T(t; z, \alpha)\phi(t; z, \alpha) \, dt
$$

where $T = \ln\left(2k^2\right)/2\gamma$. Similar to the proof of Theorem 4.14, it can be shown that $V(z, \alpha)$ satisfies (9.41) through (9.43) with $c_1 = [1 - \exp\left(-2L_1T\right)]/2L_1$, $c_2 = k^2[1 - \exp\left(-2\gamma T\right)]/2\gamma$, $c_3 = 1/2$, and $c_4 = 2k\{1 - \exp\left[-(\gamma - L_1)T\right]\}/(\gamma - L_1)$. To show that $V(z, \alpha)$ satisfies (9.44), note that the sensitivity function $\phi_\alpha(t; z, \alpha)$ satisfies the sensitivity equation

$$\frac{\partial}{\partial t}\phi_\alpha = \frac{\partial g}{\partial z}(\phi(t; z, \alpha), \alpha)\phi_\alpha + \frac{\partial g}{\partial \alpha}(\phi(t; z, \alpha), \alpha), \quad \phi_\alpha(0; z, \alpha) = 0$$

from which we obtain

$$\begin{aligned} \|\phi_\alpha(t; z, \alpha)\|_2 &\leq \int_0^t L_1\|\phi_\alpha(\tau; z, \alpha)\|_2 \, d\tau + \int_0^t L_2\|\phi(\tau; z, \alpha)\|_2 \, d\tau \\ &\leq \int_0^t L_1\|\phi_\alpha(\tau; z, \alpha)\|_2 \, d\tau + \int_0^t L_2ke^{-\gamma\tau} \, d\tau\|z\|_2 \\ &\leq \int_0^t L_1\|\phi_\alpha(\tau; z, \alpha)\|_2 \, d\tau + \frac{L_2k}{\gamma}\|z\|_2 \end{aligned}$$

Use of the Gronwall–Bellman inequality yields

$$\|\phi_\alpha(t; z, \alpha)\|_2 \leq \frac{L_2k}{\gamma}\|z\|_2 e^{L_1 t}$$

Hence,

$$\begin{aligned} \left\|\frac{\partial V}{\partial \alpha}\right\|_2 &= \left\|\int_0^T 2\phi^T(t; z, \alpha)\phi_\alpha(t; z, \alpha) \, dt\right\|_2 \\ &\leq \int_0^T 2ke^{-\gamma t}\|z\|_2 \left(\frac{L_2k}{\gamma}\right) e^{L_1 t}\|z\|_2 \, dt \\ &\leq \frac{2k^2 L_2}{\gamma(\gamma - L_1)}\left[1 - e^{-(\gamma - L_1)T}\right]\|z\|_2^2 \stackrel{\text{def}}{=} c_5\|z\|_2^2 \end{aligned}$$

which completes the proof of the lemma. □

When the frozen system (9.40) is linear, a Lyapunov function satisfying (9.41) through (9.44) can be explicitly determined by solving a parameterized Lyapunov equation. This fact is stated in the next lemma.

Lemma 9.9 *Consider the system* $\dot{z} = A(\alpha)z$, *where* $\alpha \in \Gamma$ *and* $A(\alpha)$ *is continuously differentiable. Suppose the elements of A and their first partial derivatives with respect to α are uniformly bounded; that is,*

$$\|A(\alpha)\|_2 \leq c, \quad \left\|\frac{\partial}{\partial \alpha_i}A(\alpha)\right\|_2 \leq b_i, \quad \forall\, \alpha \in \Gamma, \; \forall\, 1 \leq i \leq m$$

Suppose further that $A(\alpha)$ is Hurwitz uniformly in α; that is,

$$\text{Re}[\lambda(A(\alpha))] \le -\sigma < 0, \quad \forall\, \alpha \in \Gamma$$

Then, the Lyapunov equation

$$PA(\alpha) + A^T(\alpha)P = -I \tag{9.48}$$

has a unique positive definite solution $P(\alpha)$ for every $\alpha \in \Gamma$. Moreover, $P(\alpha)$ is continuously differentiable and satisfies

$$c_1 z^T z \le z^T P(\alpha) z \le c_2 z^T z$$

$$\left\| \frac{\partial}{\partial \alpha_i} P(\alpha) \right\|_2 \le \mu_i, \quad \forall\, 1 \le i \le m$$

for all $(z, \alpha) \in R^n \times \Gamma$, where c_1, c_2, and μ_i are positive constants independent of α. Consequently, $V(z, \alpha) = z^T P(\alpha) z$ satisfies (9.42) through (9.44) in the 2-norm with $c_3 = 1$, $c_4 = 2c_2$, and $c_5 = \sqrt{\sum_{i=1}^m \mu_i^2}$. $\diamond$

Proof: The uniform Hurwitz property of $A(\alpha)$ implies that the exponential matrix $\exp[tA(\alpha)]$ satisfies

$$\| \exp[tA(\alpha)] \| \le k(A)e^{-\beta t}, \quad \forall\, t \ge 0,\ \forall\, \alpha \in \Gamma$$

where $\beta > 0$ is independent of α, but $k(A) > 0$ depends on α. For the exponentially decaying bound to hold uniformly in α, we need to use the property that $\|A(\alpha)\|$ is bounded. The set of matrices satisfying $\text{Re}[\lambda(A(\alpha))] \le -\sigma$ and $\|A(\alpha)\| \le c$ is a compact set, which we denote by S. Let A and B be any two elements of S. Consider[8]

$$\exp[t(A+B)] = \exp[tA] + \int_0^t \exp[(t-\tau)A]B\exp[\tau(A+B)]\, d\tau$$

Using the exponentially decaying bound on $\exp[tA]$, we get

$$\| \exp[t(A+B)] \| \le k(A)e^{-\beta t} + \int_0^t k(A)e^{-\beta(t-\tau)}\|B\|\,\|\exp[\tau(A+B)]\|\, d\tau$$

Multiply through by $e^{\beta t}$,

$$e^{\beta t}\| \exp[t(A+B)] \| \le k(A) + k(A)\|B\| \int_0^t e^{\beta \tau}\|\exp[\tau(A+B)]\|\, d\tau$$

---

[8]This matrix identity follows by writing $\dot{x} = (A+B)x$ as $\dot{x} = Ax + Bx$ and viewing Bx as an input term. Substituting $x(t) = \exp[t(A+B)]x_0$ into the input term yields

$$\exp[t(A+B)]x_0 = \exp[tA]x_0 + \int_0^t \exp[(t-\tau)A]B\exp[\tau(A+B)]x_0\, d\tau$$

Since this expression holds for all $x_0 \in R^n$, we arrive at the matrix identity.

Applying the Gronwall–Bellman inequality yields

$$\| \exp[t(A+B)] \| \leq k(A) e^{-(\beta - k(A) \| B \|) t}, \quad \forall\, t \geq 0$$

Hence, there exists a positive constant $\gamma < \beta$ and a neighborhood $\mathcal{N}(A)$ of A such that if $C \in \mathcal{N}(A)$, then

$$\| \exp[tC] \| \leq k(A) e^{-\gamma t}, \quad \forall\, t \geq 0$$

Since S is compact, it is covered by a finite number of these neighborhoods. Therefore, we can find a positive constant k independent of α such that

$$\| \exp[tA(\alpha)] \| \leq k e^{-\gamma t}, \quad \forall\, t \geq 0,\ \forall\, \alpha \in \Gamma$$

Consider now the Lyapunov equation (9.48). Existence of a unique positive definite solution for every $\alpha \in \Gamma$ follows from Theorem 4.6. Moreover, the proof of that theorem shows that

$$P(\alpha) = \int_0^\infty \left[e^{tA(\alpha)} \right]^T \left[e^{tA(\alpha)} \right]\, dt$$

Since $A(\alpha)$ is continuously differentiable, so is $P(\alpha)$. We have

$$z^T P(\alpha) z \leq \int_0^\infty k^2 e^{-2\gamma t} \| z \|_2^2\, dt = \frac{k^2}{2\gamma} \| z \|_2^2 \;\Rightarrow\; c_2 = \frac{k^2}{2\gamma}$$

Let $y(t) = e^{tA(\alpha)} z$. Then, $\dot{y} = A(\alpha) y$,

$$-y^T(t) \dot{y}(t) = -y^T(t) A(\alpha) y(t) \leq \| A(\alpha) \|_2 y^T(t) y(t) \leq c\, y^T(t) y(t)$$

and

$$
\begin{aligned}
z^T P(\alpha) z &= \int_0^\infty y^T(t) y(t)\, dt \;\geq\; \int_0^\infty \frac{-1}{c} y^T(t) \dot{y}(t)\, dt \\
&= \frac{1}{2c} \int_0^\infty \frac{d}{dt}[-y^T(t) y(t)]\, dt \;=\; \frac{1}{2c} \left. [-y^T(t) y(t)] \right|_0^\infty \\
&= \frac{1}{2c} y^T(0) y(0) \;=\; \frac{1}{2c} z^T z \;\Rightarrow\; c_1 = \frac{1}{2c}
\end{aligned}
$$

Differentiate $P(\alpha) A(\alpha) + A^T(\alpha) P(\alpha) = -I$ partially with respect to any component α_i of α, and denote the derivative of $P(\alpha)$ by $P'(\alpha)$. Then,

$$P'(\alpha) A(\alpha) + A^T(\alpha) P'(\alpha) = -\{ P(\alpha) A'(\alpha) + [A'(\alpha)]^T P(\alpha) \}$$

Thus, $P'(\alpha)$ is given by

$$P'(\alpha) = \int_0^\infty \left[e^{tA(\alpha)} \right]^T \{ P(\alpha) A'(\alpha) + [A'(\alpha)]^T P(\alpha) \} \left[e^{tA(\alpha)} \right]\, dt$$

It follows that

$$\|P'(\alpha)\|_2 \leq \int_0^\infty k^2 e^{-2\gamma t} 2 \frac{k^2}{2\gamma} b_i \, dt = \frac{b_i k^4}{2\gamma^2} \Rightarrow \mu_i = \frac{b_i k^4}{2\gamma^2}$$

which completes the proof of the lemma. $\square$

It should be noted that the set Γ in Lemma 9.9 is not necessarily compact. When Γ is compact, the boundedness of $A(\alpha)$ and its partial derivatives follow from the assumption that $A(\alpha)$ is continuously differentiable.

Example 9.9 Consider the system

$$\dot{x} = A(\varepsilon t)x$$

where $\varepsilon > 0$. When ε is sufficiently small, we can treat this system as a slowly varying system. It is in the form of (9.38) with $u = \varepsilon t$ and $\Gamma = [0, \infty)$. For all $u \in \Gamma$, the origin $x = 0$ is an equilibrium point. Hence, this is a special case where $h(u) = 0$. Suppose $\mathrm{Re}[\lambda(A(\alpha))] \leq -\sigma < 0$, and $A(\alpha)$ and $A'(\alpha)$ are uniformly bounded for all $\alpha \in \Gamma$. Then, the solution of the Lyapunov equation (9.48) holds the properties stated in Lemma 9.9. Using $V(x, u) = x^T P(u)x$ as a Lyapunov function candidate for $\dot{x} = A(u)x$, we obtain

$$\begin{aligned}
\dot{V}(t, x) &= x^T[P(u(t))A(u(t)) + A^T(u(t))P(u(t))]x + x^T P'(u(t))\dot{u}(t)x \\
&\leq -x^T x + \varepsilon c_5 \|x\|_2^2 = -(1 - \varepsilon c_5)\|x\|_2^2
\end{aligned}$$

where c_5 is an upper bound on $\|P'(\alpha)\|_2$. Therefore, for all $\varepsilon < 1/c_5$, the origin $x = 0$ is an exponentially stable equilibrium point of $\dot{x} = A(\varepsilon t)x$. $\triangle$

9.7   Exercises

9.1 ([150]) Consider the Lyapunov equation $PA + A^T P = -Q$, where $Q = Q^T > 0$ and A is Hurwitz. Let $\mu(Q) = \lambda_{\min}(Q)/\lambda_{\max}(P)$.

(a) Show that $\mu(kQ) = \mu(Q)$ for any positive constant k.

(b) Let $\hat{Q} = \hat{Q}^T > 0$ have $\lambda_{\min}(\hat{Q}) = 1$. Show that $\mu(I) \geq \mu(\hat{Q})$.

(c) Show that $\mu(I) \geq \mu(Q)$, $\forall Q = Q^T > 0$.

Hint: In part (b), let P_1 and P_2 be the solutions of the Lyapunov equation for $Q = I$ and $Q = \hat{Q}$, respectively. Show that

$$P_1 - P_2 = \int_0^\infty \exp(A^T t)(I - \hat{Q}) \exp(At) \, dt \leq 0$$

9.2 Consider the system $\dot{x} = Ax + Bu$ and let $u = -Fx$ be a stabilizing state feedback control; that is, the matrix $(A - BF)$ is Hurwitz. Suppose that, due to physical limitations, we have to use a limiter to limit the value of u_i to $|u_i(t)| \leq L$. The closed-loop system can be represented by $\dot{x} = Ax - BL\,\mathrm{sat}(Fx/L)$, where $\mathrm{sat}(v)$ is a vector whose ith component is the saturation function. By adding and subtracting the term BFx, we can rewrite the closed-loop state equation as $\dot{x} = (A - BF)x - Bh(Fx)$, where $h(v) = L\,\mathrm{sat}(v/L) - v$. Thus, the effect of the limiter can be viewed as a perturbation of the nominal system without the limiter.

(a) Show that

$$|h_i(v)| \leq \frac{\delta}{(1+\delta)}|v_i|, \ \forall \ |v_i| \leq L(1+\delta)$$

where $\delta > 0$.

(b) Let P be the solution of

$$P(A - BF) + (A - BF)^T P = -I$$

Show that the derivative of $V(x) = x^T Px$ along the trajectories of the closed-loop system will be negative definite over the region $|(Fx)_i| \leq L(1 + \delta)$, $\forall\ i$, provided $\delta/(1 + \delta) < 1/(2\|PB\|_2\,\|F\|_2)$.

(c) Show that the origin is asymptotically stable and discuss how you would estimate the region of attraction.

(d) Apply the result obtained in part (c) to the case

$$A = \begin{bmatrix} 0 & 1 \\ 0.5 & 1 \end{bmatrix}, \quad B = \begin{bmatrix} 0 \\ 1 \end{bmatrix}, \quad F = \begin{bmatrix} 1 & 2 \end{bmatrix}, \quad \text{and} \quad L = 1$$

and estimate the region of attraction.

9.3 Consider the system

$$\dot{x} = f(t, x) + Bu, \quad y = Cx, \quad \text{and} \quad u = -g(t, y)$$

where $f(t, 0) = 0$, $g(t, 0) = 0$, and $\|g(t, y)\| \leq \gamma \|y\|$ for all $t \geq 0$. Suppose that the origin of $\dot{x} = f(t, x)$ is globally exponentially stable and let $V(t, x)$ be a Lyapunov function that satisfies (9.3) through (9.5) globally. Find a bound γ^* on γ such that the origin of the given system is globally exponentially stable for $\gamma < \gamma^*$.

9.4 Consider the perturbed system

$$\dot{x} = Ax + B[u + g(t, x)]$$

where $g(t, x)$ is continuously differentiable and satisfies $\|g(t, x)\|_2 \leq k\|x\|_2$, $\forall\ t \geq 0$, $\forall\ x \in B_r$ for some $r > 0$. Let $P = P^T > 0$ be the solution of the Riccati equation

$$PA + A^T P + Q - PBB^T P + 2\alpha P = 0$$

where $Q \geq k^2 I$ and $\alpha > 0$. Show that $u = -B^T P x$ stabilizes the origin of the perturbed system.

9.5 ([101]) Consider the perturbed system

$$\dot{x} = Ax + Bu + Dg(t, y), \qquad y = Cx$$

where $g(t, y)$ is continuously differentiable and satisfies $\|g(t, y)\|_2 \leq k\|y\|_2$, $\forall\, t \geq 0$, $\forall\, \|y\|_2 \leq r$ for some $r > 0$. Suppose the equation

$$PA + A^T P + \varepsilon Q - \frac{1}{\varepsilon} PBB^T P + \frac{1}{\gamma} PDD^T P + \frac{1}{\gamma} C^T C = 0$$

where $Q = Q^T > 0$, $\varepsilon > 0$, and $0 < \gamma < 1/k$ has a positive definite solution $P = P^T > 0$. Show that $u = -(1/2\varepsilon)B^T P x$ stabilizes the origin of the perturbed system.

9.6 Consider the system

$$\begin{aligned}
\dot{x}_1 &= -\alpha x_1 - \omega x_2 + (\beta x_1 - \gamma x_2)(x_1^2 + x_2^2) \\
\dot{x}_2 &= \omega x_1 - \alpha x_2 + (\gamma x_1 + \beta x_2)(x_1^2 + x_2^2)
\end{aligned}$$

where $\alpha > 0$, β, γ, and $\omega > 0$ are constants.

(a) By viewing this system as a perturbation of the linear system

$$\dot{x}_1 = -\alpha x_1 - \omega x_2, \qquad \dot{x}_2 = \omega x_1 - \alpha x_2$$

show that the origin of the perturbed system is exponentially stable with $\{\|x\|_2 \leq r\}$ included in the region of attraction, provided $|\beta|$ and $|\gamma|$ are sufficiently small. Find upper bounds on $|\beta|$ and $|\gamma|$ in terms of r.

(b) Using $V(x) = x_1^2 + x_2^2$ as a Lyapunov function candidate for the perturbed system, show that the origin is globally exponentially stable when $\beta \leq 0$ and exponentially stable with $\{\|x\|_2 < \sqrt{\alpha/\beta}\}$ included in the region of attraction when $\beta > 0$.

(c) Compare the results of (a) and (b) and comment on the conservative nature of the result of (a).

9.7 Consider the perturbed system

$$\dot{x} = f(x) + g(x)$$

Suppose the origin of the nominal system $\dot{x} = f(x)$ is asymptotically (but not exponentially) stable. Show that, for any $\gamma > 0$, there is a function $g(x)$ satisfying $\|g(x)\| \leq \gamma\|x\|$ in some neighborhood of the origin such that the origin of the perturbed system is unstable.

9.8 ([66]) Consider the perturbed system

$$\dot{x} = f(x) + g(x)$$

where $f(x)$ and $g(x)$ are continuously differentiable and $\|g(x)\| \leq \gamma\|x\|$ for all $\|x\| < r$. Suppose the origin of the nominal system $\dot{x} = f(x)$ is asymptotically stable and there is a Lyapunov function $V(x)$ that satisfies inequalities (9.11) through (9.13) for all $\|x\| < r$. Let $\Omega = \{V(x) \leq c\}$, with $c < \alpha_1(r)$.

(a) Show that there is a positive constant γ^* such that, for $\gamma < \gamma^*$, the solutions of the perturbed system starting in Ω stay in Ω for all $t \geq 0$ and are ultimately bounded by a class $\mathcal{K}$ function of γ.

(b) Suppose the nominal system has the additional property that $A = [\partial f/\partial x](0)$ is Hurwitz. Show that there is γ_1^* such that, for $\gamma < \gamma_1^*$, the solutions of the perturbed system starting in Ω converge to the origin as $t \to \infty$.

(c) Would (b) hold if A was not Hurwitz? Consider

$$f(x) = \begin{bmatrix} -x_2 - (2x_1 + x_3)^3 \\ x_1 \\ x_2 \end{bmatrix}, \quad g(x) = a \begin{bmatrix} x_1 - x_3 - (2x_1 + x_3)^3 \\ 0 \\ 0 \end{bmatrix}, \quad a \neq 0$$

Hint: For the example of part (c), use

$$V(x) = x_1^2 + \tfrac{1}{2}x_2^2 + \tfrac{1}{2}x_3^2 + x_1 x_3$$

to show that the origin of $\dot{x} = f(x)$ is asymptotically stable and then apply Theorem 4.16 to obtain a Lyapunov function that satisfies (9.11) through (9.13).

9.9 Consider the system

$$\dot{x}_1 = -x_1^3 + x_2^5 - \gamma x_2, \quad \dot{x}_2 = -x_1^3 - x_2^5 + \gamma(x_1 + x_2), \quad 0 \leq \gamma \leq \tfrac{1}{2}$$

(a) With $\gamma = 0$, show that the origin is globally asymptotically stable. Is it exponentially stable?

(b) With $0 < \gamma \leq 1/2$, show that the origin is unstable and the solutions of the system are globally ultimately bounded by an ultimate bound that is a class $\mathcal{K}$ function of γ.

9.10 ([19]) Consider the system

$$\dot{x}_1 = x_2, \quad \dot{x}_2 = -a \sin x_1 - b x_1 - c x_2 - \gamma(c x_1 + 2x_2) + q(t) \cos x_1$$

where a, $b > a$, c, and γ are positive constants and $q(t)$ is a continuous function.

(a) With $q(t) \equiv 0$, use

$$V(x) = \left(b + \tfrac{1}{2}c^2\right) x_1^2 + cx_1x_2 + x_2^2 + 2a(1 - \cos x_1)$$

to show that the origin is globally exponentially stable.

(b) Study the stability of the system when $q(t) \neq 0$ and $|q(t)| \leq k$ for all $t \geq 0$.

9.11 Consider the system

$$\dot{x}_1 = \left[(\sin x_2)^2 - 1\right] x_1, \quad \dot{x}_2 = -bx_1 - (1 + b)x_2$$

(a) With $b = 0$, show that the origin is exponentially stable and globally asymptotically stable.

(b) With $b \neq 0$, show that the origin is exponentially stable for sufficiently small $|b|$, but not globally asymptotically stable, no matter how small $|b|$ is.

(c) Discuss the results of parts (a) and (b) in view of the robustness results of Section 9.1, and show that when $b = 0$ the origin is not globally exponentially stable.

9.12 ([8]) Consider the system

$$\dot{x}_1 = -x_1 + (x_1 + a)x_2, \quad \dot{x}_2 = -x_1(x_1 + a) + bx_2, \quad a \neq 0$$

(a) Let $b = 0$. Show that the origin is globally asymptotically stable. Is it exponentially stable?

(b) Let $b > 0$. Show that the origin is exponentially stable for $b < \min\{1, a^2\}$.

(c) Show that the origin is not globally asymptotically stable for any $b > 0$.

(d) Discuss the results of parts (a) through (c) in view of the robustness results of Section 9.1, and show that when $b = 0$ the origin is not globally exponentially stable.

Hint: In part (d), note that the Jacobian matrix of the nominal system is not globally bounded.

9.13 Consider the scalar system $\dot{x} = -x/(1 + x^2)$ and $V(x) = x^4$.

(a) Show that inequalities (9.11) through (9.13) are satisfied globally with

$$\alpha_1(r) = \alpha_2(r) = r^4; \quad \alpha_3(r) = \frac{4r^4}{1 + r^2}; \quad \alpha_4(r) = 4r^3$$

(b) Verify that these functions belong to class $\mathcal{K}_\infty$.

(c) Show that the right-hand side of (9.14) approaches zero as $r \to \infty$.

(d) Consider the perturbed system $\dot{x} = -x/(1 + x^2) + \delta$, where δ is a positive constant. Show that whenever $\delta > 1/2$, the solution $x(t)$ escapes to ∞ for any initial state $x(0)$.

9.14 Verify that $D^+ W(t)$ satisfies (9.17) when $V = 0$.
Hint: Show that $V(t + h, x(t + h)) \leq 0.5 c_4 h^2 \|g(t, 0)\|^2 + h \, o(h)$, where $o(h)/h \to 0$ as $h \to 0$. Then, use the fact that $\sqrt{c_4/2c_1} \geq 1$.

9.15 Consider the linear system of Example 9.6, but change the assumption on $B(t)$ to $\int_0^\infty \|B(t)\| \, dt < \infty$. Show that the origin is exponentially stable.

9.16 Consider the linear system of Example 9.6, but change the assumption on $B(t)$ to $\int_0^\infty \|B(t)\|^2 \, dt < \infty$. Show that the origin is exponentially stable.
Hint: Use the inequality

$$\int_a^b v(t) \, dt \leq \sqrt{(b - a) \int_a^b v^2(t) \, dt}, \quad \forall \, v(t) \geq 0$$

which follows from the Cauchy–Schwartz inequality.

9.17 Consider the system $\dot{x} = A(t)x$ where $A(t)$ is continuous. Suppose $\lim_{t \to \infty} A(t) = \bar{A}$ exists and $\bar{A}$ is Hurwitz. Show that the origin is exponentially stable.

9.18 Repeat part(b) of Exercise 9.10 when $q(t)$ is bounded and $q(t) \to 0$ as $t \to \infty$.

9.19 Consider the system $\dot{x} = f(t, x)$, where $\|f(t, x) - f(0, x)\|_2 \leq \gamma(t)\|x\|_2$ for all $t \geq 0$, $x \in R^2$, $\gamma(t) \to 0$ as $t \to \infty$,

$$f(0, x) = Ax - (x_1^2 + x_2^2)Bx, \quad A = \begin{bmatrix} -\alpha & -\omega \\ \omega & -\alpha \end{bmatrix}, \quad B = \begin{bmatrix} \beta & \Omega \\ -\Omega & \beta \end{bmatrix}$$

and α, β, ω, Ω are positive constants. Show that the origin is globally exponentially stable.

9.20 Consider the system $\dot{x} = f(x) + G(x)u + w(t)$, where $\|w(t)\|_2 \leq a + c \, e^{-t}$. Suppose there exist a symmetric positive definite matrix P, a positive semidefinite function $W(x)$, and positive constants γ and σ such that

$$2x^T P f(x) + \gamma x^T P x + W(x) - 2\sigma x^T P G(x) G^T(x) P x \leq 0, \quad \forall \, x \in R^n$$

Show that with $u = -\sigma G^T(x)Px$, the trajectories of the closed-loop system are uniformly ultimately bounded by $2ak\lambda_{\max}(P)/\gamma\lambda_{\min}(P)$, for some $k > 1$.

9.21 Consider the perturbed system (9.1). Suppose there is a Lyapunov function $V(t,x)$ that satisfies (9.11) through (9.13), and the perturbation term satisfies $\|g(t,x)\| \leq \delta(t)$, $\forall\, t \geq 0$, $\forall\, x \in D$. Show that for any $\varepsilon > 0$ and $\Delta > 0$, there exist $\eta > 0$ and $\rho > 0$ such that whenever $(1/\Delta) \int_t^{t+\Delta} \delta(\tau)\, d\tau < \eta$, every solution of the perturbed system with $\|x(t_0)\| < \rho$ will satisfy $\|x(t)\| < \varepsilon$, $\forall\, t \geq t_0$.
(This result is known as total stability in the presence of perturbation that is bounded in the mean [107].)
Hint: Choose $W = \sqrt{V}$, discretize the time interval with sampling points at $t_0 + i\Delta$ for $i = 0, 1, 2, \ldots$, and show that $W(t_0 + i\Delta)$ satisfies the difference inequality

$$W(t_0 + (i+1)\Delta) \leq e^{-\sigma\Delta} W(t_0 + i\Delta) + k\eta\Delta$$

9.22 Let A be an $n \times n$ matrix with $a_{ij} \leq 0$ for all $i \neq j$ and $a_{ii} > \sum_{j \neq i} |a_{ij}|$, $i = 1, 2, \ldots, n$. Show that A is an M-matrix.
Hint: Show that $\sum_{j=1}^{n} a_{ij} > 0$ for $i = 1, \ldots, n$, and use mathematical induction to show that all the leading principal minors are positive.

9.23 Suppose the conditions of Theorem 9.3 are satisfied with

$$\phi_i(x_i) = \|x_i\| \quad \text{and} \quad c_{i1}\|x_i\|^2 \leq V_i(t, x_i) \leq c_{i2}\|x_i\|^2$$

Show that the origin is exponentially stable.

9.24 ([132]) Study the stability of the origin of the system

$$\dot{x}_1 = -x_1^3 - 1.5x_1|x_2|^3, \quad \dot{x}_2 = -x_2^5 + x_1^2 x_2^2$$

by using composite Lyapunov analysis.

9.25 Study the stability of the origin of the system

$$\dot{x}_1 = x_2 + x_2 x_3^3, \quad \dot{x}_2 = -x_1 - x_2 + x_1^2, \quad \dot{x}_3 = x_1 + x_2 - x_3^3$$

by using composite Lyapunov analysis.

9.26 Consider the linear interconnected system

$$\dot{x}_i = A_{ii}x_i + \sum_{j=1; j \neq i}^{m} A_{ij}x_j, \quad i = 1, 2, \ldots, m$$

where, for each i, x_i is an n_i-dimensional vector and A_{ii} is a Hurwitz matrix. Study the stability of the origin by using composite Lyapunov analysis.

9.27 ([175]) Complex interconnected systems could be subject to structural perturbations that cause groups of subsystems to be connected or disconnected from each other during operation. Such structural perturbations can be represented as

$$\dot{x}_i = f_i(t, x_i) + g_i(t, e_{i1}x_1, \ldots, e_{im}x_m), \quad i = 1, 2, \ldots, m$$

where e_{ij} is a binary variable that takes the value 1 when the jth subsystem acts on the ith subsystem and the value 0 otherwise. The origin of the interconnected system is said to be connectively asymptotically stable if it is asymptotically stable for all interconnection patterns, that is, for all possible values of the binary variables e_{ij}. Suppose that all the assumptions of Theorem 9.2 are satisfied, with (9.36) taking the form

$$\|g_i(t, e_{i1}x_1, \ldots, e_{im}x_m)\| \leq \sum_{i=1}^{m} e_{ij}\gamma_{ij}\phi_j(x_j)$$

Show that the origin is connectively asymptotically stable.

9.28 ([49]) The output $y(t)$ of the linear system

$$\dot{x} = Ax + Bu, \quad y = Cx$$

is required to track a reference input r. Consider the integral controller

$$\dot{z} = r - Cx, \quad u = -F_1 x - F_2 z$$

where we have assumed that the state x can be measured and the matrices F_1 and F_2 can be designed such that the matrix

$$\begin{bmatrix} A - BF_1 & -BF_2 \\ -C & 0 \end{bmatrix}$$

is Hurwitz.

(a) Show that if $r = $ constant, then $y(t) \to r$ as $t \to \infty$.

(b) Study the tracking properties of the system when $r(t)$ is a slowly varying input.

9.29 ([86]) The output $y(t)$ of the nonlinear system

$$\dot{x} = f(x, u), \quad y = h(x)$$

is required to track a reference input r. Consider the integral controller

$$\dot{z} = r - h(x), \quad u = \gamma(x, z, r)$$

where we have assumed that the state x can be measured, the function γ can be designed such that the closed-loop system

$$\dot{x} = f(x, \gamma(x, z, r)), \quad \dot{z} = r - h(x)$$

has an exponentially stable equilibrium point $(\bar{x}, \bar{z})$, and the functions f, h, and γ are twice continuously differentiable in their arguments.

(a) Show that if $r = $ constant and the initial state $(x(0), z(0))$ is sufficiently close to $(\bar{x}, \bar{z})$, then $y(t) \to r$ as $t \to \infty$.

(b) Study the tracking properties of the system when $r(t)$ is a slowly varying input.

9.30 (**[86]**) Consider the tracking problem of Exercise 9.29, but assume that we can only measure $y = h(x)$. Consider the observer-based integral controller

$$\dot{z}_1 = f(z_1, u) + G(r)[y - h(z_1)], \quad \dot{z}_2 = r - y, \quad \text{and} \quad u = \gamma(z_1, z_2, r)$$

Suppose γ and G can be designed such that the closed-loop system has an exponentially stable equilibrium point $(\bar{x}, \bar{z}_1, \bar{z}_2)$. Study the tracking properties of the system when

    (1) $r = \text{constant}$.   **(2)** $r(t)$ is slowly varying.

9.31 Consider the linear system $\dot{x} = A(t)x$ where $\|A(t)\| \leq k$ and the eigenvalues of $A(t)$ satisfy $\text{Re}[\lambda(t)] \leq -\sigma$ for all $t \geq 0$. Suppose that $\int_0^\infty \|\dot{A}(t)\|^2 \, dt \leq \rho$. Show that the origin of $\dot{x} = A(t)x$ is exponentially stable.

Chapter 10

Perturbation Theory and Averaging

Exact closed-form analytic solutions of nonlinear differential equations are possible only for a limited number of special classes of differential equations. In general, we have to resort to approximate solutions. There are two distinct categories of approximation methods that engineers and scientists should have at their disposal as they analyze nonlinear systems: (1) numerical solution methods and (2) asymptotic methods. In this and the next chapter, we introduce the reader to some asymptotic methods for the analysis of nonlinear differential equations.[1]

Suppose we are given the state equation

$$\dot{x} = f(t, x, \varepsilon)$$

where ε is a "small" scalar parameter, and, under certain conditions, the equation has an exact solution $x(t, \varepsilon)$. Equations of this type are encountered in many applications. The goal of an asymptotic method is to obtain an approximate solution $\tilde{x}(t, \varepsilon)$ such that the approximation error $x(t, \varepsilon) - \tilde{x}(t, \varepsilon)$ is small, in some norm, for small $|\varepsilon|$ and the approximate solution $\tilde{x}(t, \varepsilon)$ is expressed in terms of equations simpler than the original equation. The practical significance of asymptotic methods is in revealing underlying structural properties possessed by the original state equation for small $|\varepsilon|$. We will see, in Section 10.1, examples where asymptotic methods reveal a weak coupling structure among isolated subsystems or the structure of a weakly nonlinear system. More important, asymptotic methods reveal multiple-time-scale structures inherent in many practical problems. Quite often, the solution of the state equation exhibits the phenomenon that some variables move in time faster than other variables, leading to the classification of variables as "slow" and "fast." Both the averaging method of this chapter and the singular perturbation method of the next chapter deal with the interaction of slow and fast variables.

---

[1] Numerical solution methods are not studied in this textbook on the premise that most students are introduced to them in elementary differential equation courses and they get their in-depth study of the subject in numerical analysis courses.

Section 10.1 presents the classical perturbation method of seeking an approximate solution as a finite Taylor expansion of the exact solution. The asymptotic validity of the approximation is established in Section 10.1 on finite time intervals and in Section 10.2 on the infinite-time interval. Section 10.3 examines an autonomous system under the influence of a weak periodic perturbation. While the results of the first three sections are interesting in their own sake, they provide the technical basis for the averaging method. In Section 10.4, we introduce the averaging method in its simplest form, which is sometimes called "periodic averaging" since the right-hand side function is periodic in time. Section 10.5 gives an application of the averaging method to the study of periodic solutions of weakly nonlinear second-order systems. Finally, we present a more general form of the averaging method in Section 10.6.

10.1   The Perturbation Method

Consider the system

$$\dot{x} = f(t, x, \varepsilon) \tag{10.1}$$

where $f : [t_0, t_1] \times D \times [-\varepsilon_0, \varepsilon_0] \to R^n$ is "sufficiently smooth" in its arguments over a domain $D \subset R^n$. The required smoothness conditions will be spelled out as we proceed. Suppose we want to solve the state equation (10.1) for a given initial state

$$x(t_0) = \eta(\varepsilon) \tag{10.2}$$

where, for more generality, we allow the initial state to depend "smoothly" on ε. The solution of (10.1) and (10.2) depends on the parameter ε, a point that we emphasize by writing the solution as $x(t, \varepsilon)$. The goal of the perturbation method is to exploit the "smallness" of the perturbation parameter ε to construct approximate solutions that are valid for sufficiently small $|\varepsilon|$. The simplest approximation results by setting $\varepsilon = 0$ in (10.1) and (10.2) to obtain the nominal or unperturbed problem

$$\dot{x} = f(t, x, 0), \quad x(t_0) = \eta_0 \tag{10.3}$$

where $\eta_0 = \eta(0)$. Suppose this problem has a unique solution $x_0(t)$ defined on $[t_0, t_1]$ and $x_0(t) \in D$ for all $t \in [t_0, t_1]$. Suppose further that f is continuous in (t, x, ε) and locally Lipschitz in (x, ε), uniformly in t, and η is locally Lipschitz in ε for (t, x, ε) in $[t_0, t_1] \times D \times [-\varepsilon_0, \varepsilon_0]$. The closeness of the solutions of the perturbed and unperturbed problems follows from continuity of solutions with respect to initial states and parameters. In particular, Theorem 3.5 shows that there is a positive constant $\varepsilon_1 \leq \varepsilon_0$ such that for all $|\varepsilon| \leq \varepsilon_1$, the problem of (10.1) and (10.2) has a unique solution $x(t, \varepsilon)$ defined on $[t_0, t_1]$. Furthermore, Theorem 3.4 shows that there is a positive constant k such that

$$\|x(t, \varepsilon) - x_0(t)\| \leq k|\varepsilon|, \quad \forall |\varepsilon| < \varepsilon_1, \ \forall \, t \in [t_0, t_1] \tag{10.4}$$

When the approximation error satisfies the bound of (10.4), we say that the error is of order $O(\varepsilon)$ and write

$$x(t, \varepsilon) - x_0(t) = O(\varepsilon)$$

This order of magnitude notation will be used frequently in this chapter and the next one. It is defined next.

Definition 10.1 $\delta_1(\varepsilon) = O(\delta_2(\varepsilon))$ *if there exist positive constants k and c such that*

$$|\delta_1(\varepsilon)| \leq k|\delta_2(\varepsilon)|, \quad \forall\ |\varepsilon| < c$$

Example 10.1

- $\varepsilon^n = O(\varepsilon^m)$ for all $n \geq m$, since

$$|\varepsilon|^n = |\varepsilon|^m|\varepsilon|^{n-m} < |\varepsilon|^m, \quad \forall\ |\varepsilon| < 1$$

- $\varepsilon^2/(0.5 + \varepsilon) = O(\varepsilon^2)$, since

$$\left|\frac{\varepsilon^2}{0.5 + \varepsilon}\right| < \frac{1}{0.5 - a}|\varepsilon|^2, \quad \forall\ |\varepsilon| < a < 0.5$$

- $1 + 2\varepsilon = O(1)$, since

$$|1 + 2\varepsilon| < 1 + 2a, \quad \forall\ |\varepsilon| < a$$

- $\exp(-a/\varepsilon)$ with positive a and ε is $O(\varepsilon^n)$ for any positive integer n, since

$$\frac{e^{-a/\varepsilon}}{\varepsilon^n} \leq \left(\frac{n}{a}\right)^n e^{-n}, \quad \forall\ \varepsilon > 0$$

$\triangle$

What can we say about the numerical value of the approximation error $x(t, \varepsilon) - x_0(t)$ for a given numerical value of ε when the error is $O(\varepsilon)$? Unfortunately, we cannot translate the $O(\varepsilon)$ order of magnitude statement into a numerical bound on the error. Knowing that the error is $O(\varepsilon)$ means that its norm is less than $k|\varepsilon|$ for some positive constant k that is independent of ε. However, we do not know the value of k, which might be 1, 10, or any positive number.[2] The fact that k is independent of ε guarantees that the bound $k|\varepsilon|$ decreases monotonically as $|\varepsilon|$ decreases. Therefore, for sufficiently small $|\varepsilon|$, the error will be small. More precisely, given any tolerance δ, we know that the norm of the error will be less

---

[2]It should be noted, however, that in a well-formulated perturbation problem where variables are normalized to have dimensionless state variables, time, and perturbation parameter, one should expect the numerical value of k not to be much larger than one. See Example 10.4 for further discussion of normalization, or consult [98] and [141] for more examples.

than δ for all $|\varepsilon| < \delta/k$. If this range is too small to cover the numerical values of interest for ε, we then need to extend the range of validity by obtaining a higher order approximation. An $O(\varepsilon^2)$ approximation will meet the same δ tolerance for all $|\varepsilon| < \sqrt{\delta/k_2}$, an $O(\varepsilon^3)$ approximation will do it for all $|\varepsilon| < (\delta/k_3)^{1/3}$, and so on. Although the constants $k, k_2, k_3, \ldots$ are not necessarily equal, these intervals are increasing in length, since the tolerance δ is typically much smaller than one. Another way to look at higher order approximations is to see that, for a given "sufficiently small" value of ε, an $O(\varepsilon^n)$ error will be smaller than an $O(\varepsilon^m)$ error for $n > m$, since

$$\frac{k_1|\varepsilon|^n}{k_2|\varepsilon|^m} < 1, \quad \forall \ |\varepsilon| < \left(\frac{k_2}{k_1}\right)^{1/(n-m)}$$

Higher-order approximations for solutions of (10.1) and (10.2) can be obtained in a straightforward manner, provided the functions f and η are sufficiently smooth. Suppose f and η have continuous partial derivatives with respect to (x, ε) up to order N for $(t, x, \varepsilon) \in [t_0, t_1] \times D \times [-\varepsilon_0, \varepsilon_0]$. To obtain a higher order approximation of $x(t, \varepsilon)$, we construct a finite Taylor series

$$x(t, \varepsilon) = \sum_{k=0}^{N-1} x_k(t)\varepsilon^k + \varepsilon^N R_x(t, \varepsilon) \tag{10.5}$$

Two things need to be done here. First, we need to calculate the terms x_0, x_1, $\ldots$, x_{N-1}; in the process of doing that, it will be shown that these terms are well defined. Second, we need to show that the remainder term R_x is well defined and bounded on $[t_0, t_1]$, which will establish that $\sum_{k=0}^{N-1} x_k(t)\varepsilon^k$ is an $O(\varepsilon^N)$ (Nth-order) approximation of $x(t, \varepsilon)$. By Taylor's theorem,[3] the smoothness requirement on the initial state $\eta(\varepsilon)$ guarantees the existence of a finite Taylor series for $\eta(\varepsilon)$; that is,

$$\eta(\varepsilon) = \sum_{k=0}^{N-1} \eta_k \varepsilon^k + \varepsilon^N R_\eta(\varepsilon)$$

Therefore,

$$x_k(t_0) = \eta_k, \quad k = 0, 1, 2, \ldots, N-1$$

Substituting (10.5) into (10.1) yields

$$\sum_{k=0}^{N-1} \dot{x}_k(t)\varepsilon^k + \varepsilon^N \dot{R}_x(t, \varepsilon) \ = \ f(t, x(t, \varepsilon), \varepsilon) \ \stackrel{\text{def}}{=} \ h(t, \varepsilon)$$

$$= \ \sum_{k=0}^{N-1} h_k(t)\varepsilon^k + \varepsilon^N R_h(t, \varepsilon) \tag{10.6}$$

where the coefficients of the Taylor series of $h(t, \varepsilon)$ are functions of the coefficients of the Taylor series of $x(t, \varepsilon)$. Since (10.6) holds for all sufficiently small ε, it must hold

---

[3]See [10, Theorem 5-14].

as an identity in ε. Hence, coefficients of like powers of ε must be equal. Matching those coefficients, we can derive the equations that must be satisfied by x_0, x_1, and so on. Before we do that, we have to generate the coefficients of the Taylor series of $h(t,\varepsilon)$. The zeroth-order term $h_0(t)$ is given by

$$h_0(t) = f(t, x_0(t), 0)$$

Consequently, matching coefficients of ε^0 in (10.6), we determine that $x_0(t)$ satisfies

$$\dot{x}_0 = f(t, x_0, 0), \quad x_0(t_0) = \eta_0$$

which, not surprisingly, is the unperturbed problem (10.3). The first-order term $h_1(t)$ is given by

$$
\begin{aligned}
h_1(t) &= \left. \frac{\partial}{\partial \varepsilon} f(t, x(t, \varepsilon), \varepsilon) \right|_{\varepsilon=0} \\
&= \left. \left\{ \frac{\partial f}{\partial x}(t, x(t, \varepsilon), \varepsilon) \frac{\partial x}{\partial \varepsilon}(t, \varepsilon) + \frac{\partial f}{\partial \varepsilon}(t, x(t, \varepsilon), \varepsilon) \right\} \right|_{\varepsilon=0} \\
&= \frac{\partial f}{\partial x}(t, x_0(t), 0) \, x_1(t) + \frac{\partial f}{\partial \varepsilon}(t, x_0(t), 0)
\end{aligned}
$$

Matching coefficients of ε in (10.6), we find that $x_1(t)$ satisfies

$$\dot{x}_1 = \frac{\partial f}{\partial x}(t, x_0(t), 0) \, x_1 + \frac{\partial f}{\partial \varepsilon}(t, x_0(t), 0), \quad x_1(t_0) = \eta_1$$

Define

$$A(t) = \frac{\partial f}{\partial x}(t, x_0(t), 0), \quad g_1(t, x_0(t)) = \frac{\partial f}{\partial \varepsilon}(t, x_0(t), 0)$$

and rewrite the equation for x_1 as

$$\dot{x}_1 = A(t)x_1 + g_1(t, x_0(t)), \quad x_1(t_0) = \eta_1$$

This linear equation has a unique solution defined on $[t_0, t_1]$.

The process can be continued to derive the equations satisfied by x_2, x_3, and so on. This, however, will involve higher order differentials of f with respect to x, which makes the notation cumbersome. There is no point in writing the equations in a general form. Once the idea is clear, we can generate the equations for the specific problem of interest. Nevertheless, to set the pattern that these equations take, we will, at the risk of boring some readers, derive the equation for x_2. The second-order coefficient in the Taylor series of $h(t, \varepsilon)$ is given by

$$h_2(t) = \left. \frac{1}{2} \frac{\partial^2}{\partial \varepsilon^2} h(t, \varepsilon) \right|_{\varepsilon=0}$$

Now,

$$\frac{\partial}{\partial \varepsilon} h(t, \varepsilon) = \frac{\partial f}{\partial x}(t, x, \varepsilon) \frac{\partial x}{\partial \varepsilon}(t, \varepsilon) + \frac{\partial f}{\partial \varepsilon}(t, x, \varepsilon)$$

$$= \frac{\partial f}{\partial x}(t, x, \varepsilon)[x_1(t) + 2\varepsilon x_2(t) + \cdots] + \frac{\partial f}{\partial \varepsilon}(t, x, \varepsilon)$$

To simplify the notation, let

$$\psi(t, x, \varepsilon) = \frac{\partial f}{\partial x}(t, x, \varepsilon)\, x_1(t)$$

and continue to calculate the second derivative of h with respect to ε:

$$\frac{\partial^2}{\partial \varepsilon^2} h(t, \varepsilon) = \frac{\partial \psi}{\partial x}(t, x, \varepsilon) \frac{\partial x}{\partial \varepsilon}(t, \varepsilon) + \frac{\partial}{\partial \varepsilon} \frac{\partial f}{\partial x}(t, x, \varepsilon)\, x_1(t)$$

$$+ 2\frac{\partial f}{\partial x}(t, x, \varepsilon)\, x_2(t) + \frac{\partial}{\partial x} \frac{\partial f}{\partial \varepsilon}(t, x, \varepsilon) \frac{\partial x}{\partial \varepsilon}(t, \varepsilon)$$

$$+ \frac{\partial^2 f}{\partial \varepsilon^2}(t, x, \varepsilon) + \varepsilon[\,\cdot\,]$$

Thus,

$$h_2(t) = A(t)x_2(t) + g_2(t, x_0(t), x_1(t))$$

where

$$g_2(t, x_0(t), x_1(t)) = \frac{1}{2} \frac{\partial \psi}{\partial x}(t, x_0(t), 0)\, x_1(t) + \frac{\partial}{\partial \varepsilon} \frac{\partial f}{\partial x}(t, x_0(t), 0)\, x_1(t)$$

$$+ \frac{1}{2} \frac{\partial^2 f}{\partial \varepsilon^2}(t, x_0(t), 0)$$

Matching coefficients of ε^2 in (10.6) yields

$$\dot{x}_2 = A(t)x_2 + g_2(t, x_0(t), x_1(t)), \qquad x_2(t_0) = \eta_2$$

In summary, the Taylor series coefficients x_0, x_1, ..., x_{N-1} are obtained by solving the equations

$$\dot{x}_0 = f(t, x_0, 0), \qquad x_0(t_0) = \eta_0 \tag{10.7}$$

$$\dot{x}_k = A(t)x_k + g_k(t, x_0(t), \dots, x_{k-1}(t)), \qquad x_k(t_0) = \eta_k \tag{10.8}$$

for $k = 1, 2, \dots, N-1$, where $A(t)$ is the Jacobian $[\partial f/\partial x]$ evaluated at $x = x_0(t)$ and $\varepsilon = 0$, and the term $g_k(t, x_0(t), x_1(t), \dots, x_{k-1}(t))$ is a polynomial in $x_1, \dots, x_{k-1}$ with coefficients depending continuously on t and $x_0(t)$. The assumption that $x_0(t)$ is defined on $[t_0, t_1]$ implies that $A(t)$ is defined on the same interval; hence, the linear equations (10.8) have unique solutions defined on $[t_0, t_1]$. Let us now illustrate the calculation of the Taylor series coefficients by a second-order example.

Example 10.2 Consider the Van der Pol state equation

$$\dot{x}_1 = x_2, \qquad\qquad x_1(0) = \eta_1(\varepsilon)$$

$$\dot{x}_2 = -x_1 + \varepsilon(1 - x_1^2)x_2, \quad x_2(0) = \eta_2(\varepsilon)$$

Suppose we want to construct a finite Taylor series with $N = 3$. Let

$$x_i = x_{i0} + \varepsilon x_{i1} + \varepsilon^2 x_{i2} + \varepsilon^3 R_{x_i}, \quad i = 1, 2$$

and

$$\eta_i = \eta_{i0} + \varepsilon\eta_{i1} + \varepsilon^2\eta_{i2} + \varepsilon^3 R_{\eta_i}, \quad i = 1, 2$$

Substituting the series for x_1 and x_2 into the state equation results in

$$\dot{x}_{10} + \varepsilon\dot{x}_{11} + \varepsilon^2\dot{x}_{12} + \varepsilon^3\dot{R}_{x_1} = x_{20} + \varepsilon x_{21} + \varepsilon^2 x_{22} + \varepsilon^3 R_{x_2}$$
$$\dot{x}_{20} + \varepsilon\dot{x}_{21} + \varepsilon^2\dot{x}_{22} + \varepsilon^3\dot{R}_{x_2} = -x_{10} - \varepsilon x_{11} - \varepsilon^2 x_{12} - \varepsilon^3 R_{x_1}$$
$$+ \varepsilon\left[1 - (x_{10} + \varepsilon x_{11} + \varepsilon^2 x_{12} + \varepsilon^3 R_{x_1})^2\right]$$
$$\times (x_{20} + \varepsilon x_{21} + \varepsilon^2 x_{22} + \varepsilon^3 R_{x_2})$$

Matching coefficients of ε^0, we obtain

$$\dot{x}_{10} = x_{20}, \quad x_{10}(0) = \eta_{10}$$

$$\dot{x}_{20} = -x_{10}, \quad x_{20}(0) = \eta_{20}$$

which is the unperturbed problem at $\varepsilon = 0$. Matching coefficients of ε, we obtain

$$\dot{x}_{11} = x_{21}, \qquad\qquad x_{11}(0) = \eta_{11}$$

$$\dot{x}_{21} = -x_{11} + (1 - x_{10}^2)x_{20}, \quad x_{21}(0) = \eta_{21}$$

while matching coefficients of ε^2 results in

$$\dot{x}_{12} = x_{22}, \qquad\qquad\qquad x_{12}(0) = \eta_{12}$$

$$\dot{x}_{22} = -x_{12} + (1 - x_{10}^2)x_{21} - 2x_{10}x_{11}x_{20}, \quad x_{22}(0) = \eta_{22}$$

The latter two sets of equations are in the form of (10.8) for $k = 1, 2$. $\qquad\triangle$

Having calculated the terms x_0, x_1, ..., x_{N-1}, our task now is to show that $\sum_{k=0}^{N-1} x_k(t)\varepsilon^k$ is indeed an $O(\varepsilon^N)$ approximation of $x(t, \varepsilon)$. Consider the approximation error

$$e = x - \sum_{k=0}^{N-1} x_k(t)\varepsilon^k \tag{10.9}$$

Differentiating both sides of (10.9) with respect to t and substituting for the derivatives of x and x_k from (10.1), (10.7), and (10.8), it can be shown that e satisfies the equation

$$\dot{e} = A(t)e + \rho_1(t, e, \varepsilon) + \rho_2(t, \varepsilon), \quad e(t_0) = \varepsilon^N R_\eta(\varepsilon) \tag{10.10}$$

where

$$\rho_1(t, e, \varepsilon) = f\left(t, e + \sum_{k=0}^{N-1} x_k(t)\varepsilon^k, \varepsilon\right) - f\left(t, \sum_{k=0}^{N-1} x_k(t)\varepsilon^k, \varepsilon\right) - A(t)e$$

$$\rho_2(t, \varepsilon) = f\left(t, \sum_{k=0}^{N-1} x_k(t)\varepsilon^k, \varepsilon\right) - f(t, x_0(t), 0) - \sum_{k=1}^{N-1} \left[A(t)x_k(t) + g_k(\cdot)\right]\varepsilon^k$$

By assumption, $x_0(t)$ is bounded and belongs to D for all $t \in [t_0, t_1]$. Hence, there exist $\lambda > 0$ and $\varepsilon_1 > 0$ such that for all $\|e\| \le \lambda$ and $|\varepsilon| \le \varepsilon_1$, the functions $x_0(t)$, $\sum_{k=0}^{N-1} x_k(t)\varepsilon^k$, and $e + \sum_{k=0}^{N-1} x_k(t)\varepsilon^k$ belong to a compact subset of D. It can be easily verified that

$$\rho_1(t, 0, \varepsilon) = 0 \tag{10.11}$$

$$\|\rho_1(t, e_2, \varepsilon) - \rho_1(t, e_1, \varepsilon)\| \le k_1\|e_2 - e_1\| \tag{10.12}$$

$$\|\rho_2(t, \varepsilon)\| \le k_2|\varepsilon|^N \tag{10.13}$$

for all $t \in [t_0, t_1]$, $e_1, e_2 \in B_\lambda$, $\varepsilon \in [-\varepsilon_1, \varepsilon_1]$, for some positive constants k_1 and k_2. Equation (10.10) can be viewed as a perturbation of

$$\dot{e}_0 = A(t)e_0 + \rho_1(t, e_0, \varepsilon), \quad e_0(t_0) = 0 \tag{10.14}$$

which has the unique solution $e_0(t, \varepsilon) \equiv 0$ for $t \in [t_0, t_1]$. Applying Theorem 3.5 shows that (10.10) has a unique solution defined on $[t_0, t_1]$ for sufficiently small $|\varepsilon|$. Applying Theorem 3.4 shows that

$$\|e(t, \varepsilon)\| = \|e(t, \varepsilon) - e_0(t, \varepsilon)\| = O(\varepsilon^N)$$

We summarize our conclusion in the next theorem.

Theorem 10.1 *Suppose*

- *f and its partial derivatives with respect to (x, ε) up to order N are continuous in (t, x, ε) for $(t, x, \varepsilon) \in [t_0, t_1] \times D \times [-\varepsilon_0, \varepsilon_0]$;*

- *η and its derivatives up to order N are continuous for $\varepsilon \in [-\varepsilon_0, \varepsilon_0]$;*

- *the nominal problem given in (10.3) has a unique solution $x_0(t)$ defined on $[t_0, t_1]$ and $x_0(t) \in D$ for all $t \in [t_0, t_1]$.*

Then, there exists $\varepsilon^* > 0$ such that $\forall \, |\varepsilon| < \varepsilon^*$, the problem given by (10.1) and (10.2) has a unique solution $x(t, \varepsilon)$, defined on $[t_0, t_1]$, which satisfies

$$x(t, \varepsilon) - \sum_{k=0}^{N-1} x_k(t) \varepsilon^k = O(\varepsilon^N)$$

$\diamond$

When we approximate $x(t, \varepsilon)$ by $x_0(t)$, we need not know the value of the parameter ε, which could be an unknown parameter that represents deviations of the system's parameters from their nominal values. When we use a higher order approximation $\sum_{k=0}^{N-1} x_k(t) \varepsilon^k$ for $N \geq 2$, we need to know the value of ε to construct the series, even though we do not need it to calculate the terms x_1, x_2, and so on. If we have to know ε to construct the Taylor series approximation, we must then compare the computational effort needed to approximate the solution via a Taylor series with the effort needed to calculate the exact solution. The exact solution $x(t, \varepsilon)$ can be obtained by solving the nonlinear state equation (10.1), while the approximate solution is obtained by solving the nonlinear state equation (10.7) and a number of linear state equations (10.8), depending on the order of the approximation. Since, in both cases, we have to solve a nonlinear state equation of order n, we must ask ourselves, What do we gain by solving (10.7) instead of (10.1)? One situation where the Taylor series approximation will be clearly preferable is the case when the solution is sought for several values of ε. In the Taylor series approximation, equations (10.7) and (10.8) will be solved only once; then, different Taylor expansions will be constructed for different values of ε. Aside from this special (repeated values of ε) case, we find the Taylor series approximation to be effective when

- the unperturbed state equation (10.7) is considerably simpler than the ε-dependent state equation (10.1), and

- ε is reasonably small that an "acceptable" approximation can be achieved with a few terms in the series.

In most engineering applications of the perturbation method, adequate approximations are achieved with $N = 2$ or 3, and the process of setting $\varepsilon = 0$ simplifies the state equation considerably. In the next two examples, we look at two typical cases where setting $\varepsilon = 0$ reduces the complexity of the state equation. In the first example, we consider again the Van der Pol equation of Example 10.2, which represents a wide class of "weakly nonlinear systems" that become linear at $\varepsilon = 0$. To construct a Taylor series approximation, we only solve linear equations. In the second example, we look at a system formed of interconnected subsystems with "weak" or ε-coupling. At $\varepsilon = 0$, the system decomposes into lower order decoupled subsystems. To construct a Taylor series approximation, we always solve lower order decoupled equations as opposed to solving the original higher order equation (10.1).

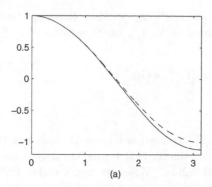 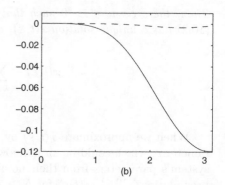

Figure 10.1: Example 10.3 at $\varepsilon = 0.1$: (a) $x_1(t, \varepsilon)$ (solid) and $x_{10}(t)$ (dashed); (b) $x_1(t, \varepsilon) - x_{10}(t)$ (solid) and $x_1(t, \varepsilon) - x_{10}(t) - \varepsilon x_{11}(t)$ (dashed).

Example 10.3 Suppose we want to solve the Van der Pol equation

$$\dot{x}_1 = x_2, \qquad\qquad x_1(0) = 1$$

$$\dot{x}_2 = -x_1 + \varepsilon(1 - x_1^2)x_2, \quad x_2(0) = 0$$

over the time interval $[0, \pi]$. We start by setting $\varepsilon = 0$ to obtain the linear unperturbed equation

$$\dot{x}_{10} = x_{20}, \quad x_{10}(0) = 1$$

$$\dot{x}_{20} = -x_{10}, \quad x_{20}(0) = 0$$

whose solution is

$$x_{10}(t) = \cos t, \quad x_{20}(t) = -\sin t$$

Clearly, all the assumptions of Theorem 10.1 are satisfied, and we conclude that the approximation error $x(t, \varepsilon) - x_0(t)$ is $O(\varepsilon)$. Calculating $x(t, \varepsilon)$ numerically at three different values of ε and using

$$E_0 = \max_{0 \le t \le \pi} \|x(t, \varepsilon) - x_0(t)\|_2$$

as a measure of the approximation error, we find that $E_0 = 0.0112$, 0.0589, and 0.1192 for $\varepsilon = 0.01$, 0.05, and 0.1, respectively. These numbers show that the error is bounded by 1.2ε for $\varepsilon \le 0.1$. Figure 10.1(a) shows the exact and approximate trajectories of the first component of the state vector when $\varepsilon = 0.1$. Suppose we want to improve the approximation at $\varepsilon = 0.1$. From Example 10.2, we know that x_{11} and x_{21} satisfy the equation

$$\dot{x}_{11} = x_{21}, \qquad\qquad x_{11}(0) = 0$$

$$\dot{x}_{21} = -x_{11} - (1 - \cos^2 t)\sin t, \quad x_{21}(0) = 0$$

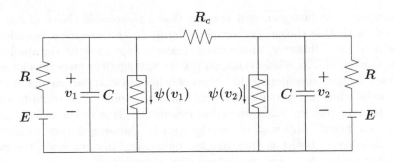

Figure 10.2: Electric circuit of Example 10.4.

whose solution is

$$
\begin{aligned}
x_{11}(t) &= -\tfrac{9}{32}\sin t - \tfrac{1}{32}\sin 3t + \tfrac{3}{8}t\cos t \\
x_{21}(t) &= \tfrac{3}{32}\cos t - \tfrac{3}{32}\cos 3t - \tfrac{3}{8}t\sin t
\end{aligned}
$$

By Theorem 10.1, the second-order approximation $x_0(t) + \varepsilon x_1(t)$ is $O(\varepsilon^2)$ close to the exact solution for sufficiently small ε. To compare the approximate solution with the exact one at $\varepsilon = 0.1$, we calculate

$$
E_1 = \max_{0 \le t \le \pi} \|x(t, 0.1) - x_0(t) - 0.1 x_1(t)\|_2 = 0.0057
$$

which shows a reduction in the approximation error by almost an order of magnitude. Figure 10.1(b) shows the approximation errors in the first component of the state vector for the first-order approximation x_0 and the second-order approximation $x_0 + \varepsilon x_1$ at $\varepsilon = 0.1$.
$\triangle$

Example 10.4 The circuit shown in Figure 10.2 contains nonlinear resistors whose I–V characteristics are given by $i = \psi(v)$. The differential equations for the voltages across the capacitors are

$$
\begin{aligned}
C\frac{dv_1}{dt} &= \frac{1}{R}(E - v_1) - \psi(v_1) - \frac{1}{R_c}(v_1 - v_2) \\
C\frac{dv_2}{dt} &= \frac{1}{R}(E - v_2) - \psi(v_2) - \frac{1}{R_c}(v_2 - v_1)
\end{aligned}
$$

The circuit has two similar RC sections connected through the resistor R_c. When R_c is "relatively large," the connection between the two sections becomes "weak." In particular, when $R_c = \infty$, the connection is open circuit and the two sections are decoupled from each other. This circuit lends itself to an ε-coupling representation where the coupling between the two sections may be parameterized by a small parameter ε. At first glance, it appears that a reasonable choice of ε is $\varepsilon = 1/R_c$. Indeed, with this choice, the coupling terms in the foregoing equations will be multiplied by ε. However, such a choice makes ε dependent on the absolute value of a physical parameter whose value, no matter how small or large, has no significance by itself without considering the values of other physical parameters in the system. In a well-formulated perturbation problem, the parameter ε would be chosen as a ratio between physical parameters that reflects the "true smallness" of ε in a relative sense. To choose ε this way, we usually start by choosing the state variables or the time variable (or both) as dimensionless quantities. In our circuit, the clear choice of state variables is v_1 and v_2. Instead of working with v_1 and v_2, we scale them in such a way that the typical extreme values of the scaled variables would be close to ± 1. Due to the weak coupling between the two identical sections, it is reasonable to use the same scaling factor α for both state variables. Define the state variables as $x_1 = v_1/\alpha$ and $x_2 = v_2/\alpha$. Taking a dimensionless time $\tau = t/RC$ and writing $dx/d\tau = \dot{x}$, we obtain the state equation

$$
\begin{aligned}
\dot{x}_1 &= \frac{E}{\alpha} - x_1 - \frac{R}{\alpha}\psi(\alpha x_1) - \frac{R}{R_c}(x_1 - x_2) \\
\dot{x}_2 &= \frac{E}{\alpha} - x_2 - \frac{R}{\alpha}\psi(\alpha x_2) - \frac{R}{R_c}(x_2 - x_1)
\end{aligned}
$$

It appears now that a reasonable choice of ε is R/R_c. Suppose that $R = 1.5 \times 10^3$ Ω, $E = 1.2\ V$, and the nonlinear resistors are tunnel diodes with

$$
\psi(v) = 10^{-3} \times \left(17.76v - 103.79v^2 + 229.62v^3 - 226.31v^4 + 83.72v^5\right)
$$

Take $\alpha = 1$ and rewrite the state equation as

$$
\begin{aligned}
\dot{x}_1 &= 1.2 - x_1 - h(x_1) - \varepsilon(x_1 - x_2) \\
\dot{x}_2 &= 1.2 - x_2 - h(x_2) - \varepsilon(x_2 - x_1)
\end{aligned}
$$

where $h(v) = 1.5 \times 10^3 \times \psi(v)$. Suppose we want to solve this equation for the initial state

$$
x_1(0) = 0.15; \quad x_2(0) = 0.6
$$

Setting $\varepsilon = 0$, we obtain the decoupled equations

$$
\dot{x}_1 = 1.2 - x_1 - h(x_1), \quad x_1(0) = 0.15
$$

$$
\dot{x}_2 = 1.2 - x_2 - h(x_2), \quad x_2(0) = 0.6
$$

which are solved independently of each other. Let $x_{10}(t)$ and $x_{20}(t)$ be the solutions. According to Theorem 10.1, they provide an $O(\varepsilon)$ approximation of the exact solution for sufficiently small ε. To obtain an $O(\varepsilon^2)$ approximation, we set up the equations for x_{11} and x_{21} as

$$
\dot{x}_{11} = -[1 + h'(x_{10}(t))]x_{11} - [x_{10}(t) - x_{20}(t)], \quad x_{11}(0) = 0
$$

$$
\dot{x}_{21} = -[1 + h'(x_{20}(t))]x_{21} - [x_{20}(t) - x_{10}(t)], \quad x_{21}(0) = 0
$$

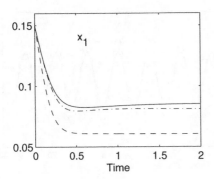 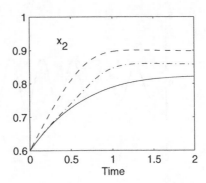

Figure 10.3: Exact solution (solid), first-order approximation (dashed), and second-order approximation (dash-dot) for Example 10.4 at $\varepsilon = 0.3$.

where $h'(\cdot)$ is the derivative of $h(\cdot)$. Figure 10.3 shows the exact solution as well as the first-order and second-order approximations for $\varepsilon = 0.3$. $\triangle$

A serious limitation of Theorem 10.1 is that the $O(\varepsilon^N)$ error bound is valid only on finite (order $O(1)$) time intervals $[t_0, t_1]$. It does not hold on intervals like $[t_0, T/\varepsilon)$ nor on the infinite-time interval $[t_0, \infty)$. The reason is that the constant k in the bound $k|\varepsilon|^N$ depends on t_1 in such a way that it grows unbounded as t_1 increases. In particular, since the constant k results from application of Theorem 3.4, it has a component of the form $\exp(Lt_1)$. In the next section, we will see how to employ stability conditions to extend Theorem 10.1 to the infinite interval. In the lack of such stability conditions, the approximation may not be valid for large t, even though it is valid on $O(1)$ time intervals. Figure 10.4 shows the exact and approximate solutions for the Van der Pol equation of Example 10.3, at $\varepsilon = 0.1$, over a large time interval. For large t, the error $x_1(t, \varepsilon) - x_{10}(t)$ is no longer $O(\varepsilon)$. More seriously, the error $x_1(t, \varepsilon) - x_{10}(t) - \varepsilon x_{11}(t)$ grows unbounded, which is a consequence of the term $t \cos t$ in $x_{11}(t)$.

10.2   Perturbation on the Infinite Interval

The perturbation result of Theorem 10.1 can be extended to the infinite time interval $[t_0, \infty)$ under some additional stability conditions. In the next theorem, we require the nominal system (10.7) to have an exponentially stable equilibrium point at the origin and use a Lyapunov function to estimate its region of attraction. There is no loss of generality in taking the equilibrium point at the origin, since any equilibrium point can be shifted to the origin by a change of variables.

Theorem 10.2 *Let $D \subset R^n$ be a domain that contains the origin and suppose*

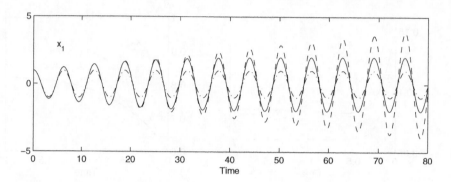

Figure 10.4: Exact solution (solid), first-order approximation (dash-dot), and second-order approximation (dashed) for the Van der Pol equation over a large time interval.

- f *and its partial derivatives with respect to* (x, ε) *up to order* N *are continuous and bounded for* $(t, x, \varepsilon) \in [0, \infty) \times D_0 \times [-\varepsilon_0, \varepsilon_0]$, *for every compact set* $D_0 \subset D$; *if* $N = 1$, $[\partial f / \partial x](t, x, \varepsilon)$ *is Lipschitz in* (x, ε), *uniformly in* t;

- η *and its derivatives up to order* N *are continuous for* $\varepsilon \in [-\varepsilon_0, \varepsilon_0]$;

- *the origin is an exponentially stable equilibrium point of the nominal system* (10.7);

- *there is a Lyapunov function* $V(t, x)$ *that satisfies the conditions of Theorem 4.9 for the nominal system* (10.7) *for* $(t, x) \in [0, \infty) \times D$ *and* $\{W_1(x) \leq c\}$ *is a compact subset of* D.

Then, for each compact set $\Omega \subset \{W_2(x) \leq \rho c, \ 0 < \rho < 1\}$, *there is a positive constant* ε^* *such that for all* $t_0 \geq 0$, $\eta_0 \in \Omega$, *and* $|\varepsilon| < \varepsilon^*$, *equations* (10.1) *and* (10.2) *have a unique solution* $x(t, \varepsilon)$, *uniformly bounded on* $[t_0, \infty)$, *and*

$$x(t, \varepsilon) - \sum_{k=0}^{N-1} x_k(t) \varepsilon^k = O(\varepsilon^N)$$

where $O(\varepsilon^N)$ *holds uniformly in* t *for all* $t \geq t_0$. $\diamond$

If the nominal system (10.7) is autonomous, the set Ω in Theorem 10.2 can be any compact subset of the region of attraction of the origin. This is a consequence of (the converse Lyapunov) Theorem 4.17, since the Lyapunov function $V(x)$ provided by the theorem has the property that any compact subset of the region of attraction can be included in the interior of a compact set of the form $\{V(x) \leq c\}$.

Proof of Theorem 10.2: Application of Theorem 9.1 shows that there is $\varepsilon_1 > 0$

such that for all $|\varepsilon| < \varepsilon_1$, $x(t, \varepsilon)$ is uniformly bounded and $x(t, \varepsilon) - x_0(t)$ is $O(\varepsilon)$, uniformly in t, for all $t \geq t_0$. It is also clear that for $\eta_0 \in \Omega$, $x_0(t)$ is uniformly bounded and $\lim_{t \to \infty} x_0(t) = 0$. Consider the linear equations (10.8). We know from bounded-input–bounded-output stability (Theorem 5.1) that the solution of (10.8) will be uniformly bounded if the origin of $\dot{z} = A(t)z$ is exponentially stable and the input term g_k is bounded. The input g_k is a polynomial in $x_1, \ldots, x_{k-1}$ with coefficients depending on t and $x_0(t)$. The dependence on t comes through the partial derivatives of f, which are bounded on compact subsets of D. Since $x_0(t)$ is bounded, the polynomial coefficients are bounded for all $t \geq t_0$. Hence, boundedness of g_k will follow from boundedness of $x_1, \ldots, x_{k-1}$. The matrix $A(t)$ is given by

$$A(t) = \frac{\partial f}{\partial x}(t, x_0(t), 0)$$

where $x_0(t)$ is the solution of the nominal system (10.7). It turns out that exponential stability of the origin as an equilibrium for (10.7) ensures that the origin of $\dot{z} = A(t)z$ will be exponentially stable for every solution $x_0(t)$ that starts in the set Ω. To see this point, let

$$A_0(t) = \frac{\partial f}{\partial x}(t, 0, 0)$$

and write

$$A(t) = A_0(t) + [A(t) - A_0(t)] \stackrel{\text{def}}{=} A_0(t) + B(t)$$

so that the linear system $\dot{z} = A(t)z$ can be viewed as a linear perturbation of $\dot{y} = A_0(t)y$. Since $[\partial f/\partial x](t, x, 0)$ is Lipschitz in x, uniformly in t,

$$\|B(t)\| = \left\| \frac{\partial f}{\partial x}(t, x_0(t), 0) - \frac{\partial f}{\partial x}(t, 0, 0) \right\| \leq L\|x_0(t)\|$$

On the other hand, by exponential stability of the origin of (10.7) and Theorem 4.15, we know that the origin of the linear system $\dot{y} = A_0(t)y$ is exponentially stable. Therefore, similar to Example 9.6, we can use $\lim_{t \to \infty} x_0(t) = 0$ to show that the origin of the linear system $\dot{z} = A(t)z$ is exponentially stable.

Since $\|x_0(t)\|$ is bounded and $g_1(t, x_0(t)) = [\partial f/\partial \varepsilon](t, x_0(t), 0)$, we see that g_1 is bounded for all $t \geq t_0$. Hence, by Theorem 5.1, we conclude that $x_1(t)$ is bounded. By a simple induction argument, we can see that $x_2(t), \ldots, x_{k-1}(t)$ are bounded.

So far, we have verified that the exact solution $x(t, \varepsilon)$ and the approximate solution $\sum_{k=0}^{N-1} x_k(t)\varepsilon^k$ are uniformly bounded on $[t_0, \infty)$ for sufficiently small $|\varepsilon|$. All that remains now is to analyze the approximation error $e = x - \sum_{k=0}^{N-1} x_k(t)\varepsilon^k$. The error analysis is quite similar to what we have done in Section 10.1. The error satisfies (10.10), where ρ_1 and ρ_2 satisfy (10.11), (10.13) and

$$\left\| \frac{\partial \rho_1}{\partial e}(t, e, \varepsilon) \right\| \leq k_1(\|e\| + |\varepsilon|)$$

for all $(t, e, \varepsilon) \in [t_0, \infty) \times B_\lambda \times [-\varepsilon_1, \varepsilon_1]$ for sufficiently small ε_1. The error equation (10.10) can be viewed as a perturbation of $\dot{e} = A(t)e$, where the perturbation term satisfies

$$\|\rho_1(t, e, \varepsilon) + \rho_2(t, \varepsilon)\| \le k_1(\|e\| + |\varepsilon|)\|e\| + k_2|\varepsilon|^N \le k_1(\lambda + |\varepsilon|)\|e\| + k_2|\varepsilon|^N$$

Noting that $\|e(t_0, \varepsilon)\| = O(\varepsilon^N)$, we conclude from Lemma 9.4 that, for sufficiently small $|\varepsilon|$, $\|e(t, \varepsilon)\| = O(\varepsilon^N)$ for all $t \ge t_0$.   □

Example 10.5 The electric circuit of Example 10.4 is represented by

$$\begin{aligned}
\dot{x}_1 &= 1.2 - x_1 - h(x_1) - \varepsilon(x_1 - x_2) \\
\dot{x}_2 &= 1.2 - x_2 - h(x_2) - \varepsilon(x_2 - x_1)
\end{aligned}$$

where

$$h(v) = 1.5 \left(17.76v - 103.79v^2 + 229.62v^3 - 226.31v^4 + 83.72v^5 \right)$$

At $\varepsilon = 0$, the unperturbed system comprises two isolated first-order subsystems:

$$\begin{aligned}
\dot{x}_1 &= 1.2 - x_1 - h(x_1) \\
\dot{x}_2 &= 1.2 - x_2 - h(x_2)
\end{aligned}$$

It can be verified that each of the two systems has three equilibrium points at 0.063, 0.285, and 0.884. The Jacobian $-1 + h'(x_i)$ is negative at $x_i = 0.063$ and $x_i = 0.884$ and positive at $x_i = 0.285$. Hence, the equilibrium points at 0.063 and 0.884 are exponentially stable, while the equilibrium point at 0.285 is unstable. When the two first-order systems are put together, the composite second-order system will have nine equilibrium points; only four of them will be exponentially stable. These are the equilibrium points $(0.063, 0.063)$, $(0.063, 0.884)$, $(0.884, 0.063)$, and $(0.884, 0.884)$. Theorem 10.2 says that if the initial state $x(0)$ belongs to a compact subset of the region of attraction of any one of these equilibrium points, the approximation calculated in Example 10.4 will be valid for all $t \ge 0$. The simulation shown in Figure 10.3 was taken over a time interval long enough for the solution to reach steady state. In this particular case, the initial state $(0.15, 0.6)$ belongs to the region of attraction of $(0.063, 0.884)$.   △

The $O(\varepsilon^N)$ estimate of Theorem 10.2 is valid only when the origin is exponentially stable. It does not necessarily hold if it is asymptotically, but not exponentially, stable, as illustrated by the next example.

Example 10.6 Consider the first-order system

$$\dot{x} = -x^3 + \varepsilon x$$

and suppose $\varepsilon > 0$. The origin of the unperturbed system

$$\dot{x} = -x^3$$

is globally asymptotically stable, but not exponentially stable. (See Example 4.23.) The perturbed system has three equilibrium points at $x = 0$ and $x = \pm\sqrt{\varepsilon}$. The equilibrium $x = 0$ is unstable, while the other two equilibria are asymptotically stable. Solving both systems with the same positive initial condition $x(0) = a$, it can be easily seen that

$$x(t, \varepsilon) \to \sqrt{\varepsilon} \quad \text{and} \quad x_0(t) \to 0 \quad \text{as} \quad t \to \infty$$

Because $\sqrt{\varepsilon}$ is not $O(\varepsilon)$, it is clear that the approximation error $x(t, \varepsilon) - x_0(t)$ is not $O(\varepsilon)$ for all $t \geq 0$. Nevertheless, since the origin is asymptotically stable, we should be able to make a statement about the asymptotic behavior of the approximation as $t \to \infty$. Indeed, we can make a statement, although it will be weaker than the statement of Theorem 10.2. Because the origin of the unperturbed system is asymptotically stable, the solution $x_0(t)$ tends to zero as $t \to \infty$; equivalently, given any $\delta > 0$, there is $T_1 > 0$ such that

$$\|x_0(t)\| < \delta/2, \quad \forall\, t \geq T_1$$

The solutions of the perturbed system are ultimately bounded by a bound that shrinks with ε. Therefore, given any $\delta > 0$, there is $T_2 > 0$ and $\varepsilon^* > 0$ such that

$$\|x(t, \varepsilon)\| < \delta/2, \quad \forall\, t \geq T_2, \ \forall\, \varepsilon < \varepsilon^*$$

Combining these two estimates, we can say that for any $\delta > 0$ the approximation error satisfies

$$\|x(t, \varepsilon) - x_0(t)\| < \delta, \quad \forall\, t \geq T, \ \forall\, \varepsilon < \varepsilon^*$$

where $T = \max\{T_1, T_2\}$. On the order $O(1)$ time interval $[0, T]$, we know from the finite time result of Theorem 10.1 that the approximation error is $O(\varepsilon)$. Therefore, we can say that for any $\delta > 0$, there is $\varepsilon^{**} > 0$ such that

$$\|x(t, \varepsilon) - x_0(t)\| < \delta, \quad \forall\, t \in [0, \infty), \ \forall\, \varepsilon < \varepsilon^{**}$$

The last inequality is equivalent to saying that the approximation error tends to zero as $\varepsilon \to 0$, uniformly in t for all $t \geq 0$, which is the best we can show, in general, in the lack of exponential stability. Of course, in this particular example, we can obtain both $x_0(t)$ and $x(t, \varepsilon)$ in closed form, and we can actually show that the approximation error is $O(\sqrt{\varepsilon})$. $\triangle$

10.3 Periodic Perturbation of Autonomous Systems

Consider the system

$$\dot{x} = f(x) + \varepsilon g(t, x, \varepsilon) \tag{10.15}$$

where f, g, and their first partial derivatives with respect to x are continuous and bounded for all $(t, x, \varepsilon) \in [0, \infty) \times D_0 \times [-\varepsilon_0, \varepsilon_0]$, for every compact set $D_0 \subset D$, where $D \subset R^n$ is a domain that contains the origin. Suppose the origin is an exponentially stable equilibrium point of the autonomous system

$$\dot{x} = f(x) \tag{10.16}$$

Equivalently,[4] the matrix $A = [\partial f / \partial x](0)$ is Hurwitz. Due to boundedness of g, we can use Theorem 4.14 and Lemma 9.2 to show that there exist $r > 0$ and $\varepsilon_1 > 0$ such that for all $\|x(0)\| \leq r$ and $|\varepsilon| \leq \varepsilon_1$, the solution of (10.15) is uniformly ultimately bounded with ultimate bound proportional to $|\varepsilon|$. In other words, all solutions approach an $O(\varepsilon)$ neighborhood of the origin as $t \to \infty$. This is true for any bounded g. In this section, we are interested in what happens inside that $O(\varepsilon)$ neighborhood when g is T-periodic in t; that is,

$$g(t + T, x, \varepsilon) = g(t, x, \varepsilon), \quad \forall\, (t, x, \varepsilon) \in [0, \infty) \times D \times [-\varepsilon_0, \varepsilon_0]$$

In particular, we are interested in the possibility that a T-periodic solution might exist within an $O(\varepsilon)$ neighborhood of the origin.

Let $\phi(t; t_0, x_0, \varepsilon)$ be the solution of (10.15) that starts at (t_0, x_0); that is, $x_0 = \phi(t_0; t_0, x_0, \varepsilon)$. For all $\|x\| < r$, define a map $P_\varepsilon(x)$ by

$$P_\varepsilon(x) = \phi(T; 0, x, \varepsilon)$$

That is, $P_\varepsilon(x)$ is the state of the system at time T when the initial state at time zero is x. This map plays a key role in studying the existence of periodic solutions of (10.15).[5]

Lemma 10.1 *Under the foregoing conditions, equation* (10.15) *has a T-periodic solution if and only if the equation*

$$x = P_\varepsilon(x) \tag{10.17}$$

has a solution. $\diamond$

Proof: Since g is T-periodic in t, the solution of (10.15) is invariant to time shifts that are integer multiples of T. In particular,

$$\phi(t + T; T, x, \varepsilon) = \phi(t; 0, x, \varepsilon), \quad \forall\, t \geq 0 \tag{10.18}$$

This can be seen by changing the time variable from t to $\tau = t - T$, which yields

$$\frac{dx}{d\tau} = f(x) + \varepsilon g(\tau + T, x, \varepsilon) = f(x) + \varepsilon g(\tau, x, \varepsilon)$$

---

[4]The equivalence follows from Theorem 4.15.

[5]This map can be interpreted [70, Section 4.1] as a Poincaré map of the $(n + 1)$-dimensional autonomous system

$$\dot{x} = f(x) + \varepsilon g(\theta, x, \varepsilon), \qquad \dot{\theta} = 1$$

On the other hand, by uniqueness of solution, we have

$$\phi(t+T;0,x,\varepsilon) = \phi(t+T;T,\phi(T;0,x,\varepsilon),\varepsilon), \quad \forall\, t \geq 0 \qquad (10.19)$$

To prove sufficiency, let

$$p_\varepsilon = P_\varepsilon(p_\varepsilon) = \phi(T;0,p_\varepsilon,\varepsilon)$$

Then

$$\begin{aligned}
\phi(t+T;0,p_\varepsilon,\varepsilon) &= \phi(t+T;T,\phi(T;0,p_\varepsilon,\varepsilon),\varepsilon)\\
&= \phi(t+T;T,p_\varepsilon,\varepsilon)\\
&= \phi(t;0,p_\varepsilon,\varepsilon) \qquad\qquad (10.20)
\end{aligned}$$

where the first equality follows from (10.19) and the last equality from (10.18). Equation (10.20) shows that the solution starting at $(0,p_\varepsilon)$ is T-periodic. To prove necessity, let $\bar{x}(t)$ be a T-periodic solution of (10.15). Set $y = \bar{x}(0)$. Then

$$\phi(t+T;0,y,\varepsilon) = \phi(t;0,y,\varepsilon), \quad \forall\, t \geq 0$$

Taking $t=0$ yields

$$\phi(T;0,y,\varepsilon) = \phi(0;0,y,\varepsilon) = y$$

which shows that y is a solution of (10.17). $\qquad\qquad\qquad\qquad\qquad\square$

Lemma 10.2 *Under the foregoing conditions, there exist positive constants k and ε_2 such that (10.17) has a unique solution in $\|x\| < k|\varepsilon|$, for all $|\varepsilon| < \varepsilon_2$.* $\qquad\diamond$

Proof: At $\varepsilon = 0$, $\phi(t;0,x,0)$ is the solution of the unperturbed system (10.16) that starts at $(0,x)$. Since $x = 0$ is an equilibrium point for (10.16), $0 = \phi(t;0,0,0)$ for all $t \geq 0$. Hence,

$$P_0(0) = \phi(T;0,0,0) = 0$$

From the implicit function theorem, it follows that if the Jacobian matrix

$$J = I - \left.\frac{\partial P_\varepsilon}{\partial x}\right|_{x=0,\varepsilon=0}$$

is nonsingular, then there is a positive constant ε_2 such that equation (10.17) has a unique solution p_ε in $|\varepsilon| < \varepsilon_2$. To check nonsingularity of the Jacobian matrix, recall that the solution $\phi(t;0,x,\varepsilon)$ is given by

$$\phi(t;0,x,\varepsilon) = x + \int_0^t \left[f(\phi(\tau;0,x,\varepsilon)) + \varepsilon g(\tau,\phi(\tau;0,x,\varepsilon),\varepsilon)\right]\, d\tau$$

Differentiating with respect to x yields

$$\frac{\partial}{\partial x}\phi(t;0,x,\varepsilon) = I + \int_0^t \left[\frac{\partial f}{\partial x}(\cdot)\,\frac{\partial \phi}{\partial x}(\cdot) + \varepsilon\,\frac{\partial g}{\partial x}(\cdot)\,\frac{\partial \phi}{\partial x}(\cdot)\right]\,d\tau$$

Let

$$U(t) = \left.\frac{\partial}{\partial x}\phi(t;0,x,\varepsilon)\right|_{x=0,\varepsilon=0}$$

Then,

$$U(t) = I + \int_0^t \frac{\partial f}{\partial x}(0)U(\tau)\,d\tau \;=\; I + \int_0^t AU(\tau)\,d\tau$$

and

$$\frac{d}{dt}U(t) = AU(t),\quad U(0) = I$$

Thus, $U(t) = \exp(At)$. Consequently,

$$I - \left.\frac{\partial P_\varepsilon}{\partial x}\right|_{x=0,\varepsilon=0} = I - \exp(AT)$$

Because A is Hurwitz, all eigenvalues of $\exp(AT)$ are strictly inside the unit circle.[6] Consequently, J is nonsingular. Hence, (10.17) has a unique solution p_ε, $\forall\,|\varepsilon| < \varepsilon_2$. On the other hand, since all solutions of (10.15) approach an $O(\varepsilon)$ neighborhood of the origin as $t \to \infty$, it must be true that p_ε is $O(\varepsilon)$, because the corresponding periodic solution passes through p_ε infinitely many times as $t \to \infty$. □

It is now clear that, for sufficiently small ε, the perturbed system (10.15) has a T-periodic solution in an $O(\varepsilon)$ neighborhood of the origin. In fact, this periodic solution has to be unique due to the uniqueness of the solution of equation (10.17). Using the Hurwitz property of A, we can go further to show that the periodic solution is exponentially stable.

Lemma 10.3 *Under the foregoing conditions, if $\bar{x}(t,\varepsilon)$ is a T-periodic solution of (10.15) such that $\|\bar{x}(t,\varepsilon)\| \le k|\varepsilon|$, then $\bar{x}(t,\varepsilon)$ is exponentially stable.* ◇

Proof: A systematic procedure to study the stability of $\bar{x}(t,\varepsilon)$ is to apply the change of variables $z = x - \bar{x}(t,\varepsilon)$ and study the stability of the equilibrium point at $z = 0$. The new variable z satisfies the equation

$$\begin{aligned}
\dot{z} &= f(z + \bar{x}(t,\varepsilon)) - f(\bar{x}(t,\varepsilon)) + \varepsilon\,[g(t, z + \bar{x}(t,\varepsilon),\varepsilon) - g(t,\bar{x}(t,\varepsilon),\varepsilon)]\\
&\stackrel{\text{def}}{=} \hat{f}(t,z)
\end{aligned}$$

---

[6]This is a well-known fact in sampled-data control theory. It can be proved by transforming A into its Jordan form.

Linearization about $z = 0$ yields

$$\left.\frac{\partial \hat{f}}{\partial z}\right|_{z=0} = \left.\frac{\partial f}{\partial x}\right|_{z=0} + \varepsilon \left.\frac{\partial g}{\partial x}\right|_{z=0}$$

$$= A + \left[\frac{\partial f}{\partial x}(\bar{x}(t,\varepsilon)) - A\right] + \varepsilon \frac{\partial g}{\partial x}(t, \bar{x}(t,\varepsilon), \varepsilon)$$

By continuity of $[\partial f/\partial x]$, we know that for any $\delta > 0$, there is $\varepsilon^* > 0$ such that

$$\left\|\frac{\partial f}{\partial x}(\bar{x}(t,\varepsilon)) - \frac{\partial f}{\partial x}(0)\right\| < \delta$$

for $\varepsilon < \varepsilon^*$. Since A is Hurwitz and $[\partial g/\partial x](t, \bar{x}, \varepsilon)$ is $O(1)$, we conclude from Lemma 9.1 that, for sufficiently small ε, the linear system

$$\dot{y} = \left[A + \left(\frac{\partial f}{\partial x}(\bar{x}(t,\varepsilon)) - A\right) + \varepsilon \frac{\partial g}{\partial x}(t, \bar{x}(t,\varepsilon), \varepsilon)\right] y$$

has an exponentially stable equilibrium point at $y = 0$. Therefore, by Theorem 4.13, $z = 0$ is an exponentially stable equilibrium point. $\square$

We summarize our findings in the next theorem.

Theorem 10.3 *Suppose*

- f, g, *and their first partial derivatives with respect to* x *are continuous and bounded for all* $(t, x, \varepsilon) \in [0, \infty) \times D_0 \times [-\varepsilon_0, \varepsilon_0]$, *for every compact set* $D_0 \subset D$, *where* $D \subset R^n$ *is a domain that contains the origin;*

- *The origin is an exponentially stable equilibrium point of the autonomous system* (10.16);

- $g(t, x, \varepsilon)$ *is* T-*periodic in* t.

Then, there exist positive constants ε^* *and* k *such that for all* $|\varepsilon| < \varepsilon^*$, *equation* (10.15) *has a unique* T-*periodic solution* $\bar{x}(t, \varepsilon)$ *with the property that* $\|\bar{x}(t,\varepsilon)\| \leq k|\varepsilon|$. *Moreover, this solution is exponentially stable.* $\diamond$

If $g(t, 0, \varepsilon) = 0$, the origin will be an equilibrium point of the perturbed system (10.15). By uniqueness of the periodic solution $\bar{x}(t, \varepsilon)$, it follows that $\bar{x}(t, \varepsilon)$ is the trivial solution $x = 0$. In this case, the theorem ensures that the origin is an exponentially stable equilibrium point of the perturbed system (10.15).

10.4   Averaging

The averaging method applies to a system of the form

$$\dot{x} = \varepsilon f(t, x, \varepsilon)$$

where ε is a small positive parameter and $f(t, x, \varepsilon)$ is T-periodic in t; that is,

$$f(t + T, x, \varepsilon) = f(t, x, \varepsilon), \quad \forall\, (t, x, \varepsilon) \in [0, \infty) \times D \times [0, \varepsilon_0]$$

for some domain $D \subset R^n$. The method approximates the solution of this system by the solution of an "average system," obtained by averaging $f(t, x, \varepsilon)$ at $\varepsilon = 0$. To motivate the averaging method, let us start by examining a scalar example.

Example 10.7 Consider the first-order linear system

$$\dot{x} = \varepsilon a(t, \varepsilon) x, \quad x(0) = \eta \tag{10.21}$$

where ε is a positive parameter, a is sufficiently smooth in its arguments, and $a(t + T, \varepsilon) = a(t, \varepsilon)$ for all $t \geq 0$. To obtain an approximate solution that is valid for small ε, we may apply the perturbation method of Section 10.1. Setting $\varepsilon = 0$ results in the unperturbed system

$$\dot{x} = 0, \quad x(0) = \eta$$

which has a constant solution $x_0(t) = \eta$. According to Theorem 10.1, the error of this approximation will be $O(\varepsilon)$ on $O(1)$ time intervals. The unperturbed system does not satisfy the conditions of Theorem 10.2. Therefore, it is not clear whether this approximation is valid on time intervals larger than $O(1)$. Because in this example we can write down a closed-form expression for the exact solution, we will examine the approximation error by direct calculations. The solution of (10.21) is given by

$$x(t, \varepsilon) = \exp\left[\varepsilon \int_0^t a(\tau, \varepsilon)\, d\tau \right] \eta$$

Hence, the approximation error is

$$x(t, \varepsilon) - x_0(t) = \left\{ \exp\left[\varepsilon \int_0^t a(\tau, \varepsilon)\, d\tau \right] - 1 \right\} \eta$$

To see how the approximation error behaves as t increases, we need to evaluate the integral term in the foregoing expression. The function $a(t, \varepsilon)$ is periodic in t. Let its mean be

$$\bar{a}(\varepsilon) = \frac{1}{T} \int_0^T a(\tau, \varepsilon)\, d\tau$$

We can write $a(t, \varepsilon)$ as

$$a(t, \varepsilon) = \bar{a}(\varepsilon) + [a(t, \varepsilon) - \bar{a}(\varepsilon)]$$

The term inside the bracket is a T-periodic function of t with zero mean. Therefore, the integral

$$\int_0^t [a(\tau, \varepsilon) - \bar{a}(\varepsilon)] \ d\tau \overset{\text{def}}{=} \Delta(t, \varepsilon)$$

is T-periodic and, hence, bounded for all $t \geq 0$. On the other hand, the integration of the term $\bar{a}(\varepsilon)$ on $[0, t]$ results in $t\bar{a}(\varepsilon)$. Thus,

$$x(t, \varepsilon) - x_0(t) = \{\exp[\varepsilon t \bar{a}(\varepsilon)] \exp[\varepsilon \Delta(t, \varepsilon)] - 1\} \eta$$

Except for the case $\bar{a}(\varepsilon) = 0$, the approximation error will be $O(\varepsilon)$ only on $O(1)$ time intervals. A careful examination of the approximation error suggests that a better approximation of $x(t, \varepsilon)$ is $\exp[\varepsilon t \bar{a}(\varepsilon)]\eta$ or even $\exp[\varepsilon t \bar{a}(0)]\eta$, since $\bar{a}(\varepsilon) - \bar{a}(0) = O(\varepsilon)$. Let us try $\bar{x}(\varepsilon t) = \exp[\varepsilon t \bar{a}(0)]\eta$ as an alternative approximation. The approximation error is given by

$$
\begin{aligned}
x(t, \varepsilon) - \bar{x}(\varepsilon t) &= \{\exp[\varepsilon t \bar{a}(\varepsilon)] \exp[\varepsilon \Delta(t, \varepsilon)] - \exp[\varepsilon t \bar{a}(0)]\} \eta \\
&= \exp[\varepsilon t \bar{a}(0)] \{\exp[\varepsilon t(\bar{a}(\varepsilon) - \bar{a}(0))] \exp[\varepsilon \Delta(t, \varepsilon)] - 1\} \eta
\end{aligned}
$$

Noting that

$$
\begin{aligned}
\exp[\varepsilon \Delta(t, \varepsilon)] &= 1 + O(\varepsilon), \ \ \forall \, t \geq 0 \\
\exp[\varepsilon t(\bar{a}(\varepsilon) - \bar{a}(0))] &= \exp[t O(\varepsilon^2)] = 1 + O(\varepsilon), \ \ \forall \, t \in [0, b/\varepsilon] \\
\exp[\varepsilon t \bar{a}(0)] &= O(1), \ \ \forall \, t \in [0, b/\varepsilon]
\end{aligned}
$$

for any finite $b > 0$, we conclude that $x(t, \varepsilon) - \bar{x}(\varepsilon t) = O(\varepsilon)$ on time intervals of order $O(1/\varepsilon)$, which confirms the conjecture that the approximation $\bar{x}(\varepsilon t) = \exp[\varepsilon t \bar{a}(0)]\eta$ is better than the approximation $x_0(t) = \eta$. Note that $\bar{x}(\varepsilon t)$ is the solution of the average system

$$\dot{x} = \varepsilon \bar{a}(0)x, \quad x(0) = \eta \tag{10.22}$$

whose right-hand side is the average of the right-hand side of (10.21) at $\varepsilon = 0$. $\quad \triangle$

In this example, we have arrived at the average system (10.22) through our knowledge of the closed-form expression of the exact solution of (10.21). Such closed-form expressions are available only in very special cases. However, the plausibility of averaging is not dependent on the special features of the example. Let us reason the idea of averaging in a different way. The right-hand side of (10.21) is multiplied by a positive constant ε. When ε is small, the solution x will vary "slowly" with t relative to the periodic fluctuation of $a(t, \varepsilon)$. It is intuitively clear that if the response of a system is much slower than the excitation, then such response will be determined predominantly by the average of the excitation. This intuition has its roots in linear system theory, where we know that if the bandwidth of the system is much smaller than the bandwidth of the input, then the system will act as a low-pass filter that rejects the high-frequency component of the input.

If the solution of (10.21) is determined predominantly by the average of the fluctuation of $a(t, \varepsilon)$, then it is reasonable, in order to get an $O(\varepsilon)$ approximation, that the function $a(t, \varepsilon)$ be replaced by its average. This two-time-scale interpretation of averaging is not dependent on the special features of Example 10.7, nor is it dependent on the linearity of the system. It is a plausible idea that works in a more general setup, as we shall see in the rest of the chapter.

Consider the system

$$\dot{x} = \varepsilon f(t, x, \varepsilon) \tag{10.23}$$

where f and its partial derivatives with respect to (x, ε) up to the second order are continuous and bounded for $(t, x, \varepsilon) \in [0, \infty) \times D_0 \times [0, \varepsilon_0]$, for every compact set $D_0 \subset D$, where $D \subset R^n$ is a domain. Moreover, $f(t, x, \varepsilon)$ is T-periodic in t for some $T > 0$ and ε is positive. We associate with (10.23) an autonomous average system

$$\dot{x} = \varepsilon f_{\mathrm{av}}(x) \tag{10.24}$$

where

$$f_{\mathrm{av}}(x) = \frac{1}{T} \int_0^T f(\tau, x, 0) \, d\tau \tag{10.25}$$

The basic problem in the averaging method is to determine in what sense the behavior of the autonomous system (10.24) approximates the behavior of the nonautonomous system (10.23). We will address this problem by showing, via a change of variables, that the nonautonomous system (10.23) can be represented as a perturbation of the autonomous system (10.24). Define

$$u(t, x) = \int_0^t h(\tau, x) \, d\tau \tag{10.26}$$

where

$$h(t, x) = f(t, x, 0) - f_{\mathrm{av}}(x) \tag{10.27}$$

Since $h(t, x)$ is T-periodic in t and has zero mean, the function $u(t, x)$ is T-periodic in t. Hence, $u(t, x)$ is bounded for all $(t, x) \in [0, \infty) \times D_0$. Moreover, $\partial u / \partial t$ and $\partial u / \partial x$, given by

$$\frac{\partial u}{\partial t} = h(t, x), \qquad \frac{\partial u}{\partial x} = \int_0^t \frac{\partial h}{\partial x}(\tau, x) \, d\tau$$

are T-periodic in t and bounded on $[0, \infty) \times D_0$. Here, we have used the fact that $\partial h / \partial x$ is T-periodic in t and has zero mean. Consider the change of variables

$$x = y + \varepsilon u(t, y) \tag{10.28}$$

Differentiating both sides with respect to t, we obtain

$$\dot{x} = \dot{y} + \varepsilon \frac{\partial u}{\partial t}(t, y) + \varepsilon \frac{\partial u}{\partial y}(t, y) \, \dot{y}$$

Substituting for $\dot{x}$ from (10.23), we find that the new state variable y satisfies the equation

$$\left[I + \varepsilon\frac{\partial u}{\partial y}\right]\dot{y} = \varepsilon f(t, y + \varepsilon u, \varepsilon) - \varepsilon\frac{\partial u}{\partial t}$$
$$= \varepsilon f(t, y + \varepsilon u, \varepsilon) - \varepsilon f(t, y, 0) + \varepsilon f_{\text{av}}(y)$$
$$\overset{\text{def}}{=} \varepsilon f_{\text{av}}(y) + \varepsilon p(t, y, \varepsilon)$$

where

$$p(t, y, \varepsilon) = [f(t, y + \varepsilon u, \varepsilon) - f(t, y, \varepsilon)] + [f(t, y, \varepsilon) - f(t, y, 0)]$$

The function $p(t, y, \varepsilon)$ is T-periodic in t and, using mean value theorem, can be expressed as

$$p(t, y, \varepsilon) = F_1(t, y, \varepsilon u, \varepsilon)\varepsilon u + F_2(t, y, \varepsilon)\varepsilon$$

Because $\partial u/\partial y$ is bounded on $[0, \infty) \times D_0$, the matrix $I + \varepsilon\partial u/\partial y$ is nonsingular for sufficiently small ε, and

$$\left[I + \varepsilon\frac{\partial u}{\partial y}\right]^{-1} = I + O(\varepsilon)$$

Therefore, the state equation for y is given by

$$\dot{y} = \varepsilon f_{\text{av}}(y) + \varepsilon^2 q(t, y, \varepsilon) \tag{10.29}$$

where $q(t, y, \varepsilon)$ is T-periodic in t and f_{av}, q, and their first partial derivatives with respect to (y, ε) are continuous and bounded on $[0, \infty) \times D_0$ for sufficiently small ε. This equation is a perturbation of the average system (10.24). By extending the arguments used in the previous three sections, we can determine the basis for approximating the solutions of (10.29) by the solutions of the average system (10.24).

The change of time variable $s = \varepsilon t$ transforms (10.29) into

$$\frac{dy}{ds} = f_{\text{av}}(y) + \varepsilon q(s/\varepsilon, y, \varepsilon) \tag{10.30}$$

where $q(s/\varepsilon, y, \varepsilon)$ is εT-periodic in s and bounded on $[0, \infty) \times D_0$ for sufficiently small ε. By applying Theorems 3.4 and 3.5 on continuity of solutions with respect to initial states and parameters, we see that if the average system

$$\frac{dy}{ds} = f_{\text{av}}(y)$$

has a unique solution $\bar{y}(s)$ defined on $[0, b]$, $\bar{y}(s) \in D$ for all $s \in [0, b]$, and $y(0, \varepsilon) - x_{\text{av}}(0) = O(\varepsilon)$, then there exists $\varepsilon^* > 0$ such that for all $0 < \varepsilon < \varepsilon^*$, the perturbed system (10.30) will have a unique solution defined for all $s \in [0, b]$ and the two solutions will be $O(\varepsilon)$ close. Since $t = s/\varepsilon$ and $x - y = O(\varepsilon)$ by (10.28), the solution of the average system (10.24) provides an $O(\varepsilon)$ approximation for the solution of (10.23) over the time interval $[0, b/\varepsilon]$ in the t time scale.

Suppose the average system (10.24) has an exponentially stable equilibrium point at the origin and D is a domain that contains the origin. Let $V(y)$ be the Lyapunov function provided by (the converse Lyapunov) Theorem 4.17. Then, for any compact subset Ω of the region of attraction of the origin, there is a constant $c > 0$ such that Ω lies in the interior of the compact set $\{V(y) \leq c\}$. Suppose $y_{\mathrm{av}}(0) \in \Omega$ and $y(0, \varepsilon) - y_{\mathrm{av}}(0) = O(\varepsilon)$. Applying Theorem 9.1 shows that the $O(\varepsilon)$ approximation will be valid for all $s \geq 0$, that is, for all $t \geq 0$.

Finally, Theorem 10.3 shows that (10.30) has a unique, exponentially stable, (εT)-periodic solution $\bar{y}(s/\varepsilon, \varepsilon)$ in an $O(\varepsilon)$ neighborhood of the origin. The periodic solution has period εT in the s time scale, that is, period T in the t time scale. By (10.28), we see that (10.23) has a T-periodic solution

$$\bar{x}(t, \varepsilon) = \bar{y}(t, \varepsilon) + \varepsilon u(t, \bar{y}(t, \varepsilon))$$

Because u is bounded, the periodic solution $\bar{x}(t, \varepsilon)$ lies in an $O(\varepsilon)$ neighborhood of the origin. We summarize these conclusions in the next theorem.

Theorem 10.4 *Let $f(t, x, \varepsilon)$ and its partial derivatives with respect to (x, ε) up to the second order be continuous and bounded for $(t, x, \varepsilon) \in [0, \infty) \times D_0 \times [0, \varepsilon_0]$, for every compact set $D_0 \subset D$, where $D \subset R^n$ is a domain. Suppose f is T-periodic in t for some $T > 0$ and ε is a positive parameter. Let $x(t, \varepsilon)$ and $x_{\mathrm{av}}(\varepsilon t)$ denote the solutions of (10.23) and (10.24), respectively.*

- *If $x_{\mathrm{av}}(\varepsilon t) \in D \; \forall \; t \in [0, b/\varepsilon]$ and $x(0, \varepsilon) - x_{\mathrm{av}}(0) = O(\varepsilon)$, then there exists $\varepsilon^* > 0$ such that for all $0 < \varepsilon < \varepsilon^*$, $x(t, \varepsilon)$ is defined and*

$$x(t, \varepsilon) - x_{\mathrm{av}}(\varepsilon t) = O(\varepsilon) \quad \text{on } [0, b/\varepsilon]$$

- *If the origin $x = 0 \in D$ is an exponentially stable equilibrium point of the average system (10.24), $\Omega \subset D$ is a compact subset of its region of attraction, $x_{\mathrm{av}}(0) \in \Omega$, and $x(0, \varepsilon) - x_{\mathrm{av}}(0) = O(\varepsilon)$, then there exists $\varepsilon^* > 0$ such that for all $0 < \varepsilon < \varepsilon^*$, $x(t, \varepsilon)$ is defined and*

$$x(t, \varepsilon) - x_{\mathrm{av}}(\varepsilon t) = O(\varepsilon) \quad \text{for all } t \in [0, \infty)$$

- *If the origin $x = 0 \in D$ is an exponentially stable equilibrium point of the average system (10.24), then there exist positive constants ε^* and k such that, for all $0 < \varepsilon < \varepsilon^*$, (10.23) has a unique, exponentially stable, T-periodic solution $\bar{x}(t, \varepsilon)$ with the property $\|\bar{x}(t, \varepsilon)\| \leq k\varepsilon$.* $\diamond$

If $f(t, 0, \varepsilon) = 0$ for all $(t, \varepsilon) \in [0, \infty) \times [0, \varepsilon_0]$, the origin will be an equilibrium point of (10.23). By the uniqueness of the T-periodic solution $\bar{x}(t, \varepsilon)$, it follows that $\bar{x}(t, \varepsilon)$ is the trivial solution $x = 0$. In this case, the theorem ensures that the origin is an exponentially stable equilibrium point of (10.23).

Example 10.8 Consider the linear system

$$\dot{x} = \varepsilon A(t)x$$

where $A(t+T) = A(t)$ and $\varepsilon > 0$. Let

$$\bar{A} = \frac{1}{T} \int_0^T A(\tau) \, d\tau$$

The average system is given by

$$\dot{x} = \varepsilon \bar{A} x$$

It has an equilibrium point at $x = 0$. Suppose the matrix $\bar{A}$ is Hurwitz. Then, it follows from Theorem 10.4 that, for sufficiently small ε, $\dot{x} = \varepsilon A(t)x$ has a unique T-periodic solution in an $O(\varepsilon)$ neighborhood of the origin $x = 0$. However, $x = 0$ is an equilibrium point for the system. Hence, the periodic solution is the trivial solution $x(t) = 0$. Consequently, we conclude that, for sufficiently small ε, $x = 0$ is an exponentially stable equilibrium point for the nonautonomous system $\dot{x} = \varepsilon A(t)x$.

$\triangle$

Example 10.9 Consider the scalar system

$$\dot{x} = \varepsilon(x \sin^2 t - 0.5x^2) = \varepsilon f(t, x)$$

The function $f(t, x)$ is π-periodic in t. The average function $f_{\mathrm{av}}(x)$ is given by

$$f_{\mathrm{av}}(x) = \frac{1}{\pi} \int_0^\pi (x \sin^2 t - 0.5x^2) \, dt = 0.5(x - x^2)$$

The average system

$$\dot{x} = 0.5\varepsilon(x - x^2)$$

has two equilibrium points at $x = 0$ and $x = 1$. The Jacobian df_{av}/dx evaluated at these equilibria is given by

$$\left. \frac{df_{\mathrm{av}}}{dx} \right|_{x=0} = \left. (0.5 - x) \right|_{x=0} = 0.5$$

$$\left. \frac{df_{\mathrm{av}}}{dx} \right|_{x=1} = \left. (0.5 - x) \right|_{x=1} = -0.5$$

Thus, for sufficiently small ε, the system has an exponentially stable π-periodic solution in an $O(\varepsilon)$ neighborhood of $x = 1$. Moreover, by sketching the function $x - x^2$, it can be seen that the region of attraction of $x = 1$ is $(0, \infty)$. Hence, for initial states in the compact interval $[a, b] \subset (0, \infty)$, solving the average system with the same initial state as the original system yields the approximation

$$x(t, \varepsilon) - x_{\mathrm{av}}(\varepsilon t) = O(\varepsilon), \quad \forall \, t \geq 0$$

Suppose we want to calculate a second-order approximation. We need to use the change of variables (10.28) to represent the problem as a standard perturbation problem and then proceed to approximate the solution, as we have done in Section 10.1. Using (10.26), we find that the function $u(t, x)$ is given by

$$u(t, x) = \int_0^t \left(x \sin^2 \tau - 0.5x^2 - 0.5x + 0.5x^2 \right) \, d\tau = -\tfrac{1}{4} x \sin 2t$$

The change of variables of (10.28) takes the form

$$x = y - \tfrac{1}{4} \varepsilon y \sin 2t = \left(1 - \tfrac{1}{4} \varepsilon \sin 2t \right) y$$

Differentiating both sides with respect to t, we obtain

$$\dot{x} = \left(1 - \tfrac{1}{4} \varepsilon \sin 2t \right) \dot{y} - \tfrac{1}{2} \varepsilon y \cos 2t$$

Hence,

$$\dot{y} = \frac{\varepsilon}{1 - (\varepsilon/4) \sin 2t} \left(x \sin^2 t - \tfrac{1}{2} x^2 + \tfrac{1}{2} y \cos 2t \right)$$

Substituting x in term of y, and expanding the term $1/[1 - (\varepsilon/4) \sin 2t]$ in the power series

$$\frac{1}{1 - (\varepsilon/4) \sin 2t} = 1 + \tfrac{1}{4} \varepsilon \sin 2t + O(\varepsilon^2)$$

we arrive at the equation

$$\dot{y} = \tfrac{1}{2} \varepsilon (y - y^2) + \tfrac{1}{16} \varepsilon^2 (y \sin 4t + 2y^2 \sin 2t) + O(\varepsilon^3)$$

where the system appears as a perturbation of the average system. In order to find a second-order approximation, we need to calculate y_0 and y_1 in the finite Taylor series

$$y = y_0 + \varepsilon y_1 + \varepsilon^2 R_y$$

We know that $y_0 = x_{\mathrm{av}}$, the solution of the average system. The equation for y_1 is given by

$$\dot{y}_1 = \varepsilon \left[\left(\tfrac{1}{2} - y_0(t) \right) y_1 + \tfrac{1}{16} y_0(t) \sin 4t + \tfrac{1}{8} y_0^2(t) \sin 2t \right], \quad y_1(0) = 0$$

where we have assumed that the initial state $x(0)$ is independent of ε. Using (10.28), we obtain a second-order approximation of x as

$$x = \left(1 - \tfrac{1}{4} \varepsilon \sin 2t \right) x_{\mathrm{av}}(\varepsilon t) + \varepsilon y_1(t, \varepsilon) + O(\varepsilon^2)$$

Figure 10.5 shows the solution of the exact system, the average system, and the second-order approximation for $x(0) = 0.7$ and $\varepsilon = 0.3$. The figure illustrates clearly how the solution of the average system averages the exact solution. The second-order approximation is almost indistinguishable from the exact solution, but we can see the difference as the solution reaches steady state. $\triangle$

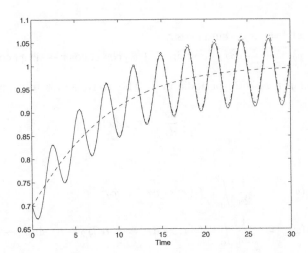

Figure 10.5: The exact (solid), average (dashed), and second-order (dash-dot) solutions of Example 10.9 with $\varepsilon = 0.3$.

Example 10.10 Consider the suspended pendulum of Section 1.2.1 and assume that the suspension point is subjected to vertical vibrations of small amplitude and high frequency. Suppose the motion of the suspension point is described by $a \sin \omega t$, where a is the amplitude and ω is the frequency. Writing Newton's law in the tangential direction (perpendicular to the rod), the equation of motion is[7]

$$m(l\ddot{\theta} - a\omega^2 \sin \omega t \sin \theta) = -mg \sin \theta - k(l\dot{\theta} + a\omega \cos \omega t \sin \theta)$$

Assume that $a/l \ll 1$ and $\omega_0/\omega \ll 1$, where $\omega_0 = \sqrt{g/l}$ is the frequency of free oscillations of the pendulum in the vicinity of the lower equilibrium position $\theta = 0$. Let $\varepsilon = a/l$ and write $\omega_0/\omega = \alpha\varepsilon$, where $\alpha = \omega_0 l/\omega a$. Let $\beta = k/m\omega_0$ and change the time scale from t to $\tau = \omega t$. In the new time scale, the equation of motion is

$$\frac{d^2\theta}{d\tau^2} + \alpha\beta\varepsilon \frac{d\theta}{d\tau} + (\alpha^2\varepsilon^2 - \varepsilon \sin \tau) \sin \theta + \alpha\beta\varepsilon^2 \cos \tau \sin \theta = 0$$

With

$$x_1 = \theta, \qquad x_2 = \frac{1}{\varepsilon} \frac{d\theta}{d\tau} + \cos \tau \sin \theta$$

as state variables, the state equation is given by

$$\frac{dx}{d\tau} = \varepsilon f(\tau, x) \tag{10.31}$$

---

[7]To derive this equation, write expressions for the x- and y-coordinates of the bob as $x = l \sin \theta$ and $y = l \cos \theta - a \sin \omega t$. Then, show that the velocity and acceleration of the bob in the tangential direction are $(l\dot{\theta} + a\omega \cos \omega t \sin \theta)$ and $(l\ddot{\theta} - a\omega^2 \sin \omega t \sin \theta)$, respectively. The friction force is assumed to be viscous friction proportional to the velocity of the bob with a friction coefficient k.

where

$$
\begin{aligned}
f_1(\tau, x) &= x_2 - \sin x_1 \cos \tau \\
f_2(\tau, x) &= -\alpha\beta x_2 - \alpha^2 \sin x_1 + x_2 \cos x_1 \cos \tau - \sin x_1 \cos x_1 \cos^2 \tau
\end{aligned}
$$

The function $f(\tau, x)$ is 2π-periodic in τ. The average system is given by

$$
\frac{dx}{d\tau} = \varepsilon f_{\mathrm{av}}(x) \tag{10.32}
$$

where

$$
\begin{aligned}
f_{\mathrm{av}1}(x) &= \frac{1}{2\pi} \int_0^{2\pi} f_1(\tau, x)\, d\tau = x_2 \\
f_{\mathrm{av}2}(x) &= \frac{1}{2\pi} \int_0^{2\pi} f_2(\tau, x)\, d\tau = -\alpha\beta x_2 - \alpha^2 \sin x_1 - \tfrac{1}{4} \sin 2x_1
\end{aligned}
$$

In arriving at these expressions, we have used the fact that the average of $\cos \tau$ is zero, while the average of $\cos^2 \tau$ is $1/2$. Both the original system (10.31) and the average system (10.32) have equilibrium points at $(x_1 = 0,\ x_2 = 0)$ and $(x_1 = \pi,\ x_2 = 0)$, which correspond to the equilibrium positions $\theta = 0$ and $\theta = \pi$. With a fixed suspension point, the equilibrium position $\theta = 0$ is exponentially stable, while the equilibrium position $\theta = \pi$ is unstable. Let us see what a vibrating suspension point will do to the system. To apply Theorem 10.4, we analyze the stability properties of the equilibrium points of the average system (10.32) via linearization. The Jacobian of $f_{\mathrm{av}}(x)$ is given by

$$
\frac{\partial f_{\mathrm{av}}}{\partial x} =
\begin{bmatrix}
0 & 1 \\
-\alpha^2 \cos x_1 - 0.5 \cos 2x_1 & -\alpha\beta
\end{bmatrix}
$$

At the equilibrium point $(x_1 = 0, x_2 = 0)$, the Jacobian

$$
\begin{bmatrix}
0 & 1 \\
-\alpha^2 - 0.5 & -\alpha\beta
\end{bmatrix}
$$

is Hurwitz for all positive values of α and β. Therefore, Theorem 10.4 says that, for sufficiently small ε, the original system (10.31) has a unique exponentially stable 2π-periodic solution in an $O(\varepsilon)$ neighborhood of the origin. Because the origin is an equilibrium point for the original system, the periodic solution is the trivial solution $x = 0$. In this case, Theorem 10.4 confirms that, for sufficiently small ε, the origin is an exponentially stable equilibrium point for the original system (10.31). In other words, exponential stability of the lower equilibrium position of the pendulum is preserved under (small-amplitude, high-frequency) vibration of the suspension point. At the equilibrium point $(x_1 = \pi, x_2 = 0)$, the Jacobian

$$
\begin{bmatrix}
0 & 1 \\
\alpha^2 - 0.5 & -\alpha\beta
\end{bmatrix}
$$

is Hurwitz for $0 < \alpha < 1/\sqrt{2}$ and $\beta > 0$. Noting, again, that $(x_1 = \pi,\ x_2 = 0)$ is an equilibrium point for the original system, and applying Theorem 10.4, we are led to the conclusion that if $\alpha < 1/\sqrt{2}$, then the upper equilibrium position $\theta = \pi$ is an exponentially stable equilibrium point for the original system (10.31) for sufficiently small ε. This is an intriguing finding, because it shows that the unstable upper equilibrium position of the pendulum can be stabilized by vibrating the suspension point vertically with small amplitude and high frequency.[8] $\triangle$

10.5 Weakly Nonlinear Second-Order Oscillators

Consider the second-order system

$$\ddot{y} + \omega^2 y = \varepsilon g(y, \dot{y}) \tag{10.33}$$

where $g(\cdot, \cdot)$ is sufficiently smooth and $|g|$ is bounded by $k|y|$ or $k|\dot{y}|$ on compact sets of $(y, \dot{y})$; k is a positive constant. Choosing $x_1 = y$ and $x_2 = \dot{y}/\omega$ as state variables, we obtain the state equation

$$
\begin{aligned}
\dot{x}_1 &= \omega x_2 \\
\dot{x}_2 &= -\omega x_1 + \frac{\varepsilon}{\omega} g(x_1, \omega x_2)
\end{aligned}
$$

Representing the system in the polar coordinates

$$x_1 = r \sin\phi, \qquad x_2 = r \cos\phi$$

we have

$$\dot{r} = \frac{1}{r}(x_1 \dot{x}_1 + x_2 \dot{x}_2) = \frac{\varepsilon}{\omega} g(r \sin\phi, \omega r \cos\phi) \cos\phi \tag{10.34}$$

$$\dot{\phi} = \frac{1}{r^2}(x_2 \dot{x}_1 - x_1 \dot{x}_2) = \omega - \frac{\varepsilon}{\omega r} g(r \sin\phi, \omega r \cos\phi) \sin\phi \tag{10.35}$$

The second term on the right-hand side of (10.35) is $O(\varepsilon)$ on bounded sets of r, as a consequence of the assumption that $|g|$ is bounded by $k|y|$ or $k|\dot{y}|$. Hence,

---

[8]The idea of introducing high-frequency, zero-mean vibrations in the parameters of a dynamic system in order to modify the properties of the system in a desired manner has been generalized into a *principle of vibrational control*. (See [22] and [127].)

the right-hand side of (10.35) is positive for sufficiently small ε. Divide (10.34) by (10.35) to obtain

$$\frac{dr}{d\phi} = \frac{\varepsilon g(r\sin\phi, \omega r\cos\phi)\cos\phi}{\omega^2 - (\varepsilon/r)g(r\sin\phi, \omega r\cos\phi)\sin\phi}$$

We rewrite this equation as

$$\frac{dr}{d\phi} = \varepsilon f(\phi, r, \varepsilon) \tag{10.36}$$

where

$$f(\phi, r, \varepsilon) = \frac{g(r\sin\phi, \omega r\cos\phi)\cos\phi}{\omega^2 - (\varepsilon/r)g(r\sin\phi, \omega r\cos\phi)\sin\phi}$$

If we view ϕ as the independent variable, then (10.36) takes the form (10.23), where $f(\phi, r, \varepsilon)$ is 2π-periodic in ϕ. The function $f_{\mathrm{av}}(r)$ is given by

$$f_{\mathrm{av}}(r) = \frac{1}{2\pi}\int_0^{2\pi} f(\phi, r, 0)\, d\phi = \frac{1}{2\pi\omega^2}\int_0^{2\pi} g(r\sin\phi, \omega r\cos\phi)\cos\phi\, d\phi$$

Suppose the average system

$$\frac{dr}{d\phi} = \varepsilon f_{\mathrm{av}}(r) \tag{10.37}$$

has an equilibrium point r^*, where $[\partial f_{\mathrm{av}}/\partial r](r^*) < 0$; then, there is $\varepsilon^* > 0$ such that $\forall\, 0 < \varepsilon < \varepsilon^*$, (10.36) has a unique exponentially stable 2π-periodic solution $r = R(\phi, \varepsilon)$ in an $O(\varepsilon)$ neighborhood of r^*. This, by itself, does not say that (10.33) has a periodic solution with respect to t. More work is needed to reach that conclusion. Substituting $r = R(\phi, \varepsilon)$ into (10.35) yields

$$\dot\phi = \omega - \frac{\varepsilon}{\omega R(\phi, \varepsilon)} g(R(\phi, \varepsilon)\sin\phi, \omega R(\phi, \varepsilon)\cos\phi)\sin\phi$$

Let $\phi^*(t, \varepsilon)$ be the solution of this equation starting at $\phi^*(0, \varepsilon) = 0$. To show that (10.33) has a periodic solution, we need to show that there exists $T = T(\varepsilon) > 0$, generally dependent on ε, such that

$$\phi^*(t + T, \varepsilon) = 2\pi + \phi^*(t, \varepsilon),\ \forall\, t \geq 0 \tag{10.38}$$

For then,

$$R(\phi^*(t + T, \varepsilon), \varepsilon) = R(2\pi + \phi^*(t, \varepsilon), \varepsilon) = R(\phi^*(t, \varepsilon), \varepsilon)$$

which implies that $R(\phi^*(t, \varepsilon), \varepsilon)$ is T-periodic in t. Because

$$\phi^*(t + \tau, \varepsilon) = \phi^*(t, \varepsilon) + \omega\tau + O(\varepsilon)$$

for bounded $\tau \geq 0$, it can be easily seen that, for sufficiently small ε, (10.38) has a unique solution $T(\varepsilon) = 2\pi/\omega + O(\varepsilon)$.

The image of the solution $r = R(\phi^*(t, \varepsilon), \varepsilon)$ in the state plane x_1–x_2 is a closed orbit in the neighborhood of the circle $r = r^*$. Since the periodic solution $r = R(\phi, \varepsilon)$ is exponentially stable, the closed orbit will attract all solutions in its neighborhood; that is, the closed orbit is a stable limit cycle.

Example 10.11 The Van der Pol equation

$$\ddot{y} + y = \varepsilon \dot{y}(1 - y^2)$$

is a special case of (10.33) with $\omega = 1$ and $g(y, \dot{y}) = \dot{y}(1 - y^2)$. The function $f_{av}(r)$ is given by

$$
\begin{aligned}
f_{av}(r) &= \frac{1}{2\pi} \int_0^{2\pi} \left(1 - r^2 \sin^2 \phi\right) r \cos^2 \phi \, d\phi \\
&= \frac{1}{2\pi} \int_0^{2\pi} r \cos^2 \phi \, d\phi - \frac{1}{2\pi} \int_0^{2\pi} r^3 \sin^2 \phi \cos^2 \phi \, d\phi \\
&= \frac{1}{2} r - \frac{1}{8} r^3
\end{aligned}
$$

The average system

$$\frac{dr}{d\phi} = \varepsilon \left(\tfrac{1}{2} r - \tfrac{1}{8} r^3\right)$$

has three equilibrium points at $r = 0$, $r = 2$, and $r = -2$. Since by definition $r \geq 0$, the negative root is rejected. We check stability of the equilibria via linearization. The Jacobian matrix is given by

$$\frac{df_{av}}{dr} = \tfrac{1}{2} - \tfrac{3}{8} r^2$$

and

$$\left. \frac{df_{av}}{dr} \right|_{r=0} = \tfrac{1}{2} > 0; \qquad \left. \frac{df_{av}}{dr} \right|_{r=2} = -1 < 0$$

Thus, the equilibrium point $r = 2$ is exponentially stable. Therefore, for sufficiently small ε, the Van der Pol equation has a stable limit cycle in an $O(\varepsilon)$ neighborhood of $r = 2$. The period of oscillation is $O(\varepsilon)$ close to 2π. This stable limit cycle was observed in Example 2.6 via simulation. $\triangle$

Let us conclude by noting that the foregoing procedure may be used to show the existence of an unstable limit cycle. This can be done by reversing time in (10.33), that is, replacing t by $\tau = -t$. If the system has a stable limit cycle in reverse time, it will have an unstable limit cycle in forward time.

10.6 General Averaging

Consider the system

$$\dot{x} = \varepsilon f(t, x, \varepsilon) \tag{10.39}$$

where f and its partial derivatives with respect to (x, ε) up to the second order are continuous and bounded for $(t, x, \varepsilon) \in [0, \infty) \times D_0 \times [0, \varepsilon_0]$, for every compact set

$D_0 \subset D$. The parameter ε is positive, and $D \subset R^n$ is a domain. The averaging method applies to the system (10.39) in cases more general than the case when $f(t, x, \varepsilon)$ is periodic in t. In particular, it applies when the function $f(t, x, 0)$ has a well-defined average $f_{\mathrm{av}}(x)$ according to the next definition.

Definition 10.2 *A continuous, bounded function* $g : [0, \infty) \times D \to R^n$ *is said to have an average* $g_{\mathrm{av}}(x)$ *if the limit*

$$g_{\mathrm{av}}(x) = \lim_{T \to \infty} \frac{1}{T} \int_t^{t+T} g(\tau, x) \, d\tau$$

exists and

$$\left\| \frac{1}{T} \int_t^{t+T} g(\tau, x) \, d\tau - g_{\mathrm{av}}(x) \right\| \le k\sigma(T), \quad \forall \, (t, x) \in [0, \infty) \times D_0$$

for every compact set $D_0 \subset D$, *where* k *is a positive constant (possibly dependent on* D_0*) and* $\sigma : [0, \infty) \to [0, \infty)$ *is a strictly decreasing, continuous, bounded function such that* $\sigma(T) \to 0$ *as* $T \to \infty$. *The function* σ *is called the convergence function.*

Example 10.12

- Let $g(t, x) = \sum_{k=1}^N g_k(t, x)$, where $g_k(t, x)$ is periodic in t of period T_k, with $T_i \ne T_j$ when $i \ne j$. The function g is not periodic[9] in t, but it has the average

$$g_{\mathrm{av}}(x) = \sum_{k=1}^N g_{k_{\mathrm{av}}}(x)$$

  where $g_{k_{\mathrm{av}}}$ is the average of the periodic function $g_k(t, x)$, as defined in Section 10.4. The convergence function σ is of order $O(1/T)$ as $T \to \infty$. We can take it as $\sigma(T) = 1/(T + 1)$.

- The average of

$$g(t, x) = \frac{1}{1 + t} h(x)$$

  is zero, and the convergence function σ can be taken as $\sigma(T) = (1/T) \ln(1 + T)$.
$$\triangle$$

Suppose now that $f(t, x, 0)$ has the average function $f_{\mathrm{av}}(x)$ with convergence function σ. Let

$$h(t, x) = f(t, x, 0) - f_{\mathrm{av}}(x) \tag{10.40}$$

---

[9]This function is called almost periodic. An introduction to the theory of almost periodic functions can be found in [59] or [75].

The function $h(t, x)$ has zero average with σ as its convergence function. Suppose the Jacobian matrix $\partial h/\partial x$ has zero average with the same convergence function σ. Define

$$w(t, x, \eta) = \int_0^t h(\tau, x) \exp[-\eta(t - \tau)] \, d\tau \qquad (10.41)$$

for some positive constant η. At $\eta = 0$, the function $w(t, x, 0)$ satisfies

$$\|w(t + \delta, x, 0) - w(t, x, 0)\| = \left\| \int_0^{t+\delta} h(\tau, x) \, d\tau - \int_0^t h(\tau, x) \, d\tau \right\|$$

$$= \left\| \int_t^{t+\delta} h(\tau, x) \, d\tau \right\| \leq k\delta\sigma(\delta) \qquad (10.42)$$

This implies, in particular, that

$$\|w(t, x, 0)\| \leq kt\sigma(t), \quad \forall \, (t, x) \in [0, \infty) \times D_0$$

since $w(0, x, 0) = 0$. Integrating the right-hand side of (10.41) by parts, we obtain

$$w(t, x, \eta) = w(t, x, 0) - \eta \int_0^t \exp[-\eta(t - \tau)] w(\tau, x, 0) \, d\tau$$

$$= \exp(-\eta t) w(t, x, 0) - \eta \int_0^t \exp[-\eta(t - \tau)] \, [w(\tau, x, 0) - w(t, x, 0)] \, d\tau$$

where the second equality is obtained by adding and subtracting

$$\eta \int_0^t \exp[-\eta(t - \tau)] \, d\tau \, w(t, x, 0)$$

to the right-hand side. Using (10.42), we obtain

$$\|w(t, x, \eta)\| \leq kt \exp(-\eta t)\sigma(t) + k\eta \int_0^t \exp[-\eta(t - \tau)](t - \tau)\sigma(t - \tau) \, d\tau \quad (10.43)$$

This inequality can be used to show that $\eta\|w(t, x, \eta)\|$ is uniformly bounded by $k\alpha(\eta)$ for some class $\mathcal{K}$ function α. For example, if $\sigma(t) = 1/(t + 1)$, then

$$\eta\|w(t, x, \eta)\| \leq k\eta \exp(-\eta t) + k\eta^2 \int_0^t \exp[-\eta(t - \tau)] \, d\tau = k\eta$$

Defining $\alpha(\eta) = \eta$, we have $\eta\|w(t, x, \eta)\| \leq k\alpha(\eta)$. If $\sigma(t) = 1/(t^r + 1)$ with $0 < r < 1$, then

$$\eta\|w(t, x, \eta)\| \leq k\eta t^{(1-r)} e^{-\eta t} + k\eta^2 \int_0^t e^{-\eta(t-\tau)}(t - \tau)^{(1-r)} \, d\tau$$

$$\leq k\eta \left(\frac{1 - r}{\eta}\right)^{1-r} e^{-(1-r)} + k\eta^2 \int_0^\infty e^{-\eta s} s^{(1-r)} \, ds$$

$$\leq k\eta \left(\frac{1 - r}{\eta}\right)^{1-r} e^{-(1-r)} + k\eta^2 \frac{\Gamma(2 - r)}{\eta^{(2-r)}} \leq k k_1 \eta^r$$

where $\Gamma(\cdot)$ denotes the standard gamma function. Defining $\alpha(\eta) = k_1 \eta^r$, we have $\eta\|w(t,x,\eta)\| \leq k\alpha(\eta)$. In general, it can be shown (Exercise 10.19) that there is a class $\mathcal{K}$ function α such that

$$\eta\|w(t,x,\eta)\| \leq k\alpha(\eta), \quad \forall\ (t,x) \in [0,\infty) \times D_0 \tag{10.44}$$

Without loss of generality, we can choose $\alpha(\eta)$ such that $\alpha(\eta) \geq c\eta$ for $\eta \in [0,1]$, where c is a positive constant. The partial derivatives $[\partial w/\partial t]$ and $[\partial w/\partial x]$ are given by

$$\frac{\partial w}{\partial t} = h(t,x) - \eta w(t,x,\eta)$$

$$\frac{\partial w}{\partial x} = \int_0^t \frac{\partial h}{\partial x}(\tau,x)\exp[-\eta(t-\tau)]\ d\tau$$

Because $[\partial h/\partial x]$ possesses the same properties of h that have been used to arrive at (10.44), it is clear that we can repeat the previous derivations to show that

$$\eta\left\|\frac{\partial w}{\partial x}\right\| \leq k\alpha(\eta), \quad \forall\ (t,x) \in [0,\infty) \times D_0 \tag{10.45}$$

There is no loss of generality in using the same class $\mathcal{K}$ function in both (10.44) and (10.45), since the calculated estimates will differ only in the positive constant that multiplies the η dependent term, so we can define α by using the larger of the two constants.

The function $w(t,x,\eta)$ that we have just defined possesses all the key properties of the function $u(t,x)$ of Section 10.4. The only difference is that the function w is parameterized in a parameter η in such a way that the bounds on w and $[\partial w/\partial x]$ are of the form $k\alpha(\eta)/\eta$ for some class $\mathcal{K}$ function α. We did not need to parameterize u in terms of any parameter. In fact, $u(t,x)$ is nothing more than the function $w(t,x,\eta)$ evaluated at $\eta = 0$. This should come as no surprise because in the periodic case, the convergence function $\sigma(t) = 1/(t+1)$; hence, $\alpha(\eta)/\eta = 1$.

From this point on, the analysis will be very similar to that of Section 10.4. We define the change of variables

$$x = y + \varepsilon w(t,y,\varepsilon) \tag{10.46}$$

The term $\varepsilon w(t,y,\varepsilon)$ is of order $O(\alpha(\varepsilon))$; thus, for sufficiently small ε, the change of variables of (10.46) is well defined, since the matrix $[I + \varepsilon\partial w/\partial y]$ is nonsingular. In particular,

$$\left[I + \varepsilon\frac{\partial w}{\partial y}\right]^{-1} = I + O(\alpha(\varepsilon))$$

Proceeding as in Section 10.4, we can show that the state equation for y is given by

$$\dot{y} = \varepsilon f_{\text{av}}(y) + \varepsilon\alpha(\varepsilon)q(t,y,\varepsilon) \tag{10.47}$$

where $q(t, y, \varepsilon)$ is bounded on $[0, \infty) \times D_0$ for sufficiently small ε. In arriving at (10.47), we have used the fact that $\alpha(\varepsilon) \geq c\varepsilon$. Equation (10.47) is a perturbation of the average system

$$\dot{x} = \varepsilon f_{\mathrm{av}}(x) \tag{10.48}$$

It is similar to (10.29), except that the coefficient of the q term is $\varepsilon\alpha(\varepsilon)$, instead of ε^2. This observation leads to the following theorem, which is similar to Theorem 10.4, except that the estimates $O(\varepsilon)$ are replaced by the estimates $O(\alpha(\varepsilon))$.

Theorem 10.5 *Let $f(t, x, \varepsilon)$ and its partial derivatives with respect to (x, ε) up to the second order be continuous and bounded for $(t, x, \varepsilon) \in [0, \infty) \times D_0 \times [0, \varepsilon_0]$, for every compact set $D_0 \subset D$, where $\varepsilon > 0$ and $D \subset R^n$ is a domain. Suppose $f(t, x, 0)$ has the average function $f_{\mathrm{av}}(x)$ on $[0, \infty) \times D$ and the Jacobian of $h(t, x) = f(t, x, 0) - f_{\mathrm{av}}(x)$ has zero average with the same convergence function as f. Let $x(t, \varepsilon)$ and $x_{\mathrm{av}}(\varepsilon t)$ denote the solutions of (10.39) and (10.48), respectively, and α be the class $\mathcal{K}$ function appearing in the estimates of (10.44) and (10.45).*

- *If $x_{\mathrm{av}}(\varepsilon t) \in D \ \forall \ t \in [0, b/\varepsilon]$ and $x(0, \varepsilon) - x_{\mathrm{av}}(0) = O(\alpha(\varepsilon))$, then there exists $\varepsilon^* > 0$ such that for all $0 < \varepsilon < \varepsilon^*$, $x(t, \varepsilon)$ is defined and*

$$x(t, \varepsilon) - x_{\mathrm{av}}(\varepsilon t) = O(\alpha(\varepsilon)) \quad \text{on } [0, b/\varepsilon]$$

- *If the origin $x = 0 \in D$ is an exponentially stable equilibrium point of the average system (10.48), $\Omega \subset D$ is a compact subset of its region of attraction, $x_{\mathrm{av}}(0) \in \Omega$, and $x(0, \varepsilon) - x_{\mathrm{av}}(0, \varepsilon) = O(\alpha(\varepsilon))$, then there exists $\varepsilon^* > 0$ such that for all $0 < \varepsilon < \varepsilon^*$, $x(t, \varepsilon)$ is defined and*

$$x(t, \varepsilon) - x_{\mathrm{av}}(\varepsilon t) = O(\alpha(\varepsilon)) \quad \text{for all } t \in [0, \infty)$$

- *If the origin $x = 0 \in D$ is an exponentially stable equilibrium point of the average system (10.48) and $f(t, 0, \varepsilon) = 0$ for all $(t, \varepsilon) \in [0, \infty) \times [0, \varepsilon_0]$, then there exists $\varepsilon^* > 0$ such that for all $0 < \varepsilon < \varepsilon^*$, the origin is an exponentially stable equilibrium point of the original system (10.39).* $\diamond$

Proof: By expressing (10.47) in the $s = \varepsilon t$ time scale, applying Theorems 3.4 and 3.5, and using the change of variables of (10.46), we can conclude the first part of the theorem. For the second part, we apply Theorem 9.1 on continuity of solutions on the infinite interval. Finally, by using $h(t, 0) = 0$, $w(t, 0, \eta) = 0$, and the bound $\|\partial w/\partial x\| \leq k\alpha(\eta)/\eta$, we see that the estimate on w can be revised to

$$\eta\|w(t, x, \eta)\| \leq k\alpha(\eta)\|x\|$$

The assumption $f(t, 0, \varepsilon) = 0$ and differentiability of f with respect to ε imply that $f(t, x, \varepsilon)$ is Lipschitz in ε, linearly in x; that is,

$$\|f(t, x, \varepsilon) - f(t, x, 0)\| \leq L_1 \varepsilon\|x\|$$

Using these estimates, it can be verified that the function $q(t, y, \varepsilon)$ in (10.47) satisfies the inequality $\|q(t, y, \varepsilon)\| \leq L\|y\|$ with some positive constant L for $(t, y, \varepsilon) \in [0, \infty) \times D_1 \times [0, \varepsilon_1]$, where $D_1 = \{\|y\| < r_1\}$ and r_1 and ε_1 are chosen small enough. By (the converse Lyapunov) Theorem 4.14 and Lemma 9.1, we conclude that, for sufficiently small ε, the origin is an exponentially stable equilibrium point for the original system (10.39). $\square$

Example 10.13 Consider the linear system

$$\dot{x} = \varepsilon A(t) x$$

where $\varepsilon > 0$. Suppose $A(t)$ and its derivatives up to the second order are continuous and bounded. Moreover, suppose $A(t)$ has an average

$$A_{\mathrm{av}} = \lim_{T \to \infty} \frac{1}{T} \int_t^{t+T} A(\tau) \, d\tau$$

in the sense of Definition 10.2. The average system is given by

$$\dot{x} = \varepsilon A_{\mathrm{av}} x$$

Suppose A_{av} is Hurwitz. By Theorem 10.5, we conclude that the origin of the original time-varying system is exponentially stable for sufficiently small ε. Suppose further that the matrix $A(t) = A_{\mathrm{tr}}(t) + A_{\mathrm{ss}}(t)$ is the sum of a transient component $A_{\mathrm{tr}}(t)$ and a steady-state component $A_{\mathrm{ss}}(t)$. The transient component decays to zero exponentially fast; that is,

$$\|A_{\mathrm{tr}}(t)\| \leq k_1 \exp(-\gamma t), \quad k_1 > 0, \ \gamma > 0$$

while the elements of the steady-state component are formed of a finite sum of sinusoids with distinct frequencies. The average of the transient component is zero, since

$$\frac{1}{T} \int_t^{t+T} \|A_{\mathrm{tr}}(\tau)\| \, d\tau \leq \frac{1}{T} \int_t^{t+T} k_1 e^{-\gamma \tau} \, d\tau = \frac{k_1 e^{-\gamma t}}{\gamma T} \left[1 - e^{-\gamma T} \right] \leq \frac{k_2}{T+1}$$

Recalling the first case of Example 10.12, we see that $A(t)$ has an average with convergence function $\sigma(T) = 1/(T+1)$. Hence, the class $\mathcal{K}$ function of Theorem 10.5 is $\alpha(\eta) = \eta$. Let $x(t, \varepsilon)$ and $x_{\mathrm{av}}(\varepsilon t)$ denote solutions of the original and average systems, which start from the same initial state. By Theorem 10.5,

$$x(t, \varepsilon) - x_{\mathrm{av}}(\varepsilon t) = O(\varepsilon), \quad \forall \, t \geq 0$$

$\triangle$

10.7 Exercises

10.1 If $\delta(\varepsilon) = O(\varepsilon)$, is it $O(\varepsilon^{1/2})$? Is it $O(\varepsilon^{3/2})$?

10.2 If $\delta(\varepsilon) = \varepsilon^{1/n}$, where $n > 1$ is a positive integer, is there a positive integer N such that $\delta(\varepsilon) = O(\varepsilon^N)$?

10.3 Consider the initial value problem

$$
\begin{aligned}
\dot{x}_1 &= -(0.2 + \varepsilon)x_1 + \frac{\pi}{4} - \tan^{-1} x_1 + \varepsilon \tan^{-1} x_2, \quad x_1(0) = \eta_1 \\
\dot{x}_2 &= -(0.2 + \varepsilon)x_2 + \frac{\pi}{4} - \tan^{-1} x_2 + \varepsilon \tan^{-1} x_1, \quad x_2(0) = \eta_2
\end{aligned}
$$

(a) Find an $O(\varepsilon)$ approximation.

(b) Find an $O(\varepsilon^2)$ approximation.

(c) Investigate the validity of the approximation on the infinite interval.

(d) Calculate, using a computer program, the exact solution, the $O(\varepsilon)$ approximation, and the $O(\varepsilon^2)$ approximation for $\varepsilon = 0.1$, $\eta_1 = 0.5$, and $\eta_2 = 1.5$ on the time interval $[0, 3]$. Comment on the accuracy of the approximation.

Hint: In parts (a) and (b), it is sufficient to give the equations defining the approximation. You are not required to find an analytic closed-form expression for the approximation.

10.4 Repeat Exercise 10.3 for the system

$$
\dot{x}_1 = x_2, \qquad \dot{x}_2 = -x_1 - x_2 + \varepsilon x_1^3
$$

In part (d), let $\varepsilon = 0.1$, $\eta_1 = 1.0$, $\eta_2 = 0.0$, and the time interval be $[0, 5]$.

10.5 Repeat Exercise 10.3 for the system

$$
\dot{x}_1 = -x_1 + x_2, \qquad \dot{x}_2 = \varepsilon x_1 - x_2 - \tfrac{1}{3}x_2^3
$$

In part (d), let $\varepsilon = 0.2$, $\eta_1 = 1.0$, $\eta_2 = 0.0$, and the time interval be $[0, 4]$.

10.6 ([166]) Repeat Exercise 10.3 for the system

$$
\dot{x}_1 = x_1 - x_1^2 + \varepsilon x_1 x_2, \qquad \dot{x}_2 = 2x_2 - x_2^2 - \varepsilon x_1 x_2
$$

In part (d), let $\varepsilon = 0.2$, $\eta_1 = 0.5$, $\eta_2 = 1.0$, and the time interval be $[0, 4]$.

10.7 Repeat Exercise 10.3 for the system

$$
\dot{x}_1 = -x_1 + x_2(1 + x_1) + \varepsilon(1 + x_1)^2, \qquad \dot{x}_2 = -x_1(x_1 + 1)
$$

In part (d), let $\varepsilon = -0.1$, $\eta_1 = -1$, and $\eta_2 = 2$. Repeat the calculation for $\varepsilon = -0.05$ and $\varepsilon = -0.2$ and comment on the accuracy of the approximation.

10.8 Consider the initial value problem

$$\begin{aligned} \dot{x}_1 &= -x_1 + \varepsilon x_2, & x_1(0) &= \eta \\ \dot{x}_2 &= -x_2 - \varepsilon x_1, & x_2(0) &= \eta \end{aligned}$$

Find an $O(\varepsilon)$ approximation. Calculate the exact and approximate solutions at $\varepsilon = 0.1$ for two different sets of initial conditions: (1) $\eta = 1$, (2) $\eta = 10$. Comment on the approximation accuracy. Explain any discrepancy with Theorem 10.1.

10.9 ([70]) Study, using the averaging method, each of the following scalar systems.

$\quad$ **(1)** $\dot{x} = \varepsilon(x - x^2)\sin^2 t$ $\qquad$ **(2)** $\dot{x} = \varepsilon(x\cos^2 t - \frac{1}{2}x^2)$

$\quad$ **(3)** $\dot{x} = \varepsilon(-x + \cos^2 t)$ $\qquad$ **(4)** $\dot{x} = -\varepsilon x \cos t$

10.10 For each of the following systems, show that, for sufficiently small $\varepsilon > 0$, the origin is exponentially stable:

$\quad$ **(1)** $\qquad \dot{x}_1 = \varepsilon x_2$
$$\dot{x}_2 = -\varepsilon(1 + 2\sin t)x_2 - \varepsilon(1 + \cos t)\sin x_1$$

$\quad$ **(2)** $\qquad \dot{x}_1 = \varepsilon[(-1 + 1.5\cos^2 t)x_1 + (1 - 1.5\sin t\cos t)x_2]$
$$\dot{x}_2 = \varepsilon[(-1 - 1.5\sin t\cos t)x_1 + (-1 + 1.5\sin^2 t)x_2]$$

$\quad$ **(3)** $\qquad \dot{x} = \varepsilon\left(-x\sin^2 t + x^2\sin t + xe^{-t}\right), \quad \varepsilon > 0$

10.11 Consider the system

$$\begin{aligned} \dot{x}_1 &= \varepsilon[(-1 + 1.5\cos^2 t)x_1 + (1 - 1.5\sin t\cos t)x_2] \\ \dot{x}_2 &= \varepsilon[(-1 - 1.5\sin t\cos t)x_1 + (-1 + 1.5\sin^2 t)x_2] + e^{-t} \end{aligned}$$

Show that there is $\varepsilon^* > 0$ such that for all $0 < \varepsilon < \varepsilon^*$ and all $x(0) \in R^2$, $x(t) \to 0$ as $t \to \infty$.

10.12 Consider the system $\dot{y} = Ay + \varepsilon g(t, y, \varepsilon)$, $\varepsilon > 0$, where the $n \times n$ matrix A has only simple eigenvalues on the imaginary axis.

(a) Show that $\exp(At)$ and $\exp(-At)$ are bounded for all $t \geq 0$.

(b) Show that the change of variables $y = \exp(At)x$ transforms the system into the form $\dot{x} = \varepsilon f(t, x, \varepsilon)$, where $f = \exp(-At)g(t, \exp(At)x, \varepsilon)$.

10.13 ([166]) Study Mathieu's equation $\ddot{y} + (1 + 2\varepsilon\cos 2t)y = 0$, $\varepsilon > 0$, using the averaging method.
Hint: Use Exercise 10.12.

10.14 (**[166]**) Study the equation $\ddot{y}+y=8\varepsilon(\dot{y})^2\cos t$ using the averaging method. Hint: Use Exercise 10.12.

10.15 Apply the averaging method to study the existence of limit cycles for each of the second-order systems that follow. If there is a limit cycle, estimate its location in the state plane and the period of oscillation, and determine whether it is stable or unstable.

$$(\mathbf{1})\ \ \ddot{y}+y=-\varepsilon\dot{y}(1-y^2) \qquad\qquad (\mathbf{2})\ \ \ddot{y}+y=\varepsilon\dot{y}(1-y^2)-\varepsilon y^3$$

$$(\mathbf{3})\ \ \ddot{y}+y=-\varepsilon\left(1-\tfrac{3\pi}{4}|y|\right)\dot{y} \qquad (\mathbf{4})\ \ \ddot{y}+y=-\varepsilon\left(1-\tfrac{3\pi}{4}|\dot{y}|\right)\dot{y}$$

$$(\mathbf{5})\ \ \ddot{y}+y=-\varepsilon(\dot{y}-y^3) \qquad\qquad (\mathbf{6})\ \ \ddot{y}+y=\varepsilon\dot{y}(1-y^2-\dot{y}^2)$$

10.16 Consider the second-order system

$$\dot{x}_1 = x_2, \qquad \dot{x}_2 = -x_1 + \varepsilon[x_1 + x_2(1 - x_1^2 - x_2^2)], \quad \varepsilon > 0$$

(a) Show that, for sufficiently small ε, the system has a stable limit cycle.

(b) Show that the system has no periodic orbits when $\varepsilon > 1$.

10.17 Consider Rayleigh's equation

$$m\frac{d^2u}{dt^2} + ku = \lambda\left[1 - \alpha\left(\frac{du}{dt}\right)^2\right]\frac{du}{dt}$$

where m, k, λ, and α are positive constants.

(a) Using the dimensionless variables $y = u/u^*$, $\tau = t/t^*$, and $\varepsilon = \lambda/\lambda^*$, where $(u^*)^2\alpha k = m/3$, $t^* = \sqrt{m/k}$, and $\lambda^* = \sqrt{km}$, show that the equation can be normalized to

$$\ddot{y}+y=\varepsilon\left(\dot{y}-\tfrac{1}{3}\dot{y}^3\right)$$

in which $\dot{y}$ denotes the derivative of y with respect to τ.

(b) Apply the averaging method to show that the normalized Rayleigh equation has a stable limit cycle. Estimate the location of the limit cycle in the plane $(y,\dot{y})$.

(c) Using a numerical algorithm, obtain the phase portrait of the normalized Rayleigh equation in the plane $(y,\dot{y})$ for

$$\text{(i) } \varepsilon = 1, \quad \text{(ii) } \varepsilon = 0.1, \quad \text{and} \quad \text{(iii) } \varepsilon = 0.01,$$

Compare with the results of part (b).

10.18 Consider Duffing's equation

$$m\ddot{y} + c\dot{y} + ky + ka^2y^3 = A\cos\omega t$$

where A, a, c, k, m, and ω are positive constants.

(a) Taking $x_1 = y$, $x_2 = \dot{y}$, $\tau = \omega t$, and $\varepsilon = 1/\omega$, show that the equation can be represented as $dx/d\tau = \varepsilon f(\tau, x, \varepsilon)$.

(b) Show that the system has an exponentially stable periodic solution for sufficiently large ω. Estimate the frequency of oscillation and the location of the periodic orbit in the phase plane.

10.19 Verify (10.44).

Hint: Start from (10.43) and use the fact that $\sigma(t)$ is bounded for $t \leq 1/\sqrt{\eta}$, while for $t \geq 1/\sqrt{\eta}$, $\sigma(t) \leq \sigma(1/\sqrt{\eta})$.

10.20 Study, using general averaging, the scalar system

$$\dot{x} = \varepsilon \left(\sin^2 t + \sin 1.5t + e^{-t}\right) x$$

10.21 (**[168]**) The output of an nth-order linear time-invariant single-input–single-output system can be represented by $y(t) = \theta^T w(t)$, where θ is a $(2n+1)$-dimensional vector of constant parameters and $w(t)$ is an auxiliary signal that can be synthesized from the system's input and output without knowing θ. Suppose that the vector θ is unknown and denote its value by θ^*. In identification experiments, the parameter $\theta(t)$ is updated by using an adaptation law of the form $\dot{\theta} = -\varepsilon e(t)w(t)$, where $e(t) = [\theta(t)-\theta^*]^T w(t)$ is the error between the actual system's output and the estimated output obtained by using $\theta(t)$. Let $\phi(t) = \theta(t) - \theta^*$ denote the parameter error.

(a) Show that $\dot{\phi} = \varepsilon A(t)\phi$, where $A(t) = -w(t)w^T(t)$.

(b) Using (general) averaging, derive a condition on $w(t)$, which ensures that, for sufficiently small ε, $\theta(t) \to \theta^*$ as $t \to \infty$.

Chapter 11

Singular Perturbations

While the perturbation method of Section 10.1 applies to state equations that depend smoothly on a small parameter ε, in this chapter we face a more difficult perturbation problem characterized by discontinuous dependence of system properties on the perturbation parameter ε. We will study the so-called *standard singular perturbation model*

$$\dot{x} = f(t, x, z, \varepsilon)$$
$$\varepsilon \dot{z} = g(t, x, z, \varepsilon)$$

where setting $\varepsilon = 0$ causes a fundamental and abrupt change in the dynamic properties of the system, as the differential equation $\varepsilon \dot{z} = g$ degenerates into the algebraic or transcendental equation

$$0 = g(t, x, z, 0)$$

The essence of the theory developed in this chapter is that the discontinuity of solutions caused by singular perturbations can be avoided if analyzed in separate time scales. This multitime-scale approach is a fundamental characteristic of the singular perturbation method.

In Section 11.1, we define the standard singular perturbation model and illustrate, via examples, some of its physical sources. In Section 11.2, we study the two-time-scale properties of the standard model and give a trajectory approximation result, based on the decomposition of the model into reduced (slow) and boundary-layer (fast) models. The approximation result is extended in Section 11.3 to the infinite-time interval. The intuition behind the time-scale decomposition becomes more transparent with a geometric viewpoint, which we present in Section 11.4. The time-scale decomposition of Section 11.2 is used in Section 11.5 to analyze the stability of equilibrium points via Lyapunov's method.

From Chapter 11 of *Nonlinear Systems*, Third Edition. Hassan K. Khalil.

11.1   The Standard Singular Perturbation Model

The singular perturbation model of a dynamical system is a state model where the derivatives of some of the states are multiplied by a small positive parameter ε; that is,

$$\dot{x} = f(t, x, z, \varepsilon) \tag{11.1}$$
$$\varepsilon\dot{z} = g(t, x, z, \varepsilon) \tag{11.2}$$

We assume that the functions f and g are continuously differentiable in their arguments for $(t, x, z, \varepsilon) \in [0, t_1] \times D_x \times D_z \times [0, \varepsilon_0]$, where $D_x \subset R^n$ and $D_z \subset R^m$ are open connected sets. When we set $\varepsilon = 0$ in (11.1) and (11.2), the dimension of the state equation reduces from $n + m$ to n because the differential equation (11.2) degenerates into the equation

$$0 = g(t, x, z, 0) \tag{11.3}$$

We say that the model (11.1)–(11.2) is in *standard form* if (11.3) has $k \geq 1$ isolated real roots

$$z = h_i(t, x), \quad i = 1, 2, \ldots, k \tag{11.4}$$

for each $(t, x) \in [0, t_1] \times D_x$. This assumption ensures that a well-defined n-dimensional reduced model will correspond to each root of (11.3). To obtain the ith reduced model, we substitute (11.4) into (11.1), at $\varepsilon = 0$, to obtain

$$\dot{x} = f(t, x, h(t, x), 0) \tag{11.5}$$

where we have dropped the subscript i from h. It will be clear from the context which root of (11.3) we are using. This model is sometimes called a *quasi-steady-state model*, because z, whose velocity $\dot{z} = g/\varepsilon$ can be large when ε is small and $g \neq 0$, may rapidly converge to a root of (11.3), which is the equilibrium of (11.2). We will discuss this two-time-scale property of (11.1) and (11.2) in the next section. The model (11.5) is also known as the *slow model*.

Modeling a physical system in the singularly perturbed form may not be easy. It is not always clear how to pick the parameters to be considered as small. Fortunately, in many applications, our knowledge of physical processes and components of the system sets us on the right track.[1] The following four examples illustrate four different "typical" ways of choosing the parameter ε. In the first example, ε is chosen as a small time constant. This is the most popular source of singularly perturbed models and, historically, the case that motivated interest in singular perturbations. Small time constants, masses, capacitances, and similar "parasitic" parameters that increase the order of a model are quite common in physical systems. In the interest of model simplification, we usually neglect these parasitic parameters to reduce the

---

[1] More about modeling physical systems in the singularly perturbed form can be found in [38], [105, Chapter 1], and [104, Chapter 4].

order of the model. Singular perturbations legitimize this ad hoc model simplification and provide tools for improving oversimplified models. In the second example, the parameter ε is the reciprocal of a high-gain parameter in a feedback system. The example represents an important source of singularly perturbed models. The use of high-gain parameters, or more precisely, parameters that are driven asymptotically toward infinity, in the design of feedback control systems is quite common. A typical approach to the analysis and design of high-gain feedback systems is to model them in the singularly perturbed form. In the third example, the parameter ε is a parasitic resistor in an electric circuit. Although neglecting the parasitic resistor reduces the order of the model, it does it in a way that is quite distinct from neglecting a parasitic time constant. Modeling the system in the standard singularly perturbed form involves a careful choice of the state variables. In the fourth example, the parameter ε is the ratio of the natural frequency of the car body to the natural frequency of the tire in an automotive suspension model. The special feature of this example is that it cannot be modeled in the standard singularly perturbed form without ε-dependent scaling of the state variables.

Example 11.1 An armature-controlled DC motor can be modeled by the second-order state equation

$$
\begin{aligned}
J\frac{d\omega}{dt} &= ki \\
L\frac{di}{dt} &= -k\omega - Ri + u
\end{aligned}
$$

where i, u, R, and L are the armature current, voltage, resistance, and inductance, J is the moment of inertia, ω is the angular speed, and ki and $k\omega$ are, respectively, the torque and the back electromotive force (e.m.f.) developed with constant excitation flux. The first state equation is a mechanical torque equation, and the second one is an equation for the electric transient in the armature circuit. Typically, L is "small" and can play the role of our parameter ε. This means that, with $\omega = x$ and $i = z$, the motor's model is in the standard form of (11.1)–(11.2) whenever $R \neq 0$. Neglecting L, we solve

$$0 = -k\omega - Ri + u$$

to obtain (the unique root)

$$i = \frac{u - k\omega}{R}$$

and substitute it into the torque equation. The resulting model

$$J\dot{\omega} = -\frac{k^2}{R}\omega + \frac{k}{R}u$$

is the commonly used first-order model of the DC motor. As we discussed in Chapter 10, it is preferable to choose the perturbation parameter ε as a dimensionless

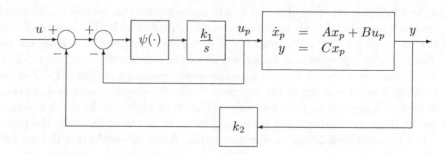

Figure 11.1: Actuator control with high-gain feedback.

ratio of two physical parameters. To that end, let us define the dimensionless variables

$$\omega_r = \frac{\omega}{\Omega}; \quad i_r = \frac{iR}{k\Omega}; \quad u_r = \frac{u}{k\Omega}$$

and rewrite the state equation as

$$T_m \frac{d\omega_r}{dt} = i_r$$

$$T_e \frac{di_r}{dt} = -\omega_r - i_r + u_r$$

where $T_m = JR/k^2$ is the mechanical time constant and $T_e = L/R$ is the electrical time constant. Since $T_m \gg T_e$, we let T_m be the time unit; that is, we introduce the dimensionless time variable $t_r = t/T_m$ and rewrite the state equation as

$$\frac{d\omega_r}{dt_r} = i_r$$

$$\frac{T_e}{T_m} \frac{di_r}{dt_r} = -\omega_r - i_r + u_r$$

This scaling has brought the model into the standard form with a physically meaningful dimensionless parameter

$$\varepsilon = \frac{T_e}{T_m} = \frac{Lk^2}{JR^2}$$

$\triangle$

Example 11.2 Consider the feedback control system of Figure 11.1. The inner loop represents actuator control with high-gain feedback. The high-gain parameter is the integrator constant k_1. The plant is a single-input–single-output nth-order system represented by the state model $\{A, B, C\}$. The nonlinearity $\psi(\cdot) \in (0, \infty]$; that is,

$$\psi(0) = 0 \text{ and } y\psi(y) > 0, \ \forall \ y \neq 0$$

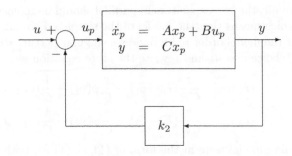

Figure 11.2: Simplified block diagram of Figure 11.1.

The state equation for the closed-loop system is

$$\dot{x}_p = Ax_p + Bu_p$$
$$\frac{1}{k_1}\dot{u}_p = \psi(u - u_p - k_2Cx_p)$$

With $\varepsilon = 1/k_1$, $x_p = x$, and $u_p = z$, the model takes the form of (11.1)–(11.2). Setting $\varepsilon = 0$, or equivalently $k_1 = \infty$, we solve

$$\psi(u - u_p - k_2Cx_p) = 0$$

to obtain

$$u_p = u - k_2Cx_p$$

which is the unique root since $\psi(\cdot)$ vanishes only at its origin. The resulting reduced model

$$\dot{x}_p = (A - Bk_2C)x_p + Bu$$

is the model of the simplified block diagram of Figure 11.2, where the whole inner loop in Figure 11.1 is replaced by a direct connection. $\triangle$

Example 11.3 Consider again the electric circuit of Example 10.4, shown in Figure 10.2. The differential equations for the voltages across the capacitors are

$$C\dot{v}_1 = \frac{1}{R}(E - v_1) - \psi(v_1) - \frac{1}{R_c}(v_1 - v_2)$$
$$C\dot{v}_2 = \frac{1}{R}(E - v_2) - \psi(v_2) - \frac{1}{R_c}(v_2 - v_1)$$

In Example 10.4, we analyzed the circuit for a "large" resistor R_c, which was idealized to be open circuit when $1/R_c$ was set to zero. This time, let us study the circuit for a "small" R_c. Setting $R_c = 0$ replaces the resistor with a short-circuit connection that puts the two capacitors in parallel. In a well-defined model for this simplified circuit, the two capacitors in parallel should be replaced by one equivalent capacitor, which means that the model of the simplified circuit will be of order one. To represent the model order reduction as a singular perturbation, let us start with the seeming choice $\varepsilon = R_c$ and rewrite the state equation as

$$\varepsilon \dot{v}_1 = \frac{\varepsilon}{CR}(E - v_1) - \frac{\varepsilon}{C}\psi(v_1) - \frac{1}{C}(v_1 - v_2)$$

$$\varepsilon \dot{v}_2 = \frac{\varepsilon}{CR}(E - v_2) - \frac{\varepsilon}{C}\psi(v_2) - \frac{1}{C}(v_2 - v_1)$$

If the preceding model were in the form of (11.1)–(11.2), both v_1 and v_2 would be considered as z variables, and (11.3) would be

$$v_1 - v_2 = 0$$

However, the roots of this equation are not isolated, which violates the basic assumption that the roots of (11.3) should be isolated. Therefore, with v_1 and v_2 as z variables, the model is not in the standard form. Let us now try another choice of the state variables. Take[2]

$$x = \tfrac{1}{2}(v_1 + v_2); \qquad z = \tfrac{1}{2}(v_1 - v_2)$$

The state equation for the new variables is

$$\dot{x} = \frac{1}{CR}(E - x) - \frac{1}{2C}[\psi(x + z) + \psi(x - z)]$$

$$\varepsilon \dot{z} = -\left(\frac{\varepsilon}{CR} + \frac{2}{C}\right)z - \frac{\varepsilon}{2C}[\psi(x + z) - \psi(x - z)]$$

Now the unique root of (11.3) is $z = 0$, which results in the reduced model

$$\dot{x} = -\frac{1}{CR}(E - x) - \frac{1}{C}\psi(x)$$

This model represents the simplified circuit of Figure 11.3, where each pair of similar parallel branches is replaced by an equivalent single branch. To obtain ε as a dimensionless parameter, we normalize x, z, and ψ as

$$x_r = \frac{x}{E}; \qquad z_r = \frac{z}{E}; \qquad \psi_r(v) = \frac{R}{E}\psi(Ev)$$

and normalize the time variable as $t_r = t/CR$ to obtain the singularly perturbed model

$$\frac{dx_r}{dt_r} = 1 - x_r - \frac{1}{2}[\psi_r(x_r + z_r) + \psi_r(x_r - z_r)]$$

$$\varepsilon \frac{dz_r}{dt_r} = -(\varepsilon + 2)z_r - \frac{\varepsilon}{2}[\psi_r(x_r + z_r) - \psi_r(x_r - z_r)]$$

where $\varepsilon = R_c/R$ is dimensionless. $\triangle$

---

[2]This choice of state variables follows from a systematic procedure described in [38].

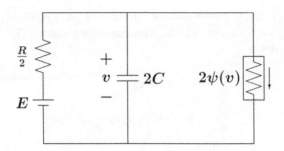

Figure 11.3: Simplified circuit when $R_c = 0$.

Example 11.4 A quarter-car model of automotive suspension is shown in Figure 11.4, where m_s and m_u are the car body and tire masses, k_s and k_t are the spring constants of the strut and tire, b_s is the damper (shock absorber) constant, and F is a force generated by a force actuator that may be used in active and semi-active suspension. When $F = 0$, we have the traditional passive suspension. The distances d_s, d_u, and d_r are the elevations of the car, tire, and road surface, respectively, from a reference point. From Newton's law, the balance of forces acting on m_s and m_u results in the equations

$$m_s \ddot{d}_s + b_s(\dot{d}_s - \dot{d}_u) + k_s(d_s - d_u) = F$$

$$m_u \ddot{d}_u + b_s(\dot{d}_u - \dot{d}_s) + k_s(d_u - d_s) + k_t(d_u - d_r) = -F$$

In a typical car, the natural frequency $\sqrt{k_t/m_u}$ of the tire is about 10 times the natural frequency $\sqrt{k_s/m_s}$ of the car body and strut. We therefore define the parameter

$$\varepsilon = \sqrt{\frac{k_s/m_s}{k_t/m_u}} = \sqrt{\frac{k_s m_u}{k_t m_s}}$$

This mass-spring system is of interest because it cannot be transformed into a standard singularly perturbed model without an ε-dependent scaling. The tire stiffness $k_t = O(1/\varepsilon^2)$ tends to infinity as $\varepsilon \to 0$. For the tire potential energy $k_t(d_u - d_r)^2/2$ to remain bounded, the displacement $d_u - d_r$ must be $O(\varepsilon)$; that is, the scaled displacement $(d_u - d_r)/\varepsilon$ must remain finite. In addition to this scaling, we normalize all variables to be dimensionless. Distances are divided by some distance ℓ, velocities by $\ell\sqrt{k_s/m_s}$, forces by ℓk_s, and time by $\sqrt{m_s/k_s}$. Thus, to express the system in the standard singularly perturbed form, we introduce the slow and fast variables as

$$x = \begin{bmatrix} (d_s - d_u)/\ell \\ (\dot{d}_s/\ell)\sqrt{m_s/k_s} \end{bmatrix}, \quad z = \begin{bmatrix} (d_u - d_r)/(\varepsilon\ell) \\ (\dot{d}_u/\ell)\sqrt{m_s/k_s} \end{bmatrix}$$

and take $u = F/(k_s\ell)$ as the control input, $w = (\dot{d}_r/\ell)\sqrt{m_s/k_s}$ as the disturbance input, and $t_r = t\sqrt{k_s/m_s}$ as the dismensionless time. The resulting singularly perturbed model is

$$\frac{dx_1}{dt_r} = x_2 - z_2$$

$$\frac{dx_2}{dt_r} = -x_1 - \beta(x_2 - z_2) + u$$

$$\varepsilon\frac{dz_1}{dt_r} = z_2 - w$$

$$\varepsilon\frac{dz_2}{dt_r} = \alpha x_1 - \alpha\beta(z_2 - x_2) - z_1 - \alpha u$$

where

$$\alpha = \sqrt{\frac{k_s m_s}{k_t m_u}}, \qquad \beta = \frac{b_s}{\sqrt{k_s m_s}}$$

For typical cars with passive suspension, the parameters α, β, and ε take values in the ranges $[0.6, 1.2]$, $[0.5, 0.8]$, and $[0.08, 0.135]$, respectively. In active/semiactive suspension, the damping constant may be reduced as the force actuator provides additional damping. Setting $\varepsilon = 0$ results in the reduced model

$$\frac{dx_1}{dt_r} = x_2 - w$$

$$\frac{dx_2}{dt_r} = -x_1 - \beta(x_2 - w) + u$$

which corresponds to the simplified one-degree-of-freedom model shown in Figure 11.4. $\triangle$

11.2   Time-Scale Properties of the Standard Model

Singular perturbations cause a multitime-scale behavior of dynamical systems characterized by the presence of slow and fast transients in the system's response to external stimuli. Loosely speaking, the slow response is approximated by the reduced model (11.5), while the discrepancy between the response of the reduced model and that of the full model (11.1)–(11.2) is the fast transient. To see this point, let us consider the problem of solving the state equation

$$\dot{x} = f(t, x, z, \varepsilon), \qquad x(t_0) = \xi(\varepsilon) \tag{11.6}$$

$$\varepsilon\dot{z} = g(t, x, z, \varepsilon), \qquad z(t_0) = \eta(\varepsilon) \tag{11.7}$$

where $\xi(\varepsilon)$ and $\eta(\varepsilon)$ depend smoothly on ε and $t_0 \in [0, t_1)$. Let $x(t, \varepsilon)$ and $z(t, \varepsilon)$ denote the solution of the full problem of (11.6) and (11.7). When we define the

Quarter-Car Model   Simplified Model

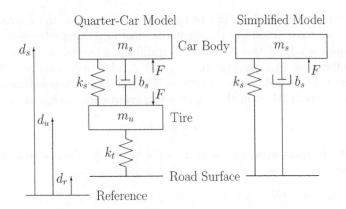

Figure 11.4: Quarter-Car Model of Automotive suspension.

corresponding problem for the reduced model (11.5), we can only specify n initial conditions, since the model is nth order. Naturally, we retain the initial state for x to obtain the reduced problem

$$\dot{x} = f(t, x, h(t, x), 0), \quad x(t_0) = \xi_0 \overset{\text{def}}{=} \xi(0) \tag{11.8}$$

Denote the solution of (11.8) by $\bar{x}(t)$. Because the variable z has been excluded from the reduced model and substituted by its "quasi-steady-state" $h(t, x)$, the only information we can obtain about z by solving (11.8) is to compute

$$\bar{z}(t) \overset{\text{def}}{=} h(t, \bar{x}(t))$$

which describes the quasi-steady-state behavior of z when $x = \bar{x}$. By contrast to the original variable z starting at t_0 from a prescribed $\eta(\varepsilon)$, the quasi-steady-state $\bar{z}$ is not free to start from a prescribed value, and there may be a large discrepancy between its initial value $\bar{z}(t_0) = h(t_0, \xi_0)$ and the prescribed initial state $\eta(\varepsilon)$. Thus, $\bar{z}(t)$ cannot be a uniform approximation of $z(t, \varepsilon)$. The best we can expect is that the estimate

$$z(t, \varepsilon) - \bar{z}(t) = O(\varepsilon)$$

will hold on an interval excluding t_0, that is, for $t \in [t_b, t_1]$, where $t_b > t_0$. On the other hand, it is reasonable to expect the estimate

$$x(t, \varepsilon) - \bar{x}(t) = O(\varepsilon)$$

to hold uniformly for all $t \in [t_0, t_1]$, since

$$x(t_0, \varepsilon) - \bar{x}(t_0) = \xi(\varepsilon) - \xi(0) = O(\varepsilon)$$

If the error $z(t, \varepsilon) - \bar{z}(t)$ is indeed $O(\varepsilon)$ over $[t_b, t_1]$, then it must be true that during the initial ("boundary-layer") interval $[t_0, t_b]$, the variable z approaches $\bar{z}$. Let us remember that the speed of z can be high, because $\dot{z} = g/\varepsilon$. In fact, having set $\varepsilon = 0$ in (11.2), we have made the transient of z instantaneous whenever $g \neq 0$. From our previous study of the stability of equilibrium points, it should be clear that we cannot expect z to converge to its quasi-steady-state $\bar{z}$, unless certain stability conditions are satisfied. Such conditions will result from the forthcoming analysis.

It is more convenient in the analysis to perform the change of variables

$$y = z - h(t, x) \tag{11.9}$$

that shifts the quasi-steady-state of z to the origin. In the new variables (x, y), the full problem is

$$
\begin{aligned}
\dot{x} &= f(t, x, y + h(t, x), \varepsilon), \quad x(t_0) = \xi(\varepsilon) \tag{11.10} \\
\varepsilon \dot{y} &= g(t, x, y + h(t, x), \varepsilon) - \varepsilon \frac{\partial h}{\partial t} \\
&\quad - \varepsilon \frac{\partial h}{\partial x} f(t, x, y + h(t, x), \varepsilon), \quad y(t_0) = \eta(\varepsilon) - h(t_0, \xi(\varepsilon)) \tag{11.11}
\end{aligned}
$$

The quasi-steady-state of (11.11) is now $y = 0$, which when substituted into (11.10) results in the reduced model (11.8). To analyze (11.11), let us note that $\varepsilon \dot{y}$ may remain finite even when ε tends to zero and $\dot{y}$ tends to infinity. We set

$$\varepsilon \frac{dy}{dt} = \frac{dy}{d\tau}; \quad \text{hence,} \quad \frac{d\tau}{dt} = \frac{1}{\varepsilon}$$

and use $\tau = 0$ as the initial value at $t = t_0$. The new time variable $\tau = (t - t_0)/\varepsilon$ is "stretched"; that is, if ε tends to zero, τ tends to infinity even for finite t only slightly larger than t_0 by a fixed (independent of ε) difference. In the τ time scale, (11.11) is represented by

$$
\begin{aligned}
\frac{dy}{d\tau} &= g(t, x, y + h(t, x), \varepsilon) - \varepsilon \frac{\partial h}{\partial t} \\
&\quad - \varepsilon \frac{\partial h}{\partial x} f(t, x, y + h(t, x), \varepsilon), \quad y(0) = \eta(\varepsilon) - h(t_0, \xi(\varepsilon)) \tag{11.12}
\end{aligned}
$$

The variables t and x in the foregoing equation will be slowly varying since, in the τ time scale, they are given by

$$t = t_0 + \varepsilon \tau, \qquad x = x(t_0 + \varepsilon \tau, \varepsilon)$$

Setting $\varepsilon = 0$ freezes these variables at $t = t_0$ and $x = \xi_0$, and reduces (11.12) to the autonomous system

$$\frac{dy}{d\tau} = g(t_0, \xi_0, y + h(t_0, \xi_0), 0), \quad y(0) = \eta(0) - h(t_0, \xi_0) \stackrel{\text{def}}{=} \eta_0 - h(t_0, \xi_0) \tag{11.13}$$

which has equilibrium at $y = 0$. If this equilibrium point is asymptotically stable and $y(0)$ belongs to its region of attraction, it is reasonable to expect that the solution of (11.13) will reach an $O(\varepsilon)$ neighborhood of the origin during the boundary-layer interval. Beyond this interval, we need a stability property that guarantees that $y(\tau)$ will remain close to zero, while the slowly varying parameters (t, x) move away from their initial values (t_0, ξ_0). To analyze this situation, we allow the frozen parameters to take values in the region of the slowly varying parameters (t, x).[3] Assume that the solution $\bar{x}(t)$ of the reduced problem is defined for $t \in [0, t_1]$ and $\bar{x}(t) \in D_x \subset R^n$, for some domain D_x. We rewrite (11.13) as

$$\frac{dy}{d\tau} = g(t, x, y + h(t, x), 0) \tag{11.14}$$

where $(t, x) \in [0, t_1] \times D_x$ are treated as fixed parameters. We will refer to (11.14) as the boundary-layer model or boundary-layer system. Sometimes, we will also refer to (11.13) as the boundary-layer model. This should cause no confusion, because (11.13) is an evaluation of (11.14) for a given initial time and initial state. The crucial stability property we need for (11.14) is exponential stability of its origin, uniformly in the frozen parameters, as stated in the next definition.

Definition 11.1 *The equilibrium point $y = 0$ of the boundary-layer system (11.14) is exponentially stable, uniformly in $(t, x) \in [0, t_1] \times D_x$, if there exist positive constants k, γ, and ρ_0 such that the solutions of (11.14) satisfy*

$$\|y(\tau)\| \leq k\|y(0)\| \exp(-\gamma \tau), \ \forall \ \|y(0)\| < \rho_0, \ \forall \ (t, x) \in [0, t_1] \times D_x, \ \forall \ \tau \geq 0 \tag{11.15}$$

Aside from trivial cases where the solution of the boundary layer model may be known in closed form, verification of exponential stability of the origin will have to be done either by linearization or via Lyapunov analysis. It can be shown (Exercise 11.5) that if the Jacobian matrix $[\partial g / \partial y]$ satisfies the eigenvalue condition

$$\mathrm{Re}\left[\lambda\left\{\frac{\partial g}{\partial y}(t, x, h(t, x), 0)\right\}\right] \leq -c < 0, \quad \forall \ (t, x) \in [0, t_1] \times D_x \tag{11.16}$$

then there exist constants k, γ, and ρ_0 for which (11.15) is satisfied. This, of course, is a local result; that is, the constant ρ_0 could be very small. Alternatively, it can be shown (Exercise 11.6) that if there is a Lyapunov function $V(t, x, y)$ that satisfies

$$c_1\|y\|^2 \leq V(t, x, y) \leq c_2\|y\|^2 \tag{11.17}$$

$$\frac{\partial V}{\partial y} g(t, x, y + h(t, x), 0) \leq -c_3\|y\|^2 \tag{11.18}$$

for $(t, x, y) \in [0, t_1] \times D_x \times D_y$, where $D_y \subset R^m$ is a domain that contains the origin, then (11.15) is satisfied with the estimates

$$\rho_0 = \rho\sqrt{c_1/c_2}, \ k = \sqrt{c_2/c_1}, \ \gamma = c_3/2c_2 \tag{11.19}$$

in which $B_\rho \subset D_y$.

---

[3]Recall from Section 9.6 that if the origin of (11.13) is exponentially stable, uniformly in the frozen parameters (t_0, ξ_0), then it will remain exponentially stable when these parameters are replaced by the slowly varying variables (t, x).

Theorem 11.1 *Consider the singular perturbation problem of (11.6) and (11.7) and let $z = h(t, x)$ be an isolated root of (11.3). Assume that the following conditions are satisfied for all*

$$[t, x, z - h(t, x), \varepsilon] \in [0, t_1] \times D_x \times D_y \times [0, \varepsilon_0]$$

for some domains $D_x \subset R^n$ and $D_y \subset R^m$, in which D_x is convex and D_y contains the origin:

- *The functions f, g, their first partial derivatives with respect to (x, z, ε), and the first partial derivative of g with respect to t are continuous; the function $h(t, x)$ and the Jacobian $[\partial g(t, x, z, 0)/\partial z]$ have continuous first partial derivatives with respect to their arguments; the initial data $\xi(\varepsilon)$ and $\eta(\varepsilon)$ are smooth functions of ε.*

- *The reduced problem (11.8) has a unique solution $\bar{x}(t) \in S$, for $t \in [t_0, t_1]$, where S is a compact subset of D_x.*

- *The origin is an exponentially stable equilibrium point of the boundary-layer model (11.14), uniformly in (t, x); let $\mathcal{R}_y \subset D_y$ be the region of attraction of (11.13) and Ω_y be a compact subset of $\mathcal{R}_y$.*

Then, there exists a positive constant ε^* such that for all $\eta_0 - h(t_0, \xi_0) \in \Omega_y$ and $0 < \varepsilon < \varepsilon^*$, the singular perturbation problem of (11.6) and (11.7) has a unique solution $x(t, \varepsilon)$, $z(t, \varepsilon)$ on $[t_0, t_1]$, and

$$x(t, \varepsilon) - \bar{x}(t) = O(\varepsilon) \tag{11.20}$$

$$z(t, \varepsilon) - h(t, \bar{x}(t)) - \hat{y}(t/\varepsilon) = O(\varepsilon) \tag{11.21}$$

hold uniformly for $t \in [t_0, t_1]$, where $\hat{y}(\tau)$ is the solution of the boundary-layer model (11.13). Moreover, given any $t_b > t_0$, there is $\varepsilon^{**} \leq \varepsilon^*$ such that

$$z(t, \varepsilon) - h(t, \bar{x}(t)) = O(\varepsilon) \tag{11.22}$$

holds uniformly for $t \in [t_b, t_1]$ whenever $\varepsilon < \varepsilon^{**}$. $\diamond$

Proof: See Appendix C.17.

This theorem is known as Tikhonov's theorem.[4] Its proof uses the stability properties of the boundary-layer model to show that

$$\|y(t, \varepsilon)\| \leq k_1 \exp\left[\frac{-\alpha(t - t_0)}{\varepsilon}\right] + \varepsilon\delta$$

The preceding bound is used in (11.10) to prove (11.20), which is plausible, since $\int_0^t \exp(-\alpha s/\varepsilon) \, ds$ is $O(\varepsilon)$. The proof ends with error analysis of (11.11) in the τ time scale to prove (11.21) and (11.22).

---

[4]There are other versions of Tikhonov's theorem which use slightly different technical assumptions. (See, for example, [105, Chapter 1, Theorem 3.1].)

Example 11.5 Consider the singular perturbation problem

$$\dot{x} = z, \qquad\qquad x(0) = \xi_0$$

$$\varepsilon \dot{z} = -x - z + u(t), \quad z(0) = \eta_0$$

for the DC motor of Example 11.1. Suppose $u(t) = t$ for $t \geq 0$ and we want to solve the state equation over the interval $[0, 1]$. The unique root of (11.3) is $h(t, x) = -x + t$ and the boundary-layer model (11.14) is

$$\frac{dy}{d\tau} = -y$$

Clearly, the origin of the boundary-layer system is globally exponentially stable. The reduced problem

$$\dot{x} = -x + t, \quad x(0) = \xi_0$$

has the unique solution

$$\bar{x}(t) = t - 1 + (1 + \xi_0)\exp(-t)$$

The boundary-layer problem

$$\frac{dy}{d\tau} = -y, \quad y(0) = \eta_0 + \xi_0$$

has the unique solution

$$\hat{y}(\tau) = (\eta_0 + \xi_0)\exp(-\tau)$$

From Theorem 11.1, we have

$$x - [t - 1 + (1 + \xi_0)\exp(-t)] = O(\varepsilon)$$

$$z - \left[(\eta_0 + \xi_0)\exp\left(\frac{-t}{\varepsilon}\right) + 1 - (1 + \xi_0)\exp(-t)\right] = O(\varepsilon)$$

for all $t \in [0, 1]$. The $O(\varepsilon)$ approximation of z clearly exhibits a two-time-scale behavior. It starts with a fast transient $(\eta_0 + \xi_0)\exp(-t/\varepsilon)$, which is the so-called boundary-layer part of the solution. After the decay of this transient, z remains close to $[1 - (1 + \xi_0)\exp(-t)]$, which is the slow (quasi-steady-state) part of the solution. The two-time-scale behavior is significant only in z, while x is predominantly slow. In fact, x has a fast (boundary-layer) transient, but it is $O(\varepsilon)$. Since this system is linear, we can characterize its two-time-scale behavior via modal analysis. It can be easily seen that the system has one slow eigenvalue λ_1, which is $O(\varepsilon)$ close to the eigenvalue of the reduced model, that is, $\lambda_1 = -1 + O(\varepsilon)$, and one fast eigenvalue $\lambda_2 = \lambda/\varepsilon$, where λ is $O(\varepsilon)$ close to the eigenvalue of the boundary-layer model, that is, $\lambda_2 = [-1 + O(\varepsilon)]/\varepsilon$. The exact solutions of x and z will be linear combinations of the slow mode $\exp(\lambda_1 t)$, the fast mode $\exp(\lambda t/\varepsilon)$, and a steady-state component due to the input $u(t) = t$. By actually calculating the modal decomposition, it can be verified that the coefficient of the fast mode in x is $O(\varepsilon)$. This can be done for linear systems in general. (See Exercise 11.14.) $\triangle$

Example 11.6 Consider the singular perturbation problem

$$\dot{x} \;=\; Ax + Bz, \qquad\qquad x(0) \;=\; \xi_0$$

$$\varepsilon\dot{z} \;=\; \psi(u(t) - z - k_2 Cx), \quad z(0) \;=\; \eta_0$$

for the high-gain feedback system of Example 11.2. Suppose $u(t) = 1$ for $t \geq 0$ and $\psi(\cdot) = \tan^{-1}(\cdot)$. The unique root of (11.3) is $h(t,x) = 1 - k_2 Cx$ and the boundary-layer model (11.14) is

$$\frac{dy}{d\tau} = \tan^{-1}(-y) = -\tan^{-1}(y)$$

The Jacobian

$$\left.\frac{\partial g}{\partial y}\right|_{y=0} = -\left.\frac{1}{1+y^2}\right|_{y=0} = -1$$

is Hurwitz; hence, the origin of the boundary-layer model is exponentially stable. It is also clear that the origin is globally asymptotically stable. Since the reduced problem

$$\dot{x} = (A - Bk_2C)x + B, \quad x(0) = \xi_0$$

is linear, it is clear that all the assumptions of Theorem 11.1 are satisfied, and we can proceed to approximate x and z in terms of the solutions of the reduced and boundary-layer problems. $\triangle$

Example 11.7 Consider the singular perturbation problem

$$\dot{x} \;=\; x^2(1+t)/z, \qquad\qquad\qquad x(0) \;=\; 1$$

$$\varepsilon\dot{z} \;=\; -[z + (1+t)x]\, z\, [z - (1+t)], \quad z(0) \;=\; \eta_0$$

Equation (11.3), which takes the form

$$0 = -[z + (1+t)x]\, z\, [z - (1+t)]$$

has three isolated roots

$$z = -(1+t)x, \quad z = 0, \quad \text{and} \quad z = 1+t$$

in the region $\{t \geq 0 \text{ and } x > k\}$, where $0 < k < 1$. Consider first the root $z = -(1+t)x$. The boundary-layer model (11.14) is

$$\frac{dy}{d\tau} = -y[y - (1+t)x][y - (1+t)x - (1+t)]$$

A sketch of the right-hand side function, Figure 11.5(a), shows that the origin is asymptotically stable with $y < (1+t)x$ as its region of attraction. Taking $V(y) = y^2$,

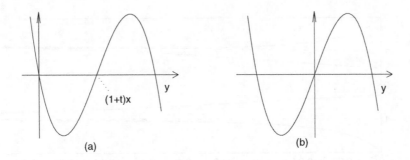

Figure 11.5: RHS of boundary-layer model: (a) $z = -(1+t)x$, (b) $z = 0$.

it can be easily verified that V satisfies (11.17) and (11.18) for $y \leq \rho < (1+t)x$. The reduced problem

$$\dot{x} = -x, \quad x(0) = 1$$

has the unique solution $\bar{x}(t) = \exp(-t)$ for all $t \geq 0$. The boundary-layer problem with $t = 0$ and $x = 1$,

$$\frac{dy}{d\tau} = -y(y-1)(y-2), \quad y(0) = \eta_0 + 1$$

has a unique decaying solution $\hat{y}(\tau)$ for $\eta_0 < 0$. Consider next the root $z = 0$. The boundary-layer model (11.14) is

$$\frac{dy}{d\tau} = -[y + (1+t)x] \, y \, [y - (1+t)]$$

A sketch of the right-hand side function, Figure 11.5(b), shows that the origin is unstable. Consequently, Theorem 11.1 does not apply to this case. Finally, the boundary-layer model for the root $z = 1 + t$ is

$$\frac{dy}{d\tau} = -[y + (1+t) + (1+t)x][y + (1+t)]y$$

Similar to the first case, it can be shown that the origin is exponentially stable uniformly in (t, x). The reduced problem

$$\dot{x} = x^2, \quad x(0) = 1$$

has the unique solution $\bar{x}(t) = 1/(1-t)$ for all $t \in [0, 1)$. Notice that $\bar{x}(t)$ has a finite escape time at $t = 1$. However, Theorem 11.1 still holds for $t \in [0, t_1]$ with $t_1 < 1$. The boundary-layer problem with $t = 0$ and $x = 1$,

$$\frac{dy}{d\tau} = -(y+2)(y+1)y, \quad y(0) = \eta_0 - 1$$

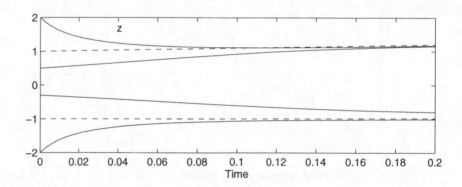

Figure 11.6: Simulation results for z of Example 11.7 at $\varepsilon = 0.1$: reduced solution (dashed); exact solution (solid).

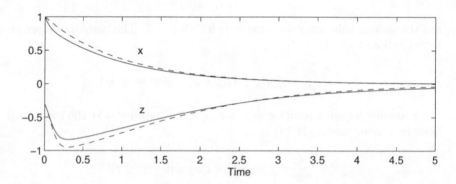

Figure 11.7: Exact (solid) and approximate (dashed) solutions for Example 11.7 at $\varepsilon = 0.1$.

has a unique decaying solution $\hat{y}(\tau)$ for $\eta_0 > 0$. Among the three roots of (11.3), only two roots, $h = -(1 + t)x$ and $h = 1 + t$, give rise to valid reduced models. Theorem 11.1 applies to the root $h = -(1+t)x$ if $\eta_0 < 0$ and to the root $h = 1+t$ if $\eta_0 > 0$. Figures 11.6 and 11.7 show simulation results at $\varepsilon = 0.1$. Figure 11.6 shows z for four different values of η_0, two for each reduced model. Figure 11.7 shows the exact and approximate solutions of x and z for $\eta_0 = -0.3$. The trajectories of Figure 11.6 clearly exhibit a two-time-scale behavior. They start with a fast transient of $z(t, \varepsilon)$ from η_0 to $\bar{z}(t)$. After the decay of this transient, they remain close to $\bar{z}(t)$. In the case $\eta_0 = -0.3$, the convergence to $\bar{z}(t)$ does not take place within the time interval $[0, 0.2]$. The same case is shown in Figure 11.7 on a longer time interval, where we can see $z(t, \varepsilon)$ approaching $\bar{z}(t)$. Figure 11.7 illustrates the $O(\varepsilon)$ asymptotic approximation result of Tikhonov's theorem. $\triangle$

11.3   Singular Perturbation on the Infinite Interval

Theorem 11.1 is valid only on $O(1)$ time intervals. This fact can be easily seen from the proof of the theorem. In particular, it is established in (C.81) that

$$\|x(t, \varepsilon) - \bar{x}(t)\| \le \varepsilon k_3 [1 + t_1 - t_0] \exp[L_6(t_1 - t_0)]$$

For any finite t_1, the foregoing estimate is $O(\varepsilon)$, but it is not $O(\varepsilon)$ uniformly in t for all $t \ge t_0$. For the latter statement to hold, we need to show that

$$\|x(t, \varepsilon) - \bar{x}(t)\| \le \varepsilon k, \quad \forall\, t \in [t_0, \infty)$$

This can be done under some additional stability conditions. In the next theorem, we require the reduced system (11.5) to have an exponentially stable equilibrium point at the origin and use a Lyapunov function to estimate its region of attraction.

Theorem 11.2 *Consider the singular perturbation problem of (11.6) and (11.7) and let $z = h(t, x)$ be an isolated root of (11.3). Assume that the following conditions are satisfied for all*

$$[t, x, z - h(t, x), \varepsilon] \in [0, \infty) \times D_x \times D_y \times [0, \varepsilon_0]$$

for some domains $D_x \subset R^n$ and $D_y \subset R^m$, which contain their respective origins:

- *On any compact subset of $D_x \times D_y$, the functions f, g, their first partial derivatives with respect to (x, z, ε), and the first partial derivative of g with respect to t are continuous and bounded, $h(t, x)$ and $[\partial g(t, x, z, 0)/\partial z]$ have bounded first partial derivatives with respect to their arguments, and $[\partial f(t, x, h(t, x), 0)/\partial x]$ is Lipschitz in x, uniformly in t; the initial data $\xi(\varepsilon)$ and $\eta(\varepsilon)$ are smooth functions of ε;*

- *the origin is an exponentially stable equilibrium point of the reduced system (11.5); there is a Lyapunov function $V(t, x)$ that satisfies the conditions of Theorem 4.9 for (11.5) for $(t, x) \in [0, \infty) \times D_x$ and $\{W_1(x) \le c\}$ is a compact subset of D_x;*

- *the origin is an exponentially stable equilibrium point of the boundary-layer system (11.14), uniformly in (t, x); let $\mathcal{R}_y \subset D_y$ be the region of attraction of (11.13) and Ω_y be a compact subset of $\mathcal{R}_y$.*

Then, for each compact set $\Omega_x \subset \{W_2(x) \le \rho c, \ 0 < \rho < 1\}$ there is a positive constant ε^* such that for all $t_0 \ge 0$, $\xi_0 \in \Omega_x$, $\eta_0 - h(t_0, \xi_0) \in \Omega_y$, and $0 < \varepsilon < \varepsilon^*$, the singular perturbation problem of (11.6) and (11.7) has a unique solution $x(t, \varepsilon)$, $z(t, \varepsilon)$ on $[t_0, \infty)$, and

$$x(t, \varepsilon) - \bar{x}(t) = O(\varepsilon) \tag{11.23}$$

$$z(t, \varepsilon) - h(t, \bar{x}(t)) - \hat{y}(t/\varepsilon) = O(\varepsilon) \tag{11.24}$$

hold uniformly for $t \in [t_0, \infty)$, where $\bar{x}(t)$ and $\hat{y}(\tau)$ are the solutions of the reduced and boundary-layer problems (11.8) and (11.13). Moreover, given any $t_b > t_0$, there is $\varepsilon^{**} \leq \varepsilon^*$ such that

$$z(t, \varepsilon) - h(t, \bar{x}(t)) = O(\varepsilon) \tag{11.25}$$

holds uniformly for $t \in [t_b, \infty)$ whenever $\varepsilon < \varepsilon^{**}$. ◇

Proof: See Appendix C.18.

If the reduced system (11.5) is autonomous, the set Ω_x in Theorem 11.2 can be any compact subset of its region of attraction. This is a consequence of (the converse Lyapunov) Theorem 4.17, which provides a Lyapunov function $V(x)$ such that any compact subset of the region of attraction is in the interior of a compact set of the form $\{V(x) \leq c\}$.

Example 11.8 Consider the singular perturbation problem

$$\dot{x} = 1 - x - \frac{1}{2}[\psi(x + z) + \psi(x - z)], \qquad x(0) = \xi_0$$

$$\varepsilon \dot{z} = -(\varepsilon + 2)z - \frac{\varepsilon}{2}[\psi(x + z) - \psi(x - z)], \quad z(0) = \eta_0$$

for the electric circuit of Example 11.3, and assume that

$$\psi(v) = a\left[\exp\left(\frac{v}{b}\right) - 1\right], \quad a > 0, \ b > 0$$

We have dropped the subscript r as we copied these equations from Example 11.3. The differentiability and Lipschitz conditions of Theorem 11.2 are satisfied on any compact set of (x, z). The reduced model

$$\dot{x} = 1 - x - a\left[\exp\left(\frac{x}{b}\right) - 1\right] \stackrel{\text{def}}{=} f_o(x)$$

has a unique equilibrium point at $x = p^*$, where p^* is the unique root of $f_o(p^*) = 0$. It can be easily seen that $0 < p^* < 1$. The Jacobian

$$\left.\frac{df_o}{dx}\right|_{x=p^*} = -1 - \frac{a}{b}\exp\left(\frac{p^*}{b}\right) < -1$$

is negative; hence, the equilibrium point $x = p^*$ is exponentially stable. Moreover, by sketching the function $f_o(x)$, it can be seen that $x = p^*$ is globally asymptotically stable. The change of variables $\tilde{x} = x - p^*$ shifts the equilibrium point to the origin. The boundary-layer model

$$\frac{dz}{d\tau} = -2z$$

is independent of x, and its origin is globally exponentially stable. Thus, all the conditions of Theorem 11.2 are satisfied globally and the estimates of (11.23) through (11.25), with $h = 0$, hold for all $t \geq 0$ and for any bounded initial state (ξ_0, η_0). △

Example 11.9 Consider the adaptive control of a plant represented by the second-order transfer function

$$\tilde{P}(s) = \frac{k_p}{(s - a_p)(\varepsilon s + 1)}$$

where a_p, $k_p > 0$, and $\varepsilon > 0$ are unknown parameters. The parameter ε represents a small "parasitic" time constant. Suppose we have neglected ε and simplified the transfer function to

$$P(s) = \frac{k_p}{s - a_p}$$

We may now proceed to design the adaptive controller for this first-order transfer function. In Section 1.2.6, a model reference adaptive controller is given by

$$
\begin{aligned}
u &= \theta_1 r + \theta_2 y_p \\
\dot{\theta}_1 &= -\gamma(y_p - y_m)r \\
\dot{\theta}_2 &= -\gamma(y_p - y_m)y_p
\end{aligned}
$$

where y_p, u, r, and y_m are the plant output, the control input, the reference input, and the reference model output, respectively. With (the first-order model of) the plant and the reference model represented by

$$\dot{y}_p = a_p y_p + k_p u$$

and

$$\dot{y}_m = a_m y_m + k_m r, \quad k_m > 0$$

it is shown in Section 1.2.6 that the closed-loop adaptive control system is represented by the third-order state equation

$$
\begin{aligned}
\dot{e}_o &= a_m e_o + k_p \phi_1 r + k_p \phi_2 (e_o + y_m) \\
\dot{\phi}_1 &= -\gamma e_o r \\
\dot{\phi}_2 &= -\gamma e_o (e_o + y_m)
\end{aligned}
$$

where $e_o = y_p - y_m$, $\phi_1 = \theta_1 - \theta_1^*$, $\phi_2 = \theta_2 - \theta_2^*$, $\theta_1^* = k_m/k_p$, and $\theta_2^* = (a_m - a_p)/k_p$. Define

$$x = [\begin{array}{ccc} e_o & \phi_1 & \phi_2 \end{array}]^T$$

as the state vector and rewrite the state equation as

$$\dot{x} = f_0(t, x)$$

where $f_0(t, 0) = 0$. We will refer to this third-order state equation as the nominal adaptive control system, which is the model we use in the stability analysis. We assume that the origin of the model is exponentially stable.[5] When the adaptive controller is applied to the actual system, the closed-loop system will be different from this nominal model. Let us represent the situation as a singular perturbation problem. The actual second-order model of the plant can be represented by the singularly perturbed model

$$\dot{y}_p = a_p y_p + k_p z$$
$$\varepsilon \dot{z} = -z + u$$

By repeating the derivations of Section 1.2.6, it can be seen that the actual adaptive control system is represented by the singularly perturbed model

$$\dot{x} = f_0(t, x) + K[z - h(t, x)]$$
$$\varepsilon \dot{z} = -z + h(t, x)$$

where

$$h(t, x) = u = (\theta_1^* + \phi_1) r(t) + (\theta_2^* + \phi_2)(e_o + y_m(t)), \quad K = [k_p, 0, 0]^T$$

The signal $y_m(t)$ is the output of a Hurwitz transfer function driven by $r(t)$. Therefore, it has the same smoothness and boundedness properties of $r(t)$. In particular, if $r(t)$ has continuous and bounded derivatives up to order N, the same will be true for $y_m(t)$. Let us analyze this singularly perturbed system. At $\varepsilon = 0$, we have $z = h(t, x)$ and the reduced model is

$$\dot{x} = f_0(t, x)$$

which is the closed-loop model of the nominal adaptive control system. We have assumed that the origin of the model is exponentially stable. The boundary-layer model

$$\frac{dy}{d\tau} = -y$$

is independent of (t, x) and its origin is globally exponentially stable. If the reference input $r(t)$ and its derivative $\dot{r}(t)$ are bounded, all the assumptions of Theorem 11.2 will be satisfied on any compact set of (x, z). Let $\bar{x}$ denote the solution of the nominal adaptive control system and $x(t, \varepsilon)$ denote the solution of the actual adaptive

---

[5]It is shown in Example 8.12 that this will be the case under a persistence of excitation condition. In particular, the origin will be exponentially stable if $r(t) = a \sin \omega t$. A word of caution at this point: Note that our analysis in this example assumes that $r(t)$ is fixed and studies the asymptotic behavior of the system for small ε. As we fix the value of ε at some small numerical value, our underlying assumption puts a constraint on $r(t)$–in particular, on the input frequency ω. If we start to increase ω, we may reach a point where the conclusions of the example are no longer valid because a high-frequency input may violate the slowly varying nature of the slow variable x. For example, the signal $\dot{r}(t)$, which is of order $O(\omega)$, may violate our assumption that $\dot{r}$ is of order $O(1)$ with respect to ε.

control system, both starting from the same initial state. By Theorem 11.2, we conclude that there exists $\varepsilon^* > 0$ such that for all $0 < \varepsilon < \varepsilon^*$,

$$x(t, \varepsilon) - \bar{x}(t) = O(\varepsilon)$$

where $O(\varepsilon)$ holds uniformly in t for all $t \geq t_0$. This result shows robustness to unmodeled fast dynamics. $\triangle$

11.4 Slow and Fast Manifolds

In this section, we give a geometric view of the two-time-scale behavior of the solutions of (11.1)–(11.2) as trajectories in R^{n+m}. In order to use the concept of invariant manifolds,[6] we restrict our discussion to autonomous systems. Furthermore, to simplify the notation, we take f and g to be independent of ε. Thus, we consider the following simpler form of the singularly perturbed system (11.1)–(11.2):

$$\dot{x} = f(x, z) \tag{11.26}$$
$$\varepsilon \dot{z} = g(x, z) \tag{11.27}$$

Let $z = h(x)$ be an isolated root of $0 = g(x, z)$ and suppose the assumptions of Theorem 11.1 are satisfied for this root. The equation $z = h(x)$ describes an n-dimensional manifold in the $(n + m)$-dimensional state space of (x, z). It is an invariant manifold for the system

$$\dot{x} = f(x, z) \tag{11.28}$$
$$0 = g(x, z) \tag{11.29}$$

since a trajectory of (11.28)–(11.29) that starts in the manifold $z = h(x)$ will remain in the manifold for all future time (for which the solution is defined). The motion in this manifold is described by the reduced model

$$\dot{x} = f(x, h(x))$$

Theorem 11.1 shows that trajectories of (11.26)–(11.27), which start in an $O(\varepsilon)$ neighborhood of $z = h(x)$, will remain within an $O(\varepsilon)$ neighborhood of $z = h(x)$. This motivates the following question: Is there an analog of the invariant manifold $z = h(x)$ for $\varepsilon > 0$? It turns out that, under the assumptions of Theorem 11.1, there is a nearby invariant manifold for (11.26)–(11.27) that lies within an $O(\varepsilon)$ neighborhood of $z = h(x)$. We seek the invariant manifold for (11.26)–(11.27) in the form

$$z = H(x, \varepsilon) \tag{11.30}$$

where H is a sufficiently smooth (that is, sufficiently many times continuously differentiable) function of x and ε. The expression (11.30) defines an n-dimensional

---

[6] Invariant manifolds have been introduced in Section 8.1.

manifold, dependent on ε, in the $(n + m)$-dimensional state space of (x, z). For $z = H(x, \varepsilon)$ to be an invariant manifold of (11.26)–(11.27), it must be true that

$$z(0, \varepsilon) - H(x(0, \varepsilon), \varepsilon) = 0 \Rightarrow z(t, \varepsilon) - H(x(t, \varepsilon), \varepsilon) \equiv 0, \quad \forall \, t \in J \subset [0, \infty)$$

where J is any time interval over which the solution $[x(t, \varepsilon), z(t, \varepsilon)]$ exists. Differentiating both sides of (11.30) with respect to t, multiplying through by ε, and substituting for $\dot{x}$, $\varepsilon\dot{z}$, and z from (11.26), (11.27), and (11.30), respectively, we obtain the *manifold condition*

$$0 = g(x, H(x, \varepsilon)) - \varepsilon \frac{\partial H}{\partial x} f(x, H(x, \varepsilon)) \tag{11.31}$$

which $H(x, \varepsilon)$ must satisfy for all x in the region of interest and all $\varepsilon \in [0, \varepsilon_0]$. At $\varepsilon = 0$, the partial differential equation (11.31) degenerates into

$$0 = g(x, H(x, 0))$$

which shows that $H(x, 0) = h(x)$. Since $0 = g(x, z)$ may have more than one isolated root $z = h(x)$, we may seek an invariant manifold for (11.26)–(11.27) in the neighborhood of each root. It can be shown[7] that there exist $\varepsilon^* > 0$ and a function $H(x, \varepsilon)$ satisfying the manifold condition (11.31) for all $\varepsilon \in [0, \varepsilon^*]$ and

$$H(x, \varepsilon) - h(x) = O(\varepsilon)$$

for bounded x. The invariant manifold $z = H(x, \varepsilon)$ is called a *slow manifold* for (11.26)–(11.27). For each slow manifold, there corresponds a slow model

$$\dot{x} = f(x, H(x, \varepsilon)) \tag{11.32}$$

which describes *exactly* the motion on that manifold.

In most cases, we cannot solve the manifold condition (11.31) exactly, but we can approximate $H(x, \varepsilon)$ arbitrarily closely as a Taylor series at $\varepsilon = 0$. The approximation procedure starts by substituting into (11.31) a Taylor series for $H(x, \varepsilon)$, namely,

$$H(x, \varepsilon) = H_0(x) + \varepsilon H_1(x) + \varepsilon^2 H_2(x) + \cdots$$

and by calculating $H_0(x)$, $H_1(x)$, and so on, by equating terms of like powers of ε. This requires the functions f and g to be continuously differentiable in their arguments a sufficient number of times. It is clear that $H_0(x) = H(x, 0) = h(x)$. The equation for $H_1(x)$ is

$$\frac{\partial g}{\partial z}(x, h(x))H_1(x) = \frac{\partial h}{\partial x} f(x, h(x))$$

---

[7]We will not prove the existence of the invariant manifold here. A proof can be done by a variation of the proof of (the center manifold) Theorem 8.1, given in Appendix C.15. (See [34, Section 2.7].) A proof under the basic assumptions of Theorem 11.1 can be found in [102].

and has a unique solution if the Jacobian $[\partial g/\partial z]$ at $z = h(x)$ is nonsingular. The nonsingularity of the Jacobian is implied by the eigenvalue condition (11.16). Similar to H_1, the equations for higher order terms will be linear and solvable if the Jacobian $[\partial g/\partial z]$ is nonsingular.

To introduce the notion of a fast manifold, we examine (11.26)–(11.27) in the $\tau = t/\varepsilon$ time scale. At $\varepsilon = 0$, $x(\tau) \equiv x(0)$, while $z(\tau)$ evolves according to

$$\frac{dz}{d\tau} = g(x(0), z)$$

approaching the equilibrium point $z = h(x(0))$. This motion describes trajectories (x, z) in R^{n+m}, which, for every given $x(0)$, lie in a fast manifold F_x defined by $x = x(0) = \text{constant}$ and rapidly descend to the manifold $z = h(x)$. For ε larger than zero, but small, the fast manifolds are "foliations" of solutions rapidly approaching the slow manifold. Let us illustrate this picture by two second-order examples.

Example 11.10 Consider the singularly perturbed system

$$\begin{aligned}
\dot{x} &= -x + z \\
\varepsilon \dot{z} &= \tan^{-1}(1 - z - x)
\end{aligned}$$

At $\varepsilon = 0$, the slow manifold is $z = h(x) = 1 - x$. The corresponding slow model

$$\dot{x} = -2x + 1 \qquad \qquad .$$

has an asymptotically stable equilibrium at $x = 0.5$. Therefore trajectories on the manifold $z = 1 - x$ will be heading toward the point $P = (0.5, 0.5)$, as indicated by the arrow heads in Figure 11.8. Notice that $(0.5, 0.5)$ is an equilibrium point of the full system. The fast manifolds at $\varepsilon = 0$ are parallel to the z-axis, with the trajectories heading toward the slow manifold $z = 1 - x$. With this information, we can construct an approximate phase portrait of the system. For example, a trajectory starting at point A will move down vertically until it hits the manifold $z = 1 - x$ at point B. From B, the trajectory moves along the manifold toward the equilibrium point P. Similarly, a trajectory starting at point C will move up vertically to point D and then along the manifold to the equilibrium point P. For $\varepsilon > 0$, but small, the phase portrait of the system will be close to the approximate picture we have drawn at $\varepsilon = 0$. Figure 11.9 shows the phase portrait for $\varepsilon = 0.1$. The proximity of the two portraits is noticeable. $\triangle$

Example 11.11 Consider the Van der Pol equation

$$\frac{d^2v}{ds^2} - \mu(1 - v^2)\frac{dv}{ds} + v = 0$$

when $\mu \gg 1$. With

$$x = -\frac{1}{\mu}\frac{dv}{ds} + v - \frac{1}{3}v^3; \quad z = v$$

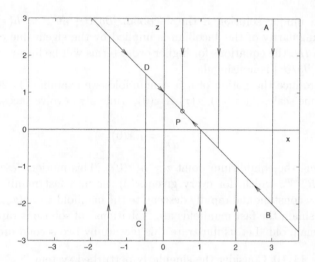

Figure 11.8: Approximate phase portrait of Example 11.10.

as state variables, $t = s/\mu$ as the time variable, and $\varepsilon = 1/\mu^2$, the system is represented by the standard singularly perturbed model

$$\dot{x} = z$$
$$\varepsilon \dot{z} = -x + z - \tfrac{1}{3}z^3$$

We already know by the Poincaré–Bendixson theorem (Example 2.9) that the Van der Pol equation has a stable limit cycle. What we would like to do here is to use singular perturbations to have a better estimate of the location of the limit cycle. At $\varepsilon = 0$, we need to solve for the roots $z = h(x)$ of

$$0 = -x + z - \tfrac{1}{3}z^3$$

The curve $-x + z - z^3/3 = 0$, the slow manifold at $\varepsilon = 0$, is sketched in Figure 11.10. For $x < -2/3$, there is only one root on the branch AB. For $-2/3 < x < 2/3$, there are three roots, one on each of the branches AB, BC, and CD. For $x > 2/3$, there is one root on the branch CD. For roots on the branch AB, the Jacobian

$$\frac{\partial g}{\partial z} = 1 - z^2 < 0, \quad \text{for } z^2 > 1$$

Thus, roots on the branch AB (excluding a neighborhood of point B) are exponentially stable. The same is true for roots on the branch CD (excluding a neighborhood of point C). On the other hand, roots on the branch BC are unstable because they lie in the region $z^2 < 1$. Let us construct an approximate phase portrait by using singular perturbations. We divide the state plane into three regions, depending

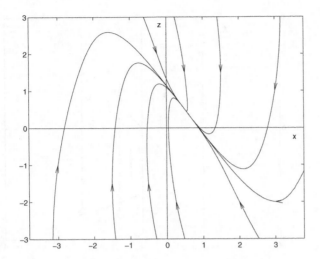

Figure 11.9: Phase portrait of Example 11.10 for $\varepsilon = 0.1$.

on the value of x. Trajectories starting in the region $x < -2/3$ will move parallel to the z-axis approaching the branch AB of the slow manifold. Trajectories starting in the region $-2/3 < x < 2/3$ will again be parallel to the z-axis, approaching either the branch AB or the branch CD, depending on the initial value of z. If the initial point is over the branch BC, the trajectory will approach AB; otherwise, it will approach CD. Finally, trajectories starting in the region $x > 2/3$ will approach the branch CD. For trajectories on the slow manifold itself, they will move along the manifold. The direction of motion can be determined by inspection of the vector field sign and is indicated in Figure 11.10. In particular, since $\dot{x} = z$, trajectories on the branch AB will be sliding down, while those on the branch CD will be climbing up. There is no point to talk about motion on the branch BC since there are no reduced models corresponding to the unstable roots on that branch. So far, we have formed an approximate phase portrait everywhere, except the branch BC and the neighborhoods of points B and C. We cannot use singular perturbation theory to predict the phase portrait in these regions. Let us investigate what happens in the neighborhood of B when ε is positive, but small. Trajectories sliding along the branch AB toward B are actually sliding along the exact slow manifold $z = H(x, \varepsilon)$. Since the trajectory is moving toward B, we must have $g < 0$. Consequently, the exact slow manifold must lie above the branch AB. Inspection of the vector field diagram in the neighborhood of B shows that the trajectory crosses the vertical line through B (that is, $x = 2/3$) at a point above B. Once the trajectory crosses this line, it belongs to the region of attraction of a stable root on the branch CD; therefore, the trajectory moves rapidly in a vertical line toward the branch CD. By a similar argument, it can be shown that a trajectory moving along the branch CD will cross the vertical line through C at a point below C and then will move

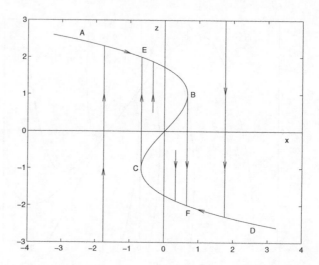

Figure 11.10: Approximate phase portrait of the Van der Pol oscillator.

vertically toward the branch AB. This completes the picture of the approximate portrait. Trajectories starting at any point are attracted to one of the two branches AB or CD, which they approach vertically. Once on the slow manifold, the trajectory will move toward the closed curve $E - B - F - C - E$, if not already on it, and will cycle through it. The exact limit cycle of the Van der Pol oscillator will lie within an $O(\varepsilon)$ neighborhood of this closed curve. The phase portrait for $\varepsilon = 0.1$, shown in Figure 11.11, confirms this prediction.

We can also estimate the period of oscillation of the periodic solution. The closed curve $E - B - F - C - E$ has two slow sides and two fast ones. Neglecting the time of the fast transients from B to F and from C to E, we estimate the period of oscillation by $t_{EB} + t_{FC}$. The time t_{EB} can be estimated from the reduced model

$$\dot{x} = z$$
$$0 = -x + z - \frac{1}{3}z^3$$

Differentiating the second equation with respect to t and equating the expressions for $\dot{x}$ from the two equations, we obtain the equation

$$\dot{z} = \frac{z}{1 - z^2}$$

which, when integrated from E to B, yields $t_{EB} = (3/2) - \ln 2$. The time t_{FC} can be estimated similarly and, due to symmetry, $t_{EB} = t_{FC}$. Thus, the period of oscillation is approximated for small ε by $3 - 2\ln 2$. $\triangle$

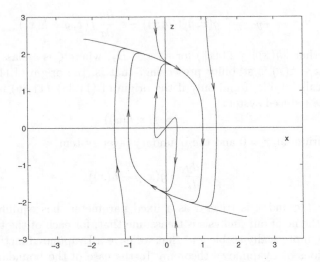

Figure 11.11: Phase portrait of the Van der Pol oscillator for $\varepsilon = 0.1$.

11.5   Stability Analysis

We consider the autonomous singularly perturbed system

$$\dot{x} = f(x, z) \tag{11.33}$$
$$\varepsilon \dot{z} = g(x, z) \tag{11.34}$$

and assume that the origin $(x = 0, z = 0)$ is an isolated equilibrium point and the functions f and g are locally Lipschitz in a domain that contains the origin. Consequently,

$$f(0,0) = 0, \quad g(0,0) = 0$$

We want to analyze the stability of the origin by examining the reduced and boundary-layer models. Let $z = h(x)$ be an isolated root of

$$0 = g(x, z)$$

defined for all $x \in D_x \subset R^n$, where D_x is a domain that contains $x = 0$. Suppose $h(0) = 0$. If $z = h(x)$ is the only root of $0 = g$, then it must vanish at the origin, since $g(0,0) = 0$. If there are two or more isolated roots, then one of them must vanish at $x = 0$, and that is the one we must work with. It is more convenient to work in the (x, y)-coordinates, where

$$y = z - h(x)$$

because this change of variables shifts the equilibrium of the boundary-layer model to the origin. In the new coordinates, the singularly perturbed system is

$$\dot{x} = f(x, y + h(x)) \tag{11.35}$$

$$\varepsilon \dot{y} \;=\; g(x, y + h(x)) - \varepsilon\, \frac{\partial h}{\partial x} f(x, y + h(x)) \tag{11.36}$$

Assuming that $\|h(x)\| \leq \zeta(\|x\|)$ for all $x \in D_x$, where ζ is a class $\mathcal{K}$ function, the map $y = z - h(x)$ is stability preserving; that is, the origin of (11.33)–(11.34) is asymptotically stable if and only if the origin of (11.35)–(11.36) is asymptotically stable. The reduced system

$$\dot{x} = f(x, h(x)) \tag{11.37}$$

has equilibrium at $x = 0$ and the boundary-layer system

$$\frac{dy}{d\tau} = g(x, y + h(x)) \tag{11.38}$$

where $\tau = t/\varepsilon$ and x is treated as a fixed parameter, has equilibrium at $y = 0$. The main theme of our analysis is to assume that, for each of the two systems, the origin is asymptotically stable and that we have a Lyapunov function that satisfies the conditions of Lyapunov's theorem. In the case of the boundary-layer system, we require asymptotic stability of the origin to hold uniformly in the frozen parameter x. We have already defined what this means in the case of an exponentially stable origin (Definition 11.1). More generally, we say that the origin of (11.38) is asymptotically stable uniformly in x if the solutions of (11.38) satisfy

$$\|y(\tau)\| \leq \beta(y(0), \tau), \quad \forall\, \tau \geq 0, \; \forall\, x \in D_x$$

where β is a class $\mathcal{KL}$ function. This conditions will be implied by the conditions we will impose on the Lyapunov function for (11.38). Viewing the full singularly perturbed system (11.35)–(11.36) as an interconnection of the reduced and boundary-layer systems, we form a composite Lyapunov function candidate for the full system as a linear combination of the Lyapunov functions for the reduced and boundary-layer systems. We then proceed to calculate the derivative of the composite Lyapunov function along the trajectories of the full system and verify, under reasonable growth conditions on f and g, that the composite Lyapunov function will satisfy the conditions of Lyapunov's theorem for sufficiently small ε.

Let $V(x)$ be a Lyapunov function for the reduced system (11.37) such that

$$\frac{\partial V}{\partial x} f(x, h(x)) \leq -\alpha_1 \psi_1^2(x) \tag{11.39}$$

for all $x \in D_x$, where $\psi_1 : R^n \to R$ is a positive definite function; that is, $\psi_1(0) = 0$ and $\psi_1(x) > 0$ for all $x \in D_x - \{0\}$. Let $W(x, y)$ be a Lyapunov function for the boundary-layer system (11.38) such that

$$\frac{\partial W}{\partial y} g(x, y + h(x)) \leq -\alpha_2 \psi_2^2(y) \tag{11.40}$$

for all $(x, y) \in D_x \times D_y$, where $D_y \subset R^m$ is a domain that contains $y = 0$, and $\psi_2 : R^m \to R$ is a positive definite function; that is, $\psi_2(0) = 0$ and $\psi_2(y) > 0$ for all $y \in D_y - \{0\}$. We allow the Lyapunov function W to depend on x, since x is a parameter of the system and Lyapunov functions may, in general, depend on the system's parameters. Because x is not a true constant parameter, we have to keep track of the effect of the dependence of W on x. To ensure that the origin of (11.38) is asymptotically stable uniformly in x, we assume that $W(x, y)$ satisfies

$$W_1(y) \leq W(x, y) \leq W_2(y), \quad \forall \ (x, y) \in D_x \times D_y \tag{11.41}$$

for some positive definite continuous functions W_1 and W_2. Now consider the composite Lyapunov function candidate

$$\nu(x, y) = (1 - d)V(x) + dW(x, y), \quad 0 < d < 1 \tag{11.42}$$

where the constant d is to be chosen. Calculating the derivative of ν along the trajectories of the full system (11.35)–(11.36), we obtain

$$
\begin{aligned}
\dot{\nu} =\ & (1 - d)\frac{\partial V}{\partial x}f(x, y + h(x)) + \frac{d}{\varepsilon}\frac{\partial W}{\partial y}g(x, y + h(x)) \\
& - d\frac{\partial W}{\partial y}\frac{\partial h}{\partial x}f(x, y + h(x)) + d\frac{\partial W}{\partial x}f(x, y + h(x)) \\
=\ & (1 - d)\frac{\partial V}{\partial x}f(x, h(x)) + \frac{d}{\varepsilon}\frac{\partial W}{\partial y}g(x, y + h(x)) \\
& + (1 - d)\frac{\partial V}{\partial x}[f(x, y + h(x)) - f(x, h(x))] \\
& + d\left[\frac{\partial W}{\partial x} - \frac{\partial W}{\partial y}\frac{\partial h}{\partial x}\right]f(x, y + h(x))
\end{aligned}
$$

We have represented the derivative $\dot{\nu}$ as the sum of four terms. The first two terms are the derivatives of V and W along the trajectories of the reduced and boundary-layer systems. These two terms are negative definite in x and y, respectively, by inequalities (11.39) and (11.40). The other two terms represent the effect of the interconnection between the slow and fast dynamics, which is neglected at $\varepsilon = 0$. These terms are, in general, indefinite. The first of these two terms

$$\frac{\partial V}{\partial x}[f(x, y + h(x)) - f(x, h(x))]$$

represents the effect of the deviation of (11.35) from the reduced system (11.37). The other term

$$\left[\frac{\partial W}{\partial x} - \frac{\partial W}{\partial y}\frac{\partial h}{\partial x}\right]f(x, y + h(x))$$

represents the deviation of (11.36) from the boundary-layer system (11.38), as well as the effect of freezing x during the boundary-layer analysis. Suppose that these perturbation terms satisfy

$$\frac{\partial V}{\partial x}[f(x, y + h(x)) - f(x, h(x))] \leq \beta_1 \psi_1(x)\psi_2(y) \tag{11.43}$$

and

$$\left[\frac{\partial W}{\partial x} - \frac{\partial W}{\partial y}\frac{\partial h}{\partial x}\right] f(x, y + h(x)) \le \beta_2 \psi_1(x)\psi_2(y) + \gamma\psi_2^2(y) \tag{11.44}$$

for some nonnegative constants β_1, β_2, and γ. Using inequalities (11.39), (11.40), (11.43), and (11.44), we obtain

$$\begin{aligned}
\dot{\nu} &\le -(1-d)\alpha_1\psi_1^2(x) - \frac{d}{\varepsilon}\alpha_2\psi_2^2(y) + (1-d)\beta_1\psi_1(x)\psi_2(y) \\
&\quad + d\beta_2\psi_1(x)\psi_2(y) + d\gamma\psi_2^2(y) \\
&= -\psi^T(x,y)\Lambda\psi(x,y)
\end{aligned}$$

where

$$\psi(x,y) = \left[\begin{array}{c} \psi_1(x) \\ \psi_2(y) \end{array}\right]$$

and

$$\Lambda = \left[\begin{array}{cc} (1-d)\alpha_1 & -\frac{1}{2}(1-d)\beta_1 - \frac{1}{2}d\beta_2 \\ -\frac{1}{2}(1-d)\beta_1 - \frac{1}{2}d\beta_2 & d((\alpha_2/\varepsilon) - \gamma) \end{array}\right]$$

The right-hand side of the last inequality is a quadratic form in ψ. The quadratic form is negative definite when

$$d(1-d)\alpha_1\left(\frac{\alpha_2}{\varepsilon} - \gamma\right) > \tfrac{1}{4}[(1-d)\beta_1 + d\beta_2]^2$$

which is equivalent to

$$\varepsilon < \frac{\alpha_1\alpha_2}{\alpha_1\gamma + \frac{1}{4d(1-d)}[(1-d)\beta_1 + d\beta_2]^2} \stackrel{\text{def}}{=} \varepsilon_d \tag{11.45}$$

The dependence of ε_d on d is sketched in Figure 11.12. It can be easily seen that the maximum value of ε_d occurs at $d^* = \beta_1/(\beta_1 + \beta_2)$ and is given by

$$\varepsilon^* = \frac{\alpha_1\alpha_2}{\alpha_1\gamma + \beta_1\beta_2} \tag{11.46}$$

It follows that the origin of (11.35)–(11.36) is asymptotically stable for all $\varepsilon < \varepsilon^*$. Theorem 11.3 summarizes our findings.

Theorem 11.3 *Consider the singularly perturbed system (11.35) and (11.36). Assume there are Lyapunov functions $V(x)$ and $W(x,y)$ that satisfy (11.39) through (11.41), (11.43), and (11.44). Let ε_d and ε^* be defined by (11.45) and (11.46). Then, the origin of (11.35) and (11.36) is asymptotically stable for all $0 < \varepsilon < \varepsilon^*$. Moreover, $\nu(x,y)$, defined by (11.42), is a Lyapunov function for $\varepsilon \in (0, \varepsilon_d)$.* $\diamond$

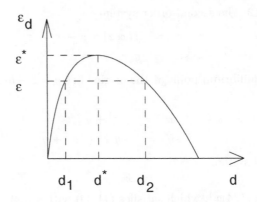

Figure 11.12: Upper bound on ε.

The stability analysis that led to Theorem 11.3 delineates a procedure for constructing Lyapunov functions for the singularly perturbed system (11.35)–(11.36). We start by studying the reduced and boundary-layer systems, searching for Lyapunov functions $V(x)$ and $W(x,y)$ that satisfy (11.39) through (11.41). Then inequalities (11.43) and (11.44), which we will refer to as the interconnection conditions, are checked. Several choices of V and W may be tried before one finds the desired Lyapunov functions. As a guideline in that search, notice that the interconnection conditions will be satisfied if

$$\left\|\frac{\partial V}{\partial x}\right\| \le k_1\psi_1(x); \quad \|f(x,h(x))\| \le k_2\psi_1(x)$$

$$\|f(x,y+h(x)) - f(x,h(x))\| \le k_3\psi_2(y)$$

$$\left\|\frac{\partial W}{\partial y}\right\| \le k_4\psi_2(y); \quad \left\|\frac{\partial W}{\partial x}\right\| \le k_5\psi_2(y)$$

A Lyapunov function $V(x)$ that satisfies (11.39) and $\|\partial V/\partial x\| \le k_1\psi_1(x)$ is known as a *quadratic-type* Lyapunov function, and ψ_1 is called a *comparison function*. Thus, the search would be successful if we could find quadratic-type Lyapunov functions V and W with comparison functions ψ_1 and ψ_2 such that $\|f(x,h(x))\|$ could be bounded by $\psi_1(x)$ and $\|f(x,y+h(x)) - f(x,h(x))\|$ could be bounded by $\psi_2(y)$. If we succeed in finding V and W, we can conclude that the origin is asymptotically stable for $\varepsilon < \varepsilon^*$. For a given $\varepsilon < \varepsilon^*$, there is a range (d_1, d_2), illustrated in Figure 11.12, such that for any $d \in (d_1, d_2)$, the function $\nu(x,y) = (1-d)V(x) + dW(x,y)$ is a valid Lyapunov function. The freedom in choosing d can be used to achieve other objectives, like improving estimates of the region of attraction.

Example 11.12 The second-order system

$$\dot{x} = f(x,z) = x - x^3 + z$$
$$\varepsilon\dot{z} = g(x,z) = -x - z$$

has a unique equilibrium point at the origin. Let $y = z - h(x) = z + x$ and rewrite the system as

$$\dot{x} = -x^3 + y$$
$$\varepsilon\dot{y} = -y + \varepsilon(-x^3 + y)$$

For the reduced system

$$\dot{x} = -x^3$$

we take $V(x) = (1/4)x^4$, which satisfies (11.39) with $\psi_1(x) = |x|^3$ and $\alpha_1 = 1$. For the boundary-layer system

$$\frac{dy}{d\tau} = -y$$

we take $W(y) = (1/2)y^2$, which satisfies (11.41) with $\psi_2(y) = |y|$ and $\alpha_2 = 1$. As for the interconnection conditions of (11.43) and (11.44), we have

$$\frac{\partial V}{\partial x}[f(x, y + h(x)) - f(x, h(x))] = x^3 y \le \psi_1\psi_2$$

and

$$\frac{\partial W}{\partial y}f(x, y + h(x)) = y(-x^3 + y) \le \psi_1\psi_2 + \psi_2^2$$

Note that $\partial W/\partial x = 0$. Hence, (11.43) and (11.44) are satisfied with $\beta_1 = \beta_2 = \gamma = 1$. Therefore, the origin is asymptotically stable for $\varepsilon < \varepsilon^* = 0.5$. In fact, since all the conditions are satisfied globally and $\nu(x, y) = (1 - d)V(x) + dW(y)$ is radially unbounded, the origin is globally asymptotically stable for $\varepsilon < 0.5$. To see how conservative this bound is, let us note that the characteristic equation of the linearization at the origin is

$$\lambda^2 + \left(\frac{1}{\varepsilon} - 1\right)\lambda = 0$$

which shows that the origin is unstable for $\varepsilon > 1$. Since our example is a simple second-order system, we may calculate the derivative of the Lyapunov function

$$\nu(x, y) = \frac{1-d}{4}x^4 + \frac{d}{2}y^2$$

along the trajectories of the full singularly perturbed system and see if we can get a less conservative upper bound on ε compared with the one provided by Theorem 11.3:

$$\dot{\nu} = (1-d)x^3(-x^3 + y) - \frac{d}{\varepsilon}y^2 + dy(-x^3 + y)$$
$$= -(1-d)x^6 + (1-2d)x^3 y - d\left(\frac{1}{\varepsilon} - 1\right)y^2$$

It is apparent that the choice $d = 1/2$ cancels the cross-product terms and yields

$$\dot{\nu} = -\frac{1}{2}x^6 - \frac{1}{2}\left(\frac{1}{\varepsilon} - 1\right)y^2$$

which is negative definite for all $\varepsilon < 1$. This estimate is indeed less conservative than that of Theorem 11.3. In fact, it is the actual range of ε for which the origin is asymptotically stable. $\triangle$

Example 11.13 The system

$$\begin{aligned}
\dot{x} &= -x + z \\
\varepsilon\dot{z} &= \tan^{-1}(1 - x - z)
\end{aligned}$$

has an equilibrium point at $(0.5, 0.5)$. The change of variables

$$\tilde{x} = x - 0.5; \quad \tilde{z} = z - 0.5$$

shifts the equilibrium point to the origin. To simplify the notation, let us drop the tilde and write the state equation as

$$\begin{aligned}
\dot{x} &= -x + z \\
\varepsilon\dot{z} &= -\tan^{-1}(x + z)
\end{aligned}$$

The equation

$$0 = -\tan^{-1}(x + z)$$

has a unique root $z = h(x) = -x$. We apply the change of variables $y = z + x$ to obtain

$$\begin{aligned}
\dot{x} &= -2x + y \\
\varepsilon\dot{y} &= -\tan^{-1} y + \varepsilon(-2x + y)
\end{aligned}$$

For the reduced system, we take $V(x) = (1/2)x^2$, which satisfies (11.39) with $\alpha_1 = 2$ and $\psi_1(x) = |x|$. For the boundary-layer system, we take $W(y) = (1/2)y^2$ and (11.40) takes the form

$$\frac{dW}{dy}[-\tan^{-1} y] = -y\tan^{-1} y \leq -\frac{\tan^{-1}\rho}{\rho}y^2$$

for all $y \in D_y = \{y \mid |y| < \rho\}$. Thus, (11.41) is satisfied with $\alpha_2 = (\tan^{-1}\rho)/\rho$ and $\psi_2(y) = |y|$. The interconnection conditions (11.43) and (11.44) are satisfied globally with $\beta_1 = 1$, $\beta_2 = 2$, and $\gamma = 1$. Hence, the origin is asymptotically stable for all $\varepsilon < \varepsilon^* = (\tan^{-1}\rho)/2\rho$. In fact, the origin is exponentially stable, since both ν and the negative definite upper bound on $\dot{\nu}$ are quadratic in (x, y). $\triangle$

The Lyapunov analysis we have just presented can be extended to nonautonomous systems. We will not give the details here;[8] instead, we consider the case of exponential stability and use converse Lyapunov theorems to prove a result of conceptual importance.

Theorem 11.4 *Consider the singularly perturbed system*

$$\dot{x} = f(t, x, z, \varepsilon) \tag{11.47}$$
$$\varepsilon\dot{z} = g(t, x, z, \varepsilon) \tag{11.48}$$

Assume that the following assumptions are satisfied for all

$$(t, x, \varepsilon) \in [0, \infty) \times B_r \times [0, \varepsilon_0]$$

- *$f(t, 0, 0, \varepsilon) = 0$ and $g(t, 0, 0, \varepsilon) = 0$.*

- *The equation*

$$0 = g(t, x, z, 0)$$

  has an isolated root $z = h(t, x)$ such that $h(t, 0) = 0$.

- *The functions f, g, h, and their partial derivatives up to the second order are bounded for $z - h(t, x) \in B_\rho$.*

- *The origin of the reduced system*

$$\dot{x} = f(t, x, h(t, x), 0)$$

  is exponentially stable.

- *The origin of the boundary-layer system*

$$\frac{dy}{d\tau} = g(t, x, y + h(t, x), 0)$$

  is exponentially stable, uniformly in (t, x).

Then, there exists $\varepsilon^* > 0$ such that for all $\varepsilon < \varepsilon^*$, the origin of (11.47)–(11.48) is exponentially stable. ◇

Proof: By Theorem 4.14, there is a Lyapunov function $V(t, x)$ for the reduced system that satisfies

$$c_1\|x\|^2 \le V(t, x) \le c_2\|x\|^2$$

$$\frac{\partial V}{\partial t} + \frac{\partial V}{\partial x} f(t, x, h(t, x), 0) \le -c_3\|x\|^2$$

$$\left\|\frac{\partial V}{\partial x}\right\| \le c_4\|x\|$$

---

[8]A detailed treatment of the nonautonomous case can be found in [105, Section 7.5].

for some positive constants c_i, $i = 1, \ldots, 4$, and for $x \in B_{r_0}$, where $r_0 \leq r$. By Lemma 9.8, there is a Lyapunov function $W(t, x, y)$ for the boundary-layer system that satisfies

$$b_1 \|y\|^2 \leq W(t, x, y) \leq b_2 \|y\|^2$$

$$\frac{\partial W}{\partial y} g(t, x, y + h(t, x), 0) \leq -b_3 \|y\|^2$$

$$\left\| \frac{\partial W}{\partial y} \right\| \leq b_4 \|y\|$$

$$\left\| \frac{\partial W}{\partial t} \right\| \leq b_5 \|y\|^2; \quad \left\| \frac{\partial W}{\partial x} \right\| \leq b_6 \|y\|^2$$

for some positive constants b_i, $i = 1, \ldots, 6$, and for $y \in B_{\rho_0}$, where $\rho_0 \leq \rho$. Apply the change of variables

$$y = z - h(t, x)$$

to transform (11.47)–(11.48) into

$$\dot{x} = f(t, x, y + h(t, x), \varepsilon) \tag{11.49}$$

$$\varepsilon \dot{y} = g(t, x, y + h(t, x), \varepsilon) - \varepsilon \frac{\partial h}{\partial t}$$

$$- \varepsilon \frac{\partial h}{\partial x} f(t, x, y + h(t, x), \varepsilon) \tag{11.50}$$

We are going to use

$$\nu(t, x, y) = V(t, x) + W(t, x, y)$$

as a Lyapunov function candidate for the system (11.49)–(11.50). In preparation for that, let us note the following estimates in the neighborhood of the origin: Since f and g vanish at the origin for all $\varepsilon \in [0, \varepsilon_0]$, they are Lipschitz in ε linearly in the state (x, y). In particular,

$$\|f(t, x, y + h(t, x), \varepsilon) - f(t, x, y + h(t, x), 0)\| \leq \varepsilon L_1 (\|x\| + \|y\|)$$

$$\|g(t, x, y + h(t, x), \varepsilon) - g(t, x, y + h(t, x), 0)\| \leq \varepsilon L_2 (\|x\| + \|y\|)$$

Also,

$$\|f(t, x, y + h(t, x), 0) - f(t, x, h(t, x), 0)\| \leq L_3 \|y\|$$

$$\|f(t, x, h(t, x), 0)\| \leq L_4 \|x\|$$

$$\left\| \frac{\partial h}{\partial t} \right\| \leq k_1 \|x\|; \quad \left\| \frac{\partial h}{\partial x} \right\| \leq k_2$$

where we have used the fact that $f(t, x, h(t, x), 0)$ and $h(t, x)$ vanish at $x = 0$ for all t. Using these estimates and the properties of the functions V and W, it can be verified that the derivative of ν along the trajectories of (11.49)–(11.50) satisfies the inequality

$$\dot{\nu} \leq -a_1\|x\|^2 + \varepsilon a_2\|x\|^2 - \frac{a_3}{\varepsilon}\|y\|^2 + a_4\|y\|^2$$
$$+ a_5\|x\|\,\|y\| + a_6\|x\|\,\|y\|^2 + a_7\|y\|^3$$

with positive a_1 and a_3 and nonnegative a_2 and a_4 to a_7. For all $\|y\| \leq \rho_0$, this inequality simplifies to

$$\dot{\nu} \leq -a_1\|x\|^2 + \varepsilon a_2\|x\|^2 - \frac{a_3}{\varepsilon}\|y\|^2 + a_8\|y\|^2 + 2a_9\|x\|\,\|y\|$$

$$= -\begin{bmatrix} \|x\| \\ \\ \|y\| \end{bmatrix}^T \begin{bmatrix} a_1 - \varepsilon a_2 & -a_9 \\ \\ -a_9 & (a_3/\varepsilon) - a_8 \end{bmatrix} \begin{bmatrix} \|x\| \\ \\ \|y\| \end{bmatrix}$$

Thus, there exists $\varepsilon^* > 0$ such that for all $0 < \varepsilon < \varepsilon^*$, we have

$$\dot{\nu} \leq -2\gamma\nu$$

for some $\gamma > 0$. It follows that

$$\nu(t, x(t), y(t)) \leq \exp[-2\gamma(t - t_0)]\nu(t_0, x(t_0), y(t_0))$$

and, from the properties of V and W,

$$\left\| \begin{array}{c} x(t) \\ y(t) \end{array} \right\| \leq K_1 \exp[-\gamma(t - t_0)] \left\| \begin{array}{c} x(t_0) \\ y(t_0) \end{array} \right\|$$

Since $y = z - h(t, x)$ and $\|h(t, x)\| \leq k_2\|x\|$, we obtain

$$\left\| \begin{array}{c} x(t) \\ z(t) \end{array} \right\| \leq K_2 \exp[-\gamma(t - t_0)] \left\| \begin{array}{c} x(t_0) \\ z(t_0) \end{array} \right\|$$

which completes the proof of the theorem.   □

Theorem 11.4 is conceptually important because it establishes robustness of exponential stability to unmodeled fast (high-frequency) dynamics. Quite often in the analysis of dynamical systems, we use reduced-order models obtained by neglecting small "parasitic" parameters. This reduction in the order of the model can be represented as a singular perturbation problem, where the full singularly perturbed model represents the actual system with the parasitic parameters and the reduced model is the simplified model used in the analysis. It is quite reasonable to assume that the boundary-layer model has an exponentially stable origin. In fact, if the dynamics associated with the parasitic elements were unstable, we should not have neglected them in the first place. The technicalities of assuming exponential stability instead of only asymptotic stability, or assuming that exponential stability holds uniformly, are quite reasonable in most applications. It is enough to mention that all these technicalities will automatically hold when the fast dynamics are linear. When the origin of the reduced model is exponentially stable, Theorem 11.4 assures us that the origin of the actual system will be exponentially stable, provided the neglected fast dynamics are sufficiently fast. The next example illustrates how this robustness property arises in control design.

Example 11.14 Consider the feedback stabilization of the system

$$\begin{aligned} \dot{x} &= f(t,x,v) \\ \varepsilon\dot{z} &= Az + Bu \\ v &= Cz \end{aligned}$$

where $f(t,0,0) = 0$ and A is a Hurwitz matrix. The system has an open-loop equilibrium point at the origin, and the control task is to design a state feedback control law to stabilize the origin. The linear part of this model represents actuator dynamics, which are, typically, much faster than the plant dynamics represented by the nonlinear equation $\dot{x} = f$. To simplify the design problem, we may neglect the actuator dynamics by setting $\varepsilon = 0$ and substituting $v = -CA^{-1}Bu$ into the plant equation. To simplify the notation, let us assume that $-CA^{-1}B = I$ and write the reduced model as

$$\dot{x} = f(t,x,u)$$

We use this model to design a state feedback control law $u = \gamma(t,x)$ such that the origin of the closed-loop model

$$\dot{x} = f(t,x,\gamma(t,x))$$

is exponentially stable. We will refer to this model as the nominal closed-loop system. Will the control law stabilize the actual system with the actuator dynamics included? When the control is applied to the actual system, the closed-loop equation is

$$\begin{aligned} \dot{x} &= f(t,x,Cz) \\ \varepsilon\dot{z} &= Az + B\gamma(t,x) \end{aligned}$$

We have a singular perturbation problem, where the full singularly perturbed model is the actual closed-loop system and the reduced model is the nominal closed-loop system. By design, the origin of the reduced model is exponentially stable. The boundary-layer model

$$\frac{dy}{d\tau} = Ay$$

is independent of (t,x) and its origin is exponentially stable since A is a Hurwitz matrix. Assuming that f and γ are smooth enough to satisfy the conditions of Theorem 11.4, we conclude that the origin of the actual closed-loop system is exponentially stable for sufficiently small ε. This result legitimizes the ad hoc model simplification process of neglecting the actuator dynamics. $\triangle$

11.6   Exercises

11.1 Consider the RC circuit of Figure 11.13 and suppose the capacitor C_2 is small relative to C_1, while $R_1 = R_2 = R$. Represent the system in the standard singularly perturbed form.

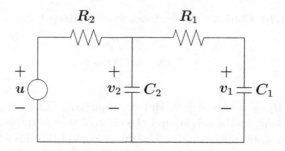

Figure 11.13: Exercises 11.1 and 11.2.

11.2 Consider the RC circuit of Figure 11.13 and suppose the resistor R_1 is small relative to R_2, while $C_1 = C_2 = C$. Represent the system in the standard singularly perturbed form.

11.3 Consider the tunnel diode circuit of Section 1.2.2 and suppose the inductance L is relatively small so that the time constant L/R is much smaller than the time constant CR. Represent the system as a standard singularly perturbed model with $\varepsilon = L/CR^2$.

11.4 ([105]) The feedback system of Figure 11.14 has a high-gain amplifier with gain k and a nonlinear element ψ. Represent the system as a standard singularly perturbed model with $\varepsilon = 1/k$.

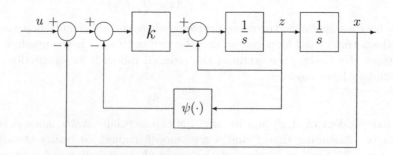

Figure 11.14: Exercise 11.4.

11.5 Show that if the Jacobian $[\partial g/\partial y]$ satisfies the eigenvalue condition (11.16), then there exist constants k, γ, and ρ_0 for which inequality (11.15) is satisfied.

11.6 Show that if there is a Lyapunov function satisfying (11.17) and (11.18), then inequality (11.15) is satisfied with the estimates of (11.19).

11.7 Consider the singular perturbation problem

$$
\begin{aligned}
\dot{x} &= x^2 + z, & x(0) &= \xi \\
\varepsilon\dot{z} &= x^2 - z + 1, & z(0) &= \eta
\end{aligned}
$$

(a) Find an $O(\varepsilon)$ approximation of x and z on the time interval $[0,1]$.

(b) Let $\xi = \eta = 0$. Simulate x and z for

$$(1)\ \varepsilon = 0.1 \quad \text{and} \quad (2)\ \varepsilon = 0.05$$

and compare with the approximation derived in part (a). In carrying out the computer simulation, note that the system has a finite escape time shortly after $t = 1$.

11.8 Consider the singular perturbation problem

$$
\begin{aligned}
\dot{x} &= x + z, & x(0) &= \xi \\
\varepsilon\dot{z} &= -\frac{2}{\pi}\tan^{-1}\left(\frac{\pi}{2}(2x + z)\right), & z(0) &= \eta
\end{aligned}
$$

(a) Find an $O(\varepsilon)$ approximation of x and z on the time interval $[0,1]$.

(b) Let $\xi = \eta = 1$. Simulate x and z for

$$(1)\ \varepsilon = 0.2 \quad \text{and} \quad (2)\ \varepsilon = 0.1$$

and compare with the approximation derived in part (a).

11.9 Consider the singularly perturbed system

$$\dot{x} = z, \qquad \varepsilon\dot{z} = -x - \varepsilon z - \exp(z) + 1 + u(t)$$

Find the reduced and boundary-layer models and analyze the stability properties of the boundary-layer model.

11.10 ([105]) Consider the singularly perturbed system

$$\dot{x} = \frac{x^2 t}{z}, \qquad \varepsilon\dot{z} = -(z + xt)(z - 2)(z - 4)$$

(a) How many reduced models can this system have?

(b) Investigate boundary-layer stability for each reduced model.

(c) Let $x(0) = 1$ and $z(0) = a$. Find an $O(\varepsilon)$ approximation of x and z on the time interval $[0, 1]$ for all values of a in the interval $[-2, 6]$.

11.11 Apply Theorem 11.2 to study the asymptotic behavior of the system

$$\dot{x} = -x + z - \sin t, \qquad \varepsilon \dot{z} = -z + \sin t$$

as $t \to \infty$.

11.12 ([105]) Find the exact slow manifold of the system

$$\dot{x} = xz^3, \qquad \varepsilon \dot{z} = -z - x^{4/3} + \tfrac{4}{3}\varepsilon x^{16/3}$$

11.13 ([105]) How many slow manifolds does the following system have? Which of these manifolds will attract trajectories of the system?

$$\dot{x} = -xz, \qquad \varepsilon \dot{z} = -(z - \sin^2 x)(z - e^{ax})(z - 2e^{2ax}), \quad a > 0$$

11.14 ([105]) Consider the linear autonomous singularly perturbed system

$$\begin{aligned} \dot{x} &= A_{11}x + A_{12}z \\ \varepsilon \dot{z} &= A_{21}x + A_{22}z \end{aligned}$$

where $x \in R^n$, $z \in R^m$, and A_{22} is a Hurwitz matrix.

(a) Show that for sufficiently small ε, the system has an exact slow manifold $z = -L(\varepsilon)x$, where L satisfies the algebraic equation

$$-\varepsilon L(A_{11} - A_{12}L) = A_{21} - A_{22}L$$

(b) Show that the change of variables $\eta = z + L(\varepsilon)x$ transforms the system into a block triangular form.

(c) Show that the eigenvalues of the system cluster into a group of n slow eigenvalues of order $O(1)$ and m fast eigenvalues of order $O(1/\varepsilon)$.

(d) Let $H(\varepsilon)$ be the solution of the linear equation

$$\varepsilon(A_{11} - A_{12}L)H - H(A_{22} + \varepsilon L A_{12}) + A_{12} = 0$$

Show that the similarity transformation

$$\begin{bmatrix} \xi \\ \eta \end{bmatrix} = \begin{bmatrix} I - \varepsilon HL & -\varepsilon H \\ L & I \end{bmatrix} \begin{bmatrix} x \\ z \end{bmatrix}$$

transforms the system into the block modal form

$$\dot{\xi} = A_s(\varepsilon)\xi, \qquad \varepsilon \dot{\eta} = A_f(\varepsilon)\eta$$

where the eigenvalues of A_s and A_f/ε are, respectively, the slow and fast eigenvalues of the full singularly perturbed system.

(e) Show that the component of the fast mode in x is $O(\varepsilon)$.

(f) Give an independent proof of Tikhonov's theorem in the current case.

11.15 Consider the linear singularly perturbed system

$$
\begin{aligned}
\dot{x} &= A_{11}x + A_{12}z + B_1u(t), & x(0) &= \xi \\
\varepsilon\dot{z} &= A_{21}x + A_{22}z + B_2u(t), & z(0) &= \eta
\end{aligned}
$$

where $x \in R^n$, $z \in R^m$, $u \in R^p$, A_{22} is Hurwitz, and $u(t)$ is uniformly bounded for all $t \geq 0$. Let $\bar{x}(t)$ be the solution of the reduced system

$$\dot{x} = A_0x + B_0u(t), \quad x(0) = \xi$$

where $A_0 = A_{11} - A_{12}A_{22}^{-1}A_{21}$, and $B_0 = B_1 - A_{12}A_{22}^{-1}B_2$.

(a) Show that $x(t,\varepsilon) - \bar{x}(t) = O(\varepsilon)$ on any compact interval $[0, t_1]$.

(b) Show that if A_0 is Hurwitz, then $x(t,\varepsilon) - \bar{x}(t) = O(\varepsilon)$ for all $t \geq 0$.

Hint: Use the transformation of the previous Exercise.

11.16 Consider the singularly perturbed system

$$\dot{x}_1 = x_2, \qquad \dot{x}_2 = -x_2 + z, \qquad \varepsilon\dot{z} = \tan^{-1}(1 - x_1 - z)$$

(a) Find the reduced and boundary-layer models.

(b) Analyze the stability properties of the boundary-layer model.

(c) Let $x_1(0) = x_2(0) = z(0) = 0$. Find an $O(\varepsilon)$ approximation of the solution. Using a numerical algorithm, calculate the exact and approximate solutions over the time interval $[0, 10]$ for $\varepsilon = 0.1$.

(d) Investigate the validity of the approximation on the infinite time interval.

(e) Show that the system has a unique equilibrium point and analyze its stability by using the singular perturbation approach. Is the equilibrium point asymptotically stable? Is it globally asymptotically stable? Is it exponentially stable? Calculate an upper bound ε^* on ε for which your stability analysis is valid.

11.17 Repeat Exercise 11.16 for the singularly perturbed system

$$\dot{x} = -2x + x^2 + z, \qquad \varepsilon\dot{z} = x - x^2 - z$$

In part (c), let $x(0) = z(0) = 1$ and the time interval be $[0, 5]$.

11.18 Repeat Exercise 11.16 for the singularly perturbed system

$$\dot{x} = xz^3 \qquad \varepsilon\dot{z} = -2x^{4/3} - 2z$$

In part (c), let $x(0) = z(0) = 1$ and the time interval be $[0, 1]$.

11.19 Repeat Exercise 11.16 for the singularly perturbed system

$$\dot{x} = -x^3 + \tan^{-1}(z), \qquad \varepsilon\dot{z} = -x - z$$

In part (c), let $x(0) = -1$, $z(0) = 2$ and the time interval be $[0, 2]$.

11.20 Repeat Exercise 11.16 for the singularly perturbed system

$$\dot{x} = -x + z_1 + z_2 + z_1 z_2, \qquad \varepsilon\dot{z}_1 = -z_1, \qquad \varepsilon\dot{z}_2 = -z_2 - (x + z_1 + xz_1)$$

In part (c), let $x(0) = z_1(0) = z_2(0) = 1$ and the time interval be $[0, 2]$.

11.21 Consider the field-controlled DC motor of Exercise 1.17. Let $v_a = V_a = $ constant, and $v_f = U = $ constant.

(a) Show that the system has a unique equilibrium point at

$$I_f = \frac{U}{R_f}, \quad I_a = \frac{c_3 V_a}{c_3 R_a + c_1 c_2 U^2 / R_f^2}, \quad \Omega = \frac{c_2 V_a U / R_f}{c_3 R_a + c_1 c_2 U^2 / R_f^2}$$

We will use (I_f, I_a, Ω) as a nominal operating point.

(b) It is typical that the armature circuit time constant $T_a = L_a/R_a$ is much smaller than the field circuit time constant $T_f = L_f/R_f$ and the mechanical time constant. Therefore, the system can be modeled as a singularly perturbed system with i_f and ω as the slow variables and i_a as the fast variable. Taking $x_1 = i_f/I_f$, $x_2 = \omega/\Omega$, $z = i_a/I_a$, $u = v_f/U$, and $\varepsilon = T_a/T_f$, and using $t' = t/T_f$ as the time variable, show that the singularly perturbed model is given by

$$\dot{x}_1 = -x_1 + u, \qquad \dot{x}_2 = a(x_1 z - x_2), \qquad \varepsilon\dot{z} = -z - bx_1 x_2 + c$$

where $a = L_f c_3 / R_f J$, $b = c_1 c_2 U^2 / c_3 R_a R_f^2$, $c = V_a / I_a R_a$, and $(\dot{\cdot})$ denotes the derivative with respect to t'.

(c) Find the reduced and boundary-layer models.

(d) Analyze the stability properties of the boundary-layer model.

(e) Find an $O(\varepsilon)$ approximation of x and z.

(f) Investigate the validity of the approximation on the infinite time interval.

(g) Using a numerical algorithm, calculate the exact and approximate solutions for a unit step input at u and zero initial states over the time interval $[0, 10]$ for $\varepsilon = 0.2$ and $\varepsilon = 0.1$. Use the numerical data $c_1 = c_2 = \sqrt{2} \times 10^{-2}$ N-m/A, $c_3 = 6 \times 10^{-6}$ N-m-s/rad, $J = 10^{-6}$ N-m-s^2/rad, $R_a = R_f = 1\ \Omega$, $L_f = 0.2$ H, $V_a = 1$ V, and $U = 0.2$ V.

11.22 ([105]) Consider the singularly perturbed system

$$\dot{x} = -\eta(x) + az, \qquad \varepsilon \dot{z} = -\frac{x}{a} - z$$

where a is a positive constant and η is a smooth nonlinear function that satisfies

$$\eta(0) = 0 \quad \text{and} \quad x\eta(x) > 0, \quad \text{for} \quad x \in (-\infty, b) - \{0\}$$

for some $b > 0$. Investigate the stability of the origin for small ε by using the singular perturbation approach.

11.23 ([105]) The singularly perturbed system

$$\dot{x} = -2x^3 + z^2, \qquad \varepsilon \dot{z} = x^3 - \tan z$$

has an isolated equilibrium point at the origin.

(a) Show that asymptotic stability of the origin cannot be shown by linearization.

(b) Using the singular perturbation approach, show that the origin is asymptotically stable for $\varepsilon \in (0, \varepsilon^*)$. Estimate ε^* and the region of attraction.

11.24 ([105]) Let the assumptions of Theorem 11.3 hold with $\psi_1(x) = \|x\|$ and $\psi_2(y) = \|y\|$ and suppose, in addition, that $V(x)$ and $W(x, y)$ satisfy

$$k_1 \|x\|^2 \leq V(x) \leq k_2 \|x\|^2$$

$$k_3 \|y\|^2 \leq W(x, y) \leq k_4 \|y\|^2$$

$\forall\, (x, y) \in D_x \times D_y$, where k_1 to k_4 are positive constants. Show that the conclusions of Theorem 11.3 hold with exponential stability replacing asymptotic stability.

11.25 ([191]) Consider the singularly perturbed system

$$\begin{aligned} \dot{x} &= f(x, y) \\ \varepsilon \dot{y} &= Ay + \varepsilon g_1(x, y) \end{aligned}$$

where A is Hurwitz and f and g_1 are sufficiently smooth functions that vanish at the origin. Suppose there is a Lyapunov function $V(x)$ such that $[\partial V/\partial x]f(x, 0) \leq -\alpha_1 \phi(x)$ in the domain of interest, where $\alpha_1 > 0$ and $\phi(x)$ is positive definite. Let P be the solution of the Lyapunov equation $PA + A^T P = -I$ and take $W(y) = y^T Py$.

(a) Suppose f and g_1 satisfy the inequalities

$$\|g_1(x,0)\|_2 \le k_1 \phi^{1/2}(x), \quad k_1 \ge 0$$

$$\frac{\partial V}{\partial x}[f(x,y) - f(x,0)] \le k_2 \phi^{1/2}(x)\|y\|_2, \quad k_2 \ge 0$$

in the domain of interest. Using the Lyapunov function candidate $\nu(x,y) = (1-d)V(x) + dW(y)$, $0 < d < 1$ and the analysis preceding Theorem 11.3, show that the origin is asymptotically stable for sufficiently small ε.

(b) As an alternative to Theorem 11.3, suppose f and g_1 satisfy the inequalities

$$\|g_1(x,0)\|_2 \le k_3 \phi^a(x), \quad k_3 \ge 0, \quad 0 < a \le \tfrac{1}{2}$$

$$\frac{\partial V}{\partial x}[f(x,y) - f(x,0)] \le k_4 \phi^b(x)\|y\|_2^c, \quad k_4 \ge 0, \quad 0 < b < 1, \quad c = \frac{1-b}{a}$$

in the domain of interest. Using the Lyapunov function candidate $\nu(x,y) = V(x) + (y^T P y)^\gamma$, where $\gamma = 1/2a$, show that the origin is asymptotically stable for sufficiently small ε.
Hint: Use Young's inequality

$$uw \le \frac{1}{\mu}u^p + \mu^{\frac{1}{p-1}} w^{\frac{p}{p-1}}, \forall\, u \ge 0,\ w \ge 0,\ \mu > 0,\ p > 1$$

to show that $\dot\nu \le -c_1 \phi - c_2 \|y\|_2^{2\gamma}$. Then show that the coefficients c_1 and c_2 can be made positive for sufficiently small ε.

(c) Give an example where the interconnection conditions of part (b) are satisfied, but not those of part (a).

11.26 ([99]) Consider the multiparameter singularly perturbed system

$$\dot{x} = f(x, z_1, \dots, z_m)$$

$$\varepsilon_i \dot{z}_i = \eta_i(x) + \sum_{j=1}^{m} a_{ij} z_j, \quad i = 1, \dots, m$$

where x is an n-dimensional vector, z_i's are scalar variables, and ε_i's are small positive parameters. Let $\varepsilon = \max_i \varepsilon_i$. This equation can be rewritten as

$$\dot{x} = f(x, z)$$

$$\varepsilon D \dot{z} = \eta(x) + Az$$

where z and η are m-dimensional vectors whose components are z_i and η_i, respectively, A is an $m \times m$ matrix whose elements are a_{ij}, and D is an $m \times m$ diagonal matrix whose ith diagonal element is $\varepsilon_i/\varepsilon$. The diagonal elements of D are positive and bounded by one. Suppose the origin of the reduced system $\dot{x} = f(x, -A^{-1}\eta(x))$ is asymptotically stable and there is a Lyapunov function $V(x)$ that satisfies the conditions of Theorem 11.3. Suppose further that there is a diagonal matrix P with positive elements such that

$$PA + A^T P = -Q, \quad Q > 0$$

Using

$$\nu(x, z) = (1 - d)V(x) + d(z + A^{-1}\eta(x))^T PD(z + A^{-1}\eta(x)), \quad 0 < d < 1$$

as a Lyapunov function candidate, analyze the stability of the origin. State and prove a theorem similar to Theorem 11.3 for the multiparameter case. Your conclusion should allow the parameters ε_i's to be arbitrary, subject only to a requirement that they be sufficiently small.

11.27 ([105]) The singularly perturbed system

$$\dot{x}_1 = (a + x_2)x_1 + 2z, \qquad \dot{x}_2 = bx_1^2, \qquad \varepsilon\dot{z} = -x_1 x_2 - z$$

where $a > 0$ and $b > 0$, has an equilibrium set $\{x_1 = 0, \ z = 0\}$. Study the asymptotic behavior of the solution, for small ε, using LaSalle's invariance principle. Hint: The asymptotic behavior of the reduced model has been studied in Example 4.10. Use a composite Lyapunov function and proceed as in Section 11.5. Notice, however, that Theorem 11.3 does not apply to the current problem.

11.28 Show that the origin of the system

$$\dot{x}_1 = x_2 + e^{-t}z, \qquad \dot{x}_2 = -x_2 + z, \qquad \varepsilon\dot{z} = -(x_1 + z) - (x_1 + z)^3$$

is globally exponentially stable for sufficiently small ε.

11.29 Consider the singularly perturbed system

$$\dot{x} = -x + \tan^{-1} z, \qquad \varepsilon\dot{z} = -x - z + u$$

(a) Find ε^* such that $\forall \ \varepsilon < \varepsilon^*$, the origin of the unforced system is globally asymptotically stable.

(b) Show that for each $\varepsilon < \varepsilon^*$, the system is input-to-state stable.

11.30 Consider the feedback connection of Figure 7.1, where the linear component is a singularly perturbed system represented by

$$
\begin{aligned}
\dot{x}_1 &= x_2 \\
\dot{x}_2 &= -x_1 - 2x_2 + z \\
\varepsilon\dot{z} &= -z + u \\
y &= 2x_1 + x_2
\end{aligned}
$$

and ψ is a smooth, memoryless, time-invariant nonlinearity that belongs to a sector $[0, k]$ for some $k > 0$.

(a) Represent the closed-loop system as a singularly perturbed system and find its reduced and boundary-layer models.

(b) Show that for every $k > 0$, there is $\varepsilon^* > 0$ such that the system is absolutely stable for all $0 < \varepsilon < \varepsilon^*$.

Chapter 12

Feedback Control

The last three chapters of the book deal with the design of feedback control. Various tools of nonlinear control design are introduced, including linearization, integral control, gain scheduling, feedback linearization, sliding mode control, Lyapunov redesign, backstepping, passivity-based control, and high-gain observers. Most of the nonlinear analysis tools we have learned so far come into play in these three chapters, solidifying our understanding of these tools. This chapter starts with a section on control problems that serves as an introduction to all three chapters. This is followed by four sections on classical tools, which proved to be useful in applications, namely, linearization, integral control, and gain scheduling. Feedback linearization is presented in Chapter 13 and various nonlinear design tools are presented in Chapter 14.

12.1   Control Problems

There are many control tasks that require the use of feedback. Depending on the design goals, there are several formulations of the control problem. The tasks of stabilization, tracking, and disturbance rejection or attenuation (and various combinations of them) lead to a number of control problems. In each problem, we may have a state feedback version where all state variables can be measured or an output feedback version where only an output vector, whose dimension is typically less than the dimension of the state, can be measured. In a typical control problem, there are additional goals for the design, like meeting certain requirements on the transient response or certain constraints on the control input. These requirements could be conflicting and the designer has to trade off various conflicting requirements. The desire to optimize this design tradeoff leads to various optimal control problems. When model uncertainty is taken into consideration, issues of sensitivity and robustness come into play. The attempt to design feedback control to cope with a wide range of model uncertainty leads to either robust or adaptive control problems. In robust control, the model uncertainty is characterized as perturbations of a nominal model. You may think of the nominal model as a point in a space and the perturbed models as points in a ball that contains the nominal model. A robust control design tries to meet the control objective for any model in the "ball of uncertainty." Adaptive control, on the other hand, parameterizes the uncertainty in terms of certain unknown parameters and tries to use feedback to learn these parameters on-line, that is, during the operation of the system. In a more elaborate adaptive scheme, the controller might be learning certain unknown nonlinear functions, rather than just learning some unknown parameters. There are also problem formulations that mix robust and adaptive control. In the current section, we describe the control problems we shall encounter in this chapter and the next two. We will limit our discussions to the basic tasks of stabilization, tracking, and disturbance rejection. We start with the stabilization problem, both state feedback and output feedback versions. Then we describe tracking and disturbance rejection problems. Some robust control problems will be described in Chapter 14, as needed.

The state feedback stabilization problem for the system

$$\dot{x} = f(t, x, u)$$

is the problem of designing a feedback control law

$$u = \gamma(t, x)$$

such that the origin $x = 0$ is a uniformly asymptotically stable equilibrium point of the closed-loop system

$$\dot{x} = f(t, x, \gamma(t, x))$$

The feedback control law $u = \gamma(t, x)$ is usually called "static feedback," because it is a memoryless function of x. Sometimes, we use a dynamic state feedback control

$$u = \gamma(t, x, z)$$

where z is the solution of a dynamical system driven by x; that is,

$$\dot{z} = g(t, x, z)$$

Common examples of dynamic state feedback control arise when we use integral control (Section 12.3) or adaptive control (Section 1.2.6).

The output feedback stabilization problem for the system

$$\begin{aligned} \dot{x} &= f(t, x, u) \\ y &= h(t, x, u) \end{aligned}$$

is the problem of designing a static output feedback control law

$$u = \gamma(t, y)$$

or a dynamic output feedback control law

$$
\begin{aligned}
u &= \gamma(t, y, z) \\
\dot{z} &= g(t, y, z)
\end{aligned}
$$

such that the origin is a uniformly asymptotically stable equilibrium point of the closed-loop system. In the case of dynamic feedback control, the origin to be stabilized is $(x = 0,\ z = 0)$. Dynamic feedback control is more common in output feedback schemes, since the lack of measurement of some of the state variables is usually compensated for by including "observers" or "observer-like" components in the feedback controller.

While the standard stabilization problem is defined as stabilization of an equilibrium point at the origin, we can use the same formulation to stabilize the system with respect to an arbitrary point x_{ss}. For that we need the existence of a steady-state value of the input u_{ss} which can maintain equilibrium at x_{ss}; namely,

$$
0 = f(t, x_{\mathrm{ss}}, u_{\mathrm{ss}}), \quad \forall\, t \geq 0
$$

The change of variables

$$
x_\delta = x - x_{\mathrm{ss}}, \qquad u_\delta = u - u_{\mathrm{ss}}
$$

results in

$$
\dot{x}_\delta = f(t, x_{\mathrm{ss}} + x_\delta, u_{\mathrm{ss}} + u_\delta) \overset{\text{def}}{=} f_\delta(t, x_\delta, u_\delta)
$$

where $f_\delta(t, 0, 0) \equiv 0$ for all $t \geq 0$. For output feedback problems, the output is redefined as

$$
y_\delta = y - h(t, x_{\mathrm{ss}}, u_{\mathrm{ss}}) = h(t, x_{\mathrm{ss}} + x_\delta, u_{\mathrm{ss}} + u_\delta) - h(t, x_{\mathrm{ss}}, u_{\mathrm{ss}}) \overset{\text{def}}{=} h_\delta(t, x_\delta, u_\delta)
$$

in which $h_\delta(t, 0, 0) \equiv 0$ for all $t \geq 0$. We can now proceed to the solve the standard stabilization problem for the system

$$
\begin{aligned}
\dot{x}_\delta &= f_\delta(t, x_\delta, u_\delta) \\
y_\delta &= h_\delta(t, x_\delta, u_\delta)
\end{aligned}
$$

where u_δ is designed as feedback control of x_δ or y_δ. The overall control $u = u_\delta + u_{\mathrm{ss}}$ has a feedback component u_δ and a feedforward component u_{ss}.

Naturally, the feedback stabilization problem is much simpler when the system is linear and time invariant:

$$
\begin{aligned}
\dot{x} &= Ax + Bu \\
y &= Cx + Du
\end{aligned}
$$

In this case, the state feedback control $u = -Kx$ preserves linearity of the open-loop system, and the origin of the closed-loop system

$$
\dot{x} = (A - BK)x
$$

is asymptotically stable if and only if the matrix $A - BK$ is Hurwitz. Thus, the state feedback stabilization problem reduces to a problem of designing a matrix K to assign the eigenvalues of $A - BK$ in the open left-half complex plane. Linear control theory[1] confirms that the eigenvalues of $A - BK$ can be arbitrarily assigned (subject only to the constraint that complex eigenvalues are in conjugate pairs) provided the pair (A, B) is controllable. Even if some eigenvalues of A are not controllable, stabilization is still possible, provided the uncontrollable eigenvalues have negative real parts. In this case, the pair (A, B) is called stabilizable, and the uncontrollable (open-loop) eigenvalues of A will be (closed-loop) eigenvalues of $A - BK$. If we can only measure the output y, we can use dynamic compensation, like the observer-based controller

$$\begin{aligned} u &= -K\hat{x} \\ \dot{\hat{x}} &= A\hat{x} + Bu + H(y - C\hat{x} - Du) \end{aligned}$$

to stabilize the system. Here, the feedback gain K is designed as in state feedback, such that $A - BK$ is Hurwitz, while the observer gain H is designed such that $A - HC$ is Hurwitz. The closed-loop eigenvalues will consist of the eigenvalues of $A - BK$ and the eigenvalues of $A - HC$.[2] The stabilization of $A - HC$ is dual to the stabilization of $A - BK$ and requires observability (or at least detectability) of the pair (A, C).

For a general nonlinear system, the problem is more difficult and less understood. The most practical way to approach the stabilization problem for nonlinear systems is to appeal to the neat results available in the linear case, that is, via linearization. In Section 12.2, a feedback control law is designed by linearizing the system about the desired equilibrium point and designing a stabilizing linear feedback control for the linearization. The validity of this idea comes from Lyapunov's indirect method stated in Theorems 4.7 and 4.13. Clearly, this approach is local; that is, it can only guarantee asymptotic stability, but cannot, in general, prescribe a region of attraction nor achieve global asymptotic stability. In Section 12.5, we describe *gain scheduling*, a technique that aims at extending the region of validity of linearization by solving the stabilization problem at different operating points and allowing the controller to move from one design to another in a smooth or abrupt way. In Chapter 13, another linearization idea is presented. There, we deal with a special class of nonlinear systems that can be transformed into linear systems via feedback and (possibly) a change of variables. After this transformation, a stabilizing linear state feedback control is designed for the linear system. This linearization approach is different from the first one in that no approximation is used; it is exact. Exactness, however, assumes perfect knowledge of the state equation and uses that knowledge to cancel the nonlinearities of the system. Since perfect knowledge of the state

---

[1]See, for example, [9], [35], [110], or [158].

[2]This fact is usually referred to as the "separation principle," since the assignment of the closed-loop eigenvalues can be carried out in separate tasks for the state feedback and observer problems.

equation and exact mathematical cancellation of terms are almost impossible, the implementation of this approach will almost always result in a closed-loop system, which is a perturbation of a nominal system whose origin is exponentially stable. The validity of the method draws upon Lyapunov theory for perturbed systems (Chapter 9), specifically regarding robustness of exponential stability.

When a linear system is stabilized by feedback, the origin of the closed-loop system is globally asymptotically stable. This is not the case for nonlinear systems where different stabilization notions can be introduced. If the nonlinear system is stabilized via linearization, then the origin of the closed-loop system will be asymptotically stable. Without further analysis of the system, the region of attraction of the origin will be unknown. In this case, we say the feedback control achieves *local stabilization*. If the feedback control guarantees that a certain set is included in the region of attraction or if an estimate of the region of attraction is given, we say that the feedback control achieves *regional stabilization*. If the origin of the closed-loop system is globally asymptotically stable, we say that the control achieves *global stabilization*. If feedback control does not achieve global stabilization, but can be designed such that any given compact set (no matter how large) can be included in the region of attraction, we say that the feedback control achieves *semiglobal stabilization*. These four stabilization notions are illustrated by the next example.

Example 12.1 Suppose we want to stabilize the scalar system

$$\dot{x} = x^2 + u$$

by using state feedback. Linearization at the origin results in the linear system $\dot{x} = u$, which can be stabilized by $u = -kx$ with $k > 0$. When this control is applied to the nonlinear system, it results in

$$\dot{x} = -kx + x^2$$

whose linearization at the origin is $\dot{x} = -kx$. Thus, by Theorem 4.7, the origin is asymptotically stable, and we say that $u = -kx$ achieves local stabilization. In this example, it is not hard to see that the region of attraction is the set $\{x < k\}$. With this information, we say that $u = -kx$ achieves regional stabilization. By increasing k, we can expand the region of attraction. In fact, given any compact set $B_r = \{|x| \leq r\}$, we can include it in the region of attraction by choosing $k > r$. Hence, $u = -kx$ achieves semiglobal stabilization. It is important to notice that $u = -kx$ does not achieve global stabilization. In fact, for any finite k, there is a part of the state space (that is, $x \geq k$), which is not in the region of attraction. While semiglobal stabilization can include any compact set in the region of attraction, the control law is dependent on the given set and will not necessarily work with a bigger set. For a given r, we can choose $k > r$. Once k is fixed and the controller is implemented, if the initial state happens to be in the region $\{x > k\}$, the solution $x(t)$ will diverge to infinity. Global stabilization can be achieved by the nonlinear control law

$$u = -x^2 - kx$$

which cancels the open-loop nonlinearity and yields the linear closed-loop system $\dot{x} = -kx$. $\triangle$

We turn now to the description of a more general control problem; namely, the tracking problem in the presence of disturbance. Here, we have a system modeled by

$$
\begin{aligned}
\dot{x} &= f(t, x, u, w) \\
y &= h(t, x, u, w) \\
y_m &= h_m(t, x, u, w)
\end{aligned}
$$

where x is the state, u is the control input, w is a disturbance input, y is the controlled output, and y_m is the measured output. The basic goal of the control problem is to design the control input so that the controlled output y tracks a reference signal r; that is,

$$
e(t) = y(t) - r(t) \approx 0, \quad \forall\, t \geq t_0
$$

where t_0 is the time at which control starts. Since the initial value of y depends on the initial state $x(t_0)$, meeting this requirement for all $t \geq t_0$ would require either presetting $x(t_0)$ or presetting the initial value of the reference signal by assuming knowledge of $x(t_0)$, which is not feasible in many applications. Therefore, we usually seek an asymptotic output tracking goal, where the tracking error e approaches zero as t tends to infinity; that is,

$$
e(t) \to 0 \ \text{as} \ t \to \infty
$$

If asymptotic output tracking is achieved in the presence of input disturbance w, we say that we have achieved asymptotic disturbance rejection. When the exogenous signals r and w are generated by a known model, such as constant signals or sinusoidal signals of known frequencies, asymptotic output tracking and disturbance rejection can be achieved by including such model in the feedback controller.[3] This is so even when the system's model contain uncertain parameters. In the important special case of constant exogenous signals, where the goal is to asymptotically regulate y to a "set point" r, asymptotic regulation and disturbance rejection can be achieved by including "integral action" in the controller. This is the only way to achieve asymptotic regulation in the presence of parametric uncertainties, which explains the popularity of PI (proportional-integral) and PID (proportional-integral-derivative) controllers in industrial applications. The principle of using integral action is not tied in with linearity. This is shown in Section 12.3 where integral control is presented for a general nonlinear system; then in Section 12.4, we show how linearization can be used to design the stabilizing component of the integral controller. In Chapter 14, Sections 14.1.4 and 14.5.3, we show how PI and PID controllers can be designed as robust regulators of a class of nonlinear systems.

---

[3]This is known as the "internal model principle." (See [32].)

For a general time-varying disturbance input $w(t)$, it might not be feasible to achieve asymptotic disturbance rejection. In such cases, we may attempt to achieve disturbance attenuation, which can take the form of a requirement to achieve ultimate boundedness of the tracking error with a prescribed tolerance; that is,

$$\|e(t)\| \leq \varepsilon, \quad \forall \, t \geq T$$

where ε is a prespecified (small) positive number. Alternatively, we may consider attenuating the closed-loop input–output map from the disturbance input w to the tracking error e. For example, if we consider w as an $\mathcal{L}_2$ signal, then our goal would be to minimize the $\mathcal{L}_2$ gain of the closed-loop input–output map from w to e, or at least, make this gain less than a prescribed tolerance.[4]

Feedback control laws for the tracking problem are classified in the same way we have seen in the stabilization problem. We speak of state feedback if x can be measured; that is, if $y_m = x$; otherwise, we speak of output feedback. Also, the feedback control law can be static or dynamic. The control law may achieve local, regional, semiglobal, or global tracking. The new element here is that these phrases refer not only to the size of the initial state, but to the size of the exogenous signals r and w as well. For example, in a typical problem, local tracking means tracking is achieved for sufficiently small initial states and sufficiently small exogenous signals, while global tracking means tracking is achieved for any initial state and any (r, w) in a prescribed class of exogenous signals.

12.2 Stabilization via Linearization

We illustrate the design-via-linearization approach by considering the stabilization problem. We start with state feedback control and then present output feedback.

For state feedback stabilization, consider the system

$$\dot{x} = f(x, u) \tag{12.1}$$

where $f(0, 0) = 0$ and $f(x, u)$ is continuously differentiable in a domain $D_x \times D_u \subset R^n \times R^p$ that contains the origin ($x = 0$, $u = 0$). We want to design a state feedback control law $u = \gamma(x)$ to stabilize the system. Linearization of (12.1) about ($x = 0$, $u = 0$) results in the linear system

$$\dot{x} = Ax + Bu \tag{12.2}$$

where

$$A = \left.\frac{\partial f}{\partial x}(x, u)\right|_{x=0, u=0} ; \quad B = \left.\frac{\partial f}{\partial u}(x, u)\right|_{x=0, u=0}$$

---

[4]This is the formulation of the H_∞ control problem. (See, for example, [20], [54], [61], [90], [199], and [219].)

Assume the pair (A, B) is controllable, or at least stabilizable. Design a matrix K to assign the eigenvalues of $A - BK$ to desired locations in the open left-half complex plane. Now apply the linear state feedback control $u = -Kx$ to the nonlinear system (12.1). The closed-loop system is

$$\dot{x} = f(x, -Kx) \tag{12.3}$$

Clearly, the origin is an equilibrium point of the closed-loop system. The linearization of (12.3) about the origin $x = 0$ is given by

$$\dot{x} = \left[\frac{\partial f}{\partial x}(x, -Kx) + \frac{\partial f}{\partial u}(x, -Kx)\,(-K) \right]_{x=0} x = (A - BK)x$$

Since $A - BK$ is Hurwitz, it follows from Theorem 4.7 that the origin is an asymptotically stable equilibrium point of the closed-loop system (12.3). Actually, according to Theorem 4.13, the origin is exponentially stable. As a byproduct of the linearization approach, we can always find a Lyapunov function for the closed-loop system. Let Q be any positive-definite symmetric matrix and solve the Lyapunov equation

$$P(A - BK) + (A - BK)^T P = -Q$$

for P. Since $(A - BK)$ is Hurwitz, the Lyapunov equation has a unique positive definite solution (Theorem 4.6). The quadratic function $V(x) = x^T Px$ is a Lyapunov function for the closed-loop system in the neighborhood of the origin. We can use $V(x)$ to estimate the region of attraction.

Example 12.2 Consider the pendulum equation

$$\ddot{\theta} = -a \sin \theta - b\dot{\theta} + cT$$

where $a = g/l > 0$, $b = k/m \geq 0$, $c = 1/ml^2 > 0$, θ is the angle subtended by the rod and the vertical axis, and T is the torque applied to the pendulum. View the torque as the control input and suppose we want to stabilize the pendulum at an angle $\theta = \delta$. For the pendulum to maintain equilibrium at $\theta = \delta$, the torque must have a steady-state component T_{ss} that satisfies

$$0 = -a \sin \delta + cT_{\text{ss}}$$

Choose the state variables as $x_1 = \theta - \delta$, $x_2 = \dot{\theta}$ and the control variable as $u = T - T_{\text{ss}}$. The state equation

$$\begin{aligned} \dot{x}_1 &= x_2 \\ \dot{x}_2 &= -a[\sin(x_1 + \delta) - \sin \delta] - bx_2 + cu \end{aligned}$$

is in the standard form (12.1), where $f(0, 0) = 0$. Linearization of the system at the origin results in

$$A = \begin{bmatrix} 0 & 1 \\ -a\cos(x_1 + \delta) & -b \end{bmatrix}_{x_1=0} = \begin{bmatrix} 0 & 1 \\ -a\cos\delta & -b \end{bmatrix}; \quad B = \begin{bmatrix} 0 \\ c \end{bmatrix}$$

The pair (A, B) is controllable. Taking $K = [k_1 \ k_2]$, it can be easily verified that $A - BK$ is Hurwitz for

$$k_1 > -\frac{a \cos \delta}{c}, \quad k_2 > -\frac{b}{c}$$

The torque is given by

$$T = \frac{a \sin \delta}{c} - Kx = \frac{a \sin \delta}{c} - k_1(\theta - \delta) - k_2 \dot{\theta}$$

We leave it to the reader (Exercise 12.1) to continue with the Lyapunov analysis of the closed-loop system. $\triangle$

For output feedback stabilization, consider the system

$$\dot{x} = f(x, u) \tag{12.4}$$
$$y = h(x) \tag{12.5}$$

where $f(0,0) = 0$, $h(0) = 0$, and $f(x,u)$, $h(x)$ are continuously differentiable in a domain $D_x \times D_u \subset R^n \times R^p$ that contains the origin ($x = 0$, $u = 0$). We want to design an output feedback control law (using only measurements of y) to stabilize the system. Linearization of (12.4)–(12.5) about ($x = 0$, $u = 0$) results in the linear system

$$\dot{x} = Ax + Bu \tag{12.6}$$
$$y = Cx \tag{12.7}$$

where A and B are defined after (12.2) and

$$C = \left. \frac{\partial h}{\partial x}(x) \right|_{x=0}$$

Assume (A, B) is stabilizable and (A, C) is detectable, and design a linear dynamic output feedback controller

$$\dot{z} = Fz + Gy \tag{12.8}$$
$$u = Lz + My \tag{12.9}$$

such that the closed-loop matrix

$$\begin{bmatrix} A + BMC & BL \\ GC & F \end{bmatrix} \tag{12.10}$$

is Hurwitz. An example of such design is the observer-based controller, where

$$z = \hat{x}, \quad F = A - BK - HC, \quad G = H, \quad L = -K, \quad M = 0$$

and K and H are designed such that $A - BK$ and $A - HC$ are Hurwitz. When the controller (12.8)–(12.9) is applied to the nonlinear system (12.4)–(12.5), it results in the closed-loop system

$$\dot{x} = f(x, Lz + Mh(x)) \tag{12.11}$$
$$\dot{z} = Fz + Gh(x) \tag{12.12}$$

It can be verified that the origin ($x = 0$, $z = 0$) is an equilibrium point of the closed-loop system (12.11)–(12.12) and linearization about the origin results in the Hurwitz matrix of (12.10). Thus, once again, we conclude that the origin is an exponentially stable equilibrium point of the closed-loop system (12.11)–(12.12). A Lyapunov function for the closed-loop system can be obtained by solving a Lyapunov equation for the Hurwitz matrix of (12.10).

Example 12.3 Reconsider the pendulum equation of Example 12.2, and suppose we measure the angle θ, but not the angular velocity $\dot{\theta}$. An output variable y can be taken as $y = x_1 = \theta - \delta$, and the state feedback controller of Example 12.2 can be implemented by using the observer

$$\dot{\hat{x}} = A\hat{x} + Bu + H(y - \hat{x}_1)$$

Taking $H = [h_1 \ h_2]^T$, it can be verified that $A - HC$ will be Hurwitz if

$$h_1 + b > 0, \quad h_1 b + h_2 + a \cos \delta > 0$$

The torque is given by

$$T = \frac{a \sin \delta}{c} - K\hat{x}$$

$\triangle$

12.3   Integral Control

In Example 12.2, we considered the problem of regulating the pendulum's angle θ to a constant value δ. We reduced the problem to a stabilization problem by shifting the desired equilibrium point to the origin. While this approach is sound when the parameters of the system are known, it could be unacceptable under parameter perturbations. The control law

$$T = \frac{a \sin \delta}{c} - k_1(\theta - \delta) - k_2\dot{\theta}$$

comprises the steady-state component $T_{ss} = (a/c) \sin \delta$, which assigns the equilibrium value of θ, say θ_{ss}, at the desired angle δ, and the feedback component $-Kx$, which makes $A - BK$ Hurwitz. While the calculation of both components depends on the parameters of the system, the feedback part can be designed to be robust to a wide range of parameter perturbations. In particular, if we know an upper bound on the ratio a/c, that is, $a/c \leq \rho$, we can ensure that $A - BK$ will be Hurwitz by choosing k_1 and k_2 to satisfy

$$k_1 > \rho, \quad k_2 > 0$$

The calculation of T_{ss}, on the other hand, could be sensitive to parameter perturbations. Suppose T_{ss} is calculated by using nominal values a_0 and c_0 of a and c, respectively. The equilibrium point of the closed-loop system is given by

$$a \sin \theta_{ss} = c \left[\frac{a_0}{c_0} \sin \delta - k_1 (\theta_{ss} - \delta) \right]$$

If $\delta = 0$ or $\delta = \pi$ (that is; the pendulum is stabilized at one of the open-loop equilibrium points), $T_{ss} = 0$ and the foregoing equation yields $\theta_{ss} = \delta$. In this case, the approach used in Example 12.2 will be robust to parameter perturbations. For other values of δ, the error in the steady-state angle could be unacceptable. For example, if $\delta = 45°$, $c = c_0/2$ (doubling the mass), $a = a_0$, and $k_1 = 3a_0/c_0$, we have $\theta_{ss} \approx 36°$.

In this section, we present an integral control approach that ensures asymptotic regulation under all parameter perturbations that do not destroy the stability of the closed-loop system. The use of integral control is not tied in with linearity nor with the use of linearization to design the feedback controller. We present the approach for a general nonlinear system and then show in the next section how linearization can be used to design the feedback controller.

Consider the system

$$\dot{x} = f(x, u, w) \tag{12.13}$$

$$y = h(x, w) \tag{12.14}$$

$$y_m = h_m(x, w) \tag{12.15}$$

where $x \in R^n$ is the state, $u \in R^p$ is the control input, $y \in R^p$ is the controlled output, $y_m \in R^m$ is the measured output, and $w \in R^l$ is a vector of unknown constant parameters and disturbances. The function f, h, and h_m are continuously differentiable in (x, u) and continuous in w in a domain $D_x \times D_u \times D_w \subset R^n \times R^p \times R^l$. Let $r \in D_r \subset R^p$ be a constant reference that is available on line and set

$$v = \begin{bmatrix} r \\ w \end{bmatrix} \in D_v \overset{\text{def}}{=} D_r \times D_w$$

We want to design feedback control such that

$$y(t) \to r \quad \text{as} \quad t \to \infty$$

We assume that y can be measured; that is, y is a subset of y_m. The regulation task will be achieved by stabilizing the system at an equilibrium point where $y = r$.

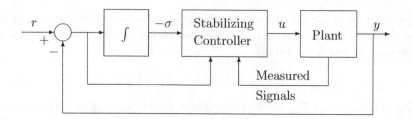

Figure 12.1: Integral control.

Towards that end, we assume that for each $v \in D_v$, there is a unique pair $(x_{\mathrm{ss}}, u_{\mathrm{ss}})$ that depends continuously on v and satisfies the equations

$$
\begin{aligned}
0 &= f(x_{\mathrm{ss}}, u_{\mathrm{ss}}, w) & (12.16) \\
r &= h(x_{\mathrm{ss}}, w) & (12.17)
\end{aligned}
$$

so that x_{ss} is the desired equilibrium point and u_{ss} is the steady-state control that is needed to maintain equilibrium at x_{ss}. To introduce integral action, we integrate the regulation error $e = y - r$:

$$\dot{\sigma} = e$$

Then we augment the integrator with the state equation (12.13) to obtain

$$
\begin{aligned}
\dot{x} &= f(x, u, w) & (12.18) \\
\dot{\sigma} &= h(x, w) - r & (12.19)
\end{aligned}
$$

For multioutput systems ($p > 1$), the integrator equation represents a stack of p integrators where each component of e is integrated. It is clear that integrating e requires both y and r to be available on line. The control task now is to design a stabilizing feedback controller that stabilizes the augmented state model (12.18)–(12.19) at an equilibrium point $(x_{\mathrm{ss}}, \sigma_{\mathrm{ss}})$ where σ_{ss} produces the desired u_{ss}. Figure 12.1 shows a block diagram representation of the integral control scheme.

The integral controller comprises two components: the integrator and the stabilizing controller. The integrator is sometimes called the internal model, since it duplicates the model of the equation $\dot{v} = 0$, which generates the exogenous constant signal v. The structure of the stabilizing controller depends on the measured signal. For example, in the case of state feedback; that is, when $y_m = x$, the stabilizing controller takes the form

$$u = \gamma(x, \sigma, e)$$

where γ is designed such that there is a unique σ_{ss} that satisfies the equation

$$\gamma(x_{\mathrm{ss}}, \sigma_{\mathrm{ss}}, 0) = u_{\mathrm{ss}}$$

and the closed-loop system

$$
\begin{aligned}
\dot{x} &= f(x, \gamma(x, \sigma, h(x, w) - r), w) \\
\dot{\sigma} &= h(x, w) - r
\end{aligned}
$$

has an asymptotically stable equilibrium point at (x_{ss}, σ_{ss}). At the equilibrium point, $y = r$, irrespective of the value of w. Hence, asymptotic regulation is achieved for all initial states in the region of attraction of (x_{ss}, σ_{ss}).

The fact that the integral controller of Figure 12.1 is robust to all parameter perturbations that do not destroy the stability of the closed-loop system can be intuitively explained as follows: The feedback controller creates an asymptotically stable equilibrium point. At this point, all signals must be constant. For the integrator $\dot{\sigma} = e$ to have a constant output σ, its input e must be zero. Thus, the inclusion of the integrator forces the regulation error to be zero at equilibrium. Parameter perturbations will change the equilibrium point, but the condition $e = 0$ at equilibrium will be maintained. Thus, as long as the perturbed equilibrium point remains asymptotically stable, regulation will be achieved.

The design of the stabilizing controller is not a trivial task because the closed-loop equation depends on the unknown vector w. In the next section, we will see a straightforward solution to this dilemma via linearization, but it will only guarantee local regulation. Nonlocal regulation can be achieved by using some of the nonlinear design tools of Chapter 14; an example is given in Section 14.1.4.

12.4   Integral Control via Linearization

We start by designing a state feedback integral controller; then we consider output feedback. We need to design $u = \gamma(x, \sigma, e)$ to stabilize the augmented state model (12.18)–(12.19) at (x_{ss}, σ_{ss}) where $u_{ss} = \gamma(x_{ss}, \sigma_{ss}, 0)$. Since we are going to use linearization, it is reasonable to consider a linear feedback control law of the form

$$u = -K_1 x - K_2 \sigma - K_3 e \tag{12.20}$$

When the control (12.20) is applied to (12.18)–(12.19), it results in the closed-loop system

$$
\begin{aligned}
\dot{x} &= f(x, -K_1 x - K_2 \sigma - K_3(h(x, w) - r), w) & (12.21) \\
\dot{\sigma} &= h(x, w) - r & (12.22)
\end{aligned}
$$

Equilibrium points $(\bar{x}, \bar{\sigma})$ of (12.21)–(12.22) satisfy the equations

$$
\begin{aligned}
0 &= f(\bar{x}, \bar{u}, w) \\
0 &= h(\bar{x}, w) - r \\
\bar{u} &= -K_1 \bar{x} - K_2 \bar{\sigma}
\end{aligned}
$$

By the assumption that the equilibrium equations (12.16) and (12.17) have a unique solution (x_{ss}, u_{ss}) in the domain of interest, we conclude that $\bar{x} = x_{ss}$ and $\bar{u} = u_{ss}$. By choosing K_2 to be nonsingular, we guarantee that there is a unique solution σ_{ss} of the equation

$$u_{ss} = -K_1 x_{ss} - K_2 \sigma_{ss}$$

Our task now is to stabilize the equilibrium point $(x_{\text{ss}}, \sigma_{\text{ss}})$. Linearization of the closed-loop system (12.21)–(12.22) about $(x_{\text{ss}}, \sigma_{\text{ss}})$ yields

$$\dot{\xi}_\delta = (\mathcal{A} - \mathcal{B}\mathcal{K})\xi_\delta$$

where

$$\xi_\delta = \begin{bmatrix} x - x_{\text{ss}} \\ \sigma - \sigma_{\text{ss}} \end{bmatrix}, \quad \mathcal{A} = \begin{bmatrix} A & 0 \\ C & 0 \end{bmatrix}, \quad \mathcal{B} = \begin{bmatrix} B \\ 0 \end{bmatrix}, \quad \mathcal{K} = \begin{bmatrix} K_1 & K_2 \end{bmatrix}$$

$$A = \left.\frac{\partial f}{\partial x}(x, u, w)\right|_{x=x_{\text{ss}}, u=u_{\text{ss}}}, \quad B = \left.\frac{\partial f}{\partial u}(x, u, w)\right|_{x=x_{\text{ss}}, u=u_{\text{ss}}}, \quad C = \left.\frac{\partial h}{\partial x}(x, w)\right|_{x=x_{\text{ss}}}$$

The matrices A, B, and C are, in general, dependent on v. Suppose now that (A, B) is controllable (respectively, stabilizable) and[5]

$$\text{rank} \begin{bmatrix} A & B \\ C & 0 \end{bmatrix} = n + p \tag{12.23}$$

Then, $(\mathcal{A}, \mathcal{B})$ is controllable (respectively, stabilizable).[6] Design $\mathcal{K}$, independent of w, such that $\mathcal{A} - \mathcal{B}\mathcal{K}$ is Hurwitz for all $v \in D_v$.[7] For any such design, the matrix K_2 will be nonsingular.[8] Thus, $(x_{\text{ss}}, \sigma_{\text{ss}})$ is an exponentially stable equilibrium point of the closed-loop system (12.21)–(12.22), and all solutions starting in its region of attraction approach it as t tends to infinity. Consequently, $y(t) - r \to 0$ as $t \to \infty$. We note that the stabilization of $(x_{\text{ss}}, \sigma_{\text{ss}})$ is independent of K_3. Therefore, we can take $K_3 = 0$, or we may use it as an extra degree of freedom to improve performance.

In summary, assuming (A, B) is stabilizable and the rank condition (12.23) is satisfied, the state feedback control can be taken as

$$\begin{aligned} u &= -K_1 x - K_2 \sigma \\ \dot{\sigma} &= e = y - r \end{aligned}$$

where $\mathcal{K} = [K_1 \ K_2]$ is designed such that $\mathcal{A} - \mathcal{B}\mathcal{K}$ is Hurwitz.

Example 12.4 Consider the pendulum equation

$$\ddot{\theta} = -a \sin \theta - b\dot{\theta} + cT$$

---

[5]The rank condition (12.23) implies that the linear state model (A, B, C) has no transmission zeros at the origin.

[6]See Exercise 12.3.

[7]This is a robust stabilization problem that has been extensively studied in the linear control literature. (See, for example, [48] and [69].) Note that if $\mathcal{K}$ is designed to stabilize $\mathcal{A} - \mathcal{B}\mathcal{K}$ at some nominal parameters, then, due to continuous dependence of the eigenvalues of a matrix on its elements, $\mathcal{A} - \mathcal{B}\mathcal{K}$ will remain Hurwitz in some neighborhood of the nominal parameters.

[8]Had K_2 been singular, $\mathcal{A} - \mathcal{B}\mathcal{K}$ would have been singular as well, which contradicts the fact that $\mathcal{A} - \mathcal{B}\mathcal{K}$ is Hurwitz.

where $a = g/l > 0$, $b = k/m \geq 0$, $c = 1/ml^2 > 0$, θ is the angle subtended by the rod and the vertical axis, and T is the torque applied to the pendulum. View T as the control input and suppose we want to regulate θ to δ. Taking $x_1 = \theta - \delta$, $x_2 = \dot{\theta}$, $u = T$, and $y = x_1$, we write the state equation as

$$\begin{aligned} \dot{x}_1 &= x_2 \\ \dot{x}_2 &= -a\sin(x_1 + \delta) - bx_2 + cu \\ y &= x_1 \end{aligned}$$

It can be easily seen that the desired equilibrium point is

$$x_{\mathrm{ss}} = \begin{bmatrix} 0 \\ 0 \end{bmatrix}, \quad u_{\mathrm{ss}} = \frac{a}{c}\sin\delta$$

The matrices A, B, and C are given by

$$A = \begin{bmatrix} 0 & 1 \\ -a\cos\delta & -b \end{bmatrix}; \quad B = \begin{bmatrix} 0 \\ c \end{bmatrix}; \quad C = \begin{bmatrix} 1 & 0 \end{bmatrix}$$

Noting that $c > 0$, it can be easily verified that (A, B) is controllable and the rank condition (12.23) is satisfied. Taking $K_1 = [k_1 \ k_2]$ and $K_2 = k_3$, it can be verified, using the Routh–Hurwitz criterion, that $A - BK$ will be Hurwitz if

$$b + k_2 c > 0, \quad (b + k_2 c)(a\cos\delta + k_1 c) - k_3 c > 0, \quad \text{and} \quad k_3 c > 0$$

Suppose we do not know the exact values of the parameters $a > 0$, $b \geq 0$, $c > 0$, but we know upper bounds ρ_1 on a/c and ρ_3 on $1/c$. Then, the choice

$$k_2 > 0, \quad k_3 > 0, \quad \text{and} \quad k_1 > \rho_1 + \frac{k_3}{k_2}\rho_2 \tag{12.24}$$

ensures that $A - BK$ will be Hurwitz. The feedback control law is given by

$$\begin{aligned} u &= -k_1(\theta - \delta) - k_2\dot{\theta} - k_3\sigma \\ \dot{\sigma} &= \theta - \delta \end{aligned}$$

which is the classical PID controller. Comparing this feedback law with the one derived in Example 12.2 shows that we no longer calculate the steady-state torque needed to maintain the equilibrium position. Regulation will be achieved for all parameter perturbations that satisfy $(b + k_2 c)(a\cos\delta + k_1 c) - k_3 c > 0$. Figure 12.2 shows simulation results for regulating the pendulum to $\delta = \pi/4$ with integral action (Example 12.4) and without integral action (Example 12.2). In the first case, the feedback gains $k_1 = 8$, $k_2 = 2$, and $k_3 = 10$ assign the eigenvalues at -15.93, -2.93, and -2.14. In the second case, the feedback gains $k_1 = 3$, $k_2 = 0.7$ assign the eigenvalues at $-4 \pm j4.59$. In both cases, the nominal parameters are $a = c = 10$ and $b = 1$. In the perturbed case, b and c are reduced to 0.5 and 5, respectively, corresponding to doubling of the mass. The simulation shows the improvement in the steady-state response with integral action, which is achieved at the expense of a longer settling time and an increased torque during the transient period. $\triangle$

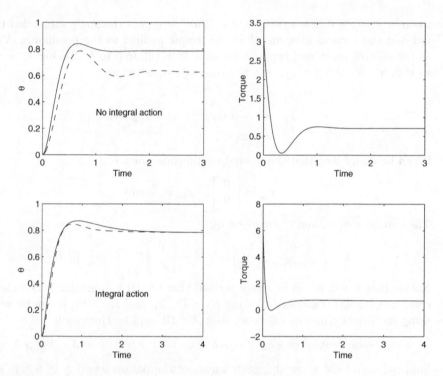

Figure 12.2: Simulation results for pendulum regulation under nominal (solid) and perturbed (dashed) parameters, with (Example 12.4) and without (Example 12.2) integral action.

In the more general case of output feeback, the integral controller can be taken as

$$\dot{\sigma} = e = y - r \tag{12.25}$$

$$\dot{z} = Fz + G_1\sigma + G_2y_m \tag{12.26}$$

$$u = Lz + M_1\sigma + M_2y_m + M_3e \tag{12.27}$$

where F, G_1, G_2, L, M_1, M_2, and M_3 are designed, independent of w, such that

$$\mathcal{A}_c = \begin{bmatrix} A + BM_2C_m + BM_3C & BM_1 & BL \\ C & 0 & 0 \\ G_2C_m & G_1 & F \end{bmatrix}$$

is Hurwitz for all $v \in D_v$, where $C_m = [\partial h_m/\partial x](x_{ss}, w)$. This will ensure that

$$\begin{bmatrix} M_1 & L \\ G_1 & F \end{bmatrix}$$

is nonsingular and the equation

$$\begin{bmatrix} M_1 & L \\ G_1 & F \end{bmatrix} \begin{bmatrix} \sigma_{\mathrm{ss}} \\ z_{\mathrm{ss}} \end{bmatrix} = \begin{bmatrix} u_{\mathrm{ss}} - M_2 h_m(x_{\mathrm{ss}}, w) \\ -G_2 h_m(x_{\mathrm{ss}}, w) \end{bmatrix}$$

has a unique solution $(\sigma_{\mathrm{ss}}, z_{\mathrm{ss}})$. Thus, $(x_{\mathrm{ss}}, \sigma_{\mathrm{ss}}, z_{\mathrm{ss}})$ is the unique equilibrium point of the closed-loop system at which $u = u_{\mathrm{ss}}$ and $e = 0$. It can be verified that $\mathcal{A}_c$ is the linearization of the closed-loop system about $(x_{\mathrm{ss}}, \sigma_{\mathrm{ss}}, z_{\mathrm{ss}})$. Hence, the equilibrium point is exponentially stable and all solutions starting in its region of attraction approach it as t tends to infinity. Consequently, $y(t) - r \to 0$ as $t \to \infty$.

12.5 Gain Scheduling

The basic limitation of the design-via-linearization approach is the fact that the controller is guaranteed to work only in some neighborhood of a single operating (equilibrium) point. In this section, we introduce *gain scheduling*, a technique that can extend the validity of the linearization approach to a range of operating points. In many situations, it is known how the dynamics of a system change with its operating points. It might even be possible to model the system in such a way that the operating points are parameterized by one or more variables, which we call *scheduling variables*. In such situations, we may linearize the system at several equilibrium points, design a linear feedback controller at each point, and implement the resulting family of linear controllers as a single controller whose parameters are changed by monitoring the scheduling variables. Such controller is called *gain-scheduled controller*.

The concept of gain scheduling originated in connection with flight control systems.[9] The nonlinear equations of motion of an airplane or a missile are linearized about selected operating points that capture the key modes of operation throughout the flight envelope. Linear controllers are designed to achieve the desired stability and performance requirements for the linearizations about the selected operating points. The parameters of the controllers are then interpolated as functions of gain scheduling variables; typical variables are dynamic pressure, Mach number, altitude, and angle of attack. Finally, the gain-scheduled controller is implemented on the nonlinear system. We start with a simple example to illustrate the idea of gain scheduling.

Example 12.5 Consider the tank system of Exercise 1.19 where the cross-sectional area A varies with height. The system can be modeled by the equation

$$\frac{d}{dt} \left(\int_0^h A(y) \, dy \right) = w_i - k\sqrt{\rho g h}$$

---

[9]See [159] for a survey of research on gain scheduling and applications to flight control and automotive engine control.

where h is the liquid height in the tank, w_i is the input flow rate, ρ is the liquid density, g is the acceleration due to gravity, and k is a positive constant. Taking $x = h$ as the state variable and $u = w_i$ as the control input, the state model is given by

$$\dot{x} = \frac{1}{A(x)} \left(u - c\sqrt{x} \right) \stackrel{\text{def}}{=} f(x, u)$$

where $c = k\sqrt{\rho g}$ will be treated as an uncertain parameter. Suppose we want to design a controller such that x tracks a reference signal r. We define $y = x$ as the controlled output and use r as the scheduling variable. When $r = \alpha$ (a positive constant), the output y should be regulated to α. To cope with the uncertainty in c, we use integral control. The equilibrium equations (12.16) and (12.17) take the form

$$0 = u_{\text{ss}} - c\sqrt{x_{\text{ss}}}, \quad \alpha = x_{\text{ss}}$$

Hence, $x_{\text{ss}} = \alpha$ and $u_{\text{ss}} = c\sqrt{\alpha}$. Augmenting the integrator $\dot{\sigma} = e = y - r$ with the state equation, we obtain

$$
\begin{aligned}
\dot{x} &= f(x, u) \\
\dot{\sigma} &= x - r
\end{aligned}
$$

We use the PI controller

$$u = -k_1(\alpha)e - k_2(\alpha)\sigma$$

to stabilize the augmented state equation at $(x_{\text{ss}}, \sigma_{\text{ss}})$, where $\sigma_{\text{ss}} = -u_{\text{ss}}/k_2(\alpha)$, provided $k_2 \neq 0$. The closed-loop system is given by

$$
\begin{aligned}
\dot{x} &= f(x, -k_1(\alpha)(x - r) - k_2(\alpha)\sigma) \\
\dot{\sigma} &= x - r
\end{aligned}
$$

When $r = \alpha$, the system has an equilibrium point at $(x_{\text{ss}}, \sigma_{\text{ss}})$. Linearization of the closed-loop system about $(x, \sigma) = (x_{\text{ss}}, \sigma_{\text{ss}})$ and $r = \alpha$ yields

$$\dot{\xi}_\delta = \begin{bmatrix} a(\alpha) - b(\alpha)k_1(\alpha) & -b(\alpha)k_2(\alpha) \\ 1 & 0 \end{bmatrix} \xi_\delta + \begin{bmatrix} b(\alpha)k_1(\alpha) \\ -1 \end{bmatrix} r_\delta, \quad y_\delta = x_\delta$$

where $\xi_\delta = [x_\delta \ \ \sigma_\delta]^T$, $x_\delta = x - \alpha$, $\sigma_\delta = \sigma - \sigma_{\text{ss}}$, $r_\delta = r - \alpha$,

$$
\begin{aligned}
a(\alpha) &= \left. \frac{\partial f}{\partial x} \right|_{x=\alpha, u=c\sqrt{\alpha}} = \left[\frac{1}{A(x)} \left(\frac{-c}{2\sqrt{x}} \right) - \frac{A'(x)}{A^2(x)} \left(u - c\sqrt{x} \right) \right]_{x=\alpha, u=c\sqrt{\alpha}} \\
&= -\frac{c\sqrt{\alpha}}{2\alpha A(\alpha)}
\end{aligned}
$$

and

$$b(\alpha) = \left. \frac{\partial f}{\partial u} \right|_{x=\alpha, u=c\sqrt{\alpha}} = \frac{1}{A(\alpha)}$$

Assuming we know an upper bound on c, we choose k_1 and k_2 as

$$k_1(\alpha) = \frac{2\zeta\omega_n}{b(\alpha)}, \quad k_2(\alpha) = \frac{\omega_n^2}{b(\alpha)}$$

where $0 < \zeta < 1$, and $2\zeta\omega_n \gg |a(\alpha)|$, to (approximately) assign the closed-loop eigenvalues at the roots of

$$s^2 + 2\zeta\omega_n s + \omega_n^2 = 0$$

Thus, the linearization of the closed-loop system under the fixed-gain controller is

$$\dot{\xi}_\delta = A_f(\alpha)\xi_\delta + B_f r_\delta, \quad y_\delta = C_f \xi_\delta$$

where

$$A_f(\alpha) = \begin{bmatrix} a(\alpha) - 2\zeta\omega_n & -\omega_n^2 \\ 1 & 0 \end{bmatrix}, \quad B_f = \begin{bmatrix} 2\zeta\omega_n \\ -1 \end{bmatrix}, \quad \text{and} \quad C_f = \begin{bmatrix} 1 & 0 \end{bmatrix}$$

The closed-loop transfer function from the command input r_δ to the output y_δ is

$$\frac{2\zeta\omega_n s + \omega_n^2}{s^2 + [2\zeta\omega_n - a(\alpha)]s + \omega_n^2}$$

Now, leaving aside the hypothetical situation where r was assumed to be constant, let us deal with time-varying r. A gain-scheduled PI controller is taken as

$$u = -k_1(r)e - k_2(r)\sigma, \quad \dot{\sigma} = e = x - r$$

where α is replaced by r so that the gains k_1 and k_2 vary directly with r. The closed-loop nonlinear system under the gain-scheduled controller is

$$\begin{aligned} \dot{x} &= f(x, -k_1(r)(x-r) - k_2(r)\sigma) \\ \dot{\sigma} &= x - r \end{aligned}$$

When $r = \alpha$, the system has an equilibrium point at (x_{ss}, σ_{ss}). This shows that the closed-loop nonlinear system under the gain-scheduled controller achieves the desired operating point for every α. Linearization about $(x, \sigma) = (x_{ss}, \sigma_{ss})$ and $r = \alpha$ yields

$$\dot{\xi}_\delta = A_s(\alpha)\xi_\delta + B_s(\alpha)r_\delta, \quad y_\delta = C_s \xi_\delta$$

where

$$A_s(\alpha) = \begin{bmatrix} a(\alpha) - 2\zeta\omega_n & -\omega_n^2 \\ 1 & 0 \end{bmatrix}, \quad B_s(\alpha) = \begin{bmatrix} 2\zeta\omega_n + \gamma(\alpha) \\ -1 \end{bmatrix}, \quad C_s = \begin{bmatrix} 1 & 0 \end{bmatrix}$$

and $\gamma(\alpha) = -b(\alpha)k_2'(\alpha)\sigma_{ss}(\alpha) = A'(\alpha)c\sqrt{\alpha}/A^2(\alpha)$. The closed-loop transfer function from the command input r_δ to the output y_δ is

$$\frac{[2\zeta\omega_n + \gamma(\alpha)]s + \omega_n^2}{s^2 + [2\zeta\omega_n - a(\alpha)]s + \omega_n^2}$$

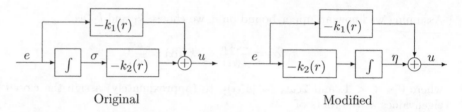

Figure 12.3: Modification of the gain-scheduled PI controller of Example 12.5.

Let us note the difference between the two linear models represented by (A_f, B_f, C_f) and (A_s, B_s, C_s). The first model is the linearization of the closed-loop system under the fixed-gain controller, while the second model is the linearization of the closed-loop system under the gain-scheduled controller. In both cases, the linearization is about the desired operating point. Ideally, we would like these two models to be equivalent, for then we know that the local behavior of the closed-loop system near the desired operating point matches the behavior predicted by the design model. Comparing the two models shows that $A_s = A_f$ and $C_s = C_f$, but $B_s \neq B_f$, resulting in a different zero location in the closed-loop transfer function. Despite this difference, the two transfer functions have the same poles and the property of zero steady-state regulation error to step inputs. If these are the only design objectives, we can say that the gain-scheduled controller is acceptable. On the other hand, if other performance issues are of concern, like the transient part of the step response, which is affected by the zero location, then we have to study the effect of the zero shift by linear analysis or simulation of the model (A_s, B_s, C_s) (or both). Alternatively, we may modify the gain-scheduled controller with the objective of arriving at a linear model that is equivalent to (A_f, B_f, C_f) for every α. This can be achieved by modifying the gain-scheduled controller to[10]

$$u = -k_1(r)e + \eta, \quad \dot{\eta} = -k_2(r)e$$

For constant gain k_2, the modification can be interpreted as commuting the gain $-k_2$ with the integrator. (See Figure 12.3.) The closed-loop nonlinear system under the modified gain-scheduled controller is

$$\begin{aligned} \dot{x} &= f(x, -k_1(r)(x - r) + \eta) \\ \dot{\eta} &= -k_2(r)(x - r) \end{aligned}$$

When $r = \alpha$, the system has an equilibrium point at $x = x_{ss}$ and $\eta = u_{ss}$. Linearization about $(x, \eta) = (x_{ss}, u_{ss})$ and $r = \alpha$ yields

$$\dot{z}_\delta = A_{ms}(\alpha)z_\delta + B_{ms}(\alpha)r_\delta, \quad y_\delta = C_{ms}z_\delta$$

where

$$A_{ms}(\alpha) = \begin{bmatrix} a(\alpha) - 2\zeta\omega_n & b(\alpha) \\ -\omega_n^2/b(\alpha) & 0 \end{bmatrix}, \quad B_{ms}(\alpha) = \begin{bmatrix} 2\zeta\omega_n \\ \omega_n^2/b(\alpha) \end{bmatrix}, \quad C_{ms} = \begin{bmatrix} 1 & 0 \end{bmatrix}$$

---

[10]This modification is the velocity algorithm of [96]. Another modification is given in [114].

$z_\delta = [x_\delta \quad \eta_\delta]^T$, and $\eta_\delta = \eta - u_{\mathrm{ss}}$. The derivative k_2' does not appear in this model because k_2 is a multiple of e, which vanishes at the equilibrium point. It can be easily seen that the models (A_f, B_f, C_f) and (A_{ms}, B_{ms}, C_{ms}) are equivalent by the similarity transformation

$$\xi_\delta = \begin{bmatrix} 1 & 0 \\ 0 & -b(\alpha)/\omega_n^2 \end{bmatrix} z_\delta$$

Hence, both models have the same transfer function from r_δ to y_δ. $\qquad \triangle$

In view of this example, we can describe the development of a gain-scheduled tracking controller for nonlinear systems by the following steps:

1. Linearize the nonlinear model about a family of operating (equilibrium) points, parameterized by the scheduling variables.

2. Using linearization, design a parameterized family of linear controllers to achieve the specified performance at each operating point.

3. Construct a gain-scheduled controller such that

   - for each constant value of the exogenous input, the closed-loop system under the gain-scheduled controller has the same equilibrium point as the closed-loop system under the fixed-gain controller;

   - the linearization of the closed-loop system under the gain-scheduled controller is equivalent to the linearization of the closed-loop system under the fixed-gain controller.

4. Check the nonlocal performance of the gain-scheduled controller by simulating the nonlinear closed-loop model.

The second step can be achieved by solving the design problem for a family of linear models that depend continuously on the scheduling variables, as we have done in the foregoing example, or by solving the problem only at a finite number of operating points by using the same controller structure for all of them, but allowing the controller parameters to change from one operating point to another. Then, the controller parameters are interpolated at intermediate operating points to produce the parameterized family of linear controllers. This interpolation process is usually ad hoc in nature and relies on physical insight.[11] In the forthcoming development we limit ourselves to the case where the design problem is solved for a family of linear models that depend continuously on the scheduling variables.

Consider the system

$$\dot{x} = f(x, u, v, w) \tag{12.28}$$
$$y = h(x, w) \tag{12.29}$$
$$y_m = h_m(x, w) \tag{12.30}$$

---

[11]See [159] for further discussion of this interpolation process.

where f, h, and h_m are twice continuously differentiable functions in (x, u, v) and continuous in w in a domain $D_x \times D_u \times D_v \times D_w \subset R^n \times R^p \times R^q \times R^l$. Here, x is the state, u is the control input, v is a measured exogenous input, w is a vector of unknown constant parameters and disturbances, $y \in R^p$ is the controlled output, and $y_m \in R^m$ is the measured output. We assume that y can be measured; that is, y is a subset of y_m. Let $r \in D_r \subset R^p$ be a reference signal. We want to design an output feedback controller that achieves small tracking error $e = y - r$ in response to the exogenous input

$$\rho = \left[\begin{array}{c} r \\ v \end{array} \right] \in D_\rho \stackrel{\text{def}}{=} D_r \times D_v$$

We use integral control to achieve zero steady-state error when $v = \alpha$ (a constant vector) and rely on gain scheduling to achieve small error for slowly varying ρ. We partition α as $\alpha = [\alpha_r^T, \ \alpha_v^T]^T$, where α_r and α_v are constant values for r and v, respectively. We use ρ as the scheduling variable.[12] For the design of integral control, we assume that there is a unique pair $(x_{\text{ss}}, u_{\text{ss}}) : D_\rho \times D_w \to D_x \times D_u$, continuously differentiable in α and continuous in w, such that

$$0 \ = \ f(x_{\text{ss}}(\alpha, w), u_{\text{ss}}(\alpha, w), \alpha_v, w) \tag{12.31}$$

$$\alpha_r \ = \ h(x_{\text{ss}}(\alpha, w), w) \tag{12.32}$$

for all $(\alpha, w) \in D_\rho \times D_w$. When $\rho = \alpha$, we can use linearization, as in the previous section, to design an integral controller of the form

$$\dot{\sigma} \ = \ e = y - r \tag{12.33}$$

$$\dot{z} \ = \ F(\alpha)z + G_1(\alpha)\sigma + G_2(\alpha)y_m \tag{12.34}$$

$$u \ = \ L(\alpha)z + M_1(\alpha)\sigma + M_2(\alpha)y_m + M_3(\alpha)e \tag{12.35}$$

where the controller gains F, G_1, G_2, L, M_1, M_2, and M_3 are continuously differentiable functions of α, designed such that

$$\mathcal{A}_c(\alpha, w) = \left[\begin{array}{ccc} A + BM_2C_m + BM_3C & BM_1 & BL \\ C & 0 & 0 \\ G_2C_m & G_1 & F \end{array} \right]$$

is Hurwitz for all $(\alpha, w) \in D_\rho \times D_w$, where

$$A = \frac{\partial f}{\partial x}, \quad B = \frac{\partial f}{\partial u}, \quad C = \frac{\partial h}{\partial x}, \quad \text{and} \quad C_m = \frac{\partial h_m}{\partial x}$$

---

[12]In the gain scheduling literature, the scheduling variable is also allowed to depend on the measured output y_m. (See [159].)

with all Jacobian matrices evaluated at $(x, u, v) = (x_{\text{ss}}, u_{\text{ss}}, \alpha_v)$. The new element here is allowing the controller gains to depend on α (the frozen value of the scheduling variable ρ). In the state feedback case, we can drop z and its state equation (12.34) and take $y_m = x$, $L = 0$, $M_1 = -K_2$, $M_2 = -K_1$, and $M_3 = 0$, where $K = [K_1 \ K_2]$ is designed such that

$$\begin{bmatrix} A - BK_1 & -BK_2 \\ C & 0 \end{bmatrix}$$

is Hurwitz for every $(\alpha, w) \in D_\rho \times D_w$.

The closed-loop system under the fixed-gain controller (12.33)–(12.35) is

$$\begin{align}
\dot{x} &= f(x, Lz + M_1\sigma + M_2 h_m(x, w) + M_3 e, v, w) \tag{12.36} \\
\dot{\sigma} &= e = h(x, w) - r \tag{12.37} \\
\dot{z} &= Fz + G_1\sigma + G_2 h_m(x, w) \tag{12.38} \\
y &= h(x, w) \tag{12.39}
\end{align}$$

When $\rho = \alpha$, the system has an equilibrium point at $(x_{\text{ss}}, \sigma_{\text{ss}}, z_{\text{ss}})$ at which $e = 0$. Linearization about $(x, \sigma, z) = (x_{\text{ss}}, \sigma_{\text{ss}}, z_{\text{ss}})$ and $\rho = \alpha$ yields

$$\begin{align}
\dot{\xi}_\delta &= A_f(\alpha, w)\xi_\delta + B_f(\alpha, w)\rho_\delta \tag{12.40} \\
y_\delta &= C_f(\alpha, w)\xi_\delta \tag{12.41}
\end{align}$$

where

$$\xi_\delta = \begin{bmatrix} x - x_{\text{ss}} \\ \sigma - \sigma_{\text{ss}} \\ z - z_{\text{ss}} \end{bmatrix}, \quad \rho_\delta = \rho - \alpha = \begin{bmatrix} r_\delta \\ v_\delta \end{bmatrix}, \quad y_\delta = y - \alpha_r$$

$$A_f = \mathcal{A}_c, \quad B_f = \begin{bmatrix} -BM_3 & E \\ -I & 0 \\ 0 & 0 \end{bmatrix}, \quad C_f = \begin{bmatrix} C & 0 & 0 \end{bmatrix}$$

$$E = \frac{\partial f}{\partial v}(x, u, v, w)\Big|_{x=x_{\text{ss}}, u=u_{\text{ss}}, v=\alpha_v}$$

Hence, when $\rho = \alpha$, the equilibrium point $(x_{\text{ss}}, \sigma_{\text{ss}}, z_{\text{ss}})$ is exponentially stable.

A gain-scheduled controller can be obtained from the fixed-gain controller (12.33)–(12.35) by scheduling the gains F, G_1, G_2 L, M_1, M_2, and M_3 as functions of the scheduling variable ρ, that is, replacing α by ρ. It can be verified that the closed-loop system under this controller will have the desired equilibrium point and its linearization $(A_s(\alpha, w), B_s(\alpha, w), C_s(\alpha, w))$ will have $A_s = A_f = \mathcal{A}_c$, $C_s = C_f$, but, in general, $B_s \neq B_f$ due to partial differentiation of the scheduled gains with respect to ρ. The fact that $\mathcal{A}_c(\alpha, w)$ is Hurwitz for all $(\alpha, w) \in D_\rho \times D_w$ shows that the gain-scheduled controller will produce an exponentially stable equilibrium point with zero steady-state tracking error when $\rho = \alpha$. However, the closed-loop transfer function from ρ_δ to y_δ could be different from the corresponding transfer function of the design model. Therefore, we must check the local performance of the gain-scheduled controller via analysis or simulation. If the performance is acceptable, we may go ahead and implement the gain-scheduled controller. It turns out, however, that we can do better than that. As in Example 12.5, we can modify the gain-scheduled controller to achieve equivalence between the linearized models of the closed-loop systems under the fixed-gain and gain-scheduled controllers. In the example, we commuted the gain k_2 and the integrator; that is, we moved the integrator from the input side of the controller to its output side, so that both gains k_1 and k_2 are multiples of e, which vanishes at steady-state. This is basically what we would like to do for the controller (12.33)–(12.35). However, the current situation is complicated by the presence of the dynamic equation (12.34), which has two driving inputs: σ and y_m. While σ is the output of an integrator and it makes sense to talk about moving the integrator to the output side of the controller, y_m is not the output of an integrator. This difficulty can be overcome if we can measure $\dot{y}_m$, the derivative of y_m. For, then, we can represent the controller (12.33)–(12.35) as

$$\begin{aligned}
\dot{\lambda} &= \psi \\
\dot{z} &= F(\alpha)z + G(\alpha)\lambda \\
u &= L(\alpha)z + M(\alpha)\lambda + M_3(\alpha)e
\end{aligned}$$

where

$$\psi = \begin{bmatrix} e \\ \dot{y}_m \end{bmatrix}, \quad G = \begin{bmatrix} G_1 & G_2 \end{bmatrix}, \quad \text{and} \quad M = \begin{bmatrix} M_1 & M_2 \end{bmatrix}$$

The transfer function from ψ to u,

$$\{L(\alpha)[sI - F(\alpha)]^{-1}G(\alpha) + M(\alpha)\}\frac{1}{s}$$

is equivalent to

$$\frac{1}{s}\{L(\alpha)[sI - F(\alpha)]^{-1}G(\alpha) + M(\alpha)\}$$

Hence, the controller can be realized by

$$\begin{aligned}
\dot{\varphi} &= F(\alpha)\varphi + G(\alpha)\psi \\
\dot{\eta} &= L(\alpha)\varphi + M(\alpha)\psi \\
u &= \eta + M_3(\alpha)e
\end{aligned}$$

Figure 12.4 shows the original and modified realizations of the fixed-gain controller. Scheduling the gains F, G, L, M, and M_3 in the modified realization as functions of the scheduling variable ρ, we obtain the gain-scheduled controller

$$\begin{aligned}
\dot{\varphi} &= F(\rho)\varphi + G_1(\rho)e + G_2(\rho)\dot{y}_m & (12.42) \\
\dot{\eta} &= L(\rho)\varphi + M_1(\rho)e + M_2(\rho)\dot{y}_m & (12.43) \\
u &= \eta + M_3(\rho)e & (12.44)
\end{aligned}$$

When this controller is applied to the nonlinear system (12.28)–(12.30), it results in the closed-loop system

$$
\dot{\mathcal{X}} = g(\mathcal{X}, \rho, w) \tag{12.45}
$$
$$
y = h(x, w) \tag{12.46}
$$

where

$$
\mathcal{X} = \begin{bmatrix} x \\ \varphi \\ \eta \end{bmatrix}, \quad g(\mathcal{X}, \rho, w) = \begin{bmatrix} f(x, \eta + M_3(\rho)e, v, w) \\ F(\rho)\varphi + G_1(\rho)e + G_2(\rho)\dot{y}_m \\ L(\rho)\varphi + M_1(\rho)e + M_2(\rho)\dot{y}_m \end{bmatrix}
$$

$$
e = h(x, w) - r, \quad \dot{y}_m = \frac{\partial h_m}{\partial x}(x, w) f(x, \eta + M_3(\rho)e, v, w)
$$

When $\rho = \alpha$, the system (12.45)–(12.46) has a unique equilibrium point

$$
\mathcal{X}_{ss}(\alpha, w) = \begin{bmatrix} x_{ss}(\alpha, w) \\ 0 \\ u_{ss}(\alpha, w) \end{bmatrix} \tag{12.47}
$$

at which $y = \alpha_r$. Linearization of (12.45)–(12.46) about $\mathcal{X} = \mathcal{X}_{ss}$ and $\rho = \alpha$ yields[13]

$$
\dot{\mathcal{X}}_\delta = A_{ms}(\alpha, w)\mathcal{X}_\delta + B_{ms}(\alpha, w)\rho_\delta \tag{12.48}
$$
$$
y_\delta = C_{ms}(\alpha, w)\mathcal{X}_\delta \tag{12.49}
$$

where

$$
\mathcal{X}_\delta = \mathcal{X} - \mathcal{X}_{ss}, \quad A_{ms} = \begin{bmatrix} A + BM_3C & 0 & B \\ G_1C + G_2C_m(A + BM_3C) & F & G_2C_mB \\ M_1C + M_2C_m(A + BM_3C) & L & M_2C_mB \end{bmatrix}
$$

$$
B_{ms} = \begin{bmatrix} -BM_3 & E \\ -G_1 - G_2C_mBM_3 & G_2C_mE \\ -M_1 - M_2C_mBM_3 & M_2C_mE \end{bmatrix}, \quad C_{ms} = \begin{bmatrix} C & 0 & 0 \end{bmatrix}
$$

We leave it as an exercise for the reader (Exercise 12.6) to verify that the matrix

$$
P = \begin{bmatrix} I & 0 & 0 \\ G_2C_m & G_1 & F \\ M_2C_m & M_1 & L \end{bmatrix} \tag{12.50}
$$

is nonsingular and

$$
P^{-1}A_{ms}P = A_f, \quad P^{-1}B_{ms} = B_f, \quad \text{and} \quad C_{ms}P = C_f \tag{12.51}
$$

Hence, the linear model (12.48)–(12.49) is equivalent to the linear model (12.40)–(12.41).

---

[13]While calculating the matrices A_{ms} and B_{ms}, note that partial derivatives that appear as coefficients of φ, e, or f vanish at the operating point.

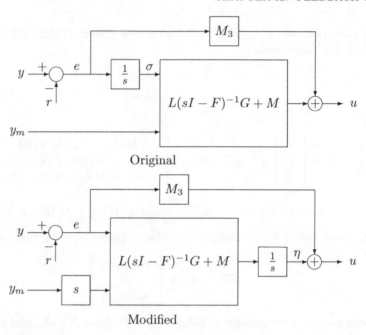

Figure 12.4: Modification of the gain-scheduled controller.

So far, our analysis of the closed-loop system under the gain-scheduled controller has focused on the local behavior in the neighborhood of a constant operating point. Can we say more about the behavior of the nonlinear system? What if the scheduling variable is not constant? In applications of gain scheduling, the practice has been that you can schedule on time-varying variables as long as they are slow enough relative to the dynamics of the system. This practice is justified by the next theorem.

Theorem 12.1 *Consider the closed-loop system* (12.45)–(12.46) *under the stated assumptions. Suppose $\rho(t)$ is continuously differentiable, $\rho(t) \in S$ (a compact subset of D_ρ), and $\|\dot{\rho}(t)\| \leq \mu$ for all $t \geq 0$. Then, there exist positive constants k_1, k_2, k, and T such that if $\mu < k_1$ and $\|\mathcal{X}(0) - \mathcal{X}_{\text{ss}}(\rho(0), w)\| < k_2$, then $\mathcal{X}(t)$ will be uniformly bounded for all $t \geq 0$ and*

$$\|e(t)\| \leq k\mu, \qquad \forall\, t \geq T$$

Furthermore, if $\rho(t) \to \rho_{\text{ss}}$ and $\dot{\rho}(t) \to 0$ as $t \to \infty$, then

$$e(t) \to 0 \ \text{ as } \ t \to \infty$$

$\diamond$

Proof: See Appendix C.19.

The theorem shows that if the scheduling variable is slowly varying and the initial state is sufficiently close to the equilibrium point at the initial time, then the tracking error will, eventually, be of the order of the derivative of the scheduling variable and will tend to zero if the scheduling variable approaches a constant limit.

If measurement of $\dot{y}_m$ is not available, we can use the gain-scheduled controller

$$\dot{\varphi} = F(\rho)\varphi + G_1(\rho)e + G_2(\rho)\vartheta \tag{12.52}$$

$$\dot{\eta} = L(\rho)\varphi + M_1(\rho)e + M_2(\rho)\vartheta \tag{12.53}$$

$$u = \eta + M_3(\rho)e \tag{12.54}$$

where $\dot{y}_m$ is replaced by its estimate ϑ, provided by the filter

$$\varepsilon\dot{\zeta} = -\zeta + y_m \tag{12.55}$$

$$\vartheta = \frac{1}{\varepsilon}(-\zeta + y_m) \tag{12.56}$$

where ε is a "sufficiently small" positive constant and the filter is always initiated at $\zeta(0)$ such that

$$\|\zeta(0) - y_m(0)\| \le k\varepsilon \tag{12.57}$$

for some $k > 0$. Since y_m is measured, we can always meet this initial condition. Furthermore, whenever the system is initited from an equilibrium point, the condition (12.57) is automatically satisfied, since, at equilibrium, $y_m = \zeta$. The filter (12.55)–(12.56) acts as a derivative approximator when ε is sufficiently small, as it can be seen from its transfer function

$$\frac{s}{\varepsilon s + 1}I$$

which approximates the differentiator transfer function sI for frequencies much smaller than $1/\varepsilon$.[14] The closed-loop system under the gain-scheduled controller (12.52)–(12.56) takes the singularly perturbed form

$$\dot{\mathcal{X}} = g(\mathcal{X}, \rho, w) + N(\rho)(\vartheta - \dot{y}_m) \tag{12.58}$$

$$\varepsilon\dot{\vartheta} = -\vartheta + \dot{y}_m \tag{12.59}$$

$$y = h(x, w) \tag{12.60}$$

where

$$\dot{y}_m = \frac{\partial h_m}{\partial x}(x, w)f(x, \eta + M_3(\rho)e, v, w), \qquad N = \begin{bmatrix} 0 \\ G_2 \\ M_2 \end{bmatrix}$$

---

[14]Approximating the derivative $\dot{y}_m$ can be achieved by using the high-gain observer of Section 14.5. In fact, the filter (12.55)–(12.56) is a reduced-order high-gain observer for a second-order system whose output is y_m. The condition (12.57) eliminates peaking of the transient response. If this condition cannot be enforced, the estimate ϑ should be saturated to eliminate peaking, as discussed in Section 14.5.

Setting $\varepsilon = 0$ results in $\vartheta = \dot{y}_m$ and the system (12.58)–(12.60) reduces to the system (12.45)–(12.46). The next theorem justifies the use of the filter (12.55)–(12.56) for sufficiently small ε.

Theorem 12.2 *Consider the closed-loop system* (12.58)–(12.60) *under the stated assumptions. Suppose $\rho(t)$ is continuously differentiable, $\rho(t) \in S$ (a compact subset of D_ρ), and $\|\dot{\rho}(t)\| \leq \mu$ for all $t \geq 0$. Then, there exist positive constants k_1, k_2, k_3, k, and T such that if $\mu < k_1$, $\|\mathcal{X}(0) - \mathcal{X}_{\mathrm{ss}}(\rho(0), w)\| < k_2$, and $\varepsilon < k_3$, then $\mathcal{X}(t)$ will be uniformly bounded for all $t \geq 0$ and*

$$\|e(t)\| \leq k\mu, \quad \forall\, t \geq T$$

Furthermore, if $\rho(t) \to \rho_{\mathrm{ss}}$ and $\dot{\rho}(t) \to 0$ as $t \to \infty$, then

$$e(t) \to 0 \quad \text{as} \quad t \to \infty$$

$\diamond$

Proof: See Appendix C.20.

The theorem shows that if the scheduling variable is slowly varying, the initial state is sufficiently close to the equilibrium point at the initial time, and ε is sufficiently small, then the tracking error will, eventually, be of the order of the derivative of the scheduling variable and will tend to zero if the scheduling variable approaches a constant limit.

Example 12.6 Consider the second-order system

$$\begin{aligned}
\dot{x}_1 &= \tan x_1 + x_2 \\
\dot{x}_2 &= x_1 + u \\
y &= x_2
\end{aligned}$$

where y is the only measured signal; that is, $y_m = y$. We want y to track a reference signal r. We use r as the scheduling variable. When $r = \alpha = \text{constant}$, the equilibrium equations (12.31) and (12.32) have the unique solution

$$x_{\mathrm{ss}}(\alpha) = \begin{bmatrix} -\tan^{-1}\alpha \\ \alpha \end{bmatrix}, \quad u_{\mathrm{ss}}(\alpha) = \tan^{-1}\alpha$$

We use the observer-based integral controller

$$\begin{aligned}
\dot{\sigma} &= e = y - r & (12.61) \\
\dot{\hat{x}} &= A(\alpha)\hat{x} + Bu + H(\alpha)(y - C\hat{x}) & (12.62) \\
u &= -K_1(\alpha)\hat{x} - K_2(\alpha)\sigma & (12.63)
\end{aligned}$$

where

$$A(\alpha) = \begin{bmatrix} 1 + \alpha^2 & 1 \\ 1 & 0 \end{bmatrix}, \quad B = \begin{bmatrix} 0 \\ 1 \end{bmatrix}, \quad C = \begin{bmatrix} 0 & 1 \end{bmatrix}$$

$$K_1(\alpha) = \left[\ (1+\alpha^2)(3+\alpha^2) + 3 + \tfrac{1}{1+\alpha^2} \qquad 3+\alpha^2 \ \right], \quad K_2(\alpha) = -\frac{1}{1+\alpha^2}$$

$$H(\alpha) = \left[\begin{array}{c} 10 + (4+\alpha^2)(1+\alpha^2) \\ (4+\alpha^2) \end{array} \right]$$

The feedback gains $K_1(\alpha)$ and $K_2(\alpha)$ are designed to assign the closed-loop eigenvalues at -1, $-(1/2) \pm j(\sqrt{3}/2)$. The observer gain $H(\alpha)$ is designed to assign the observer eigenvalues at $-(3/2) \pm j(3\sqrt{3}/2)$. We have chosen the eigenvalues independent of α for convenience, but we could have allowed them to depend on α as long as their real parts are less than a negative number independent of α. This fixed-gain controller is a special case of (12.33)–(12.35) with $z = \hat{x}$, $F = A - BK_1 - HC$, $G_1 = -BK_2$, $G_2 = H$, $L = -K_1$, $M_1 = -K_2$, $M_2 = 0$, and $M_3 = 0$. Since $\dot{y}$ is not available, we implement the gain-scheduled controller (12.52)–(12.56) with $\varepsilon = 0.01$. Figure 12.5 shows the response of the closed-loop system to a sequence of step changes in the reference signal. A step change in the reference signal resets the equilibrium point of the system, and the initial state of the system at time 0_+ is the equilibrium state at time 0_-. If the initial state is within the region of attraction of the new equilibrium point, the system reaches steady state at that point. Since our controller is based on linearization, it guarantees only local stabilization. Therefore, in general, step changes in the reference signal will have to be limited. Reaching a large value of the reference signal can be done by a sequence of step changes, as in the figure, allowing enough time for the system to settle down after each step change. Another method to change the reference set point is to

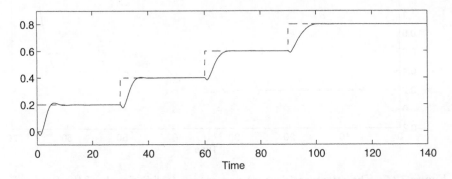

Figure 12.5: The reference (dashed) and output (solid) signals of the gain-scheduled controller of Example 12.6.

move slowly from one set point to another. Figure 12.6 shows the response of the closed-loop system to a slow ramp that takes the set point from zero to one over a period of 100 seconds. This response is consistent with our conclusions about the behavior of gain-scheduled controllers under slowly varying scheduling variables. The same figure shows the response to a faster ramp signal. As the slope of the ramp increases, tracking performance deteriorates. If we keep increasing the slope

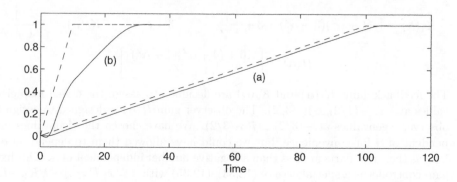

Figure 12.6: The reference (dashed) and output (solid) signals of the gain-scheduled controller of Example 12.6 with ramp reference: (a) ramp slope = 0.01; (b) ramp slope = 0.1.

of the ramp, the system will eventually go unstable. To appreciate what we gain by gain scheduling, Figure 12.7 shows the response of the closed-loop system to the same sequence of step changes of Figure 12.5 when a fixed-gain controller evaluated at $\alpha = 0$ is used. For small reference inputs, the response is as good as the one with the gain-scheduled controller, but as the reference signal increases, the performance deteriorates and the system goes unstable. Finally, to see why we may have to mod-

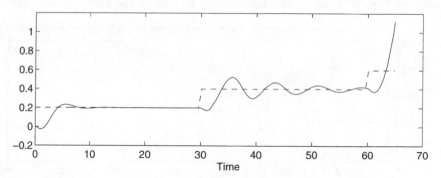

Figure 12.7: The reference (dashed) and output (solid) signals of the fixed gain controller of Example 12.6.

ify the gain-scheduled controller as in Figure 12.4, Figure 12.8 shows the response of the closed-loop system under an unmodified controller (obtained by simply replacing α by r in the foregoing controller equations) to the same sequence of step changes of Figure 12.5. While stability and zero steady-state tracking error are achieved, as predicted by our analysis, the transient response deteriorates rapidly as the reference signal increases. This is due to additional zeros in the closed-loop transfer function. Such bad transient behavior could lead to instability as it could

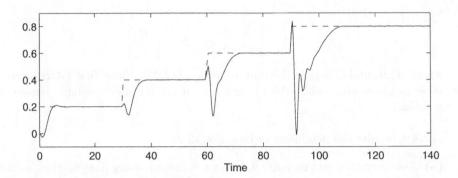

Figure 12.8: The reference (dashed) and output (solid) signals of the unmodified gain-scheduled controller of Example 12.6.

take the state of the system out of the finite region of attraction, although instability was not observed in this example.   △

12.6   Exercises

12.1 Consider the closed-loop system of Example 12.2. Assume $a = c = 10$, $\delta = \pi/4$, $b = 0$, $k_1 = 2.5$, and $k_2 = 1$. Find a Lyapunov function for the system, and use it to estimate the region of attraction.

12.2 For each of the following systems, use linearization to

(a) design a state feedback controller to stabilize the origin.

(b) design an output feedback controller to stabilize the origin.

$$(1) \quad \begin{cases} \dot{x}_1 &= x_1 + x_2 \\ \dot{x}_2 &= 3x_1^2 x_2 + x_1 + u \\ y &= -x_1^3 + x_2 \end{cases}$$

$$(2) \quad \begin{cases} \dot{x}_1 &= x_1 + x_2 \\ \dot{x}_2 &= x_1 x_2^2 - x_1 + x_3 \\ \dot{x}_3 &= u \\ y &= -x_1^3 + x_2 \end{cases}$$

$$(3) \quad \begin{cases} \dot{x}_1 &= -x_1 + x_2 \\ \dot{x}_2 &= x_1 - x_2 - x_1 x_3 + u \\ \dot{x}_3 &= x_1 + x_1 x_2 - 2x_3 \\ y &= x_1 \end{cases}$$

12.3 Let

$$\mathcal{A} = \begin{bmatrix} A & 0 \\ C & 0 \end{bmatrix}, \quad \mathcal{B} = \begin{bmatrix} B \\ 0 \end{bmatrix}$$

where A, B, and C satisfy the rank condition (12.23). Show that $(\mathcal{A}, \mathcal{B})$ is controllable (respectively, stabilizable) if and only if (A, B) is controllable (respectively, stabilizable)

12.4 Consider the pendulum of Example 12.2.

(a) Assuming that you measure θ, but not $\dot{\theta}$, design, using linearization, an output feedback integral controller to stabilize the pendulum at an angle $\theta = \delta$.

(b) Assuming that you measure both θ and $\dot{\theta}$, design a gain-scheduled, state feedback, integral controller so that the angle θ tracks a reference angle θ_r. Study the performance of the gain-scheduled controller by computer simulation.

(c) Assuming that you measure θ, but not $\dot{\theta}$, design a gain-scheduled, observer-based, integral controller so that the angle θ tracks a reference angle θ_r. Study the performance of the gain-scheduled controller by computer simulation.

Use the following numerical data: a $= 10$, $b = 0.1$, and $c = 10$.

12.5 Consider the linear system

$$\dot{x} = A(\alpha)x + B(\alpha)u$$

where $A(\alpha)$ and $B(\alpha)$ are continuously differentiable functions of the constant vector α and $\alpha \in \Gamma$, a compact subset of R^m. Let $W(\alpha)$ be the controllability Gramian, defined by

$$W(\alpha) = \int_0^\tau \exp[-A(\alpha)\sigma]B(\alpha)B^T(\alpha)\exp[-A^T(\alpha)\sigma]\,d\sigma$$

for some $\tau > 0$, independent of α. Suppose (A, B) is controllable, uniformly in α, in the sense that there are positive constants c_1 and c_2, independent of α, such that

$$c_1 I \leq W(\alpha) \leq c_2 I, \quad \forall\,\alpha \in \Gamma$$

Let

$$Q(\alpha) = \int_0^\tau e^{-2c\sigma}\exp[-A(\alpha)\sigma]B(\alpha)B^T(\alpha)\exp[-A^T(\alpha)\sigma]\,d\sigma, \quad c > 0$$

(a) Show that

$$c_1 e^{-2c\tau} I \leq Q(\alpha) \leq c_2 I, \quad \forall\,\alpha \in \Gamma$$

(b) Let
$$u = -K(\alpha)x \overset{\text{def}}{=} -\tfrac{1}{2}B^T(\alpha)P(\alpha)x$$

where $P(\alpha) = Q^{-1}(\alpha)$. Using $V = x^T P(\alpha)x$ as a Lyapunov function candidate for

$$\dot{x} = [A(\alpha) - B(\alpha)K(\alpha)]x$$

show that $\dot{V} \leq -2cV$.

(c) Show that $[A(\alpha) - B(\alpha)K(\alpha)]$ is Hurwitz uniformly in α for all $\alpha \in \Gamma$.

12.6 Show that $P(\alpha)$, defined by (12.50), is nonsingular and satisfies (12.51).

12.7 A simplified model of the low-frequency motion of a ship is given by [60]

$$\tau\ddot{\psi} + \dot{\psi} = k\delta$$

where ψ is the heading angle of the ship and δ is the rudder angle, viewed here as the control input. The time constant τ and the gain k depend on the forward speed of the ship v, according to the expressions $\tau = \tau_0 v_0/v$ and $k = k_0 v/v_0$, where τ_0, k_0, and v_0 are constants.

(a) Assuming a constant forward speed, design a state feedback integral controller so that ψ tracks a desired angle ψ_r.

(b) Use gain scheduling to compensate for varying forward speed.

12.8 The magnetic suspension system of Exercise 1.18 is modeled by

$$
\begin{aligned}
\dot{x}_1 &= x_2 \\
\dot{x}_2 &= g - \frac{k}{m}x_2 - \frac{L_0 a x_3^2}{2m(a+x_1)^2} \\
\dot{x}_3 &= \frac{1}{L(x_1)}\left[-Rx_3 + \frac{L_0 a x_2 x_3}{(a+x_1)^2} + u\right]
\end{aligned}
$$

where $x_1 = y$, $x_2 = \dot{y}$, $x_3 = i$, and $u = v$. Use the following numerical data: $m = 0.1$ kg, $k = 0.001$ N/m/sec, $g = 9.81$ m/sec^2, $a = 0.05$ m, $L_0 = 0.01$ H, $L_1 = 0.02$ H, and $R = 1$ Ω.

(a) Find the steady-state values I_{ss} and V_{ss} of i and v, respectively, which are needed to balance the ball at a desired position $y = r > 0$.

(b) Show that the equilibrium point obtained by taking $u = V_{ss}$ is unstable.

(c) Using linearization, design a state feedback control law to stabilize the ball at $y = 0.05$ m.

(d) Assume the permissible range of y is 0 to 0.1 m and the permissible range of the input voltage is 0 to 15 V. Starting with the ball at equilibrium, move it a small distance up (and then down) and let it go. Repeat this experiment, gradually increasing the amount of initial disturbance. Using simulation, determine the largest range of initial disturbance for which the ball will return to the equilibrium point without violating the constraints on y and v. To account for the constraint on v, include a limiter in your simulation.

(e) Using simulation, investigate the effect of perturbations in the mass m. Simulate the closed-loop system with the nominal controller, but with the mass changing from its nominal value. Find the range of m for which the controller will still balance the ball and investigate the steady-state error.

(f) Repeat the design of part (c) using integral control. Repeat parts (d) and (e) for this design. Comment on the effect of integral control on the transient response and steady-state error.

(g) Repeat the design of part (c) assuming you can only measure y. Repeat parts (d) and (e) for this design.

(h) Repeat the design of part (c) assuming you can only measure y and i. Repeat parts (d) and (e) for this design.

(i) Repeat the integral control design of part (f) assuming you can only measure y. Repeat parts (d) and (e) for this design.

(j) Repeat the integral control design of part (f) assuming you can only measure y and i. Repeat parts (d) and (e) for this design.

(k) Design a gain-scheduled, observer-based, integral controller so that the ball position y tracks a reference position r. Assume you can measure y and i. Using simulation, study the performance of the gain-scheduled controller when r changes slowly from 0.03 to 0.07.

(l) If you can only measure i, can you design a linear output feedback control law to stabilize the ball at $y = r$? Can you design a linear output feedback integral controller?

12.9 A field-controlled DC motor is described in Exercise 1.17. When the field circuit is driven by a current source, we can view the field current as the control input and model the system by the second-order state model

$$\dot{x}_1 = -\theta_1 x_1 - \theta_2 x_2 u + \theta_3$$
$$\dot{x}_2 = -\theta_4 x_2 + \theta_5 x_1 u$$
$$y = x_2$$

where x_1 is the armature current, x_2 is the speed, u is the field current, and θ_1 to θ_5 are positive constants. It is required to design a speed control system so that y asymptotically tracks a constant speed reference r. It is assumed that $r^2 < \theta_3^2\theta_5/4\theta_1\theta_2\theta_4$ and the domain of operation is restricted to $x_1 > \theta_3/2\theta_1$.

(a) Find the steady-state input u_{ss} needed to maintain the output r. Verify that that the open-loop control $u = u_{\text{ss}}$ results in an exponentially stable equilibrium point.

(b) Starting with the motor at rest $(y = 0)$, apply a small step change in the reference signal and simulate the response. Repeat this experiment, gradually increasing the amount of step change. Determine the largest range of initial step for which the motor will reach steady-state at the desired speed.

(c) Using computer simulation, study the performance of the system when the rotor inertia changes by $\pm 50\%$.

(d) Using linearization, design a state feedback integral controller to achieve the desired speed regulation. Repeat parts (b) and (c) for this controller and compare its performance with the open-loop controller of part (a).

(e) Suppose you measure the speed x_2, but not the armature current x_1. Repeat part (d) by using an observer to estimate the armature current. Repeat parts (b) and (c) for this controller and compare its performance with the one designed in part (d).

(f) Design a gain-scheduled, observer-based, integral controller so that the speed x_2 tracks a reference speed r

In parts (b) through (e), use the following numerical data: $\theta_1 = 60$, $\theta_2 = 0.5$, $\theta_3 = 40$, $\theta_4 = 6$, and $\theta_5 = 4 \times 10^4$.

12.10 Consider the inverted pendulum of Exercise 1.15.

(a) Using $x_1 = \theta$, $x_2 = \dot{\theta}$, $x_3 = y$, and $x_4 = \dot{y}$ as state variables and $u = F$ as control input, write down the state equation.

(b) Show that the open-loop system has an equilibrium set.

(c) Suppose we want to stabilize the pendulum at the vertical position $(\theta = 0)$. Find an open-loop equilibrium point at which $\theta = 0$, and show that it is unstable.

(d) Linearize the nonlinear state equation at the desired equilibrium point, and verify that the linearized state equation is controllable.

(e) Using linearization, design a state feedback control law to stabilize the system at the desired equilibrium point.

(f) Using computer simulation, study the transient behavior and the effect of $\pm 20\%$ perturbation in the mass of the pendulum and its moment of inertia.

(g) Starting with the pendulum at equilibrium, move it a small angle to the right (and then to the left) and let it go. Repeat this experiment, gradually increasing the amount of initial disturbance. Using simulation, determine the largest range of initial disturbance for which the pendulum will return to equilibrium.

(h) Suppose you can only measure the angle θ and the cart position y. Using linearization, design an output feedback controller to stabilize the pendulum at $\theta = 0$. Repeat parts (f) and (g) for this controller.

(i) Repeat part (h) if it is desired to stabilize the pendulum at an angle $\theta = \theta_r$, where $-\pi/2 < \theta_r < \pi/2$.

In parts (e) to (i), use the following numerical data: $m = 0.1$ kg, $M = 1$ kg, $k = 0.1$ N/m/sec, $I = 0.025/3$ kg m^2, $g = 9.81$ m/sec^2, and $L = 0.5$ m.

Chapter 13

Feedback Linearization

We consider a class of nonlinear systems of the form

$$\begin{aligned} \dot{x} &= f(x) + G(x)u \\ y &= h(x) \end{aligned}$$

and pose the question of whether there exist a state feedback control

$$u = \alpha(x) + \beta(x)v$$

and a change of variables

$$z = T(x)$$

that transform the nonlinear system into an equivalent linear system. In Section 13.1, we motivate the idea by simple examples and introduce the notions of *full-state linearization*, where the state equation is completely linearized, and *input–output linearization*, where the input–output map is linearized, while the state equation may be only partially linearized. In Section 13.2, we study input–output linearization, introducing the notions of relative degree, zero dynamics, and minimum phase systems. In Section 13.3, we characterize the class of nonlinear systems that can be feedback linearized. To simplify the presentation, Sections 13.2 and 13.3 deal only with single-input–single-output systems. State feedback control of feedback (or partially feedback) linearizable systems is discussed in Section 13.4, where we deal with both stabilization and tracking.

13.1 Motivation

To introduce the idea of feedback linearization, let us start with the problem of stabilizing the origin of the pendulum equation

$$\begin{aligned} \dot{x}_1 &= x_2 \\ \dot{x}_2 &= -a[\sin(x_1 + \delta) - \sin \delta] - bx_2 + cu \end{aligned}$$

From Chapter 13 of *Nonlinear Systems*, Third Edition. Hassan K. Khalil.

Inspection of the state equation shows that we can choose u as

$$u = \frac{a}{c}[\sin(x_1 + \delta) - \sin \delta] + \frac{v}{c}$$

to cancel the nonlinear term $a[\sin(x_1 + \delta) - \sin \delta]$. This cancellation results in the linear system

$$\begin{aligned}
\dot{x}_1 &= x_2 \\
\dot{x}_2 &= -bx_2 + v
\end{aligned}$$

Thus, the stabilization problem for the nonlinear system has been reduced to a stabilization problem for a controllable linear system. We can proceed to design a stabilizing linear state feedback control

$$v = -k_1 x_1 - k_2 x_2$$

to locate the eigenvalues of the closed-loop system

$$\begin{aligned}
\dot{x}_1 &= x_2 \\
\dot{x}_2 &= -k_1 x_1 - (k_2 + b)x_2
\end{aligned}$$

in the open left-half plane. The overall state feedback control law is given by

$$u = \left(\frac{a}{c}\right)[\sin(x_1 + \delta) - \sin \delta] - \frac{1}{c}(k_1 x_1 + k_2 x_2)$$

How general is this idea of nonlinearity cancellation? Clearly, we should not expect to be able to cancel nonlinearities in every nonlinear system. There must be a certain structural property of the system that allows us to perform such cancellation. It is not hard to see that to cancel a nonlinear term $\alpha(x)$ by subtraction, the control u and the nonlinearity $\alpha(x)$ must always appear together as a sum $u + \alpha(x)$. To cancel a nonlinear term $\gamma(x)$ by division, the control u and the nonlinearity $\gamma(x)$ must always appear as a product $\gamma(x)u$. If the matrix $\gamma(x)$ is nonsingular in the domain of interest, then it can be cancelled by $u = \beta(x)v$, where $\beta(x) = \gamma^{-1}(x)$ is the inverse of the matrix $\gamma(x)$. Therefore, the ability to use feedback to convert a nonlinear state equation into a controllable linear state equation by cancelling nonlinearities requires the nonlinear state equation to have the structure

$$\dot{x} = Ax + B\gamma(x)[u - \alpha(x)] \tag{13.1}$$

where A is $n \times n$, B is $n \times p$, the pair (A, B) is controllable, the functions $\alpha : R^n \to R^p$ and $\gamma : R^n \to R^{p \times p}$ are defined in a domain $D \subset R^n$ that contains the origin, and the matrix $\gamma(x)$ is nonsingular for every $x \in D$. If the state equation takes the form (13.1), then we can linearize it via the state feedback

$$u = \alpha(x) + \beta(x)v \tag{13.2}$$

where $\beta(x) = \gamma^{-1}(x)$, to obtain the linear state equation

$$\dot{x} = Ax + Bv \tag{13.3}$$

For stabilization, we design $v = -Kx$ such that $A - BK$ is Hurwitz. The overall nonlinear stabilizing state feedback control is

$$u = \alpha(x) - \beta(x)Kx \tag{13.4}$$

Suppose the nonlinear state equation does not have the structure of (13.1). Does this mean we cannot linearize the system via feedback? The answer is no. Recall that the state model of a system is not unique. It depends on the choice of the state variables. Even if the state equation does not have the structure of (13.1) for one choice of state variables, it might do so for another choice. Consider, for example, the system

$$
\begin{aligned}
\dot{x}_1 &= a \sin x_2 \\
\dot{x}_2 &= -x_1^2 + u
\end{aligned}
$$

We cannot simply choose u to cancel the nonlinear term $a \sin x_2$. However, if we first change the variables by the transformation

$$
\begin{aligned}
z_1 &= x_1 \\
z_2 &= a \sin x_2 = \dot{x}_1
\end{aligned}
$$

then z_1 and z_2 satisfy

$$
\begin{aligned}
\dot{z}_1 &= z_2 \\
\dot{z}_2 &= a \cos x_2 \left(-x_1^2 + u \right)
\end{aligned}
$$

and the nonlinearities can be cancelled by the control

$$u = x_1^2 + \frac{1}{a \cos x_2} v$$

which is well defined for $-\pi/2 < x_2 < \pi/2$. The state equation in the new coordinates (z_1, z_2) can be found by inverting the transformation to express (x_1, x_2) in terms of (z_1, z_2); that is,

$$
\begin{aligned}
x_1 &= z_1 \\
x_2 &= \sin^{-1}\left(\frac{z_2}{a} \right)
\end{aligned}
$$

which is well defined for $-a < z_2 < a$. The transformed state equation is given by

$$
\begin{aligned}
\dot{z}_1 &= z_2 \\
\dot{z}_2 &= a \cos\left(\sin^{-1}\left(\frac{z_2}{a} \right) \right) \left(-z_1^2 + u \right)
\end{aligned}
$$

When a change of variables $z = T(x)$ is used to transform the state equation from the x-coordinates to the z-coordinates, the map T must be invertible; that is, it must have an inverse map $T^{-1}(\cdot)$ such that $x = T^{-1}(z)$ for all $z \in T(D)$, where D is the domain of T. Moreover, because the derivatives of z and x should be continuous, we require both $T(\cdot)$ and $T^{-1}(\cdot)$ to be continuously differentiable. A continuously differentiable map with a continuously differentiable inverse is known as a *diffeomorphism*. If the Jacobian matrix $[\partial T/\partial x]$ is nonsingular at a point $x_0 \in D$, then it follows from the inverse function theorem[1] that there is a neighborhood N of x_0 such that T restricted to N is a diffeomorphism on N. A map T is said to be a global diffeomorphism if it is a diffeomorphism on R^n and $T(R^n) = R^n$.[2] Now we have all the elements we need to define feedback linearizable systems.

Definition 13.1 *A nonlinear system*

$$\dot{x} = f(x) + G(x)u \tag{13.5}$$

where $f : D \to R^n$ and $G : D \to R^{n \times p}$ are sufficiently smooth[3] on a domain $D \subset R^n$, is said to be feedback linearizable (or input–state linearizable) if there exists a diffeomorphism $T : D \to R^n$ such that $D_z = T(D)$ contains the origin and the change of variables $z = T(x)$ transforms the system (13.5) into the form

$$\dot{z} = Az + B\gamma(x)[u - \alpha(x)] \tag{13.6}$$

with (A, B) controllable and $\gamma(x)$ nonsingular for all $x \in D$.

When certain output variables are of interest, as in tracking control problems, the state model is described by state and output equations. Linearizing the state equation does not necessarily linearize the output equation. For example, if the system

$$\begin{aligned} \dot{x}_1 &= a \sin x_2 \\ \dot{x}_2 &= -x_1^2 + u \end{aligned}$$

has an output $y = x_2$, then the change of variables and state feedback control

$$z_1 = x_1, \quad z_2 = a \sin x_2, \quad \text{and} \quad u = x_1^2 + \frac{1}{a \cos x_2} v$$

yield

$$\begin{aligned} \dot{z}_1 &= z_2 \\ \dot{z}_2 &= v \\ y &= \sin^{-1}\left(\frac{z_2}{a}\right) \end{aligned}$$

---

[1]See [10, Theorem 7-5].

[2]T is a global diffeomorphism if and only if $[\partial T/\partial x]$ is nonsingular for all $x \in R^n$ and T is proper; that is, $\lim_{\|x\| \to \infty} \|T(x)\| = \infty$. (See [165] or [212] for a proof of this statement.)

[3]By "sufficiently smooth," we mean that all the partial derivatives, that will appear later on, are defined and continuous.

While the state equation is linear, solving a tracking control problem for y is still complicated by the nonlinearity of the output equation. Inspection of both the state and output equations in the x-coordinates shows that, if we use the state feedback control $u = x_1^2 + v$, we can linearize the input–output map from u to y, which will be described by the linear model

$$
\begin{aligned}
\dot{x}_2 &= v \\
y &= x_2
\end{aligned}
$$

We can now proceed to solve the tracking control problem using linear control theory. This discussion shows that sometimes it is more beneficial to linearize the input–output map even at the expense of leaving part of the state equation nonlinear. In this case, the system is said to be input–output linearizable. One catch about input–output linearization is that the linearized input–output map may not account for all the dynamics of the system. In the foregoing example, the full system is described by

$$
\begin{aligned}
\dot{x}_1 &= a \sin x_2 \\
\dot{x}_2 &= v \\
y &= x_2
\end{aligned}
$$

Note that the state variable x_1 is not connected to the output y. In other words, the linearizing feedback control has made x_1 unobservable from y. When we design tracking control, we should make sure that the variable x_1 is well behaved; that is, stable or bounded in some sense. A naive control design that uses only the linear input–output map may result in an ever-growing signal $x_1(t)$. For example, suppose we design a linear control to stabilize the output y at a constant value r. Then, $x_1(t) = x_1(0) + t\, a \sin r$ and, for $\sin r \neq 0$, $x_1(t)$ will grow unbounded. This internal stability issue will be addressed by using the concept of zero dynamics.

13.2 Input–Output Linearization

Consider the single-input–single-output system

$$
\begin{aligned}
\dot{x} &= f(x) + g(x)u & (13.7) \\
y &= h(x) & (13.8)
\end{aligned}
$$

where f, g, and h are sufficiently smooth in a domain $D \subset R^n$. The mappings $f : D \to R^n$ and $g : D \to R^n$ are called vector fields on D. The derivative $\dot{y}$ is given by

$$
\dot{y} = \frac{\partial h}{\partial x}[f(x) + g(x)u] \stackrel{\text{def}}{=} L_f h(x) + L_g h(x)\, u
$$

where

$$
L_f h(x) = \frac{\partial h}{\partial x} f(x)
$$

is called the *Lie Derivative* of h with respect to f or along f. This is the familiar notion of the derivative of h along the trajectories of the system $\dot{x} = f(x)$. The new notation is convenient when we repeat the calculation of the derivative with respect to the same vector field or a new one. For example, the following notation is used:

$$
\begin{aligned}
L_g L_f h(x) &= \frac{\partial(L_f h)}{\partial x} g(x) \\
L_f^2 h(x) &= L_f L_f h(x) = \frac{\partial(L_f h)}{\partial x} f(x) \\
L_f^k h(x) &= L_f L_f^{k-1} h(x) = \frac{\partial(L_f^{k-1} h)}{\partial x} f(x) \\
L_f^0 h(x) &= h(x)
\end{aligned}
$$

If $L_g h(x) = 0$, then $\dot{y} = L_f h(x)$, independent of u. If we continue to calculate the second derivative of y, denoted by $y^{(2)}$, we obtain

$$
y^{(2)} = \frac{\partial(L_f h)}{\partial x} [f(x) + g(x)u] = L_f^2 h(x) + L_g L_f h(x)\, u
$$

Once again, if $L_g L_f h(x) = 0$, then $y^{(2)} = L_f^2 h(x)$, independent of u. Repeating this process, we see that if $h(x)$ satisfies

$$
L_g L_f^{i-1} h(x) = 0, \quad i = 1, 2, \ldots, \rho - 1; \quad L_g L_f^{\rho-1} h(x) \neq 0
$$

then u does not appear in the equations of y, $\dot{y}$, ..., $y^{(\rho-1)}$ and appears in the equation of $y^{(\rho)}$ with a nonzero coefficient:

$$
y^{(\rho)} = L_f^\rho h(x) + L_g L_f^{\rho-1} h(x)\, u
$$

The foregoing equation shows clearly that the system is input–output linearizable, since the state feedback control

$$
u = \frac{1}{L_g L_f^{\rho-1} h(x)} \left[-L_f^\rho h(x) + v \right]
$$

reduces the input–output map to

$$
y^{(\rho)} = v
$$

which is a chain of ρ integrators. In this case, the integer ρ is called the *relative degree* of the system, according to the following definition:

Definition 13.2 *The nonlinear system* (13.7)–(13.8) *is said to have relative degree* ρ, $1 \leq \rho \leq n$, *in a region* $D_0 \subset D$ *if*

$$
L_g L_f^{i-1} h(x) = 0, \quad i = 1, 2, \ldots, \rho - 1; \quad L_g L_f^{\rho-1} h(x) \neq 0 \tag{13.9}
$$

for all $x \in D_0$.

Example 13.1 Consider the controlled van der Pol equation

$$\dot{x}_1 = x_2$$
$$\dot{x}_2 = -x_1 + \varepsilon(1 - x_1^2)x_2 + u, \quad \varepsilon > 0$$

with output $y = x_1$. Calculating the derivatives of the output, we obtain

$$\dot{y} = \dot{x}_1 = x_2$$
$$\ddot{y} = \dot{x}_2 = -x_1 + \varepsilon(1 - x_1^2)x_2 + u$$

Hence, the system has relative degree two in R^2. For the output $y = x_2$,

$$\dot{y} = -x_1 + \varepsilon(1 - x_1^2)x_2 + u$$

and the system has relative degree one in R^2. For the output $y = x_1 + x_2^2$,

$$\dot{y} = x_2 + 2x_2[-x_1 + \varepsilon(1 - x_1^2)x_2 + u]$$

and the system has relative degree one in $D_0 = \{x \in R^2 \mid x_2 \neq 0\}$. $\triangle$

Example 13.2 Consider the system

$$\dot{x}_1 = x_1$$
$$\dot{x}_2 = x_2 + u$$
$$y = x_1$$

Calculating the derivatives of y, we obtain

$$\dot{y} = \dot{x}_1 = x_1 = y$$

Consequently, $y^{(n)} = y = x_1$ for all $n \geq 1$. In this case, the system does not have a well-defined relative degree. Because the example is simple, it is not difficult to see why this is so: The output $y(t) = x_1(t) = e^t x_1(0)$ is independent of the input u. $\triangle$

Example 13.3 A field-controlled DC motor with negligible shaft damping can be modeled by the state equation (Exercise 1.17)

$$\dot{x}_1 = -ax_1 + u$$
$$\dot{x}_2 = -bx_2 + k - cx_1x_3$$
$$\dot{x}_3 = \theta x_1 x_2$$

where x_1, x_2, and x_3 are the field current, armature current, and angular velocity, respectively, and a, b, c, k, and θ are positive constants. For speed control, we choose the output as $y = x_3$. The derivatives of the output are given by

$$\dot{y} = \dot{x}_3 = \theta x_1 x_2$$
$$\ddot{y} = \theta x_1 \dot{x}_2 + \theta \dot{x}_1 x_2 = (\cdot) + \theta x_2 u$$

where $(\cdot)$ contains terms which are functions of x. The system has relative degree two in the region $D_0 = \{x \in R^3 \mid x_2 \neq 0\}$. $\triangle$

Example 13.4 Consider a linear system represented by the transfer function

$$H(s) = \frac{b_m s^m + b_{m-1} s^{m-1} + \cdots + b_0}{s^n + a_{n-1} s^{n-1} + \cdots + a_0}$$

where $m < n$ and $b_m \neq 0$. A state model for the system can be taken as

$$\dot{x} = Ax + Bu$$
$$y = Cx$$

where

$$A = \begin{bmatrix} 0 & 1 & 0 & \ldots & & & \ldots & 0 \\ 0 & 0 & 1 & \ldots & & & \ldots & 0 \\ \vdots & & \ddots & & & & & \vdots \\ & & & \ddots & & & & \\ & & & & \ddots & & & \vdots \\ \vdots & & & & & \ddots & & 0 \\ 0 & & & & & & 0 & 1 \\ -a_0 & -a_1 & \ldots & \ldots & -a_m & \ldots & \ldots & -a_{n-1} \end{bmatrix}_{n \times n}, \quad B = \begin{bmatrix} 0 \\ 0 \\ \vdots \\ \\ \vdots \\ 0 \\ 1 \end{bmatrix}_{n \times 1}$$

$$C = \begin{bmatrix} b_0 & b_1 & \ldots & \ldots & b_m & 0 & \ldots & 0 \end{bmatrix}_{1 \times n}$$

This linear state model is a special case of (13.7)–(13.8), where $f(x) = Ax$, $g = B$, and $h(x) = Cx$. To check the relative degree of the system, we calculate the derivatives of the output. The first derivative is

$$\dot{y} = CAx + CBu$$

If $m = n - 1$, then $CB = b_{n-1} \neq 0$ and the system has relative degree one. Otherwise, $CB = 0$ and we continue to calculate the second derivative $y^{(2)}$. Noting that CA is a row vector obtained by shifting the elements of C one position to the right, while CA^2 is obtained by shifting the elements of C two positions to the right, and so on, we see that

$$CA^{i-1}B = 0, \quad \text{for } i = 1, 2, \ldots, n - m - 1, \quad \text{and} \quad CA^{n-m-1}B = b_m \neq 0$$

Thus, u appears first in the equation of $y^{(n-m)}$, given by

$$y^{(n-m)} = CA^{n-m}x + CA^{n-m-1}Bu$$

and the relative degree of the system is $n - m$ (the difference between the degrees of the denominator and numerator polynomials of $H(s)$).[4] $\triangle$

---

[4] The terminology "relative degree" of a nonlinear system is consistent with the use of the term relative degree in linear control theory, which is defined as $n - m$.

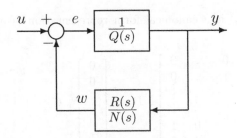

Figure 13.1: Feedback representation of $H(s)$.

To probe further into the control of input–output linearizable systems and issues of internal stability, let us start with the linear system of the foregoing example. The transfer function $H(s)$ can be written as

$$H(s) = \frac{N(s)}{D(s)}$$

where $\deg D = n$ and $\deg N = m < n$. The relative degree $\rho = n - m$. By Euclidean division, we can write $D(s)$ as

$$D(s) = Q(s)N(s) + R(s)$$

where $Q(s)$ and $R(s)$ are the quotient and remainder polynomials, respectively. From Euclidean division rules, we know that

$$\deg Q = n - m = \rho, \quad \deg R < m$$

and the leading coefficient of $Q(s)$ is $1/b_m$. With this representation of $D(s)$, we can rewrite $H(s)$ as

$$H(s) = \frac{N(s)}{Q(s)N(s) + R(s)} = \frac{\frac{1}{Q(s)}}{1 + \frac{1}{Q(s)} \frac{R(s)}{N(s)}}$$

Thus, $H(s)$ can be represented as a negative feedback connection with $1/Q(s)$ in the forward path and $R(s)/N(s)$ in the feedback path. (See Figure 13.1.) The ρth-order transfer function $1/Q(s)$ has no zeros and can be realized by the ρth-order state vector

$$\xi = \begin{bmatrix} y, & \dot{y}, & \dots, & y^{(\rho-1)} \end{bmatrix}^T$$

to obtain the state model

$$\dot{\xi} = (A_c + B_c \lambda^T)\xi + B_c b_m e$$
$$y = C_c \xi$$

where (A_c, B_c, C_c) is a canonical form representation of a chain of ρ integrators; that is,

$$A_c = \begin{bmatrix} 0 & 1 & 0 & \dots & 0 \\ 0 & 0 & 1 & \dots & 0 \\ \vdots & & \ddots & & \vdots \\ \vdots & & & 0 & 1 \\ 0 & \dots & \dots & 0 & 0 \end{bmatrix}, \; B_c = \begin{bmatrix} 0 \\ 0 \\ \vdots \\ 0 \\ 1 \end{bmatrix}, \; C_c = \begin{bmatrix} 1 & 0 & \dots & 0 & 0 \end{bmatrix} \quad (13.10)$$

and $\lambda \in R^\rho$. Let (A_0, B_0, C_0) be a minimal realization of the transfer function $R(s)/N(s)$; that is,

$$\begin{aligned} \dot{\eta} &= A_0\eta + B_0 y \\ w &= C_0\eta \end{aligned}$$

The eigenvalues of A_0 are the zeros of the polynomial $N(s)$, which are the zeros of the transfer function $H(s)$. From the feedback connection, we see that $H(s)$ can be realized by the state model

$$\begin{aligned} \dot{\eta} &= A_0\eta + B_0 C_c \xi & (13.11) \\ \dot{\xi} &= A_c\xi + B_c(\lambda^T\xi - b_m C_0\eta + b_m u) & (13.12) \\ y &= C_c\xi & (13.13) \end{aligned}$$

Using the special structure of (A_c, B_c, C_c), it is straightforward to verify that

$$y^{(\rho)} = \lambda^T\xi - b_m C_0\eta + b_m u$$

The (input–output linearizing) state feedback control

$$u = \frac{1}{b_m}[-\lambda^T\xi + b_m C_0\eta + v]$$

results in the system

$$\begin{aligned} \dot{\eta} &= A_0\eta + B_0 C_c\xi \\ \dot{\xi} &= A_c\xi + B_c v \\ y &= C_c\xi \end{aligned}$$

whose input–output map is a chain of ρ integrators, and whose state subvector η is unobservable from the output y. Suppose we want to stabilize the output at a constant reference r. This requires stabilizing ξ at $\xi^* = (r, 0, \dots, 0)^T$. Shifting the equilibrium point to the origin by the change of variables $\zeta = \xi - \xi^*$ reduces the problem to a stabilization problem for $\dot{\zeta} = A_c\zeta + B_c v$. Taking $v = -K\zeta = -K(\xi - \xi^*)$, where $A_c - B_c K$ is Hurwitz, completes the design of the control law as

$$u = \frac{1}{b_m}[-\lambda^T\xi + b_m C_0\eta - K(\xi - \xi^*)]$$

The corresponding closed-loop system is given by

$$\begin{aligned}
\dot{\eta} &= A_0\eta + B_0 C_c(\xi^* + \zeta) \\
\dot{\zeta} &= (A_c - B_c K)\zeta
\end{aligned}$$

Because $A_c - B_c K$ is Hurwitz, for any initial state $\zeta(0)$, we have $\zeta(t) \to 0$ as $t \to \infty$. Consequently, $y(t) \to r$ as $t \to \infty$. What about η? Equation (13.11) is driven by $y = C_c\xi$ as input. To ensure that $\eta(t)$ will be bounded for all possible waveforms of $y(t)$ and all possible initial states $\eta(0)$, we must require A_0 to be Hurwitz. Equivalently, the zeros of $H(s)$ must lie in the open left-half plane. A transfer function having all zeros in the open-left half plane is called *minimum phase*. From a pole placement viewpoint, the state feedback control, we have just designed via input–output linearization, assigns the closed-loop eigenvalues into two groups: ρ eigenvalues are assigned in the open-left half plane as the eigenvalues of $A_c - B_c K$, and $n - \rho$ eigenvalues are assigned at the open-loop zeros.[5]

Our analysis of the linear system of Example 13.4 sheds some light on the meaning of the state feedback control that reduces the input–output map to a chain of integrators and how to characterize internal stability. The key tool that allowed us to develop this understanding is the state model (13.11)–(13.13). Our next task is to develop a nonlinear version of (13.11)–(13.13) for the nonlinear system (13.7)–(13.8) when it has relative degree ρ. The ξ variables are taken the same as in the linear case, since the input–output map will still be a chain of ρ integrators. We would like to choose the η variables to produce a nonlinear version of (13.11). The key feature of (13.11) is the absence of the control input u. A change of variables that would transform (13.7)–(13.8) into a nonlinear version of (13.11)–(13.13) can be taken as

$$z = T(x) = \begin{bmatrix} \phi_1(x) \\ \vdots \\ \phi_{n-\rho}(x) \\ --- \\ h(x) \\ \vdots \\ L_f^{\rho-1}h(x) \end{bmatrix} \stackrel{\mathrm{def}}{=} \begin{bmatrix} \phi(x) \\ --- \\ \psi(x) \end{bmatrix} \stackrel{\mathrm{def}}{=} \begin{bmatrix} \eta \\ --- \\ \xi \end{bmatrix} \tag{13.14}$$

where ϕ_1 to $\phi_{n-\rho}$ are chosen such that $T(x)$ is a diffeomorphism on a domain $D_0 \subset D$ and

$$\frac{\partial \phi_i}{\partial x} g(x) = 0, \quad \text{for } 1 \le i \le n - \rho, \ \forall \ x \in D_0 \tag{13.15}$$

The next theorem shows that ϕ_1 to $\phi_{n-\rho}$ exist, at least locally.

---

[5]It should be noted that stabilizing the output at a constant reference does not require the system to be minimum phase. This requirement is a consequence of our choice to assign some of the closed-loop eigenvalues at the open-loop zeros.

Theorem 13.1 *Consider the system* (13.7)–(13.8), *and suppose it has relative degree* $\rho \leq n$ *in* D. *If* $\rho = n$, *then for every* $x_0 \in D$, *a neighborhood* N *of* x_0 *exists such that the map*

$$
T(x) = \begin{bmatrix} h(x) \\ L_f h(x) \\ \vdots \\ L_f^{n-1} h(x) \end{bmatrix}
$$

restricted to N, *is a diffeomorphism on* N. *If* $\rho < n$, *then, for every* $x_0 \in D$, *a neighborhood* N *of* x_0 *and smooth functions* $\phi_1(x), \ldots, \phi_{n-\rho}(x)$ *exist such that* (13.15) *is satisfied for all* $x \in N$ *and the map* $T(x)$ *of* (13.14), *restricted to* N, *is a diffeomorphism on* N.   ◇

Proof: See Appendix C.21.

The condition (13.15) ensures that when we calculate

$$
\dot{\eta} = \frac{\partial \phi}{\partial x}[f(x) + g(x)u]
$$

the u term cancels out. It is now easy to verify that the change of variables (13.14) transforms (13.7)–(13.8) into

$$
\begin{aligned}
\dot{\eta} &= f_0(\eta, \xi) & (13.16) \\
\dot{\xi} &= A_c \xi + B_c \gamma(x)[u - \alpha(x)] & (13.17) \\
y &= C_c \xi & (13.18)
\end{aligned}
$$

where $\xi \in R^\rho$, $\eta \in R^{n-\rho}$, (A_c, B_c, C_c) is a canonical form representation of a chain of ρ integrators,

$$
f_0(\eta, \xi) = \frac{\partial \phi}{\partial x} f(x) \bigg|_{x = T^{-1}(z)} \tag{13.19}
$$

$$
\gamma(x) = L_g L_f^{\rho-1} h(x) \quad \text{and} \quad \alpha(x) = -\frac{L_f^\rho h(x)}{L_g L_f^{\rho-1} h(x)} \tag{13.20}
$$

We have kept α and γ in (13.17), expressed in the original coordinates. These functions are uniquely determined by (13.20) in terms of f, g, and h. They are independent of the choice of ϕ. They can be expressed in the new coordinates by setting

$$
\alpha_0(\eta, \xi) = \alpha\left(T^{-1}(z)\right) \quad \text{and} \quad \gamma_0(\eta, \xi) = \gamma\left(T^{-1}(z)\right)
$$

which, of course, will depend on the choice of ϕ. In this case, (13.17) can be rewritten as

$$
\dot{\xi} = A_c \xi + B_c \gamma_0(\eta, \xi)[u - \alpha_0(\eta, \xi)]
$$

If x^* is an open-loop equilibrium point of (13.7), then (η^*, ξ^*), defined by

$$\eta^* = \phi(x^*), \quad \xi^* = \begin{bmatrix} h(x^*) & 0 & \cdots & 0 \end{bmatrix}$$

is an equilibrium point of (13.16)–(13.17). If y vanishes at $x = x^*$, that is, $h(x^*) = 0$, we can transform x^* into the origin point $(\eta = 0, \ \xi = 0)$ by choosing $\phi(x)$ such that $\phi(x^*) = 0$.

Equations (13.16) through (13.18) are said to be in the *normal form*. This form decomposes the system into an external part ξ and an internal part η. The external part is linearized by the state feedback control

$$u = \alpha(x) + \beta(x)v$$

where $\beta(x) = \gamma^{-1}(x)$, while the internal part is made unobservable by the same control. The internal dynamics are described by (13.16). Setting $\xi = 0$ in that equation results in

$$\dot{\eta} = f_0(\eta, 0) \tag{13.21}$$

which is called the *zero dynamics*, a name that matches nicely with the fact that for linear systems, (13.21) is given by $\dot{\eta} = A_0\eta$, where the eigenvalues of A_0 are the zeros of the transfer function $H(s)$. The system is said to be *minimum phase* if (13.21) has an asymptotically stable equilibrium point in the domain of interest. In particular, if $T(x)$ is chosen such that the origin $(\eta = 0, \ \xi = 0)$ is an equilibrium point of (13.16)–(13.18), then the system is said to be minimum phase if the origin of the zero dynamics (13.21) is asymptotically stable. It is useful to know that the zero dynamics can be characterized in the original coordinates. Noting that

$$y(t) \equiv 0 \Rightarrow \xi(t) \equiv 0 \Rightarrow u(t) \equiv \alpha(x(t))$$

we see that if the output is identically zero, the solution of the state equation must be confined to the set

$$Z^* = \{x \in D_0 \mid h(x) = L_f h(x) = \cdots = L_f^{\rho-1} h(x) = 0\}$$

and the input must be

$$u = u^*(x) \stackrel{\text{def}}{=} \alpha(x)|_{x \in Z^*}$$

The restricted motion of the system is described by

$$\dot{x} = f^*(x) \stackrel{\text{def}}{=} [f(x) + g(x)\alpha(x)]_{x \in Z^*}$$

In the special case $\rho = n$, the normal form (13.16)–(13.18) reduces

$$\dot{z} = A_c z + B_c \gamma(x)[u - \alpha(x)] \tag{13.22}$$
$$y = C_c z \tag{13.23}$$

where $z = \xi = [h(x), \cdots, L_f^{n-1} h(x)]^T$ and the η variable does not exist. In this case, the system has no zero dynamics and, by default, is said to be minimum phase.

Example 13.5 Consider the controlled van der Pol equation

$$\begin{aligned}
\dot{x}_1 &= x_2 \\
\dot{x}_2 &= -x_1 + \varepsilon(1 - x_1^2)x_2 + u \\
y &= x_2
\end{aligned}$$

We have seen in Example 13.1 that the system has relative degree one in R^2. Taking $\xi = y$ and $\eta = x_1$, we see that the system is already in the normal form. The zero dynamics are given by $\dot{x}_1 = 0$, which does not have an asymptotically stable equilibrium point. Hence, the system is not minimum phase. $\triangle$

Example 13.6 The system

$$\begin{aligned}
\dot{x}_1 &= -x_1 + \frac{2 + x_3^2}{1 + x_3^2}\, u \\
\dot{x}_2 &= x_3 \\
\dot{x}_3 &= x_1 x_3 + u \\
y &= x_2
\end{aligned}$$

has an open-loop equilibrium point at the origin. The derivatives of the output are

$$\begin{aligned}
\dot{y} &= \dot{x}_2 = x_3 \\
\ddot{y} &= \dot{x}_3 = x_1 x_3 + u
\end{aligned}$$

Therefore, the system has relative degree two in R^3. Using $L_g L_f h(x) = 1$ and $L_f^2 h(x) = x_1 x_3$ in (13.20), we obtain

$$\gamma = 1 \quad \text{and} \quad \alpha(x) = -x_1 x_3$$

To characterize the zero dynamics, restrict x to

$$Z^* = \{x \in R^3 \mid x_2 = x_3 = 0\}$$

and take $u = u^*(x) = 0$. This process yields

$$\dot{x}_1 = -x_1$$

which shows that the system is minimum phase. To transform it into the normal form, we want to choose a function $\phi(x)$ such that

$$\phi(0) = 0, \quad \frac{\partial \phi}{\partial x} g(x) = 0$$

and

$$T(x) = \begin{bmatrix} \phi(x) & x_2 & x_3 \end{bmatrix}^T$$

is a diffeomorphism on some domain containing the origin. The partial differential equation

$$\frac{\partial \phi}{\partial x_1} \cdot \frac{2 + x_3^2}{1 + x_3^2} + \frac{\partial \phi}{\partial x_3} = 0$$

can be solved by separating variables to obtain

$$\phi(x) = -x_1 + x_3 + \tan^{-1} x_3$$

which satisfies the condition $\phi(0) = 0$. The mapping $T(x)$ is a global diffeomorphism, as can be seen by the fact that for any $z \in R^3$, the equation $T(x) = z$ has a unique solution. Thus, the normal form

$$
\begin{aligned}
\dot{\eta} &= \left(-\eta + \xi_2 + \tan^{-1} \xi_2\right)\left(1 + \frac{2 + \xi_2^2}{1 + \xi_2^2}\xi_2\right) \\
\dot{\xi}_1 &= \xi_2 \\
\dot{\xi}_2 &= \left(-\eta + \xi_2 + \tan^{-1} \xi_2\right)\xi_2 + u \\
y &= \xi_1
\end{aligned}
$$

is defined globally. $\triangle$

Example 13.7 The field-controlled DC motor of Example 13.3 has relative degree two in $D_0 = \{x \in R^3 \mid x_2 \neq 0\}$. Using (13.20), we obtain

$$\gamma = \theta x_2 \quad \text{and} \quad \alpha(x) = -\frac{\theta x_2(-a x_1) + \theta x_1(-b x_2 + k - c x_1 x_3)}{\theta x_2}$$

To characterize the zero dynamics, restrict x to

$$Z^* = \{x \in D_0 \mid x_3 = 0 \text{ and } x_1 x_2 = 0\} = \{x \in D_0 \mid x_3 = 0 \text{ and } x_1 = 0\}$$

and take $u = u^*(x) = 0$, to obtain

$$\dot{x}_2 = -b x_2 + k$$

The zero dynamics have an asymptotically stable equilibrium point at $x_2 = k/b$. Hence, the system is minimum phase. To transform it into the normal form, we want to find a function $\phi(x)$ such that $[\partial \phi / \partial x]g = \partial \phi / \partial x_1 = 0$ and $T = [\phi(x), x_3, \theta x_1 x_2]^T$ is a diffeomorphism on some domain $D_x \subset D_0$. The choice $\phi(x) = x_2 - k/b$ satisfies $\partial \phi / \partial x_1 = 0$, makes $T(x)$ a diffeomorphism on $D_x = \{x \in R^3 \mid x_2 > 0\}$, and transforms the equilibrium point of the zero dynamics to the origin. $\triangle$

Example 13.8 Consider a single-input–single-output nonlinear system represented by the nth-order differential equation

$$
\begin{aligned}
y^{(n)} &= p\left(z, z^{(1)}, \ldots, z^{(m-1)}, y, y^{(1)}, \ldots, y^{(n-1)}\right) \\
&\quad + q\left(z, z^{(1)}, \ldots, z^{(m-1)}, y, y^{(1)}, \ldots, y^{(n-1)}\right) z^{(m)}, \quad m < n \quad (13.24)
\end{aligned}
$$

where z is the input, y is the output, $p(\cdot)$ and $q(\cdot)$ are sufficiently smooth functions in a domain of interest, and $q(\cdot) \neq 0$. This nonlinear input–output model reduces to the transfer function model of Example 13.4 for linear systems. We extend the dynamics of the system by adding a series of m integrators at the input side and define $u = z^{(m)}$ as the control input of the extended system.[6] The extended system is of order $(n+m)$. A state model of the extended system can be obtained by taking the state variables as

$$
\zeta = \begin{bmatrix} z \\ z^{(1)} \\ \vdots \\ z^{(m-1)} \end{bmatrix}, \quad \xi = \begin{bmatrix} y \\ y^{(1)} \\ \vdots \\ \vdots \\ y^{(n-1)} \end{bmatrix}, \quad \text{and} \quad x = \begin{bmatrix} \zeta \\ \xi \end{bmatrix}
$$

The state model is given by

$$
\begin{aligned}
\dot{\zeta} &= A_u \zeta + B_u u \\
\dot{\xi} &= A_c \xi + B_c [p(x) + q(x)u] \\
y &= C_c \xi
\end{aligned}
$$

where (A_c, B_c, C_c) is a canonical form representation of a chain of n integrators and (A_u, B_u) is a controllable canonical pair that represents a chain of m integrators. Let $D \subset R^{n+m}$ be a domain over which p and q are sufficiently smooth and $q \neq 0$. Using the special structure of (A_c, B_c, C_c), it can be easily seen that

$$
y^{(i)} = C_c A_c^i \xi, \quad \text{for} \quad 1 \leq i \leq n-1, \quad \text{and} \quad y^{(n)} = p(x) + q(x)u
$$

Hence, the system has relative degree n. To find the zero dynamics, notice that $L_f^{i-1} h(x) = \xi_i$. Consequently, $Z^* = \{x \in R^{n+m} \mid \xi = 0\}$ and $u^*(x) = -p(x)/q(x)$ evaluated at $\xi = 0$. Thus, the zero dynamics are given by

$$
\dot{\zeta} = A_u \zeta + B_u u^*(x)
$$

Recalling the definition of ζ, it can be easily seen that $\zeta_1 = z$ satisfies the mth-order differential equation

$$
0 = p\left(z, z^{(1)}, \ldots, z^{(m-1)}, 0, 0, \ldots, 0\right) + q\left(z, z^{(1)}, \ldots, z^{(m-1)}, 0, 0, \ldots, 0\right) z^{(m)}
$$
$$
(13.25)
$$

which is the same equation obtained from (13.24) upon setting $y(t) \equiv 0$. For linear systems, (13.25) reduces to a linear differential equation that corresponds to the

---

[6]In this example, we show that the extended system is input–output linearizable, which allows us to design feedback control using input–output linearization techniques. When such control is applied to the original system, the m integrators become part of the dynamics of the controller.

numerator polynomial of the transfer function. The minimum phase property of the system can be determined by studying (13.25). To transform the system into the normal form, we note that ξ is already a vector of y and its derivatives up to $y^{(n-1)}$. So, we only need to find a function $\phi = \phi(\zeta, \xi) : R^{n+m} \to R^m$ such that

$$\frac{\partial \phi}{\partial \zeta} B_u + \frac{\partial \phi}{\partial \xi} B_c q(x) = 0$$

which is equivalent to

$$\frac{\partial \phi_i}{\partial \zeta_m} + \frac{\partial \phi_i}{\partial \xi_n} q(x) = 0, \quad \text{for } 1 \le i \le m \tag{13.26}$$

In some special cases, there are obvious solutions for these partial differential equations. For example, if q is constant, ϕ can be taken as

$$\phi_i = \zeta_i - \frac{1}{q} \xi_{n-m+i}, \quad \text{for } 1 \le i \le m$$

Another case is pursued in Exercise 13.5. △

13.3   Full-State Linearization

The single-input system

$$\dot{x} = f(x) + g(x)u \tag{13.27}$$

where f and g are sufficiently smooth in a domain $D \subset R^n$, is feedback linearizable if a sufficiently smooth function $h : D \to R$ exists such that the system

$$\dot{x} = f(x) + g(x)u \tag{13.28}$$
$$y = h(x) \tag{13.29}$$

has relative degree n in a region $D_0 \subset D$. This statement follows from the fact that for systems with relative degree n, the normal form reduces to

$$\dot{z} = A_c z + B_c \gamma(x)[u - \alpha(x)] \tag{13.30}$$
$$y = C_c z \tag{13.31}$$

On the other hand, if the system (13.27) is feedback linearizable per Definition 13.1, then there is a change of variables $\zeta = S(x)$ that transforms the system into

$$\dot{\zeta} = A\zeta + B\bar{\gamma}(x)[u - \bar{\alpha}(x)]$$

where (A, B) is controllable and $\bar{\gamma}(x) \ne 0$ in some domain. For any controllable pair (A, B), we can find a nonsingular matrix M that transforms (A, B) into a controllable canonical form;[7] that is, $MAM^{-1} = A_c + B_c\lambda^T$ and $MB = B_c$, where (A_c, B_c) represents a chain of n integrators. The change of variables

$$z = M\zeta = MS(x) \stackrel{\text{def}}{=} T(x)$$

transforms the system (13.27) into

$$\dot{z} = A_c z + B_c \gamma(x)[u - \alpha(x)]$$

where $\gamma(x) = \bar{\gamma}(x)$ and $\alpha(x) = \bar{\alpha}(x) - \lambda^T MS(x)/\gamma(x)$. Because

$$\dot{z} = \frac{\partial T}{\partial x}\dot{x}$$

the equality

$$A_c T(x) + B_c \gamma(x)[u - \alpha(x)] = \frac{\partial T}{\partial x}[f(x) + g(x)u]$$

must hold for all x and u in the domain of interest. By taking $u = 0$, we split the foregoing equation into two:

$$\frac{\partial T}{\partial x} f(x) = A_c T(x) - B_c \alpha(x)\gamma(x) \qquad\qquad (13.32)$$

$$\frac{\partial T}{\partial x} g(x) = B_c \gamma(x) \qquad\qquad (13.33)$$

Equation (13.32) is equivalent to

$$\frac{\partial T_1}{\partial x} f(x) = T_2(x)$$

$$\frac{\partial T_2}{\partial x} f(x) = T_3(x)$$

$$\vdots$$

$$\frac{\partial T_{n-1}}{\partial x} f(x) = T_n(x)$$

$$\frac{\partial T_n}{\partial x} f(x) = -\alpha(x)\gamma(x)$$

and (13.33) is equivalent to

$$\frac{\partial T_1}{\partial x} g(x) = 0$$

$$\frac{\partial T_2}{\partial x} g(x) = 0$$

$$\vdots$$

$$\frac{\partial T_{n-1}}{\partial x} g(x) = 0$$

$$\frac{\partial T_n}{\partial x} g(x) = \gamma(x) \neq 0$$

---

[7]See, for example, [158].

Setting $h(x) = T_1(x)$, we see that

$$T_{i+1}(x) = L_f T_i(x) = L_f^i h(x), \quad i = 1, 2, \ldots, n-1$$

$h(x)$ satisfies the partial differential equations

$$L_g L_f^{i-1} h(x) = 0, \quad i = 1, 2, \ldots, n-1 \tag{13.34}$$

subject to the condition

$$L_g L_f^{n-1} h(x) \neq 0 \tag{13.35}$$

and α, γ are given by

$$\gamma(x) = L_g L_f^{n-1} h(x), \quad \alpha(x) = - \frac{L_f^n h(x)}{L_g L_f^{n-1} h(x)} \tag{13.36}$$

In summary, the system (13.27) is feedback linearizable if and only if a function $h(x)$ exists such that the system (13.28)–(13.29) has relative degree n, or, equivalently, h satisfies the partial differential equations (13.34) subject to the condition (13.35). The existence of h can be characterized by necessary and sufficient conditions on the vector fields f and g. These conditions use the notions of *Lie brackets* and *invariant distributions*, which we introduce next.

For two vector fields f and g on $D \subset R^n$, the *Lie bracket* $[f, g]$ is a third vector field defined by

$$[f, g](x) = \frac{\partial g}{\partial x} f(x) - \frac{\partial f}{\partial x} g(x)$$

where $[\partial g/\partial x]$ and $[\partial f/\partial x]$ are Jacobian matrices. We may repeat bracketing of g with f. The following notation is used to simplify this process:

$$\begin{aligned}
ad_f^0 g(x) &= g(x) \\
ad_f g(x) &= [f, g](x) \\
ad_f^k g(x) &= [f, ad_f^{k-1} g](x), \quad k \geq 1
\end{aligned}$$

It is obvious that $[f, g] = -[g, f]$ and for constant vector fields f and g, $[f, g] = 0$.

Example 13.9 Let

$$f(x) = \begin{bmatrix} x_2 \\ -\sin x_1 - x_2 \end{bmatrix}, \quad g = \begin{bmatrix} 0 \\ x_1 \end{bmatrix}$$

Then,

$$\begin{aligned}
[f, g](x) &= \begin{bmatrix} 0 & 0 \\ 1 & 0 \end{bmatrix} \begin{bmatrix} x_2 \\ -\sin x_1 - x_2 \end{bmatrix} - \begin{bmatrix} 0 & 1 \\ -\cos x_1 & -1 \end{bmatrix} \begin{bmatrix} 0 \\ x_1 \end{bmatrix} \\
&= \begin{bmatrix} -x_1 \\ x_1 + x_2 \end{bmatrix} \stackrel{\text{def}}{=} ad_f g
\end{aligned}$$

$$\begin{aligned}
ad_f^2 g &= [f, ad_f g] \\
&= \begin{bmatrix} -1 & 0 \\ 1 & 1 \end{bmatrix} \begin{bmatrix} x_2 \\ -\sin x_1 - x_2 \end{bmatrix} - \begin{bmatrix} 0 & 1 \\ -\cos x_1 & -1 \end{bmatrix} \begin{bmatrix} -x_1 \\ x_1 + x_2 \end{bmatrix} \\
&= \begin{bmatrix} -x_1 - 2x_2 \\ x_1 + x_2 - \sin x_1 - x_1 \cos x_1 \end{bmatrix}
\end{aligned}$$

$\triangle$

Example 13.10 If $f(x) = Ax$ and g is a constant vector field, then

$$ad_f g(x) = [f, g](x) = -Ag$$

$$ad_f^2 g = [f, ad_f g] = -A(-Ag) = A^2 g$$

and

$$ad_f^k g = (-1)^k A^k g$$

$\triangle$

For vector fields f_1, f_2, ..., f_k on $D \subset R^n$, let

$$\Delta(x) = \text{span}\{f_1(x), f_2(x), \ldots, f_k(x)\}$$

be the subspace of R^n spanned by the vectors $f_1(x)$, $f_2(x)$, ..., $f_k(x)$ at any fixed $x \in D$. The collection of all vector spaces $\Delta(x)$ for $x \in D$ is called a distribution and referred to by

$$\Delta = \text{span}\{f_1, f_2, \ldots, f_k\}$$

The dimension of $\Delta(x)$, defined by

$$\dim(\Delta(x)) = \text{rank } [f_1(x), f_2(x), \ldots, f_k(x)]$$

may vary with x, but if $\Delta = \text{span}\{f_1, \ldots, f_k\}$, where $\{f_1(x), \ldots, f_k(x)\}$ are linearly independent for all $x \in D$, then $\dim(\Delta(x)) = k$ for all $x \in D$. In this case, we say that Δ is a nonsingular distribution on D, generated by f_1, ..., f_k. A distribution Δ is *involutive* if

$$g_1 \in \Delta \text{ and } g_2 \in \Delta \Rightarrow [g_1, g_2] \in \Delta$$

If Δ is a nonsingular distribution on D, generated by f_1, ..., f_k, then it can be verified (Exercise 13.9) that Δ is involutive if and only if

$$[f_i, f_j] \in \Delta, \quad \forall \, 1 \leq i, j \leq k$$

Example 13.11 Let $D = R^3$ and $\Delta = \text{span}\{f_1, f_2\}$, where

$$f_1 = \begin{bmatrix} 2x_2 \\ 1 \\ 0 \end{bmatrix}, \quad f_2 = \begin{bmatrix} 1 \\ 0 \\ x_2 \end{bmatrix}$$

It can be verified that $\dim(\Delta(x)) = 2$ for all $x \in D$ and

$$[f_1, f_2] = \frac{\partial f_2}{\partial x} f_1 - \frac{\partial f_1}{\partial x} f_2 = \begin{bmatrix} 0 \\ 0 \\ 1 \end{bmatrix}$$

$[f_1, f_2] \in \Delta$ if and only if rank $[f_1(x), f_2(x), [f_1, f_2](x)] = 2$, for all $x \in D$. However,

$$\text{rank } [f_1(x), f_2(x), [f_1, f_2](x)] = \text{rank} \begin{bmatrix} 2x_2 & 1 & 0 \\ 1 & 0 & 0 \\ 0 & x_2 & 1 \end{bmatrix} = 3, \quad \forall \, x \in D$$

Hence, Δ is not involutive. $\triangle$

Example 13.12 Let $D = \{x \in R^3 \mid x_1^2 + x_3^2 \neq 0\}$ and $\Delta = \text{span}\{f_1, f_2\}$, where

$$f_1 = \begin{bmatrix} 2x_3 \\ -1 \\ 0 \end{bmatrix}, \quad f_2 = \begin{bmatrix} -x_1 \\ -2x_2 \\ x_3 \end{bmatrix}$$

It can be verified that $\dim(\Delta(x)) = 2$ for all $x \in D$,

$$[f_1, f_2] = \frac{\partial f_2}{\partial x} f_1 - \frac{\partial f_1}{\partial x} f_2 = \begin{bmatrix} -4x_3 \\ 2 \\ 0 \end{bmatrix}$$

and

$$\text{rank } [f_1(x), f_2(x), [f_1, f_2](x)] = \text{rank} \begin{bmatrix} 2x_3 & -x_1 & -4x_3 \\ -1 & -2x_2 & 2 \\ 0 & x_3 & 0 \end{bmatrix} = 2, \quad \forall \, x \in D$$

Therefore, $[f_1, f_2] \in \Delta$. Since $[f_2, f_1] = -[f_1, f_2]$, we conclude that Δ is involutive. $\triangle$

We are now ready to characterize the class of feedback linearizable systems.

Theorem 13.2 *The system* (13.27) *is feedback linearizable if and only if there is a domain $D_0 \subset D$ such that*

1. the matrix $\mathcal{G}(x) = [g(x), ad_f g(x), \ldots, ad_f^{n-1} g(x)]$ has rank n for all $x \in D_0$;

2. *the distribution* $\mathcal{D} = \text{span} \{g, ad_f g, \ldots, ad_f^{n-2} g\}$ *is involutive in* D_0.   ◇

Proof: See Appendix C.22.

In the next three examples, we illustrate the application of Theorem 13.2 and the solution of the partial differential equations (13.34). In all examples, we assume that the system (13.27) has an equilibrium point x^* when $u = 0$. We choose $h(x)$ such that $h(x^*) = 0$. Consequently, the change of variables $z = T(x)$ maps the equilibrium point $x = x^*$ into the origin $z = 0$.

Example 13.13 Reconsider the system

$$\dot{x} = \begin{bmatrix} a \sin x_2 \\ -x_1^2 \end{bmatrix} + \begin{bmatrix} 0 \\ 1 \end{bmatrix} u \stackrel{\text{def}}{=} f(x) + gu$$

from Section 13.1. We have

$$ad_f g = [f, g] = -\frac{\partial f}{\partial x} g = \begin{bmatrix} -a \cos x_2 \\ 0 \end{bmatrix}$$

The matrix

$$\mathcal{G} = [g, ad_f g] = \begin{bmatrix} 0 & -a \cos x_2 \\ 1 & 0 \end{bmatrix}$$

has rank two for all x such that $\cos x_2 \neq 0$. The distribution $\mathcal{D} = \text{span}\{g\}$ is involutive. Hence, the conditions of Theorem 13.2 are satisfied in the domain $D_0 = \{x \in R^2 \mid \cos x_2 \neq 0\}$. To find the change of variables that transforms the system into the form (13.6), we want to find $h(x)$ that satisfies

$$\frac{\partial h}{\partial x} g = 0; \quad \frac{\partial (L_f h)}{\partial x} g \neq 0, \quad \text{and} \quad h(0) = 0$$

From the condition $[\partial h/\partial x]g = 0$, we have

$$\frac{\partial h}{\partial x} g = \frac{\partial h}{\partial x_2} = 0$$

Thus, h must be independent of x_2. Therefore,

$$L_f h(x) = \frac{\partial h}{\partial x_1} a \sin x_2$$

The condition

$$\frac{\partial (L_f h)}{\partial x} g = \frac{\partial (L_f h)}{\partial x_2} = \frac{\partial h}{\partial x_1} a \cos x_2 \neq 0$$

is satisfied in the domain D_0 by any choice of h for which $(\partial h/\partial x_1) \neq 0$. Taking $h(x) = x_1$ results in the transformation we used earlier. Other choices of h can be made. For example, $h(x) = x_1 + x_1^3$ gives another change of variables that transforms the system into the form (13.6).   △

Example 13.14 A single link manipulator with flexible joints and negligible damping can be represented by a fourth-order model of the form (Exercise 1.5)

$$\dot{x} = f(x) + gu$$

where

$$f(x) = \begin{bmatrix} x_2 \\ -a\sin x_1 - b(x_1 - x_3) \\ x_4 \\ c(x_1 - x_3) \end{bmatrix}, \quad g = \begin{bmatrix} 0 \\ 0 \\ 0 \\ d \end{bmatrix}$$

and a, b, c, and d are positive constants. The unforced system has equilibrium at $x = 0$. We have

$$ad_f g = [f, g] = -\frac{\partial f}{\partial x} g = \begin{bmatrix} 0 \\ 0 \\ -d \\ 0 \end{bmatrix}$$

$$ad_f^2 g = [f, ad_f g] = -\frac{\partial f}{\partial x} ad_f g = \begin{bmatrix} 0 \\ bd \\ 0 \\ -cd \end{bmatrix}$$

$$ad_f^3 g = [f, ad_f^2 g] = -\frac{\partial f}{\partial x} ad_f^2 g = \begin{bmatrix} -bd \\ 0 \\ cd \\ 0 \end{bmatrix}$$

The matrix

$$\mathcal{G} = [g, ad_f g, ad_f^2 g, ad_f^3 g] = \begin{bmatrix} 0 & 0 & 0 & -bd \\ 0 & 0 & bd & 0 \\ 0 & -d & 0 & cd \\ d & 0 & -cd & 0 \end{bmatrix}$$

has full rank for all $x \in R^4$. The distribution $\Delta = \text{span}(g, ad_f g, ad_f^2)$ is involutive, since g, $ad_f g$, and $ad_f^2 g$ are constant vector fields. Thus, the conditions of Theorem 13.2 are satisfied for all $x \in R^4$. To find the change of variables that transforms the state equation into the form (13.6), we want to find $h(x)$ that satisfies

$$\frac{\partial(L_f^{i-1} h)}{\partial x} g = 0, \quad i = 1, 2, 3, \quad \frac{\partial(L_f^3 h)}{\partial x} g \neq 0, \quad \text{and} \quad h(0) = 0$$

From the condition $[\partial h/\partial x]g = 0$, we have $(\partial h/\partial x_4) = 0$, so we must choose h independent of x_4. Therefore,

$$L_f h(x) = \frac{\partial h}{\partial x_1} x_2 + \frac{\partial h}{\partial x_2}[-a\sin x_1 - b(x_1 - x_3)] + \frac{\partial h}{\partial x_3} x_4$$

From the condition $[\partial(L_f h)/\partial x]g = 0$, we have

$$\frac{\partial(L_f h)}{\partial x_4} = 0 \;\Rightarrow\; \frac{\partial h}{\partial x_3} = 0$$

So, we choose h independent of x_3. Therefore, $L_f h$ simplifies to

$$L_f h(x) = \frac{\partial h}{\partial x_1} x_2 + \frac{\partial h}{\partial x_2}[-a\sin x_1 - b(x_1 - x_3)]$$

and

$$L_f^2 h(x) = \frac{\partial(L_f h)}{\partial x_1} x_2 + \frac{\partial(L_f h)}{\partial x_2}[-a\sin x_1 - b(x_1 - x_3)] + \frac{\partial(L_f h)}{\partial x_3} x_4$$

Finally,

$$\frac{\partial(L_f^2 h)}{\partial x_4} = 0 \;\Rightarrow\; \frac{\partial(L_f h)}{\partial x_3} = 0 \;\Rightarrow\; \frac{\partial h}{\partial x_2} = 0$$

and we choose h independent of x_2. Hence,

$$L_f^3 h(x) = \frac{\partial(L_f^2 h)}{\partial x_1} x_2 + \frac{\partial(L_f^2 h)}{\partial x_2}[-a\sin x_1 - b(x_1 - x_3)] + \frac{\partial(L_f^2 h)}{\partial x_3} x_4$$

and the condition $[\partial(L_f^3 h)/\partial x]g \neq 0$ is satisfied whenever $(\partial h/\partial x_1) \neq 0$. Therefore, we take $h(x) = x_1$. The change of variables

$$
\begin{aligned}
z_1 &= h(x) &=& x_1 \\
z_2 &= L_f h(x) &=& x_2 \\
z_3 &= L_f^2 h(x) &=& -a\sin x_1 - b(x_1 - x_3) \\
z_4 &= L_f^3 h(x) &=& -ax_2\cos x_1 - b(x_2 - x_4)
\end{aligned}
$$

transforms the state equation into

$$
\begin{aligned}
\dot{z}_1 &= z_2 \\
\dot{z}_2 &= z_3 \\
\dot{z}_3 &= z_4 \\
\dot{z}_4 &= -(a\cos z_1 + b + c)z_3 + a(z_2^2 - c)\sin z_1 + bdu
\end{aligned}
$$

which is of the form (13.6). Unlike the previous example, in the current one the state equation in the z-coordinates is valid globally because $z = T(x)$ is a global diffeomorphism.   △

Example 13.15 In Examples 13.3 and 13.7 we considered a field-controlled DC motor represented by the third-order model

$$\dot{x} = f(x) + gu$$

where

$$f(x) = \begin{bmatrix} -ax_1 \\ -bx_2 + k - cx_1x_3 \\ \theta x_1 x_2 \end{bmatrix}, \quad g = \begin{bmatrix} 1 \\ 0 \\ 0 \end{bmatrix}$$

and a, b, c, θ, and k are positive constants. We saw that, with the output $y = x_3$, the system has relative degree two and hence is partially feedback linearizable. Let us investigate whether the state equation is fully linearizable. We have

$$ad_f g = [f, g] = \begin{bmatrix} a \\ cx_3 \\ -\theta x_2 \end{bmatrix}; \quad ad_f^2 g = [f, ad_f g] = \begin{bmatrix} a^2 \\ (a+b)cx_3 \\ (b-a)\theta x_2 - \theta k \end{bmatrix}$$

The determinant of

$$\mathcal{G} = [g, ad_f g, ad_f^2 g] = \begin{bmatrix} 1 & a & a^2 \\ 0 & cx_3 & (a+b)cx_3 \\ 0 & -\theta x_2 & (b-a)\theta x_2 - \theta k \end{bmatrix}$$

is given by

$$\det \mathcal{G} = c\theta(-k + 2bx_2)x_3$$

Hence, $\mathcal{G}$ has rank three for $x_2 \neq k/2b$ and $x_3 \neq 0$. The distribution $\mathcal{D} = \text{span}\{g, ad_f g\}$ is involutive if $[g, ad_f g] \in \mathcal{D}$. We have

$$[g, ad_f g] = \frac{\partial(ad_f g)}{\partial x} g = \begin{bmatrix} 0 & 0 & 0 \\ 0 & 0 & c \\ 0 & -\theta & 0 \end{bmatrix} \begin{bmatrix} 1 \\ 0 \\ 0 \end{bmatrix} = \begin{bmatrix} 0 \\ 0 \\ 0 \end{bmatrix}$$

Hence, $\mathcal{D}$ is involutive and the conditions of Theorem 13.2 are satisfied in the domain

$$D_0 = \{x \in R^3 \mid x_2 > \frac{k}{2b} \text{ and } x_3 > 0\}$$

We proceed now to find a function h that satisfies (13.34) and (13.35). The unforced system has an equilibrium set at $x_1 = 0$ and $x_2 = k/b$. We take the desired operating point as $x^* = [0, k/b, \omega_0]^T$, where ω_0 is a desired set point for the angular velocity x_3. We want to find $h(x)$ that satisfies

$$\frac{\partial h}{\partial x} g = 0; \quad \frac{\partial(L_f h)}{\partial x} g = 0; \quad \frac{\partial(L_f^2 h)}{\partial x} g \neq 0$$

with $h(x^*) = 0$, From the condition

$$\frac{\partial h}{\partial x} g = \frac{\partial h}{\partial x_1} = 0$$

we see that h must be independent of x_1. Therefore,

$$L_f h(x) = \frac{\partial h}{\partial x_2}[-bx_2 + k - cx_1x_3] + \frac{\partial h}{\partial x_3}\theta x_1 x_2$$

From the condition $[\partial(L_f h)/\partial x]g = 0$, we have

$$cx_3 \frac{\partial h}{\partial x_2} = \theta x_2 \frac{\partial h}{\partial x_3}$$

which is satisfied if h takes the form

$$h = c_1[\theta x_2^2 + cx_3^2] + c_2$$

for some constants c_1 and c_2. We choose $c_1 = 1$ and, to satisfy the condition $h(x^*) = 0$, we take

$$c_2 = -\theta\left(x_2^*\right)^2 - c\left(x_3^*\right)^2 = -\theta(k/b)^2 - c\omega_0^2$$

With this choice of h, $L_f h$ and $L_f^2 h$ are given by

$$L_f h(x) = 2\theta x_2(k - bx_2), \quad L_f^2 h(x) = 2\theta(k - 2bx_2)(-bx_2 + k - cx_1 x_3)$$

Hence,

$$\frac{\partial(L_f^2 h)}{\partial x}g = \frac{\partial(L_f^2 h)}{\partial x_1} = -2c\theta(k - 2bx_2)x_3$$

and the condition $[\partial(L_f^2 h)/\partial x]g \neq 0$ is satisfied whenever $x_2 \neq k/2b$ and $x_3 \neq 0$. Assuming $x_3^* > 0$, it can be easily verified (Exercise 13.15) that the map $z = T(x)$ is a diffeomorphism on D_0 and the state equation in the z-coordinates is well defined in the domain

$$D_z = T(D_0) = \left\{ z \in R^3 \mid z_1 > \theta\phi^2(z_2) - \theta(k/b)^2 - c\omega_0^2 \text{ and } z_2 < \frac{\theta k^2}{2b} \right\}$$

where $\phi(\cdot)$ is the inverse of the map $2\theta x_2(k - bx_2)$, which is well defined for $x_2 > k/2b$. The domain D_z contains the origin $z = 0$. $\triangle$

13.4   State Feedback Control

13.4.1   Stabilization

Consider a partially feedback linearizable system of the form

$$\dot{\eta} = f_0(\eta, \xi) \tag{13.37}$$
$$\dot{\xi} = A\xi + B\gamma(x)[u - \alpha(x)] \tag{13.38}$$

where

$$z = \begin{bmatrix} \eta \\ \xi \end{bmatrix} = T(x) = \begin{bmatrix} T_1(x) \\ T_2(x) \end{bmatrix}$$

$T(x)$ is a diffeomorphism on a domain $D \subset R^n$, $D_z = T(D)$ contains the origin, (A, B) is controllable, $\gamma(x)$ is nonsingular for all $x \in D$, $f_0(0,0) = 0$, and $f_0(\eta, \xi)$,

$\alpha(x)$, and $\gamma(x)$ are continuously differentiable. Our goal is to design a state feedback control law to stabilize the origin $z = 0$. The form (13.37)–(13.38) is clearly motivated by the normal form (13.16)–(13.18) of input–output linearizable systems. However, (13.18) is dropped since the output y plays no role in the state feedback stabilization problem. The system (13.37)–(13.38) includes also feedback linearizable systems by dropping equation (13.37). We do not restrict our discussions to single-input systems or to a pair (A, B) in the controllable canonical form. We proceed to discuss the more general system (13.37)–(13.38) and our conclusions will apply to the normal form (13.16)–(13.18) or to feedback linearizable systems as special cases.

The state feedback control

$$u = \alpha(x) + \beta(x)v$$

where $\beta(x) = \gamma^{-1}(x)$, reduces (13.37)–(13.38) to the "triangular" system

$$\dot{\eta} = f_0(\eta, \xi) \tag{13.39}$$
$$\dot{\xi} = A\xi + Bv \tag{13.40}$$

Equation (13.40) can be easily stabilized by $v = -K\xi$, where K is designed such that $(A - BK)$ is Hurwitz. Asymptotic stability of the origin of the full closed-loop system

$$\dot{\eta} = f_0(\eta, \xi) \tag{13.41}$$
$$\dot{\xi} = (A - BK)\xi \tag{13.42}$$

follows from asymptotic stability of the origin of $\dot{\eta} = f_0(\eta, 0)$, as shown in the next lemma.

Lemma 13.1 *The origin of* (13.41)–(13.42) *is asymptotically stable if the origin of* $\dot{\eta} = f_0(\eta, 0)$ *is asymptotically stable.* ◇

Proof: By (the converse Lyapunov) Theorem 4.16, there is a continuously differentiable Lyapunov function $V_1(\eta)$ such that

$$\frac{\partial V_1}{\partial \eta} f_0(\eta, 0) \leq -\alpha_3(\|\eta\|)$$

in some neighborhood of $\eta = 0$, where α_3 is a class $\mathcal{K}$ function. Let $P = P^T > 0$ be the solution of the Lyapunov equation $P(A - BK) + (A - BK)^T P = -I$ and use $V(\eta, \xi) = V_1(\eta) + k\sqrt{\xi^T P \xi}$, with $k > 0$, as a Lyapunov function candidate for (13.41)–(13.42).[8] The derivative $\dot{V}$ is given by

$$\dot{V} = \frac{\partial V_1}{\partial \eta} f_0(\eta, \xi) + \frac{k}{2\sqrt{\xi^T P \xi}} \xi^T [P(A - BK) + (A - BK)^T P]\xi$$

---

[8]The function $V(\eta, \xi)$ is continuously differentiable everywhere around the origin, except on the manifold $\xi = 0$. Both $V(\eta, \xi)$ and $\dot{V}(\eta, \xi)$ are defined and continuous around the origin. It can be easily seen that the statement of Theorem 4.1 is still valid.

$$= \frac{\partial V_1}{\partial \eta} f_0(\eta, 0) + \frac{\partial V_1}{\partial \eta} [f_0(\eta, \xi) - f_0(\eta, 0)] - \frac{k \xi^T \xi}{2\sqrt{\xi^T P \xi}}$$

On any bounded neighborhood of the origin, we can use continuous differentiability of V_1 and f_0 to obtain

$$\dot{V} \leq -\alpha_3(\|\eta\|) + k_1\|\xi\| - kk_2\|\xi\|$$

for some positive constants k_1 and k_2. Choosing $k > k_1/k_2$ ensures that $\dot{V}$ is negative definite. Hence, the origin is asymptotically stable. $\square$

The foregoing discussion shows that a minimum phase input–output linearizable system can be stabilized by the state feedback control

$$u = \alpha(x) - \beta(x)KT_2(x) \tag{13.43}$$

The control (13.43) is independent of $T_1(x)$. Therefore, it is independent of the function ϕ that satisfies the partial differential equation (13.15).

The proof of Lemma 13.1 is valid only on bounded sets. Hence, it cannot be extended to show global asymptotic stability. We can show global asymptotic stability by requiring the system $\dot{\eta} = f_0(\eta, \xi)$ to be input-to-state stable when ξ is viewed as the input.

Lemma 13.2 *The origin of* (13.41)–(13.42) *is globally asymptotically stable if the system* $\dot{\eta} = f_0(\eta, \xi)$ *is input-to-state stable* $\diamond$

Proof: Apply Lemma 4.7. $\square$

Input-to-state stability of $\dot{\eta} = f_0(\eta, \xi)$ does not follow from global asymptotic, or even exponential, stability of the origin of $\dot{\eta} = f_0(\eta, 0)$, as we saw in Section 4.10. Consequently, knowing that an input–output linearizable system is "globally" minimum phase does not automatically guarantee that the control (13.43) will globally stabilize the system. It will be globally stabilizing if the origin of $\dot{\eta} = f_0(\eta, 0)$ is globally exponentially stable and $f_0(\eta, \xi)$ is globally Lipschitz in (η, ξ), since in that case Lemma 4.6 confirms that the system $\dot{\eta} = f_0(\eta, \xi)$ will be input-to-state stable. Otherwise, we have to establish input-to-state stability by further analysis. Global Lipschitz conditions are sometimes referred to as *linear growth conditions*. The next two examples illustrate some of the difficulties that may arise in the absence of linear growth conditions.

Example 13.16 Consider the second-order system

$$\begin{aligned} \dot{\eta} &= -\eta + \eta^2 \xi \\ \dot{\xi} &= v \end{aligned}$$

While the origin of $\dot{\eta} = -\eta$ is globally exponentially stable, the system $\dot{\eta} = -\eta + \eta^2 \xi$ is not input-to-state stable. This fact can be seen by noting that $\xi(t) \equiv 1$ and

$\eta(0) \geq 2$ imply that $\dot{\eta}(t) \geq 2$. Therefore, η grows unbounded. On the other hand, by Lemma 13.1, we see that the linear control $v = -k\xi$, with $k > 0$, stabilizes the origin of the full system. In fact, the origin will be exponentially stable. However, this linear control does not make the origin globally asymptotically stable. Taking $\nu = \eta\xi$ and noting that

$$\dot{\nu} = \eta\dot{\xi} + \dot{\eta}\xi = -k\eta\xi - \eta\xi + \eta^2\xi^2 = -(1+k)\nu + \nu^2$$

we see that the set $\{\eta\xi < 1+k\}$ is positively invariant. On the boundary $\eta\xi = 1+k$, the trajectory is given by $\eta(t) = e^{kt}\eta(0)$ and $\xi(t) = e^{-kt}\xi(0)$. Thus, $\eta(t)\xi(t) \equiv 1+k$. Inside the set $\{\eta\xi < 1+k\}$, $\nu(t)$ will be strictly decreasing and after a finite time T, $\nu(t) \leq 1/2$ for all $t \geq T$. Then, $\eta\dot{\eta} \leq -(1/2)\eta^2$, for all $t \geq T$, which shows that the trajectory approaches the origin as t tends to infinity. Hence, the set $\{\eta\xi < 1 + k\}$ is the exact region of attraction. While this conclusion shows that the origin is not globally asymptotically stable, it also shows that the region of attraction expands as k increases. In fact by choosing k large enough, we can include any compact set in the region of attraction. Thus, the linear feedback control $v = -k\xi$ can achieve semiglobal stabilization. $\triangle$

If the origin of $\dot{\eta} = f_0(\eta, 0)$ is globally asymptotically stable, one might think that the triangular system (13.39)–(13.40) can be globally stabilized, or at least semiglobally stabilized, by designing the linear feedback control $v = -K\xi$ to assign the eigenvalues of $(A - BK)$ far to the left in the complex plane so that the solution of $\dot{\xi} = (A - BK)\xi$ decays to zero arbitrarily fast. Then, the solution of $\dot{\xi} = f_0(\eta, \xi)$ will quickly approach the solution of $\dot{\eta} = f_0(\eta, 0)$, which is well behaved, because its origin is globally asymptotically stable. It may even appear that this strategy is the one used to achieve semiglobal stabilization in the preceding example. The next example shows why such strategy may fail.[9]

Example 13.17 Consider the third-order system

$$\begin{aligned}
\dot{\eta} &= -\tfrac{1}{2}(1 + \xi_2)\eta^3 \\
\dot{\xi}_1 &= \xi_2 \\
\dot{\xi}_2 &= v
\end{aligned}$$

The linear feedback control

$$v = -k^2\xi_1 - 2k\xi_2 \stackrel{\text{def}}{=} -K\xi$$

assigns the eigenvalues of

$$A - BK = \begin{bmatrix} 0 & 1 \\ -k^2 & -2k \end{bmatrix}$$

---

[9]See, however, Exercise 13.20 for a special case where this strategy will work.

at $-k$ and $-k$. The exponential matrix

$$e^{(A-BK)t} = \begin{bmatrix} (1+kt)e^{-kt} & te^{-kt} \\ -k^2te^{-kt} & (1-kt)e^{-kt} \end{bmatrix}$$

shows that as $k \to \infty$, the solution $\xi(t)$ will decay to zero arbitrarily fast. Notice, however, that the coefficient of the (2,1) element of the exponential matrix is a quadratic function of k. It can be shown that the absolute value of this element reaches a maximum value k/e at $t = 1/k$. While this term can be made to decay to zero arbitrarily fast by choosing k large, its transient behavior exhibits a peak of the order of k. The phenomenon is known as *the peaking phenomenon*.[10] The interaction of peaking with nonlinear growth could destabilize the system. In particular, for the initial states $\eta(0) = \eta_0$, $\xi_1(0) = 1$, and $\xi_2(0) = 0$, we have $\xi_2(t) = -k^2te^{-kt}$ and

$$\dot{\eta} = -\tfrac{1}{2}\left(1 - k^2te^{-kt}\right)\eta^3$$

During the peaking period, the coefficient of η^3 is positive, causing $|\eta(t)|$ to grow. Eventually, the coefficient of η^3 will become negative, but that might not happen soon enough, since the system might have a finite escape time. Indeed, the solution

$$\eta^2(t) = \frac{\eta_0^2}{1 + \eta_0^2[t + (1+kt)e^{-kt} - 1]}$$

shows that if $\eta_0^2 > 1$, the system will have a finite escape time if k is chosen large enough.   △

We will come back to the triangular system (13.39)–(13.40) in Sections 14.3 and 14.4 and show how to design v as a nonlinear function of ξ and η to achieve global stabilization. This will be done by using backstepping in Section 14.3 and passivity-based control in Section 14.4. We will even deal with cases where $\dot{\eta} = f_0(\eta,\xi)$ is not input-to-state stable.

While feedback linearization provides a simple and systematic procedure for stabilizing a class of nonlinear systems, there are legitimate concerns about the robustness and efficiency of such design. In the remainder of this section, we shed some light on these two issues.

Feedback linearization is based on exact mathematical cancellation of the nonlinear terms α and γ, which requires exact knowledge of α, $\beta = \gamma^{-1}$, and T_2. This is almost impossible for several practical reasons such as model simplification, parameter uncertainty, and computational errors. Most likely, the controller will be implementing functions $\hat{\alpha}$, $\hat{\beta}$, and $\hat{T}_2$, which are approximations of α, β, and T_2; that is to say, the actual controller will be implementing the feedback control law

$$u = \hat{\alpha}(x) - \hat{\beta}(x)K\hat{T}_2(x)$$

---

[10]To read more about the peaking phenomenon, see [188]. For an illustration of the peaking phenomenon in high-gain observers, see Section 14.5.

The closed-loop system under this feedback control is

$$\begin{aligned}
\dot{\eta} &= f_0(\eta, \xi) \\
\dot{\xi} &= A\xi + B\gamma(x)[\hat{\alpha}(x) - \hat{\beta}(x)K\hat{T}_2(x) - \alpha(x)]
\end{aligned}$$

By adding and subtracting the term $BK\xi$ to the right-hand side of the second equation, we can rewrite the closed-loop system as

$$\begin{aligned}
\dot{\eta} &= f_0(\eta, \xi) & (13.44) \\
\dot{\xi} &= (A - BK)\xi + B\delta(z) & (13.45)
\end{aligned}$$

where

$$\delta(z) = \gamma(x)\{\hat{\alpha}(x) - \alpha(x) + [\beta(x) - \hat{\beta}(x)]KT_2(x) + \hat{\beta}(x)K[T_2(x) - \hat{T}_2(x)]\}\Big|_{x=T^{-1}(z)}$$

Thus, the closed-loop system appears as a perturbation of the nominal system

$$\begin{aligned}
\dot{\eta} &= f_0(\eta, \xi) \\
\dot{\xi} &= (A - BK)\xi
\end{aligned}$$

In view of the perturbation results of Chapter 10, we do not expect a serious problem from a small error $\delta(z)$. The next two lemmas confirm this expectation. We start with feedback linearizable systems where the closed-loop equation simplifies to

$$\dot{z} = (A - BK)z + B\delta(z) \qquad (13.46)$$

Lemma 13.3 *Consider the closed-loop system* (13.46), *where* $(A - BK)$ *is Hurwitz. Let* $P = P^T > 0$ *be the solution of the Lyapunov equation*

$$P(A - BK) + (A - BK)^T P = -I$$

and k *be a nonnegative constant less than* $1/(2\|PB\|_2)$.

- *If* $\|\delta(z)\| \leq k\|z\|$ *for all* z, *the origin of* (13.46) *will be globally exponentially stable.*

- *If* $\|\delta(z)\| \leq k\|z\| + \varepsilon$ *for all* z, *the state* z *will be globally ultimately bounded by* εc *for some* $c > 0$.

Proof: Let $V(z) = z^T P z$. Then

$$\begin{aligned}
\dot{V} &= z^T[P(A - BK) + (A - BK)^T P]z + 2z^T PB\delta(z) \\
&\leq -\|z\|_2^2 + 2\|PB\|_2\|z\|_2\|\delta(z)\|_2
\end{aligned}$$

If $\|\delta(z)\|_2 \leq k\|z\|_2 + \varepsilon$, we have

$$\begin{aligned}
\dot{V} &\leq -\|z\|_2^2 + 2k\|PB\|_2\|z\|_2^2 + 2\varepsilon\|PB\|_2\|z\|_2 \\
&= -(1 - \theta_1)\|z\|_2^2 - \theta_1\|z\|_2^2 + 2k\|PB\|_2\|z\|_2^2 + 2\varepsilon\|PB\|_2\|z\|_2
\end{aligned}$$

where $\theta_1 \in (0,1)$ is chosen close enough to one such that $k < \theta_1/(2\|PB\|_2)$. Consequently,

$$\dot{V} \leq -(1 - \theta_1)\|z\|_2^2 + 2\varepsilon\|PB\|_2\|z\|_2$$

If $\|\delta(z)\|_2 \leq k\|z\|_2$, we set $\varepsilon = 0$ in the preceding inequality and conclude that the origin is globally exponentially stable. If $\varepsilon > 0$,

$$\dot{V} \leq -(1 - \theta_1)(1 - \theta_2)\|z\|_2^2, \quad \forall \, \|z\|_2 \geq \frac{2\varepsilon\|PB\|_2}{(1 - \theta_1)\theta_2} \overset{\text{def}}{=} \varepsilon c_0$$

where $\theta_2 \in (0,1)$. Application of Theorem 4.18 shows that $z(t)$ is globally ultimately bounded by $\varepsilon c_0 \sqrt{\lambda_{\max}(P)/\lambda_{\min}(P)}$. $\qquad \square$

It is clear from the proof that if the bound on $\delta(z)$ is satisfied only in a neighborhood of the origin, we can prove a local version of the lemma.

Example 13.18 Consider the pendulum equation

$$\begin{aligned} \dot{x}_1 &= x_2 \\ \dot{x}_2 &= -a\sin(x_1 + \delta_1) - bx_2 + cu \end{aligned}$$

where $x_1 = \theta - \delta_1$, $x_2 = \dot{\theta}$, and $u = T$ is a torque input. The goal is to stabilize the pendulum at the angle $\theta = \delta_1$. A linearizing–stabilizing feedback control is given by

$$u = \left(\frac{a}{c}\right)\sin(x_1 + \delta_1) - \left(\frac{1}{c}\right)(k_1x_1 + k_2x_2)$$

where k_1 and k_2 are chosen such that

$$A - BK = \begin{bmatrix} 0 & 1 \\ -k_1 & -(k_2 + b) \end{bmatrix}$$

is Hurwitz. Suppose that, due to uncertainties in the parameters a and c, the actual control is

$$u = \left(\frac{\hat{a}}{\hat{c}}\right)\sin(x_1 + \delta_1) - \left(\frac{1}{\hat{c}}\right)(k_1x_1 + k_2x_2)$$

where $\hat{a}$ and $\hat{c}$ are estimates of a and c. The closed-loop system is given by

$$\begin{aligned} \dot{x}_1 &= x_2 \\ \dot{x}_2 &= -k_1x_1 - (k_2 + b)x_2 + \delta(x) \end{aligned}$$

where

$$\delta(x) = \left(\frac{\hat{a}c - a\hat{c}}{\hat{c}}\right)\sin(x_1 + \delta_1) - \left(\frac{c - \hat{c}}{\hat{c}}\right)(k_1x_1 + k_2x_2)$$

The error term $\delta(x)$ satisfies the bound $|\delta(x)| \leq k\|x\|_2 + \varepsilon$ globally, where

$$k = \left|\frac{\hat{a}c - a\hat{c}}{\hat{c}}\right| + \left|\frac{c - \hat{c}}{\hat{c}}\right|\sqrt{k_1^2 + k_2^2}, \qquad \varepsilon = \left|\frac{\hat{a}c - a\hat{c}}{\hat{c}}\right||\sin\delta_1|$$

The constants k and ε are measures of the size of the error in estimating the parameters a and c. Let

$$P = \begin{bmatrix} p_{11} & p_{12} \\ p_{12} & p_{22} \end{bmatrix}$$

be the solution of the Lyapunov equation $P(A - BK) + (A - BK)^T P = -I$. If

$$k < \frac{1}{2\sqrt{p_{12}^2 + p_{22}^2}}$$

then the solutions of the system are globally ultimately bounded by a bound that is proportional to ε. If $\sin \delta_1 = 0$, the foregoing bound on k ensures global exponential stability of the origin. $\triangle$

We turn now to the more general closed-loop system (13.44)–(13.45).

Lemma 13.4 *Consider the closed-loop system* (13.44)–(13.45), *where* $A - BK$ *is Hurwitz.*

- *If* $\|\delta(z)\| \leq \varepsilon$ *for all* z *and* $\dot{\eta} = f_0(\eta, \xi)$ *is input-to-state stable, then the state* z *is globally ultimately bounded by a class* $\mathcal{K}$ *function of* ε.

- *If* $\|\delta(z)\| \leq k\|z\|$ *in some neighborhood of* $z = 0$, *with sufficiently small* k, *and the origin of* $\dot{\eta} = f_0(\eta, 0)$ *is exponentially stable, then* $z = 0$ *is an exponentially stable equilibrium point of the system* (13.44)–(13.45).

$\diamond$

Proof: Let $V(\xi) = \xi^T P \xi$, where $P = P^T > 0$ is the solution of the Lyapunov equation $P(A - BK) + (A - BK)^T P = -I$. Then

$$\begin{aligned} \dot{V} &= \xi^T [P(A - BK) + (A - BK)^T P]\xi + 2\xi^T PB\delta(z) \\ &\leq -\|\xi\|_2^2 + 2\|PB\|_2 \|\xi\|_2 \|\delta(z)\|_2 \end{aligned}$$

If $\|\delta(z)\|_2 \leq \varepsilon$, we have

$$\dot{V} \leq -\|\xi\|_2^2 + 2\varepsilon\|PB\|_2\|\xi\|_2 \leq -\tfrac{1}{2}\|\xi\|_2^2, \quad \forall \ \|\xi\|_2 \geq 4\varepsilon\|PB\|_2$$

Hence, applying Theorem 4.18 shows that a finite time t_0 and a positive constant c exist such that

$$\|\xi(t)\|_2 \leq c\varepsilon, \quad \forall \ t \geq t_0$$

By input-to-state stability of $\dot{\eta} = f_0(\eta, \xi)$, we have

$$\|\eta(t)\|_2 \leq \beta_0(\|\eta(t_0)\|_2, t - t_0) + \gamma_0(\sup_{t \geq t_0} \|\xi(t)\|_2) \leq \beta_0(\|\eta(t_0)\|_2, t - t_0) + \gamma_0(c\varepsilon)$$

where β_0 and γ_0 are class $\mathcal{KL}$ and class $\mathcal{K}$ functions, respectively. The term $\beta_0(\|\eta(t_0)\|_2, t - t_0)$ satisfies $\beta_0 \leq \varepsilon$ after some finite time. Therefore, $\|z(t)\|_2$ is ultimately bounded by $c\varepsilon + \varepsilon + \gamma_0(c\varepsilon)$, which is a class $\mathcal{K}$ function of ε. To prove the second case of the lemma, recall from Theorem 4.14 that a Lyapunov function $V_1(\eta)$ exists in some neighborhood of $\eta = 0$ such that

$$c_1\|\eta\|_2^2 \le V_1(\eta) \le c_2\|\eta\|_2^2, \quad \frac{\partial V_1}{\partial \eta}f_0(\eta,0) \le -c_3\|\eta\|_2^2, \quad \left\|\frac{\partial V_1}{\partial \eta}\right\|_2 \le c_4\|\eta\|_2$$

Using $V(z) = bV_1(\eta) + \xi^T P\xi$, with $b > 0$, as a Lyapunov function candidate for (13.44)–(13.45), we obtain

$$
\begin{aligned}
\dot{V} =\ & b\frac{\partial V_1}{\partial \eta}f_0(\eta,0) + b\frac{\partial V_1}{\partial \eta}[f_0(\eta,\xi) - f_0(\eta,0)] \\
& + \xi^T[P(A-BK) + (A-BK)^T P]\xi + 2\xi^T PB\delta(z) \\
\le\ & -bc_3\|\eta\|_2^2 + bc_4 L\|\eta\|_2\|\xi\|_2 - \|\xi\|_2^2 + 2k\|PB\|_2\|\xi\|_2^2 + 2k\|PB\|_2\|\xi\|_2\|\eta\|_2 \\
=\ & -\begin{bmatrix} \|\eta\|_2 \\ \|\xi\|_2 \end{bmatrix}^T \begin{bmatrix} bc_3 & -(k\|PB\|_2 + bc_4 L/2) \\ -(k\|PB\|_2 + bc_4 L/2) & 1 - 2k\|PB\|_2 \end{bmatrix}\begin{bmatrix} \|\eta\|_2 \\ \|\xi\|_2 \end{bmatrix} \\
\overset{\text{def}}{=}\ & -\begin{bmatrix} \|\eta\|_2 \\ \|\xi\|_2 \end{bmatrix}^T Q \begin{bmatrix} \|\eta\|_2 \\ \|\xi\|_2 \end{bmatrix}
\end{aligned}
$$

where L is a Lipschitz constant of f_0 with respect to ξ. Taking $b = k$, it can be verified that Q is positive definite for sufficiently small k. Therefore, the origin is exponentially stable. $\square$

In Exercises 13.22 through 13.24, we present a few variations of Lemma 13.4. If $\dot{\eta} = f_0(\eta,\xi)$ is not input-to-state stable, but the origin of $\dot{\eta} = f_0(\eta,0)$ is asymptotically stable, we can prove a local version of the first case of the lemma (Exercise 13.22). If $f(\eta,\xi)$ is globally Lipschitz and the origin of $\dot{\eta} = f_0(\eta,0)$ is globally exponentially stable, we can prove a global version of the second case (Exercise 13.23). If the origin of $\dot{\eta} = f_0(\eta,0)$ is asymptotically, but not exponentially, stable, we can prove asymptotic stability of the origin of the closed-loop system by restricting the dependence of δ on η (Exercise 13.24).

The feedback control $u = \alpha(x) - \beta(x)K\xi$ has a linearizing component $u = \alpha(x) + \beta(x)v$ and a stabilizing component $v = -K\xi$. The foregoing Lyapunov analysis shows that the stabilizing component achieves a certain degree of robustness to model uncertainty.[11] We will see in Chapter 14 that the stabilizing component can be designed to achieve a much higher degree of robustness by exploiting the fact that the perturbation term $B\delta(z)$ in (13.45) belongs to the range space of the input matrix B. Such perturbation is said to satisfy the *matching condition*. The techniques of Chapter 14 can guarantee robustness to any $\delta(z)$ provided an upper bound on δ is known.

---

[11]Another type of model uncertainty that is not considered here is the sensitivity of the relative degree and the minimum phase property to parameter perturbations. To read more about this issue, see [92] and [169].

The basic philosophy of feedback linearization is to cancel the nonlinear terms of the system. Aside from the issues of whether or not we can cancel the nonlinear terms, effect of uncertainties, implementation factors, and so on, we should examine the philosophy itself: Is it a good idea to cancel nonlinear terms? Our motivation to do so has been mathematically driven. We wanted to linearize the system to make it more tractable and to use the relatively well-developed linear control theory. From a performance viewpoint, however, a nonlinear term could be "good" or "bad" and the decision whether we should use feedback to cancel a nonlinear term is, in reality, problem dependent. Let us use a couple of examples to illustrate this point.

Example 13.19 Consider the scalar system

$$\dot{x} = ax - bx^3 + u$$

where a and b are positive constants. A linearizing–stabilizing feedback control can be taken as

$$u = -(k+a)x + bx^3, \quad k > 0$$

which results in the closed-loop system $\dot{x} = -kx$. This feedback control cancels the nonlinear term $-bx^3$, but this term provides "nonlinear damping." In fact, without any feedback control, such nonlinear damping would guarantee boundedness of the solutions despite the fact that the origin is unstable. So, why should we cancel it? If we simply use the linear control

$$u = -(k+a)x, \quad k > 0$$

we will obtain the closed-loop system

$$\dot{x} = -kx - bx^3$$

whose origin is globally exponentially stable and its trajectories approach the origin faster than the trajectories of $\dot{x} = -kx$. Moreover, the linear control is simpler and uses less control effort. $\triangle$

Example 13.20 Consider the second-order system

$$
\begin{aligned}
\dot{x}_1 &= x_2 \\
\dot{x}_2 &= -h(x_1) + u
\end{aligned}
$$

where $h(0) = 0$ and $x_1 h(x_1) > 0$ for all $x_1 \neq 0$. The system is clearly feedback linearizable and a linearizing–stabilizing feedback control can be taken as

$$u = h(x_1) - (k_1 x_1 + k_2 x_2)$$

where k_1 and k_2 are chosen to assign the closed-loop eigenvalues at desired locations in the left-half complex plane. On the other hand, our study of passive systems in Chapter 7 shows that with the feedback control

$$u = -\sigma(x_2)$$

where σ is any locally Lipschitz function that satisfies $\sigma(0) = 0$ and $y\sigma(y) > 0$ for $y \neq 0$, the closed-loop system will be passive, and the derivative of the Lyapunov function $V = \int_0^{x_1} h(z) \ dz + (1/2)x_2^2$ is given by

$$\dot{V} = -x_2\sigma(x_2)$$

Because

$$x_2(t) \equiv 0 \ \Rightarrow \ \dot{x}_2(t) \equiv 0 \ \Rightarrow \ h(x_1(t)) \equiv 0 \ \Rightarrow \ x_1(t) \equiv 0$$

asymptotic stability of the origin follows from the invariance principle. The control $u = -\sigma(x_2)$ has two advantages over the linearizing feedback control. First, it does not use a model of the nonlinear function h. Hence, it is robust to uncertainty in modeling h. Second, the flexibility in choosing the function σ can be used to reduce the control effort. For example, we can meet any constraint of the form $|u| \leq k$, by choosing $u = -k \ \text{sat}(x_2)$. However, the control $u = -\sigma(x_2)$ cannot arbitrarily assign the rate of decay of $x(t)$. Linearization of the closed-loop system at the origin yields the characteristic equation

$$s^2 + \sigma'(0)s + h'(0) = 0$$

One of the two roots of the foregoing equation cannot be moved to the left of $\text{Re}[s] = -\sqrt{h'(0)}$. Feedback control laws that exploit passivity properties will be discussed in Section 14.4. $\triangle$

These two examples make the point that there are situations where nonlinearities are beneficial and cancelling them should not be an automatic choice. We should try our best to understand the effect of the nonlinear terms and decide whether or not cancellation is appropriate. Admittedly, this is not an easy task.

The robustness and efficiency concerns we raised regarding feedback linearization as a design procedure should not undermine the feedback linearization theory we developed in this chapter. The theory provides us with valuable tools to characterize a class of nonlinear systems whose structure is open to feedback control design, with or without nonlinearity cancellation. The concepts of relative degree and zero dynamics of nonlinear systems bring into focus the common input–output structure of linear and nonlinear systems and play a crucial role in extending to nonlinear systems some of the feedback design procedures that were successfully used for linear systems, such as high-gain feedback. The ability to transform a system into a normal form, where nonlinear terms enter the state equation at the same point as the control input, brings in the matching condition structure that will be used in Chapter 14 to develop some useful robust control techniques.

13.4.2 Tracking

Consider a single-input–single-output, input–output linearizable system represented in the normal form (13.16)–(13.18):

$$\dot{\eta} \ = \ f_0(\eta, \xi)$$

$$
\begin{aligned}
\dot{\xi} &= A_c\xi + B_c\gamma(x)[u - \alpha(x)] \\
y &= C_c\xi
\end{aligned}
$$

Without loss of generality, we assume that $f_0(0,0) = 0$. We want to design a state feedback control law such that the output y asymptotically tracks a reference signal $r(t)$. When the system has relative degree $\rho = n$, it has no nontrivial zero dynamics. In this case, the η variable and its equation are dropped, but the rest of the development remains the same. We assume that

- $r(t)$ and its derivatives up to $r^{(\rho)}(t)$ are bounded for all $t \geq 0$ and the ρth derivative $r^{(\rho)}(t)$ is a piecewise continuous function of t;

- the signals $r, \ldots, r^{(\rho)}$ are available on-line.

The reference signal $r(t)$ could be specified, together with its derivatives, as some given functions of time, or it could be the output of a *reference model* driven by some input signal $w(t)$. In the latter case, the assumptions on r can be met by appropriately choosing the reference model. For example, for a relative degree two system, a reference model could be a second-order linear time-invariant system represented by the transfer function

$$
\frac{\omega_n^2}{s^2 + 2\zeta\omega_n s + \omega_n^2}
$$

where the positive constants ζ and ω_n are chosen to shape the reference signal $r(t)$ for a given input signal $w(t)$. The signal $r(t)$ can be generated on-line by using the state model

$$
\begin{aligned}
\dot{y}_1 &= y_2 \\
\dot{y}_2 &= -\omega_n^2 y_1 - 2\zeta\omega_n y_2 + \omega_n^2 w \\
r &= y_1
\end{aligned}
$$

Therefore, $r(t)$, $\dot{r}(t)$, and $\ddot{r}(t)$ will be available on-line. If $w(t)$ is a piecewise continuous bounded function of t, then $r(t)$, $\dot{r}(t)$, and $\ddot{r}(t)$ will satisfy the required assumptions.

Let

$$
\mathcal{R} = \begin{bmatrix} r \\ \vdots \\ r^{(\rho-1)} \end{bmatrix}, \quad e = \begin{bmatrix} \xi_1 - r \\ \vdots \\ \xi_\rho - r^{(\rho-1)} \end{bmatrix} = \xi - \mathcal{R}
$$

The change of variables $e = \xi - \mathcal{R}$ yields

$$
\begin{aligned}
\dot{\eta} &= f_0(\eta, e + \mathcal{R}) \\
\dot{e} &= A_c e + B_c \left\{ \gamma(x)[u - \alpha(x)] - r^{(\rho)} \right\}
\end{aligned}
$$

The state feedback control

$$u = \alpha(x) + \beta(x)\left[v + r^{(\rho)}\right]$$

where $\beta(x) = 1/\gamma(x)$, reduces the normal form to the cascade system

$$\begin{aligned}
\dot{\eta} &= f_0(\eta, e + \mathcal{R}) \\
\dot{e} &= A_c e + B_c v
\end{aligned}$$

Our control objective can be met by any design of v that stabilizes the second equation while maintaining η bounded for all $t \geq 0$. With $v = -Ke$, where $A_c - B_c K$ is Hurwitz, the complete state feedback control is given by[12]

$$u = \alpha(x) + \beta(x)\left\{-K[T_2(x) - \mathcal{R}] + r^{(\rho)}\right\} \tag{13.47}$$

and the closed-loop system is given by

$$\begin{aligned}
\dot{\eta} &= f_0(\eta, e + \mathcal{R}) & (13.48) \\
\dot{e} &= (A_c - B_c K)e & (13.49)
\end{aligned}$$

For minimum phase systems, the origin of $\dot{\eta} = f_0(\eta, 0)$ is asymptotically stable. It follows from (the converse Lyapunov function) Theorem 4.16 and Theorem 4.18 that for sufficiently small $e(0)$, $\eta(0)$, and $\mathcal{R}(t)$, the state $\eta(t)$ will be bounded for all $t \geq 0$. Thus, the state feedback control (13.47) solves the local tracking problem. To extend the validity of the control to global tracking, where $\mathcal{R}(t)$ can be any bounded function of t, we face the same issues we encountered in global stabilization. A sufficient condition to ensure global tracking is input-to-state stability of the system $\dot{\eta} = f_0(\eta, \xi)$.

Example 13.21 Consider the pendulum equation

$$\begin{aligned}
\dot{x}_1 &= x_2 \\
\dot{x}_2 &= -a\sin x_1 - bx_2 + cu \\
y &= x_1
\end{aligned}$$

The system has relative degree two in R^2 and is already represented in the normal form. It has no nontrivial zero dynamics, so it is minimum phase by default. We want the output y to track a reference signal $r(t)$, with bounded derivatives $\dot{r}(t)$ and $\ddot{r}(t)$. Taking

$$e_1 = x_1 - r, \quad e_2 = x_2 - \dot{r}$$

we obtain

$$\begin{aligned}
\dot{e}_1 &= e_2 \\
\dot{e}_2 &= -a\sin x_1 - bx_2 + cu - \ddot{r}
\end{aligned}$$

---

[12]As in Section 13.2, T_2 comprises the last ρ components of the diffeomorphism $T(x)$ that transforms the system into the normal form.

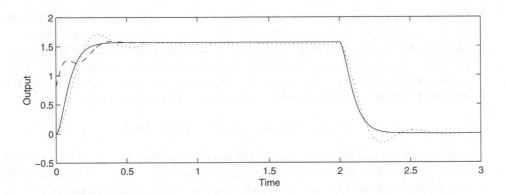

Figure 13.2: Simulation of the tracking control of Example 13.21.

The state feedback control (13.47) is given by

$$u = \frac{1}{c}[a \sin x_1 + b x_2 + \ddot{r} - k_1 e_1 - k_2 e_2]$$

where $K = [k_1, k_2]$ is designed to assign the eigenvalues of $A_c - B_c K$ at desired locations in the open left-half complex plane. Because all the assumptions hold globally, this control achieves global tracking. Figure 13.2 shows the response of the system when $a = c = 10$, $b = 1$, $k_1 = 400$, and $k_2 = 20$ to some reference signal. The solid curve is both the reference signal and output signal in the nominal case; they are identical. Here, tracking is achieved for all t and not just asymptotically, because $x(0) = \mathcal{R}(0)$. If $x(0) \neq \mathcal{R}(0)$, tracking will be achieved asymptotically, which is shown by the dashed curve. Finally, the dotted curve shows the response of the system when b and c are perturbed to $b = 0.5$ and $c = 5$, which correspond to doubling the mass. $\triangle$

In many control problems, the designer has some freedom in choosing the reference signal r. For example, one of the typical problems in controlling robot manipulators is moving the manipulator from an initial to a final point within some time interval. The first task in approaching this problem is planning the path between the two points, which has to comply with any physical constraints due to the presence of obstacles. Then, the motion trajectory is planned by specifying velocities and accelerations of the moving parts as functions of time. The outcome of this trajectory planning process is the reference signal that the output variable has to track.[13] The freedom in choosing the reference signal can be used to improve the performance of the system, especially in the presence of constraints on the control signal. The next example illustrates this point.

---

[13]To read about trajectory planning in robot manipulators, see [171].

Example 13.22 Reconsider the pendulum equation of the previous example with the nominal parameters $a = c = 10$ and $b = 1$. Suppose the pendulum is resting at the open-loop equilibrium point $x = 0$ and we want to move it to a new equilibrium point at $x_1 = \pi/2$ and $x_2 = 0$. Taking the reference signal r as the output of the second-order transfer function $1/(\tau s + 1)^2$ driven by a step input w will provide the desired motion if the jump in w is taken as $\pi/2$. The tracking control is taken as

$$u = 0.1(10 \sin x_1 + x_2 + \ddot{r} - k_1 e_1 - k_2 e_2)$$

where $k_1 = 400$ and $k_2 = 20$. Taking the initial conditions of the reference model to be zero, we find that the tracking error $e(t) = x(t) - \mathcal{R}(t)$ will be identically zero and the motion of the pendulum will track the desired reference signal for all t. The choice of the time constant τ determines the speed of motion from the initial to the final position. If there were no constraint on the magnitude of the control u, we could have chosen τ arbitrarily small and achieved arbitrarily fast transition from $x_1 = 0$ to $x_1 = \pi/2$. However, the control input u is the torque of a motor and there is a maximum torque that the motor can supply. This constraint puts a limit on how quick we can move the pendulum. By choosing τ to be compatible with the torque constraint, we can achieve better performance. Figure 13.3 shows two different choices of τ when the control is constrained to $|u| \leq 2$. For $\tau = 0.05$ sec, the output $y(t)$ deviates from the reference $r(t)$, reflecting the fact that the reference signal demands a control effort that cannot be delivered by the motor. On the other hand, with $\tau = 0.25$ sec, the output signal achieves a good tracking of the reference signal. In both cases, we could not achieve a settling time better than about 1.2 seconds, but by choosing $\tau = 0.25$, we were able to avoid the overshoot that took place when $\tau = 0.05$. △

13.5　Exercises

13.1 Consider the third-order model of a synchronous generator connected to an infinite bus from Exercise 1.8. Consider two possible choices of the output:

$$(1)\ \ y = \delta; \quad (2)\ \ y = \delta + \gamma\dot{\delta},\ \gamma \neq 0$$

In each case, study the relative degree of the system and transform it into the normal form. Specify the region over which the transformation is valid. If there are nontrivial zero dynamics, find whether or not the system is minimum phase.

13.2 Consider the system

$$\dot{x}_1 = -x_1 + x_2 - x_3, \quad \dot{x}_2 = -x_1 x_3 - x_2 + u, \quad \dot{x}_3 = -x_1 + u, \quad y = x_3$$

(a) Is the system input–output linearizable?

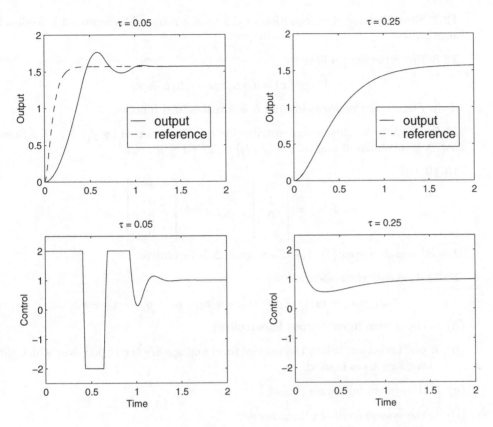

Figure 13.3: Simulation of the tracking control of Example 13.22.

(b) If yes, transform it into the normal form and specify the region over which the transformation is valid.

(c) Is the system minimum phase?

13.3 Consider the inverted pendulum of Exercise 1.15 and let θ be the output. Is the system input–output linearizable? Is it minimum phase?

13.4 Consider the system of Example 12.6. Is the system input–output linearizable? Is it minimum phase?

13.5 With reference to Example 13.8, consider the partial differential equations (13.26). Suppose $q(x)$ is independent of ζ_m and ξ_n. Show that $\phi_i = \zeta_i$ for $1 \leq i \leq m - 1$ and $\phi_m = \zeta_m - \xi_n/q(x)$ satisfy the partial differential equations.

13.6 Show that the state equation of Exercise 6.11 is feedback linearizable.

13.7 Show that the state equation of the m-link robot of Exercise 1.4 is feedback linearizable.

13.8 Prove the Jacobi identity

$$L_{[f,g]}h(x) = L_f L_g h(x) - L_g L_f h(x)$$

where f and g are vector fields and h is a real-valued function.

13.9 Let Δ be a nonsingular distribution on D, generated by $f_1, \ldots, f_r$. Show that Δ is involutive if and only if $[f_i, f_j] \in \Delta$, $\forall\, 1 \le i, j \le r$.

13.10 Let

$$f_1(x) = \begin{bmatrix} x_1 \\ 1 \\ 0 \\ x_3 \end{bmatrix}, \quad f_2(x) = \begin{bmatrix} -e^{x_2} \\ 0 \\ 0 \\ 0 \end{bmatrix}$$

$D = R^4$ and $\Delta = \text{span}\{f_1, f_2\}$. Show that Δ is involutive.

13.11 Consider the system

$$\dot{x}_1 = x_1 + x_2, \quad \dot{x}_2 = 3x_1^2 x_2 + x_1 + u, \quad y = -x_1^3 + x_2$$

(a) Is the system input–output linearizable?

(b) If yes, transform it into the normal form and specify the region over which the transformation is valid.

(c) Is the system minimum phase?

(d) Is the system feedback linearizable?

(e) If yes, find a feedback control law and a change of variables that linearize the state equation.

13.12 Repeat the previous exercise for the system

$$\dot{x}_1 = -x_1 + x_1 x_2, \quad \dot{x}_2 = x_2 + x_3, \quad \dot{x}_3 = \delta(x) + u, \quad y = x_1 + x_2$$

where $\delta(x)$ is a locally Lipschitz function of x.

13.13 An articulated vehicle (a semitrailer-like vehicle) can be modeled by the state equation

$$\dot{x}_1 = \tan(x_3)$$

$$\dot{x}_2 = -\frac{\tan(x_2)}{a\cos(x_3)} + \frac{1}{b\cos(x_2)\cos(x_3)}\tan(u)$$

$$\dot{x}_3 = \frac{\tan(x_2)}{a\cos(x_3)}$$

where a and b are positive constants. Show that system is feedback linearizable. Find the domain of validity of the exact linear model.

13.14 Consider the system

$$\dot{x}_1 = -x_1 + x_2 - x_3, \quad \dot{x}_2 = -x_1 x_3 - x_2 + u, \quad \dot{x}_3 = -x_1 + u$$

(a) Is the system feedback linearizable?

(b) If yes, find a feedback control law and a change of variables that linearize the state equation.

13.15 Verify that the map $z = T(x)$ in Example 13.15 is a diffeomorphism on D_0, and the state equation in the z coordinates is well defined on $D_z = T(D_0)$.

13.16 Consider the pendulum of Example 12.2 with the numerical data of Exercise 12.1. Design a stabilizing state feedback control law via feedback linearization, locating the closed-loop eigenvalues at the same locations used in Exercise 12.1. Compare the performance of the closed-loop system with that of Exercise 12.1.

13.17 Show that the system

$$\dot{x}_1 = -x_1 + x_2, \quad \dot{x}_2 = x_1 - x_2 - x_1 x_3 + u, \quad \dot{x}_3 = x_1 + x_1 x_2 - 2x_3$$

is feedback linearizable and design a state feedback control law to globally stabilize the origin.

13.18 Consider the system

$$\dot{x}_1 = x_2, \quad \dot{x}_2 = a \sin x_1 - bu \cos x_1$$

where a and b are positive constants.

(a) Show that the system is feedback linearizable.

(b) Using feedback linearization, design a state feedback controller to stabilize the system at $x_1 = \theta$, where $0 \le \theta < \pi/2$. Can you make this equilibrium point globally asymptotically stable?

13.19 Consider the link manipulator of Example 13.14. Suppose the parameters a, b, c, and d are not known exactly, but we know their estimates $\hat{a}$, $\hat{b}$, $\hat{c}$, and $\hat{d}$. Design a linearizing state feedback control law in terms of $\hat{a}$, $\hat{b}$, $\hat{c}$, and $\hat{d}$ and represent the closed-loop system as a perturbation of a nominal linear system.

13.20 Consider a special case of the system (13.37)–(13.38), where $f_0(\eta, \xi)$ depends only on ξ_1, and $(A, B) = (A_c, B_c)$ is a controllable canonical form that represents a chain of ρ integrators. Such system is said to be in a special normal form. Assume that the origin of $\dot{\eta} = f_0(\eta, 0)$ is globally asymptotically stable and there is a radially unbounded Lyapunov function $V_0(\eta)$ such that

$$\frac{\partial V_0}{\partial \eta} f_0(\eta, 0) \le -W(\eta)$$

for all η, where $W(\eta)$ is a positive definite function.

(a) Show that the control $u = \alpha(x) + \beta(x)v$ where $\beta(x) = \gamma^{-1}(x)$, and the change of variables

$$z_1 = \xi_1, \ z_2 = \varepsilon\xi_2, \dots, z_\rho = \varepsilon^{\rho-1}\xi_\rho, \ w = \varepsilon^\rho v$$

brings the system into the form

$$\dot{\eta} = f_0(\eta, z_1), \qquad \varepsilon\dot{z} = A_c z + B_c w$$

(b) Let K be chosen such that $A_c - B_c K$ is Hurwitz and P be the positive definite solution of the Lyapunov equation $P(A_c - B_c K) + (A_c - B_c K)^T P = -I$. Taking $w = -Kz$ and using $V(\eta, z) = V_0(\eta) + \sqrt{z^T P z}$ as a Lyapunov function candidate for the closed-loop system, show that, for sufficiently small ε, the origin ($\eta = 0$, $z = 0$) is asymptotically stable and the set $\{V(\eta, z) \leq c\}$, with an arbitrary $c > 0$, is included in the region of attraction.

(c) Show that the feedback control achieves semiglobal stabilization; that is, initial states (η_0, ξ_0) in any compact subset of R^n can be included in the region of attraction.

(d) In view of Example 13.17, investigate whether the current controller exhibits a peaking phenomenon, and if so, explain why is it possible to achieve semiglobal stabilization despite the presence of peaking.

13.21 Consider the system

$$
\begin{aligned}
\dot{x}_1 &= x_2 + x_1 x_2 - x_2^2 + u \\
\dot{x}_2 &= x_1 x_2 - x_2^2 + u \\
\dot{x}_3 &= x_1 + x_1 x_2 - x_2^2 - (x_3 - x_1)^3 + u \\
y &= x_1 - x_2
\end{aligned}
$$

(a) Show that the system has a globally defined special normal form.

(b) Show that the origin of the zero dynamics is globally asymptotically stable.

(c) Design a semiglobally stabilizing state feedback control law.

Hint: See Exercise 13.20.

13.22 Consider the system (13.44)–(13.45), where $A - BK$ is Hurwitz, the origin of $\dot{\eta} = f_0(\eta, 0)$ is asymptotically stable, and $\|\delta(z)\| \leq \varepsilon$. Show that there is a neighborhood D of $z = 0$ and $\varepsilon^* > 0$ such that for every every $z(0) \in D$ and $\varepsilon \leq \varepsilon^*$, the state z is ultimately bounded by a class $\mathcal{K}$ function of ε.

13.23 Consider the system (13.44)–(13.45), where $A - BK$ is Hurwitz, the origin of $\dot{\eta} = f_0(\eta, 0)$ is globally exponentially stable, f_0 is globally Lipschitz, and $\|\delta\| \leq k\|z\|$ for all z. Show that, for sufficiently small k, the origin $z = 0$ is globally exponentially stable.

13.24 Consider the system (13.44)–(13.45), where $A - BK$ is Hurwitz, the origin of $\dot{\eta} = f_0(\eta, 0)$ is asymptotically stable with a Lyapunov function $V_0(\eta)$ such that $[\partial V_0 / \partial \eta] f_0(\eta, 0) \leq -W(\eta)$ for some positive definite function $W(\eta)$. Suppose $\|\delta\| \leq k[\|\xi\| + W(\eta)]$. Using a composite Lyapunov function of the form $V = V_0(\eta) + \lambda \sqrt{\xi^T P \xi}$, where P is the solution of $P(A - BK) + (A - BK)^T P = -I$, show that, for sufficiently small k, the origin $z = 0$ is asymptotically stable

13.25 Consider the system

$$\dot{x}_1 = x_2 + 2x_1^2, \quad \dot{x}_2 = x_3 + u, \quad \dot{x}_3 = x_1 - x_3, \quad y = x_1$$

Design a state feedback control law such that the output y asymptotically tracks the reference signal $r(t) = \sin t$.

13.26 Repeat the previous exercise for the system

$$\dot{x}_1 = x_2 + x_1 \sin x_1, \quad \dot{x}_2 = x_1 x_2 + u, \quad y = x_1$$

13.27 The magnetic suspension system of Exercise 1.18 is modeled by

$$
\begin{aligned}
\dot{x}_1 &= x_2 \\
\dot{x}_2 &= g - \frac{k}{m} x_2 - \frac{L_0 a x_3^2}{2m(a + x_1)^2} \\
\dot{x}_3 &= \frac{1}{L(x_1)} \left[-R x_3 + \frac{L_0 a x_2 x_3}{(a + x_1)^2} + u \right]
\end{aligned}
$$

where $x_1 = y$, $x_2 = \dot{y}$, $x_3 = i$, and $u = v$. Use the following numerical data: $m = 0.1$ kg, $k = 0.001$ N/m/sec, $g = 9.81$ m/sec^2, $a = 0.05$ m, $L_0 = 0.01$ H, $L_1 = 0.02$ H, and $R = 1$ Ω.

(a) Show that the system is feedback linearizable.

(b) Using feedback linearization, design a state feedback control law to stabilize the ball at $y = 0.05$ m. Repeat parts (d) and (e) of Exercise 12.8 and compare the performance of this controller with the one designed in part (c) of that exercise.

(c) Show that, with the ball position y as the output, the system is input–output linearizable.

(d) Using feedback linearization, design a state feedback control law so that the output y asymptotically tracks $r(t) = 0.05 + 0.01 \sin t$. Simulate the closed-loop system.

13.28 A field-controlled DC motor is described in Exercise 1.17. When the field circuit is driven by a current source, we can view the field current as the control input and model the system by the second-order state model

$$\dot{x}_1 = -\theta_1 x_1 - \theta_2 x_2 u + \theta_3$$
$$\dot{x}_2 = -\theta_4 x_2 + \theta_5 x_1 u$$
$$y = x_2$$

where x_1 is the armature current, x_2 is the speed, u is the field current, and θ_1 to θ_5 are positive constants. It is desired to design a state feedback controller such that the output y asymptotically tracks a time-varying reference signal $r(t)$, where both $r(t)$ and $\dot{r}(t)$ are continuous and bounded for all $t \geq 0$. Assume that the domain of operation is restricted to $x_1 > \theta_3/2\theta_1$.

(a) Show that the system is input–output linearizable and has relative degree one.

(b) Show that it is minimum phase.

(c) Using feedback linearization, design a state feedback control to achieve the desired tracking.

(d) Using computer simulation, study the performance of the system when r is the output of a first-order filter $1/(\tau s + 1)$ driven by a step command w. The time constant τ can be chosen to adjust the rate of change of r. In the simulation, take the initial conditions as $x_1(0) = \theta_3/\theta_1$ and $x_2(0) = 0$ and use the following numerical data: $\theta_1 = 60$, $\theta_2 = 0.5$, $\theta_3 = 40$, $\theta_4 = 6$, and $\theta_5 = 4 \times 10^4$. Let the step command w change from 0 to 100 at $t = 1$. Also, add saturation at the input of the plant such that the control signal is limited to ± 0.05.

   (i) Adjust τ and the feedback controller parameters to achieve a settling time of 0.5.

   (ii) Adjust τ and the feedback controller parameters to achieve a settling time of 0.1.

   (iii) Go back to the values used in part (i) and study the performance of the system when the rotor inertia changes by $\pm 50\%$.

   (iv) Can you adjust the feedback controller parameters to improve its robustness to the parameter perturbations described in the previous part?